Probability Distributions:
An Introduction to Probability Theory with Applications

9/23/75

Probability Distributions:
An Introduction to Probability Theory with Applications

Chris P. Tsokos

*Department of Statistics
and
Statistical Laboratory*

*Virginia Polytechnic Institute
and
State University*

Blacksburg, Virginia

Duxbury Press, a Division of Wadsworth Publishing Company, Inc., Belmont, California

To "Jan"

Duxbury Press
A division of Wadsworth
Publishing Company, Inc.

ISBN—0–87872–011–1

L. C. Cat. Card No.—74–184636

Printed in the United States
of America

1 2 3 4 5 6 7 8 9 10—76 75 74 73 72

Preface

It is intended that this book be used in an introductory course in probability theory with special emphasis on distribution theory and applications. The usual first two terms of calculus are prerequisites for anyone using this book, since it is written for the science student at the junior level or above. In addition, this book could serve as a reference for research workers in the natural sciences who need to familiarize themselves with the classical probability distributions.

This book meets the needs of students with a wide variety of interests. To achieve this, we have included examples and exercises from all areas of science. The book should be used in a one-semester or a two-quarter course in introduction to probability theory with special emphasis on distribution theory and applications. Chapters 1–6 could be covered in a one-semester course with additional material from the remaining chapters included at the instructor's discretion. It is suggested, however, that in a two-semester course the complete book be covered.

In the study of probability theory the most important concept beyond the definition of probability is that of a random variable. In fact, one of the prime tasks in probability theory is to determine the distribution of a random variable because knowledge of this distribution automatically contributes knowledge of the laws which govern the random variable involved. The importance of this last statement has led to the distribution theme of this book.

Distinguishing features of the book include the following:
(1) Each new concept, theorem, definition, and corollary is followed by one or more examples as an aid to thorough understanding.
(2) New concepts are illustrated both graphically and analytically.
(3) A brief summary appears at the end of each chapter that includes the main objectives and highlights of the chapter.
(4) There are numerous exercises at the end of each chapter. These are divided into two sections: theoretical and applied.

Chapter 0 is designed to serve as a review of some of the mathematics essential to the study of probability and which is sometimes not covered in the ordinary calculus sequence. Such topics as gamma and beta functions, Jacobians, some matrix theory, and counting methods are included. It is not intended that this chapter be included in a course on probability; rather, it should be consulted by the student as it suits his individual needs.

In Chapter 1 probability is defined and developed from an historical point of view, with emphasis on the classical definition as a device for evaluating probabilities and the axiomatic approach as a manipulative method.

The definition of a random variable is introduced early in the book. We then treat one-dimensional discrete random variables, followed by one-dimensional continuous random variables. Next, the concept of derived distributions is considered. Here, emphasis is placed on continuous functions of one-dimensional discrete random variables and continuous functions of continuous one-dimensional random variables. We then turn to n-dimensional discrete random variables and n-dimensional continuous variates. Consideration is devoted to probability densities, cumulative distribution functions, and many of their properties. Strong emphasis is placed upon the expected value of a random variable, moments, moment-generating functions, and characteristic functions.

In Chapter 9 we present from an applied point of view an extensive study of a special class of stochastic processes. This class consists of finite Markov chains with a discrete parameter. State and tree diagrams are included as illustrative aids. The usefulness of Markov chains is illustrated by a number of practical examples from biology, physics, genetics, and games of chance.

At the end of each chapter a supplemental list of textbooks related to the material in the chapter is given. Many useful tables are provided in an appendix at the end of the text.

I am grateful to my colleagues and friends for their many stimulating and helpful conversations during the writing of this book. To my students at Virginia Polytechnic Institute and State University, I express my sincere thanks for their comments and assistance during the classroom testing of the manuscript. I would also like to thank the reviewers for their constructive criticisms and suggestions. Finally, I would like to say that without the support of my wife I would never have written this book.

Blacksburg, Virginia   Chris P. Tsokos

Contents

Preliminary Mathematics

0

0.0 Introduction

In this chapter, we shall discuss basic concepts of mathematics. This discussion will serve as a review for those who have studied these topics in introductory courses in mathematics, and it will fulfill the minimum requirement for those who have had very little training in mathematics. Also, we shall introduce some topics of mathematics that are usually not included in introductory courses in calculus—the concepts of Jacobians, Gamma and Beta functions, some useful identities and series, and some matrix theory. You should be familiar with these mathematical concepts in order to better understand the material covered in the rest of the book. We shall define these concepts, state some of their important properties, and illustrate with examples a few of their applications.

The material in this chapter provides you with a brief review of some concepts necessary for studying probability theory. If you wish to cover certain areas in greater detail, you are referred to other sources of information.

0.1 Sum and Product Notations

We shall use the symbol y_i to denote the ith value of the n values y_1, $y_2, y_3, \ldots, y_n$. The sum of these values, $y_1 + y_2 + \cdots + y_n$, is designated by

$$\sum_{i=1}^{n} y_i \quad \text{or} \quad \sum_{i=1}^{n} y_i.$$

The Greek letter $\sum$ (capital sigma) tells you to *sum* elements of a sequence. The letter i is referred to as the *summation index*, and y_i is called the *summand*.

1

Example 0.1.1

(a) $\displaystyle\sum_{i=1}^{r} ay_i = ay_1 + ay_2 + \cdots + ay_r$

$\qquad\qquad = a(y_1 + y_2 + \cdots + y_r)$

$\qquad\qquad = a \displaystyle\sum_{i=1}^{r} y_i \,.$

(b) $\displaystyle\sum_{j=1}^{k} x_j y_j^{j-1} = x_1 + x_2 y_2^{1} + \cdots + x_k y_k^{k-1}.$

(c) $\displaystyle\sum_{j=1}^{n} (x_j - a)^2 = (x_1 - a)^2 + (x_2 - a)^2 + \cdots + (x_n - a)^2.$

(d) $\displaystyle\sum_{i=2}^{6} (-2)^{i-1} x_{i-1}^{i} = -2x_1^2 + 4x_2^3 - 8x_3^4 + 16x_4^5 - 32x_5^6.$

Therefore, we see that the sum of terms is obtained by letting the summation index, say i, take on those integral values between and including the limits of interest.

If, instead of summing the terms y_i, $i = 1, 2, \ldots, n$, we wish to obtain their *product*, we write

$$y_1 y_2 y_3 \cdots y_n = \prod_{i=1}^{n} y_i,$$

where the Greek letter $\prod$ (capital pi) tells you to *multiply* elements of a sequence.

Example 0.1.2

(a) $\displaystyle\prod_{i=1}^{r} \left(a + \frac{i}{b}\right)^i = \left(a + \frac{1}{b}\right)\left(a + \frac{2}{b}\right)^2 \left(a + \frac{3}{b}\right)^3 \cdots \left(a + \frac{r}{b}\right)^r.$

(b) $\displaystyle\prod_{j=1}^{k} \left[c + \left(-\frac{1}{2}\right)^{j-1}\right] = c\left(c - \frac{1}{2}\right)\left(c + \frac{1}{4}\right)\cdots\left[c + \left(-\frac{1}{2}\right)^{k-1}\right].$

0.2   Set Theory

In this section, we shall treat some of the basic ideas and concepts of set theory that are essential for a modern introduction to probability.

A *set* is a collection of distinct objects. For example, one of the most familiar sets N is the set of positive integers 1, 2, 3, ... Every object belonging to a set is called an *element* of the set. Let A_1 be a given set; and, if *a is an element of* A_1, we write

$$a \in A_1.$$

If *a is not an element of* the set A_1, we write

$$a \notin A_1.$$

A set is described either by listing its elements or by stating the properties that characterize the elements of the set. For example, to specify the set A_1 of all positive integers less than 12, we may write

$$A_1 = \begin{cases} \{1, 2, 3, 4, 5, 6, 7, 8, 9, 10, 11\} \\ \{\text{all positive integers less than 12}\} \\ \{x : x < 12, \quad x \text{ a positive integer}\}. \end{cases}$$

A set A_2 is a *subset* of a set A_1 if every element of A_2 is also an element of A_1. We shall denote this by writing

$$A_2 \subseteq A_1,$$

which is read "A_1 contains A_2" or "A_2 is contained in A_1." For example, if

$$A_2 = \{x : x \le 5, \quad x \text{ a positive integer}\},$$

it is obvious that A_2 is a subset of A_1. Also, every set is a subset of itself. Two sets, A_1 and A_3, are *equal*

$$A_1 = A_3,$$

if and only if $A_1 \subseteq A_3$ and $A_3 \subseteq A_1$. A set A_2 is a *proper subset* of the set A_1 if every element of A_2 is an element of A_1 and A_1 contains at least one element that is not an element of A_2. We denote this relationship by

$$A_2 \subset A_1.$$

That is, if

$$A_1 = \{x : x = 1, 2, 3, 4, 5\}$$

and

$$A_2 = \{x : x = 1, 2, 3\},$$

then A_2 is a proper subset of A_1. The set which contains no elements is called the *empty* set or *null* set and we shall denote the empty set by the symbol $\varnothing$. The null set is a subset of every set.

0.2.1 Set Operations Let A_1 and A_2 be arbitrary sets. The *union* of these sets, denoted by

$$A_1 \cup A_2,$$

is that set containing the elements of A_1 or A_2 or both. That is,

$$A_1 \cup A_2 = \{x : x \in A_1 \quad \text{or} \quad x \in A_2\}.$$

The symbol $A_1 \cup A_2$ is read "the union of A_1 and A_2."

Example 0.2.1   If $A_1 = \{x : 0 \leq x \leq 3\}$ and $A_2 = \{x : -2 \leq x \leq 2\}$, then

$$A_1 \cup A_2 = \{x : -2 \leq x \leq 3\}.$$

The *intersection* of two sets A_1 and A_2 is that set containing only those elements common to A_1 and A_2. We shall denote the intersection of the sets A_1 and A_2 by

$$A_1 \cap A_2 \quad \text{or} \quad A_1 A_2,$$

that is,

$$A_1 \cap A_2 = A_1 A_2 = \{x : x \in A_1 \text{ and } x \in A_2\}.$$

The symbol $A_1 \cap A_2$ is read "the intersection of A_1 and A_2."

Example 0.2.2   If

$$A_1 = \{x : x = 1, 2, 3, 4, 5, 6, 7\}$$

and

$$A_2 = \{x : x = 4, 5, 6, 7, 8, 9\},$$

then

$$A_1 \cap A_2 = \{x : x = 4, 5, 6, 7\}.$$

If the sets A_1 and A_2 have no elements in common, that is, if $A_1 \cap A_2 = \varnothing$, then the sets A_1 and A_2 are said to be *disjoint* or *mutually exclusive* sets.

The *universal set, U,* refers to the totality of elements under consideration; that is, the smallest possible set that is required so that every other set we may consider will be a subset of U. The *complement* of the set $A_1 \subset U$ is the set of all elements that are not in A_1 but are in U. The complement of the set A_1 will be denoted by $\bar{A}_1$. The difference of any two sets, A_1 and A_2, denoted by $A_1 - A_2$, is equal to $A_1 \cap \bar{A}_2$ or $A_2 - A_1$ is equal to $A_2 \cap \bar{A}_1$. Therefore,

$$\bar{A}_1 = \{x : x \notin A_1 \quad \text{but} \quad x \in U\}.$$

Example 0.2.3   If $U = \{x : 0 \le x \le 25\}$ and $A_1 = \{x : 5 \le x \le 10\}$, then

$$\bar{A}_1 = \{x : 0 \le x < 5 \quad \text{or} \quad 10 < x \le 25\}.$$

The usual notation for the complement of a subset A_1 of the universal set U is

$$\bar{A}_1 = U - A_1.$$

Venn diagrams are very useful for helping to clarify these set operations. In Figure 0.2.1(a), the shaded area represents the operation $A_1 \cup A_2 \cup A_3$ and U is the universal set. Similarly, the shaded area in the Venn diagrams (b), (d), (e), and (f) represent $A_1 \cap A_2$, $\overline{A_1 \cap A_2}$, $A_1 - (A_1 \cap A_2)$, and $\overline{A_1 - (A_1 \cap A_2)}$ respectively, whereas (c) shows that $A_2 \subset A_1$.

We shall now state some of the basic and important properties of the algebra of sets. Let U be the universal set, A_1, A_2, and A_3 be subsets of U, and $\emptyset$ be the empty set. The properties of the set operations, that is union, intersection, and complementation, are given by Theorem 0.2.1.

Theorem 0.2.1   If A_1, A_2, and A_3 are subsets of the universal set U, then the following laws hold.

(1)   *Idempotent law*
   $A_1 \cup A_1 = A_1,$ $A_1 \cap A_1 = A_1$;
(2)   *Commutative law*
   $A_1 \cup A_2 = A_2 \cup A_1,$ $A_1 \cap A_2 = A_2 \cap A_1$;
(3)   *Associative law*
   $(A_1 \cup A_2) \cup A_3 = A_1 \cup (A_2 \cup A_3),$
   $(A_1 \cap A_2) \cap A_3 = A_1 \cap (A_2 \cap A_3);$
(4)   *Distributive law*
   $A_1 \cup (A_2 \cap A_3) = (A_1 \cup A_2) \cap (A_1 \cup A_3),$
   $A_1 \cap (A_2 \cup A_3) = (A_1 \cap A_2) \cup (A_1 \cap A_3);$

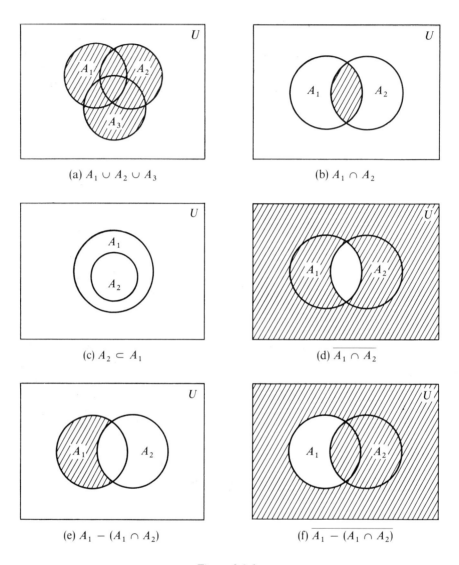

(a) $A_1 \cup A_2 \cup A_3$

(b) $A_1 \cap A_2$

(c) $A_2 \subset A_1$

(d) $\overline{A_1 \cap A_2}$

(e) $A_1 - (A_1 \cap A_2)$

(f) $\overline{A_1 - (A_1 \cap A_2)}$

Figure 0.2.1

(5) *Identity law*
    (a) $A_1 \cup U = U,$ $A_1 \cap U = A_1$;
    (b) $A_1 \cup \emptyset = A_1,$ $A_1 \cap \emptyset = \emptyset$;
(6) *Complement law*
     $A_1 \cup \bar{A_1} = U,$ $A_1 \cap \bar{A_1} = \emptyset$;
(7) *De Morgan's law*
     $\overline{A_1 \cup A_2} = \bar{A_1} \cap \bar{A_2},$ $\overline{A_1 \cap A_2} = \bar{A_1} \cup \bar{A_2}.$

The two sets A and B are said to be in *one-to-one correspondence* if each element $a \in A$ is paired with one and only one element $b \in B$ in such a manner that each element of B is paired with exactly one element of A.

Sets are classified as *finite* or *infinite*. A set is *finite* if it contains exactly n objects, where n is a non-negative integer. A set is *infinite* if it is not finite.

Example 0.2.4   If $A_1 = \{x : x = a_1, a_2, a_3, a_4\}$ and $A_2 = \{x : x = 1, 2, 3, 4\}$, then A_1 and A_2 are equivalent sets; that is, the elements of A_1 are in a 1:1 correspondence with the elements of A_2.

Example 0.2.5   If A_1 is a set containing all the positive integers less than or equal to 100, that is, if

$$A_1 = \{x : x = 1, 2, 3, \ldots 100\},$$

then A_1 is a finite set

Example 0.2.6   If A_2 is a set containing all the positive odd integers, that is, if

$$A_2 = \{x : x = 1, 3, 5, \ldots\},$$

then A_2 is an infinite set.

A set whose elements can be put into a one-to-one correspondence with the set of all positive integers is referred to as being a *countably infinite* set. Also a set is said to be *countable, denumerable, or enumerable* if it is finite or countably infinite.

Example 0.2.7   The set defined in Example 0.2.6, that is,

$$A_2 = \{x : x = 1, 3, 5 \ldots\},$$

is composed of elements which can be put into a one-to-one correspondence with the set of all positive integers. Thus, this set is countably infinite.

Example 0.2.8   If $A_1 = \{x : 0 \leq x \leq 5, \ x \text{ a real number}\}$, then the set A_1 is not a countable set, because any interval on the real line contains an infinite number of elements. However, a rigorous proof is beyond the scope of this text.

The *product* or *Cartesian product* of the sets A and B is denoted by $A \times B$ and consists of all ordered pairs (a, b), where $a \in A$ and $b \in B$, that is,

$$A \times B = \{(a, b) : a \in A, b \in B\}.$$

Example 0.2.9   If

$$A = \{x : x = a_1, a_2, a_3\} \quad \text{and} \quad B = \{x : x = 1, 2\},$$

then

$$A \times B = \{(a_1, 1), (a_1, 2), (a_2, 1), (a_2, 2), (a_3, 1), (a_3, 2)\}.$$

The Cartesian product of the sets A, B, and C is given by

$$A \times B \times C = \{(a, b, c) : a \in A, b \in B, c \in C\}.$$

That is, the product set $A \times B \times C$ consists of all possible ordered 3-tuples. Hence, the notion of a Cartesian set can be extended to any finite number of sets; that is, $A_1 \times A_2 \times \cdots \times A_n$ is the set of all ordered n-tuples, $(a_1, a_2, \ldots, a_n)$, where $a_1 \in A_1$, $a_2 \in A_2$, $\ldots$, $a_n \in A_n$.

These basic concepts of set theory constitute only a very brief survey of the area. They are intended to serve only as a helpful review for a better understanding of the formulation of the fundamental concepts of probability theory. For a more extensive development of this subject, you are referred to References [1], [3], and [7].

0.3 Permutations, Combinations, and Stirling's Formula

We shall begin this section by stating two very basic rules that are commonly used in combinatorial mathematics. That is, if a particular happening or event can take place in m different ways and a second event can occur in n different ways, then (1) the number of ways that either the first or second event may occur is $m + n$; and (2) the number of ways that both the first and the second event may occur is $m \cdot n$.

The arrangement of a set of objects in some form or order in a straight line is called a *permutation* of these objects. That is, if we have a set of n distinct elements and we wish to arrange r of them in some order in a straight line, we refer to this arrangement as a permutation of n distinct elements taken r at a time: and we denote the total number of such arrangements by P_r^n. Other symbols which are commonly used are $P(n, r)$, ^nP_r, $_nP_r$, P_{nr}, $(n)_r$.

Example 0.3.1   Find the total number of permutations of the elements a_1, a_2, and a_3 taken two at a time, that is, P_2^3.

Solution   Any one of these three elements can be put in the first position and either one of the two remaining elements can be put in the second position. Therefore, by Rule 2, there are $3 \cdot 2 = 6$ permutations. These are

$$
\begin{array}{lll}
a_1, a_2; & a_1, a_3; & a_2, a_3; \\
a_2, a_1; & a_3, a_1; & a_3, a_2.
\end{array}
$$

Example 0.3.2   The number of permutations of the four elements a_1, a_2, a_3, and a_4, taken three at a time, is similarly $4 \cdot 3 \cdot 2 \cdot 1 = 24$. These are listed below:

$$a_1, a_2, a_3; \quad a_1, a_2, a_4; \quad a_1, a_3, a_4; \quad a_2, a_3, a_4; \quad a_3, a_1, a_2;$$
$$a_1, a_3, a_2; \quad a_1, a_4, a_2; \quad a_1, a_4, a_3; \quad a_2, a_4, a_3; \quad a_4, a_1, a_2;$$
$$a_2, a_1, a_3; \quad a_2, a_1, a_4; \quad a_3, a_1, a_4; \quad a_3, a_2, a_4; \quad a_4, a_1, a_3;$$
$$a_2, a_3, a_1; \quad a_2, a_4, a_1; \quad a_3, a_4, a_1; \quad a_3, a_4, a_2; \quad a_4, a_2, a_3;$$
$$a_3, a_2, a_1; \quad a_4, a_2, a_1; \quad a_4, a_3, a_1; \quad a_4, a_3, a_2.$$

By considering similar examples with larger numbers of objects, one arrives at the following formula:

$$P_n^n = n(n-1)(n-2) \cdots 3 \cdot 2 \cdot 1. \tag{0.3.1}$$

That is, the first position can be filled by any one of the n distinct objects, the next position by any one of the remaining $n-1$, and so on. We shall denote the product of the positive integers, as shown in (0.3.1), by $n!$, which is read n *factorial*. Hence, $5! = 5 \cdot 4 \cdot 3 \cdot 2 \cdot 1$, $(r-1)! = (r-1)$ $(r-2) \cdots 3 \cdot 2 \cdot 1$. We shall define $0! = 1$, the reason for which will be shown in a later section. If r is less than n, we have

$$P_r^n = n(n-1)(n-2) \cdots (n-r+1)$$

$$= \frac{n(n-1)(n-2) \cdots (n-r+1)(n-r)(n-r-1) \cdots 3 \cdot 2 \cdot 1}{(n-r)(n-r-1) \cdots 3 \cdot 2 \cdot 1}$$

$$= \frac{n!}{(n-r)!}. \tag{0.3.2}$$

Thus, the number of permutations of 10 objects taken four at a time is

$$P_4^{10} = \frac{10!}{(10-4)!} = \frac{10!}{6!} = 5040.$$

If we are interested in finding the total number of ways in which we can choose r objects out of n, disregarding the order in which they are chosen, we speak of a *combination of n distinct objects taken r at a time*; and we shall denote this by the symbol $\binom{n}{r}$. Other symbols which are commonly used are $C_{n,r}$, C_r^n, $_nC_r$, and $C(n, r)$.

Example 0.3.3   The number of combinations of the elements a_1, a_2, and a_3, taken two at a time, is three, that is, a_1, a_2; a_1, a_3; and a_2, a_3. Each of these combinations give rise to $2!$ permutations, as shown in Example 0.3.1. Thus, eliminating the order of the arrangements, we see that

$$\binom{3}{2} = \frac{P_2^3}{2!} = \frac{3!}{2!(3-2)!} = 3.$$

Example 0.3.4   The number of combinations of the elements a_1, a_2, a_3, and a_4, taken three at a time, is four, that is, a_1, a_2, and a_3; a_1, a_2, and a_4; a_1, a_3, and a_4; and a_2, a_3, and a_4. Eliminating the order of arrangement in Example 0.3.2, we have

$$\binom{4}{3} = \frac{P_3^4}{3!} = \frac{4!}{3!(4-3)!} = 4.$$

Therefore, we can conclude that the total number of ways that we can choose r objects out of n, $r \leq n$, disregarding the order of choice, gives

$$\binom{n}{r} = \frac{P_r^n}{r!} = \frac{n!}{r!(n-r)!}.$$

Note that $\binom{n}{n} = \binom{n}{0} = 1$ and $\binom{n}{1} = n$. Also, $\binom{n}{r} = \binom{n}{n-r}$, which implies

that, if we select r objects out of n distinct objects, we select at the same time $n-r$ objects to be left alone.

Example 0.3.5

(a) $\binom{9}{6} = \frac{9!}{6!(9-6)!} = 84.$

(b) $\binom{a}{a-2} = \frac{a!}{(a-2)![a-(a-2)]!} = \frac{a!}{2!(a-2)!} = \frac{a(a-1)}{2}.$

(c) $\binom{n-1}{3} = \frac{(n-1)!}{3!(n-4)!} = \frac{(n-1)(n-2)(n-3)(n-4)!}{3!(n-4)!}$

$$= \frac{(n-1)(n-2)(n-3)}{3 \cdot 2 \cdot 1}.$$

The important point in this section: Permutations take order into consideration, whereas combinations do not.

When n, the number of elements in a set, is large, the direct evaluation of $n!$ is impractical. A good approximation for $n!$ is given by *Stirling's formula*

$$n! \approx n^n e^{-n} \sqrt{2\pi n},$$

where e is the Napierian base, $2.71828 \cdots$.
Using logarithmic tables, it is very easy to compute the value of the above expression for any number n. For a more detailed presentation of the above topics, we suggest References [6] and [11].

0.4   Binomial and Multinomial Theorems

One of the important theorems in elementary algebra is the *binomial theorem*. This theorem gives the expansion of the binomial expression $(x + y)^n$, where n is any positive integer, as follows:

$$(x + y)^n = x^n + \tfrac{n}{1}x^{n-1}y + \frac{n(n-1)}{1 \cdot 2} x^{n-2}y^2 + \frac{n(n-1)(n-2)}{1 \cdot 2 \cdot 3} x^{n-3}y^3 + \cdots$$

$$+ \frac{n(n-1)(n-2)\cdots(n-r+1)}{1 \cdot 2 \cdot 3 \cdot \cdots \cdot r} x^{n-r}y^r + \cdots + y^n.$$

The proof of this theorem is made by mathematical induction. If the sign in the binomial expression is negative, the expansion begins with a plus and then alternates its sign.

Example 0.4.1   Expand and simplify.

(a) $\left(\dfrac{x}{2} + y^2\right)^5 = \dfrac{1}{32} x^5 + \dfrac{5}{16} x^4 y^2 + \dfrac{5}{4} x^3 y^4 + \dfrac{5}{2} x^2 y^6 + \dfrac{5}{2} xy^8 + y^{10}.$

(b) $\left(2x - \dfrac{y^2}{2}\right)^6 = 64x^6 - 96x^5 y^2 + 60x^4 y^4$

$$- 20x^3 y^6 + \frac{15}{4} x^2 y^8 - \frac{3}{8} xy^{10} + \frac{1}{64} y^{12}.$$

The binomial theorem can also be expressed in terms of combinations, as follows:

$$(x + y)^n = \binom{n}{0}x^n + \binom{n}{1}x^{n-1}y + \binom{n}{2}x^{n-2}y^2 + \cdots + \binom{n}{n-1}xy^{n-1} + \binom{n}{n}y^n$$

$$= \sum_{i=0}^{n} \binom{n}{i} x^{n-i} y^i.$$

This form of the theorem is relatively simple to work with in various applications. For example, the coefficient of the sixth term in the expansion of $(x + y)^{20}$ is given by $\binom{20}{5} = \dfrac{20!}{5!15!}$ or, in general, the coefficient of the jth term in the expansion of $(x + y)^n$ is

$$\binom{n}{j-1} = \frac{n!}{(j-1)!(n-j+1)!}.$$

A generalization of the binomial theorem is the *multinomial theorem,* which may be expressed as

$$(x_1 + x_2 + \cdots + x_k)^n = \sum \binom{n}{n_1, n_2, \ldots, n_k} x_1^{n_1} x_2^{n_2} \cdots x_k^{n_k}$$

$$= \sum \frac{n!}{n_1! \, n_2! \cdots n_k!} x_1^{n_1} x_2^{n_2} \cdots x_k^{n_k},$$

where the sum is taken over all permutations of nonnegative integers $n_1, n_2, \ldots, n_k$ such that $n_1 + n_2 + \cdots + n_k = n$.

A physical interpretation of the coefficient of any one of the terms in the multinomial expansion can be thought of as follows: Consider a set A to contain n elements and let $n_1, n_2, \ldots, n_k$ be positive integers such that $n_1 + n_2 + \cdots + n_k = n$. Then we are interested in the total number of ways in which n_1 objects of one kind, n_2 objects of a second kind, $\ldots$, and n_k objects of a kth kind may be arranged in n cells. This number is given by $\binom{n}{n_1, n_2, \ldots, n_k}$. In most applications of this theorem, we are interested in obtaining the coefficients of specific terms of generating functions. For example, the coefficient of $x_1^2 x_2^4 x_3^0 x_4^3$, which is a term of the generating function or polynomial $(x_1 + x_2 + x_3 + x_4)^9$, is $\dfrac{9!}{2! 4! 0! 3!}$. This number is simply the total number of ways in which two of one kind, four of a second kind, none of a third kind, and three of a fourth kind can be selected and arranged.

Example 0.4.2   The coefficient of the term $x_1^2 x_2^3 x_3^4 x_4^0 x_5^1$ in the expansion of the polynomial $(x_1 + x_2 + x_3 + x_4 + x_5)^{10}$ is

$$\binom{10}{2, 3, 4, 0, 1} = \frac{10!}{2! 3! 4! 0! 1!}.$$

We shall now state some of the identities and series which will be found useful in the study of probability theory.

(a) If, in the binomial theorem, we let $x = p$ and $y = q$ such that $p + q = 1$, then

$$(p + q)^n = \sum_{i=0}^{n} \binom{n}{i} p^{n-i} q^i = 1.$$

(b) $\dfrac{(1 - x^n)}{(1 - x)} = \sum_{i=0}^{n-1} x^i.$

(c) $\dfrac{1}{(1-x)^n} = \displaystyle\sum_{i=0}^{\infty} \binom{n+i-1}{i} x^i.$

(d) $\dfrac{n(n+1)}{2} = \displaystyle\sum_{i=1}^{n} i,$ $\dfrac{n(n+1)(2n+1)}{6} = \displaystyle\sum_{i=1}^{n} i^2.$

(e) $\dbinom{n+m}{r} = \displaystyle\sum_{i=0}^{r} \binom{n}{i}\binom{m}{r-i}.$

(f) $e^x = \exp(x) = \displaystyle\sum_{i=0}^{\infty} \dfrac{x^i}{i!}.$

For further discussion of the above topics, you are referred to References [10], [11], and [12].

0.5 *Jacobians*

In many basic mathematical calculations, it is essential to make various transformations, that is, to change from a function of several variables to that of others. When the transformation is from one variable to another variable, the differential is enough to formulate the new function; however, when it is necessary to make transformations which involve more than one variable, we need the concept of *Jacobians*.

In this section, we show how Jacobians are obtained, and we illustrate the procedure with examples.

Suppose that we are given a function $f(x, y)$ and we are interested in obtaining a new function $h(u, v)$, where the relation between the new and old variables is given by the following mapping:

$$u = h_1 (x, y) \quad \text{and} \quad v = h_2 (x, y).$$

Under the assumption that this mapping is a one-to-one transformation, then its inverse exists:

$$x = g_1 (u, v) \quad \text{and} \quad y = g_2 (u, v).$$

This relationship may be interpreted as mapping a region G_1 of the xy plane into a region G_2 of the uv plane. Then, under the condition that both $g_1 (u, v)$ and $g_2 (u, v)$ have continuous partial derivatives with respect to u and v, we can obtain the new function $h(u, v)$ as follows:

$$h\,(u,\,v) = f\,[g_1\,(u,\,v),\,g_2\,(u,\,v)]\,|J|,$$

so that

$$\iint_{G_1} f(x,\,y)\,dx\,dy = \iint_{G_2} f\,[g_1(u,\,v),\,g_2(u,\,v)]\,|J|\,du\,dv.$$

where the "J" is the so-called *Jacobian* of the transformation and is defined by the determinant

$$J = \frac{\partial(x,\,y)}{\partial(u,\,v)} = \begin{vmatrix} \dfrac{\partial x}{\partial u} & \dfrac{\partial x}{\partial v} \\[2mm] \dfrac{\partial y}{\partial u} & \dfrac{\partial y}{\partial v} \end{vmatrix}.$$

Similarly, the above notion can be extended to a transformation involving three or more variables. Assuming again that we have continuous partial derivatives with respect to u, v, and w and that they are one-to-one, we shall now illustrate how the Jacobian is obtained for the following transformation:

$$x = g_1(u,\,v,\,w)$$
$$y = g_2(u,\,v,\,w)$$
$$z = g_3(u,\,v,\,w)$$

$$J = \frac{\partial(x,\,y,\,z)}{\partial(u,\,v,\,w)} = \begin{vmatrix} \dfrac{\partial x}{\partial u} & \dfrac{\partial x}{\partial v} & \dfrac{\partial x}{\partial w} \\[2mm] \dfrac{\partial y}{\partial u} & \dfrac{\partial y}{\partial v} & \dfrac{\partial y}{\partial w} \\[2mm] \dfrac{\partial z}{\partial u} & \dfrac{\partial z}{\partial v} & \dfrac{\partial z}{\partial w} \end{vmatrix}.$$

Example 0.5.1   Find the Jacobian of transformation of

$$x = 5u - 3v$$
$$y = 3u + 2v.$$

Solution

$$J = \frac{\partial(x,\,y)}{\partial(u,\,v)} = \begin{vmatrix} \dfrac{\partial x}{\partial u} & \dfrac{\partial x}{\partial v} \\[2mm] \dfrac{\partial y}{\partial u} & \dfrac{\partial y}{\partial v} \end{vmatrix} = \begin{vmatrix} 5 & -3 \\ 3 & 2 \end{vmatrix} = 1.$$

Example 0.5.2   Find the Jacobian of transformation of the polar coordinate functions of the form

$$t = r \sin \theta$$
$$z = r \cos \theta.$$

Solution

$$J = \frac{\partial(t, z)}{\partial(r, \theta)} = \begin{vmatrix} \dfrac{\partial t}{\partial r} & \dfrac{\partial t}{\partial \theta} \\[2mm] \dfrac{\partial z}{\partial r} & \dfrac{\partial z}{\partial \theta} \end{vmatrix} = \begin{vmatrix} \sin \theta & r \cos \theta \\ \cos \theta & -r \sin \theta \end{vmatrix}$$

$$= -r \sin^2 \theta - r \cos^2 \theta = -r(\sin^2 \theta + \cos^2 \theta) = -r.$$

Therefore,

$$|J| = r.$$

A precise theoretical development of this subject can be found in References [5], [8], and [9].

0.6 Gamma Functions

The one-parameter integral

$$\Gamma(p) = \int_0^\infty x^{p-1} e^{-x} \, dx, \quad p > 0 \tag{0.6.1}$$

is called the *gamma function*. If, in Equation (0.6.1), we replace p with $p + 1$ and integrate it by parts, we find that

$$\Gamma(p + 1) = \int_0^\infty x^p e^{-x} \, dx = -x^p e^{-x} \Big|_0^\infty + p \int_0^\infty x^{p-1} e^{-x} \, dx$$

$$= p \int_0^\infty x^{p-1} e^{-x} \, dx$$

$$= p\Gamma(p). \tag{0.6.2}$$

If we replace p with $p - 1$ in Equation (0.6.2), this becomes

$$\Gamma(p) = (p - 1)\Gamma(p - 1). \tag{0.6.3}$$

Continuing in this way, we find that

$$\Gamma(p) = (p-1)(p-2)\Gamma(p-2)$$
$$= (p-1)(p-2)(p-3)\Gamma(p-3)$$
$$= (p-1)(p-2)(p-3)(p-4)\cdots\Gamma(1),$$

where

$$\Gamma(1) = \int_0^\infty e^{-x}\, dx = -e^{-x}\Big|_0^\infty = 1.$$

For example:

$$\Gamma(2) = 1\Gamma(1) = 1, \qquad \Gamma(3) = 2\Gamma(2) = 2\cdot 1\Gamma(1) = 2;$$
$$\Gamma(4) = 3\Gamma(3) = 3\cdot 2\Gamma(2) = 3\cdot 2\cdot 1\Gamma(1) = 6$$

and

$$\Gamma(5) = 4\Gamma(4) = 4\cdot 3\Gamma(3) = 4\cdot 3\cdot 2\Gamma(2) = 4\cdot 3\cdot 2\cdot 1\Gamma(1) = 24.$$

Therefore, for any positive integer n, we have

$$\Gamma(n) = (n-1)(n-2)\cdots 3\cdot 2\cdot 1 = (n-1)!$$

Solving Equation (0.6.3) for $\Gamma(p-1)$ gives

$$\Gamma(p-1) = \frac{\Gamma(p)}{p-1}.$$

This expression may be used to evaluate values of $\Gamma(p)$ when $p < 0$.

In a number of applications of the gamma function, p is either a positive integer or a multiple of 1/2. Hence, it is important to be able to compute $(1/2)!$, that is, $\Gamma(3/2)$.

$$\Gamma\left(\frac{3}{2}\right) = \left(\frac{1}{2}\right)\Gamma\left(\frac{1}{2}\right) = \frac{1}{2}\int_0^\infty x^{-1/2}e^{-x}\, dx. \qquad (0.6.4)$$

Let $x = t^2/2$, $dx = t\, dt$ in Equation (0.6.4), and we obtain

$$\Gamma\left(\frac{3}{2}\right) = \frac{1}{\sqrt{2}}\int_0^\infty e^{-(1/2)t^2}\, dt.$$

It will be shown in a later chapter that

$$\frac{1}{\sqrt{2\pi}}\int_0^\infty e^{-(1/2)t^2}\,dt = \frac{1}{2}.$$

Therefore, $\Gamma(1/2)=\sqrt{\pi}$, and $\Gamma(3/2) = \dfrac{\sqrt{\pi}}{2} = (1/2)!$

Example 0.6.1   Evaluate the following factorials.

(a) $\left(\dfrac{3}{2}\right)! = \left(\dfrac{3}{2}\right)\left(\dfrac{1}{2}\right)! = \dfrac{3\sqrt{\pi}}{4}$

(b) $\left(\dfrac{7}{2}\right)! = \left(\dfrac{7}{2}\right)\cdot\left(\dfrac{5}{2}\right)! = \left(\dfrac{7}{2}\right)\left(\dfrac{5}{2}\right)\cdot\left(\dfrac{3}{2}\right)! = \left(\dfrac{7}{2}\right)\left(\dfrac{5}{2}\right)\left(\dfrac{3}{2}\right)\left(\dfrac{1}{2}\right)!$

$$= \left(\dfrac{7}{2}\right)\left(\dfrac{5}{2}\right)\left(\dfrac{3}{2}\right)\left(\dfrac{\sqrt{\pi}}{2}\right) = \dfrac{105\sqrt{\pi}}{16}.$$

Example 0.6.2   Evaluate the following integrals.

(a) $\displaystyle\int_0^\infty x^{6/7}e^{-x}\,dx = \Gamma\!\left(\dfrac{13}{7}\right)$

(b) $\displaystyle\int_0^\infty x^{-1/3}e^{-x}\,dx = \Gamma\!\left(\dfrac{2}{3}\right)$

(c) $\displaystyle\int_0^\infty x^3e^{-3x}\,dx$; let $t = 3x$, $\dfrac{dt}{3} = dx$. Then $\displaystyle\int_0^\infty x^3e^{-3x}\,dx$ becomes

$$\frac{1}{81}\int_0^\infty t^3e^{-t}\,dt = \frac{1}{81}\Gamma(4) = \frac{2}{27}.$$

For any positive value of p, the gamma function may very well be interpreted as the area under the function $f(x) = x^{p-1}e^{-x}$ from $x = 0$ to $x = \infty$, as shown in Figure 0.6.1 for various values of p.
The following Figure 0.6.2 can be used to approximate $\Gamma(p)$ for various positive and negative values of p when the gamma function is difficult to evaluate.

Example 0.6.3   From Figure 0.6.2, we can approximate the following gamma functions:

(a) $\Gamma(1.10) \approx .96$
(b) $\Gamma(1.30) \approx .89$
(c) $\Gamma(1.70) \approx .91$
(d) $\Gamma(1.90) \approx .96.$

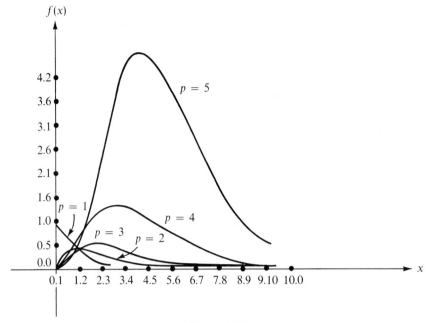

Figure 0.6.1

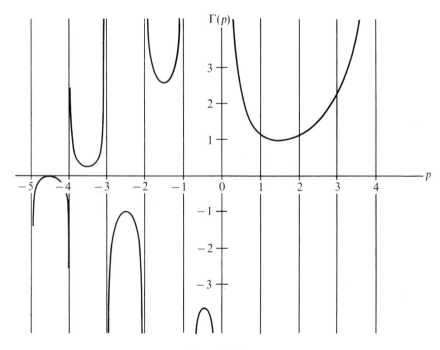

Figure 0.6.2

0.7   Beta Function

The two-parameter integral defined by

$$B(p, q) = \int_0^1 y^{p-1}(1-y)^{q-1} \, dy, \quad p > 0, q > 0$$

is called the *beta function*. This function is related to the gamma function in the following way.

$$B(p, q) = \frac{\Gamma(p)\,\Gamma(q)}{\Gamma(p+q)}. \tag{0.7.1}$$

This relationship can be shown as follows:
In the function $\Gamma(p)$, if we apply the transformation $x = y^2$, $dx = 2y \, dy$, we obtain

$$\Gamma(p) = \int_0^\infty x^{p-1} e^{-x} \, dx = 2 \int_0^\infty y^{2p-1} e^{-y^2} \, dy. \tag{0.7.2}$$

Similarly,

$$\Gamma(q) = 2 \int_0^\infty z^{2q-1} e^{-z^2} \, dz. \tag{0.7.3}$$

Multiplying the functions (0.7.2) and (0.7.3) gives

$$\Gamma(p)\Gamma(q) = 4 \int_0^\infty z^{2q-1} e^{-z^2} \, dz \cdot \int_0^\infty y^{2p-1} e^{-y^2} \, dy$$

$$= 4 \int_0^\infty \int_0^\infty z^{2q-1} y^{2p-1} e^{-(z^2+y^2)} \, dz \, dy. \tag{0.7.4}$$

In order to simplify the double integral (0.7.4), we must change to polar coordinates. That is, for a positive radius vector r as shown in Figure 0.7.1, we have

$$r = +\sqrt{z^2 + y^2}$$
$$z = r \cos \phi$$
$$y = r \sin \phi.$$

Substituting these values into Equation (0.7.4), multiplying by $|J|$, the absolute value of the Jacobian, which was shown in Example 0.5.2 of Section

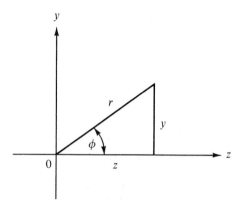

Figure 0.7.1

0.5 to be equal to r, and restricting ourselves to the first quadrant, that is, ϕ varying from 0 to $\pi/2$ and r from 0 to ∞, we obtain

$$\Gamma(p)\Gamma(q) = 4 \int_0^{\frac{\pi}{2}} \left\{ \int_0^\infty (r \cos \phi)^{2q-1}(r \sin \phi)^{2p-1} e^{-r^2} r \, dr \right\} d\phi$$

$$= 4 \int_0^{\frac{\pi}{2}} \left\{ \int_0^\infty e^{-r^2} r^{2q+2p-1} \cos^{2q-1}\phi \sin^{2p-1}\phi \, dr \right\} d\phi$$

$$= \left\{ 2 \int_0^\infty e^{-r^2} r^{2q+2p-1} \, dr \right\} \left\{ 2 \int_0^{\frac{\pi}{2}} \cos^{2q-1}\phi \sin^{2p-1}\phi \, d\phi \right\}.$$

$$(0.7.5)$$

Replacing q with $p + q$ and z with r in the function (0.7.3), we have

$$\Gamma(p + q) = 2 \int_0^\infty r^{2(p+q)-1} e^{-r^2} \, dr. \tag{0.7.6}$$

Now, if we apply the trigonometric transformation $y = \sin^2 \phi$, which implies $1 - y = \cos^2 \phi$, and $dy = 2 \cos \phi \sin \phi \, d\phi$ to the beta function, we obtain

$$B(p, q) = \int_0^1 y^{p-1}(1 - y)^{q-1} \, dy$$

$$= 2 \int_0^{\frac{\pi}{2}} \sin^{2p-1}\phi \cos^{2q-1}\phi \, d\phi. \tag{0.7.7}$$

Inspecting Equations (0.7.5), (0.7.6), and (0.7.7), it is clear that the relationship

$$B(p, q) = \frac{\Gamma(p)\Gamma(q)}{\Gamma(p+q)}, \quad p, q > 0,$$

is valid. This relationship of the beta function to the gamma function shows that $B(p, q)$ is symmetrical with respect to the parameters p and q; that is,

$$B(p, q) = B(q, p).$$

Example 0.7.1   Evaluate the following definite integrals.

(a) $\displaystyle\int_0^1 y^4(1 - y)^5 dy = \Gamma(5, 6) = \frac{\Gamma(5)\Gamma(6)}{B(11)} = \frac{1}{1260}.$

(b) $\displaystyle\int_0^1 \frac{y^2 dy}{\sqrt{1 - y^2}}$;   let $u = y^2, \dfrac{du}{2\sqrt{u}} = dy$

$$\int_0^1 \frac{y^2 dy}{\sqrt{1 - y^2}} = \int_0^1 u^{1/2}(1 - u)^{-1/2} du = \frac{1}{2} B\left(\frac{3}{2}, \frac{1}{2}\right)$$

$$= \frac{1}{2} \frac{\Gamma\left(\frac{3}{2}\right)\Gamma\left(\frac{1}{2}\right)}{\Gamma(2)} = \frac{\Pi}{4}.$$

(c) $\displaystyle\int_0^2 y^3\left(1 - \left(\frac{y}{2}\right)\right)^2 dy$;   let $u = \frac{1}{2} y, 2\, du = dy$

$$\int_0^2 y^3\left(1 - \left(\frac{y}{2}\right)\right)^2 dy = 16 \int_0^1 u^3(1 - u)^2\, du = 16\, B(4, 3)$$

$$= 16 \frac{\Gamma(4)\Gamma(3)}{\Gamma(7)} = \frac{4}{15}.$$

Note that Example 0.7.1 (c) illustrates an interesting point: the range of the variable y need not be restricted between 0 and 1, because a linear transformation gives us the domain of the beta function.

For various positive values of p and q, the beta function may be interpreted as the area under the function $f(x) = x^{p-1}(1 - x)^{q-1}$ from $x = 0$ to $x = 1$, as shown in Figure 0.7.2. It is important to observe that the parameters p and q determine the shape of the curves.

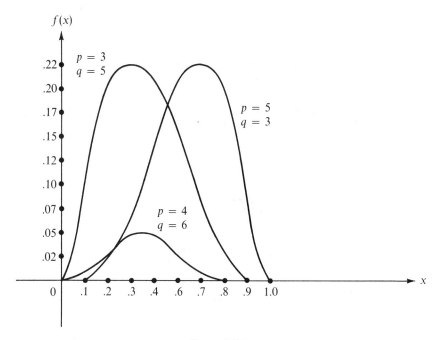

Figure 0.7.2

0.8   Matrices

In this section, we shall present a brief review of some of the basic definitions and operations of matrix algebra. This review will be helpful to you when you begin to study the formulation of the basic concepts of finite Markov chains in Chapter 9.

A matrix is a rectangular array of elements of the form

$$
A = \begin{bmatrix}
a_{11} & a_{12} & a_{13} & \cdots & a_{1n} \\
a_{21} & a_{22} & a_{23} & \cdots & a_{2n} \\
\vdots & \vdots & \vdots & & \vdots \\
a_{m1} & a_{m2} & a_{m3} & \cdots & a_{mn}
\end{bmatrix}
$$

The letters a_{ij} denote real numbers or functions, which we shall refer to as the *elements* of the matrix. The i in the double subscript of a_{ij} indicates the row, and the second subscript j indicates the column of the array in which the element is located.

We shall denote the $m \times n$ matrix A as $[a_{ij}]$, where it is understood that $i = 1, 2, \ldots, m$, and $j = 1, 2, \ldots, n$. The integers m and n denote the number of rows and columns respectively that constitute the array. We usually refer to a matrix by stating its dimensions (order); that is, A is an $m \times n$ matrix.

A matrix having the same number of rows and columns, that is, $m = n$, is called a *square matrix* of the order n or m. In a square matrix, the elements $a_{11}, a_{22}, \ldots, a_{nn}$ are called the *diagonal elements* and the sum of these elements is called the *trace* of the matrix. If $m = 1$, that is, if the matrix consists of a single row, we call it a *row vector*. Analogously, if $n = 1$, the matrix consists of a single column, and we call it a *column vector*. Thus, we can display these two vectors, terming them a and b, as follows:

$$a = [a_1, a_2, a_3, \ldots, a_n], \qquad b = \begin{bmatrix} b_1 \\ b_2 \\ b_3 \\ \vdots \\ b_m \end{bmatrix}.$$

Two matrices A and B are *equal*, $A = B$, if and only if they have the same dimensions and each element of A is equal to the corresponding element of B, that is, if and only if

$$a_{ij} = b_{ij}, \quad i = 1, 2, \ldots, m, \quad j = 1, 2, 3, \ldots, n.$$

Similarly, we say $A > B$ if $a_{ij} > b_{ij}$ for all i and j. That is, each element of A is greater than the corresponding element of B.

A square matrix with elements in the main diagonal equal to one and all other elements equal to zero is called a *unit matrix*, and we denote it by I. A zero matrix is a matrix with all of its elements being zero, and we denote it by 0.

We shall now define some of the basic operations and relations of matrices.

(a) If A is a matrix with elements a_{ij} and if c is a scalar, then $cA = [c\, a_{ij}]$. That is, multiplying a matrix A by a constant means multiplying each element of the matrix by this constant.

Example 0.8.1 If

$$A = \begin{bmatrix} 3 & -1 \\ 0 & 2 \end{bmatrix},$$

then

$$nA = \begin{bmatrix} 3n & -n \\ 0 & 2n \end{bmatrix}.$$

(b) Let $A = [a_{ij}]$ and $B = [b_{ij}]$ be two $m \times n$ matrices. The *sum* of the matrices, $A + B$, is defined as an $m \times n$ matrix C, where each element of C is the sum of the corresponding elements of A and B. That is,

$$A + B = [a_{ij} + b_{ij}] = [c_{ij}] = C.$$

The difference of two matrices is defined similarly, that is,

$$A - B = [a_{ij} - b_{ij}] = [d_{ij}] = D.$$

Example 0.8.2   If

$$A = \begin{bmatrix} -1 & 2 \\ 3 & 0 \\ 1 & 4 \end{bmatrix} \quad \text{and} \quad B = \begin{bmatrix} 2 & 4 \\ 5 & 6 \\ -2 & 1 \end{bmatrix},$$

then

$$A + B = \begin{bmatrix} 1 & 6 \\ 8 & 6 \\ -1 & 5 \end{bmatrix} \quad \text{and} \quad A - B = \begin{bmatrix} -3 & -2 \\ -2 & -6 \\ 3 & 3 \end{bmatrix}.$$

Note: Two matrices of different order cannot be added or subtracted; we speak of such matrices as not being *conformable* for addition or subtraction. Two matrices which can be added or subtracted are conformable.

(c)   Let A be an $m \times n$ and B an $n \times k$ matrix. The *product* of these matrices, AB, is an $m \times k$ matrix whose elements are given by $\sum_{t=1}^{n} a_{it} b_{tj}$, $i = 1, 2, \ldots, m$, $j = 1, 2, \ldots, k$. That is, the product operation is *row by column*; each element of the row is multiplied by the corresponding element of the column and these products are summed.

Example 0.8.3   If

$$A = \begin{bmatrix} a_{11} & a_{12} & a_{13} \\ a_{21} & a_{22} & a_{23} \end{bmatrix} \quad (2 \times 3)$$

and

$$B = \begin{bmatrix} b_{11} & b_{12} \\ b_{21} & b_{22} \\ b_{31} & b_{32} \end{bmatrix} \quad (3 \times 2)$$

then

$$AB = \begin{bmatrix} a_{11}b_{11} + a_{12}b_{21} + a_{13}b_{31} & a_{11}b_{12} + a_{12}b_{22} + a_{13}b_{32} \\ a_{21}b_{11} + a_{22}b_{21} + a_{23}b_{31} & a_{21}b_{12} + a_{22}b_{22} + a_{23}b_{32} \end{bmatrix} \quad (2 \times 2)$$

Example 0.8.4   If C is an $m \times 1$ matrix and D a $1 \times n$ matrix, then the product CD in that order is an $m \times n$ matrix. For example, if

$$C = \begin{bmatrix} c_{11} \\ c_{21} \\ \vdots \\ c_{m1} \end{bmatrix} \quad \text{and} \quad D = [d_{11} \, d_{21} \, \cdots \, d_{n1}] \quad (1 \times n),$$
$$(m \times 1)$$

then

$$CD = \begin{bmatrix} c_{11}d_{11} & c_{11}d_{21} & \cdots & c_{11}d_{n1} \\ c_{21}d_{11} & c_{21}d_{21} & \cdots & c_{21}d_{n1} \\ c_{m1}d_{11} & c_{m1}d_{21} & \cdots & c_{m1}d_{n1} \end{bmatrix} \quad (m \times n)$$

Example 0.8.5   If

$$A = \begin{bmatrix} -2 & 1 \\ 3 & 4 \end{bmatrix}_{(2 \times 2)} \quad \text{and} \quad B = \begin{bmatrix} -1 & 4 & 0 \\ 5 & 3 & -2 \end{bmatrix} \quad (2 \times 3)$$

then

$$AB = \begin{bmatrix} 7 & -5 & -2 \\ 17 & 24 & -8 \end{bmatrix} \quad (2 \times 3).$$

Example 0.8.6   If E is a $1 \times m$ matrix and F is an $m \times 1$ matrix, then EF is a 1×1 matrix. That is, if

$$E = [e_{11} \, e_{12}, \ldots, e_{1m}](1 \times m) \quad \text{and} \quad F = \begin{bmatrix} f_{11} \\ f_{21} \\ \vdots \\ f_{m1} \end{bmatrix},$$
$$(m \times 1)$$

then

$$EF = e_{11}f_{11} + e_{12}f_{21} + \cdots + e_{1m}f_{m1}$$

$$= \sum_{k=1}^{m} e_{1k}f_{k1}.$$

However, the product FE is an $m \times m$ matrix whose ijth element is $f_{i1}e_{ij}$, $i, j = 1, 2, \ldots, m$.

Hence, in order for the product of two matrices to exist, the number of columns of the first matrix must be equal to the number of rows of the second matrix. Also, if A and B are $n \times n$ matrices, then the ijth element of the product AB and BA are respectively

$$\sum_{k=1}^{n} a_{ik}b_{kj}, \quad \sum_{k=1}^{n} b_{ik}a_{kj}.$$

With respect to the above matrix operations, we state the following theorem.

Theorem 0.8.1   If the matrices A, B, and C are conformable to the indicated operation, then we have

(1)   commutative law: $A + B = B + A$;
(2)   associative law: (a) $[A + B] + C = A + [B + C]$,
                                (b) $[AB]C = A[BC]$;
(3)   scalar law: $cA + cB = c[A + B] = [A + B]c$;
(4)   distributive law: (a) $AB + AC = A[B + C]$,
                                  (b) $AC + BC = [A + B]C$.

Let A be a square matrix whose elements are real numbers. By the *determinant* of the matrix A, we mean a unique real number denoted by $|A|$ or det A and obtained by

$$|A| = \det A = \sum_r \alpha_{i_1 i_2 \cdots i_n} a_{1 i_1} a_{2 i_2} \cdots a_{n i_n},$$

where the second subscripts of the product $a_{1 i_1}$, $a_{2 i_2}$, ..., $a_{n i_n}$, when arranged in the sequence $i_1, i_2, \ldots, i_n$ is one of the $n!$ permutations of the integers $1, 2, \ldots, n$; and where $\alpha_{i_1 i_2 \cdots i_n}$ is -1 or $+1$ according to whether the permutation is odd or even, respectively, that is, whether the number of inversions in the subscript of α is odd or even, respectively. Note that one and only one element in the product comes from any row and one and only one element comes from any column. The summation is over all permutations $i_1, i_2, \ldots, i_n$ of the integers $1, 2, 3, \ldots, n$. To determine when $\alpha_{i, i_2 \ldots i_n}$ is -1 or $+1$, we obtain the number of inversions in the permutation of the second subscript of the elements of the product. For example, α_{1234} is $+1$ because the number of inversions of the permutation 1234 is zero, or an even number. α_{1243} is -1 because the number of inversions of the permutation 1243 is one, or an odd number; and it has one inversion: 4 precedes 3. α_{1432} is -1 because the number of inversions of the permutation 1432 is 3 or an odd number: 4 precedes 3, 4 precedes 2, and 3 precedes 2.

The determinant of an $n \times n$ matrix is said to be of the order n. The following examples will clarify and illustrate the manner in which we utilize the above definition to obtain the determinant of a square matrix.

Example 0.8.7   If

$$A = \begin{bmatrix} a_{11} & a_{12} \\ a_{21} & a_{22} \end{bmatrix},$$

then the determinant of A is

$$|A| = \begin{vmatrix} a_{11} & a_{12} \\ a_{21} & a_{22} \end{vmatrix} = \alpha_{12} a_{11} a_{22} + \alpha_{21} a_{12} a_{21}$$

$$= a_{11} a_{22} - a_{12} a_{21}.$$

Note that the sign of α_{12} is $+1$ because there is no inversion in the permutation 12, but α_{21} is -1 because the number of inversions of the permutation 21 is one or an odd number (because 2 precedes 1).

Example 0.8.8   If

$$A = \begin{bmatrix} a_{11} & a_{12} & a_{13} \\ a_{21} & a_{22} & a_{23} \\ a_{31} & a_{32} & a_{33} \end{bmatrix},$$

then

$$|A| = \begin{vmatrix} a_{11} & a_{12} & a_{13} \\ a_{21} & a_{22} & a_{23} \\ a_{31} & a_{32} & a_{33} \end{vmatrix} = \alpha_{123}a_{11}a_{22}a_{33} + \alpha_{132}a_{11}a_{23}a_{32} + \alpha_{213}a_{12}a_{21}a_{33}$$
$$+ \alpha_{231}a_{12}a_{23}a_{31} + \alpha_{312}a_{13}a_{21}a_{32} + \alpha_{321}a_{13}a_{22}a_{31}.$$

Note that α_{123} is $+1$ because there are no inversions in the permutation 123; α_{132} is -1 for one inversion in the permutation 132 : 3 precedes 2; α_{213} is -1 because there is one inversion: 2 precedes 1; α_{231} is $+1$ because there are two inversions (even) in the permutation of 231: 2 precedes 1 and 3 precedes 1; α_{312} is $+1$; α_{321} is -1.
Therefore,

$$|A| = a_{11}a_{22}a_{33} - a_{11}a_{23}a_{32} - a_{12}a_{21}a_{33} + a_{12}a_{23}a_{31} + a_{13}a_{21}a_{32}$$
$$- a_{13}a_{22}a_{31}.$$

Example 0.8.9   If

$$A = \begin{bmatrix} 3 & 6 & 0 \\ 2 & 4 & -2 \\ -1 & 2 & -3 \end{bmatrix},$$

then

$$|A| = -36 + 12 + 36 + 12 + 0 + 0 = 24.$$

Let A be a square matrix. By the *minor* of the element a_{ij} of the matrix A, we mean the new matrix obtained when the ith row and jth column are eliminated. It is denoted by m_{ij}. That is, the minor of a_{11} in the 3×3 matrix

$$\begin{bmatrix} a_{11} & a_{12} & a_{13} \\ a_{21} & a_{22} & a_{23} \\ a_{31} & a_{32} & a_{33} \end{bmatrix}$$

is given by

$$m_{11} = \begin{bmatrix} a_{22} & a_{23} \\ a_{32} & a_{33} \end{bmatrix}.$$

By the *cofactor* of the element of the *i*th row and *j*th column, we mean the determinant of the minor, that is, $|m_{ij}|$ multiplied by $(-1)^{i+j}$. Therefore, the cofactor of a_{23} in the above 3 × 3 matrix is given by

$$(-1)^{2+3}\begin{vmatrix} a_{11} & a_{12} \\ a_{31} & a_{32} \end{vmatrix} = -(a_{11}a_{32} - a_{12}a_{31}).$$

Example 0.8.10   If

$$A = \begin{bmatrix} 3 & -1 & 2 \\ 4 & 1 & 7 \\ 0 & 4 & -3 \end{bmatrix},$$

then the cofactor of 4 is given by

$$(-1)^{3+2}\begin{vmatrix} 3 & 2 \\ 4 & 7 \end{vmatrix} = -(21 - 8) = -13$$

or

$$(-1)^{2+1}\begin{vmatrix} -1 & 2 \\ 4 & -3 \end{vmatrix} = -(3 - 8) = 5.$$

The determinant of a square matrix can also be defined by the sum of the products formed by multiplying each element of any row or column by its cofactor. That is,

$$|A| = \sum_{j=1}^{n} a_{ij}\{\text{cof } a_{ij}\} = \sum_{i=1}^{n} a_{ij}\{\text{cof } a_{ij}\}.$$

Example 0.8.11   If

$$A = \begin{bmatrix} a_{11} & a_{12} & a_{13} \\ a_{21} & a_{22} & a_{23} \\ a_{31} & a_{32} & a_{33} \end{bmatrix},$$

then, choosing the second column, we have

$$|A| = (-1)^{1+2} a_{12}\begin{vmatrix} a_{21} & a_{23} \\ a_{31} & a_{33} \end{vmatrix} + (-1)^{2+2} a_{22}\begin{vmatrix} a_{11} & a_{13} \\ a_{31} & a_{33} \end{vmatrix}$$

$$+ (-1)^{3+2} a_{32}\begin{vmatrix} a_{11} & a_{13} \\ a_{21} & a_{23} \end{vmatrix}$$

$$= -a_{12}(a_{21}a_{33} - a_{23}a_{31}) + a_{22}(a_{11}a_{33} - a_{13}a_{31}) - a_{32}(a_{11}a_{23} - a_{13}a_{21}).$$

The method of cofactors is perhaps the easiest method for obtaining the determinant of a square matrix.

Example 0.8.12   If

$$A = \begin{bmatrix} 3 & 2 & -3 \\ 0 & 4 & -2 \\ 1 & -1 & 0 \end{bmatrix},$$

then

$$|A| = (-1)^{1+1} 3 \begin{vmatrix} 4 & -2 \\ -1 & 0 \end{vmatrix} + (-1)^{2+1} 0 \begin{vmatrix} 2 & -3 \\ -1 & 0 \end{vmatrix} + (-1)^{3+1} 1 \begin{vmatrix} 2 & -3 \\ 4 & -2 \end{vmatrix}$$

$$= 3(-2) - 0 + 1(8) = 2.$$

We shall now list some of the important properties of determinants.

(a) Interchanging two rows or columns of a square matrix yields a determinant that is the negative of the original determinant.

(b) If two rows or columns of a square matrix are identical, then the determinant is equal to zero.

(c) Interchanging the rows and columns of a square matrix does not change the value of the determinant.

(d) If any row or column of a square matrix is multiplied by a nonzero constant, the resulting determinant is equal to the constant times the original determinant of the matrix.

(e) A common factor of all elements of a row or column of a square matrix may be removed and placed as a multiplier of the resulting determinant.

(f) If a multiple of the elements of any row or column of a square matrix is added to or subtracted from the elements of any other row or column the value of the resulting determinant is the same as that of the original determinant.

(g) If A and B are $n \times n$ matrices, then $|AB| = |A||B|$.

The *transpose* of a matrix A, denoted by A^T, is obtained by changing the rows to columns and the columns to rows; that is, the ijth entry of A is the jith entry of A^T. A *diagonal* matrix is one whose only nonzero entries are on the main diagonal. If an $n \times n$ matrix A is such that $|A| \neq 0$, then A is of *rank n*, and A is said to be *nonsingular*.

The *inverse* of a nonsingular square matrix A is denoted by A^{-1}, and it is defined by

$$A^{-1} = \left[\frac{\text{cof } a_{ji}}{|A|} \right] = \left[\frac{\text{cof } a_{ij}}{|A|} \right]^T.$$

It can be easily seen that $AA^{-1} = A^{-1}A = I$ and $(A^T)^{-1} = (A^{-1})^T$.

Example 0.8.13   Find the inverse of the matrix A as defined in Example 0.8.12.

Solution   We know that $|A| = 2$, and

$$A^{-1} = \left[\frac{\text{cof } a_{ij}}{|A|} \right]^T$$

$$= \begin{bmatrix} (-1)^{1+1} \dfrac{\begin{vmatrix} 4 & -2 \\ -1 & 0 \end{vmatrix}}{2} & (-1)^{1+2} \dfrac{\begin{vmatrix} 0 & -2 \\ 1 & 0 \end{vmatrix}}{2} & (-1)^{1+3} \dfrac{\begin{vmatrix} 0 & 4 \\ 1 & -1 \end{vmatrix}}{2} \\[3mm] (-1)^{2+1} \dfrac{\begin{vmatrix} 2 & -3 \\ -1 & 0 \end{vmatrix}}{2} & (-1)^{2+2} \dfrac{\begin{vmatrix} 3 & -3 \\ 1 & 0 \end{vmatrix}}{2} & (-1)^{2+3} \dfrac{\begin{vmatrix} 3 & 2 \\ 1 & -1 \end{vmatrix}}{2} \\[3mm] (-1)^{3+1} \dfrac{\begin{vmatrix} 2 & -3 \\ 4 & -2 \end{vmatrix}}{2} & (-1)^{3+2} \dfrac{\begin{vmatrix} 3 & -3 \\ 0 & -2 \end{vmatrix}}{2} & (-1)^{3+3} \dfrac{\begin{vmatrix} 3 & 2 \\ 0 & 4 \end{vmatrix}}{2} \end{bmatrix}^T$$

$$= \begin{bmatrix} \dfrac{1}{2}(-2) & -\dfrac{1}{2}(2) & +\dfrac{1}{2}(-4) \\[3mm] -\dfrac{1}{2}(-3) & \dfrac{1}{2}(3) & -\dfrac{1}{2}(-5) \\[3mm] \dfrac{1}{2}(8) & -\dfrac{1}{2}(-6) & \dfrac{1}{2}(12) \end{bmatrix}^T$$

$$= \begin{bmatrix} -1 & -1 & -2 \\[2mm] \dfrac{3}{2} & \dfrac{3}{2} & \dfrac{5}{2} \\[2mm] 4 & 3 & 6 \end{bmatrix}^T = \begin{bmatrix} -1 & \dfrac{3}{2} & 4 \\[2mm] -1 & \dfrac{3}{2} & 3 \\[2mm] -2 & \dfrac{5}{2} & 6 \end{bmatrix}.$$

Note that

$$AA^{-1} = \begin{bmatrix} 3 & 2 & -3 \\ 0 & 4 & -2 \\ 1 & -1 & 0 \end{bmatrix}_{(3 \times 3)} \cdot \begin{bmatrix} -1 & \dfrac{3}{2} & 4 \\[2mm] -1 & \dfrac{3}{2} & 3 \\[2mm] -2 & \dfrac{5}{2} & 6 \end{bmatrix}_{(3 \times 3)} = \begin{bmatrix} 1 & 0 & 0 \\ 0 & 1 & 0 \\ 0 & 0 & 1 \end{bmatrix}_{(3 \times 3)} = I.$$

These basic concepts of matrix algebra constitute only a very brief introduction to the subject. They will be a helpful review prior to your study of Chapter 9 on Finite Markov Chains. For a more extensive development of matrix analysis, we refer you to References [2], [4], and [8].

Exercises

0.0. Evaluate the following sums:

(a) $\displaystyle\sum_{i=1}^{6} x_i^2$

(b) $\displaystyle\left(\sum_{j=1}^{4} x_j\right)^{1/2}$

(c) $\displaystyle\sum_{i=1}^{3} x_i y_j$

(d) $\displaystyle\left(\sum_{i=1}^{2} x_i\right)\left(\sum_{j=1}^{4} y_j\right)$

(e) $\displaystyle\sum_{i=1}^{4} (-1)^{i-1} i y^i$

(f) $\displaystyle\sum_{j=1}^{4}\sum_{i=1}^{3} (x_i + 1)(yi)$

(g) $\displaystyle\sum_{j=1}^{2}\sum_{i=j+1}^{5} i^{j+1}$

0.1. Evaluate the following products.

(a) $\displaystyle\prod_{i=1}^{5} x_{i-1}$

(b) $\displaystyle\prod_{i=1}^{r} \frac{x_i}{y_{i-1}}$

(c) $\displaystyle\prod_{i=1}^{3} (-1)^i \frac{x_i}{i+1}$

0.2. Let the universal set U and the subsets A_1, A_2, A_3 be defined as follows:
$$U = \{a, b, c, d, e, f, g, h, i, j, k, l\},$$
$$A_1 = \{a, b, e, f\}, \quad A_2 = \{c, e, g, h, l\}, \quad A_3 = \{a, b, d, k, l\}.$$

Find the following sets.

(a) $A_1 \cup A_2 \cup A_3$ (b) $A_1 \cap A_3$ (c) $A_1 \cap A_2 \cap A_3$
(d) $A_2 \cap U$ (e) $\bar{A}_1 \cup \bar{A}_2$ (f) $A_3 \cup (A_1 \cap A_2)$
(g) $\overline{(A_1 \cap A_3)}$ (h) $\overline{(U \cup \varnothing)}$ (i) $(A_1 \cap A_2) \cup (\bar{A}_1 \cap A_3)$

0.3. Let the universal set and the subsets A_1, A_2, and A_3 be defined as follows:
$$U = \{x : 0 \le x \le 100\},$$
$$A_1 = \{x : 16 < x \le 41\}, \quad A_2 = \{x : 29 \le x \le 56\}, \quad A_3 = \{x : 11 \le x < 66\}.$$

Find the following sets.

(a) $A_1 \cup A_3$ (b) $A_1 \cap A_3$
(c) $A_1 \cup (\varnothing \cap \bar{A}_2)$ (d) $A_1 \cap (\varnothing \cup \bar{A}_2)$
(e) $(A_3 \cup A_3) \cap (A_2 \cup \varnothing)$ (f) $(\bar{A}_3 \cap \bar{A}_2) \cup (A_3 \cap A_2)$
(g) $A_3 \cap (A_1 \cup A_2)$ (h) $(A_3 \cap A_1) \cup A_3$
(i) $A_3 \cup (A_2 \cap A_1)$

0.4. If $A = \{a_1, a_2, a_3\}$ and $B = \{b_1, b_2, b_3\}$, find the set of all ordered pairs $A \times B$ and $B \times A$.

0.5. The universal set U consists of four elements:

$$U = \{x: x = 1, 2, 3, 4\}.$$

Write all possible subsets of U.

0.6. How many different subsets are there in a set containing k distinct elements?

0.7. Draw Venn diagrams for the following sets and shade the indicated area.

(a) $(A_1 \cup A_2) \cap (A_3 \cup A_4)$
(b) $(A_1 \cup \bar{A}_2) \cap (A_3 \cup \bar{A}_4)$
(c) $(A_1 \cup \bar{A}_2) \cap (A_1 \cup \bar{A}_2)$
(d) $(A_1 \cup \bar{A}_2) \cap (\bar{A}_1 \cup A_3)$
(e) $(A_1 \cup \bar{A}_1) \cap (A_2 \cap \bar{A}_3 \cap A_4)$
(f) $\{(A_1 \cup \bar{A}_1) \cap (A_2 \cup \bar{A}_2)\} \cup (A_3 \cap \bar{A}_3)$

0.8. Prove that the following identities are valid using Venn diagrams.

(a) $\bar{A}_1 \cap \bar{A}_2 = \overline{A_1 \cup A_2}$ (b) $\overline{A_1 \cap A_2} = \bar{A}_1 \cup \bar{A}_2$

0.9. Prove that the following relations are valid using Venn diagrams.

(a) $A_1 \cap A_2 = A_1 - (A_1 - A_2)$
(b) $A_1 - A_2 = A_1 - (A_1 \cap A_2)$
(c) $(A_1 \cap A_2) - A_3 = A_1 \cap (A_2 - A_3)$
(d) $A_1 \cup A_2 = A_1 \cup (A_2 - A_1)$

0.10. Prove that

$$A_1 \subset A_2$$

implies the following relations:

(a) $A_1 \cup A_2 = A_2$ (b) $A_1 \cap A_2 = A_1$.

0.11. Evaluate:

(a) P_5^{17} (b) $P_0{}^5$ (c) P_{r+1}^n (d) P_{r-1}^{n-1}.

0.12. How many different arrangements of books are there on a shelf accommodating four books if seven books are available?

0.13. How many three-digit numbers can be formed from the numbers 0, 1, 2, 3, 4, 5 under the following conditions if 0 is not the leading digit?

(a) repetition of the numbers is allowed;
(b) repetition of the numbers is not allowed.

0.14. Evaluate:

(a) $\binom{17}{5}$ (b) $\binom{7}{i}$ (c) $\binom{n}{r+1}$ (d) $\binom{n-r+1}{r}$

0.15. (a) If $\binom{n}{12} = \binom{n}{8}$, find n.

(b) If $\binom{6}{k} = \binom{6}{k-2}$, find k.

0.16. Show that $n\binom{n}{r} = (r+1)\binom{n}{r+1} + r\binom{n}{r}$.

0.17. In how many ways can a committee of four be chosen from a 12-man group?

0.18. (a) How many subsets of size four does a set of seven possess?
(b) What is the total number of subsets that a set of seven possesses?

0.19. Show that $\binom{n}{r} = \binom{n}{n-r}$.

0.20. How many four-digit numbers can be formed from the numbers 1, 2, 3, 4, 5 if duplication is not allowed?

0.21. In how many ways can we draw a five-card hand from a deck of 52 cards?

0.22. In how many ways can one select three operable and two defective components from a lot of 16 operable and six defective components?

0.23. In how many ways can a football coach choose one or more players from 16 qualified candidates?

0.24. Using Stirling's formula evaluate the following:

(a) 333!   (b) 1321!

0.25. Expand and simplify:

    (a) $(x^{1/2} + 2y)^5$ (b) $\left(2x - \dfrac{1}{2}y^2\right)^6$

0.26. Using combinations, expand $(p + q)^n$.

0.27. Evaluate $\displaystyle\sum_{i=1}^{3-j} \binom{6}{i}\binom{4}{3-j-i}$

0.28. Find the coefficient of the following:

    (a) $y^8 x^2$ in the binomial expansion of $(y^2 - 2x)^6$,

    (b) $y^4 x^2$ in the binomial expansion of $(2y + x^2)^5$.

0.29. Find the coefficient of the following:

    (a) $x_1{}^2 x_2{}^2 x_3{}^3 x_4{}^3$ in the multinomial expansion of $(x_1 + x_2 + x_3 + x_4)^{10}$,

    (b) $x_1{}^0 x_2{}^4 x_3{}^3$ in the expansion of the trinomial $(x_1 - 2x_2 - x_3)^7$.

0.30. In how many ways can five dimes and six quarters be distributed among 11 boys each receiving a coin?

0.31. In how many different ways can five copies of four different books be arranged on a shelf?

0.32. How many different signals can you make using 10 flags—three yellow, three white, two green, and two red?

0.33. Find the Jacobian of transformation of

$$t = 3x - \frac{1}{2}y$$

$$h = -x + 4y.$$

0.34. Find the Jacobian of transformation of the polar coordinate functions of the form

$$z = -r \sin \theta$$
$$y = r \cos \theta.$$

0.35. Evaluate the following integrals:

    (a) $\displaystyle\int_0^\infty x^t e^{-tx}dx \quad t \geq 0$ (b) $\displaystyle\int_0^\infty x^4 e^{-x}dx$

    (c) $\displaystyle\int_0^\infty x^6 e^{-2x}dx$ (d) $\displaystyle\int_0^\infty x^{1/2} e^{-x^3}dx$

(e) $\displaystyle\int_0^\infty 4^{-9x^2} dx$

0.36. Evaluate the following integrals:

(a) $\displaystyle\int_0^1 x^5(1-x)^4 \, dx$

(b) $\displaystyle\int_0^2 x^2(2-x)^{-1/2} \, dx$

(c) $\displaystyle\int_0^1 x^{-1/5}(1-x)^{-2/5} \, dx$

(d) $\displaystyle\int_2^4 (x-2)^{-1/6}(4-x)^{-5/6} \, dx$

(e) $\displaystyle\int_2^3 (2-x)^2(x-3)^3 \, dx$

0.37. Given the matrices

$$A = \begin{bmatrix} 5 & 0 & 2 \\ 1 & 2 & -3 \\ 1 & -1 & 1 \end{bmatrix}, \quad B = \begin{bmatrix} 4 & 2 & 5 \\ 3 & -1 & 2 \\ 2 & 0 & 3 \end{bmatrix}, \quad C = \begin{bmatrix} 0 & 3 & 2 \\ 4 & 1 & 2 \\ 1 & -2 & 3 \end{bmatrix},$$

compute Parts a–e; verify Part f.

(a) $A + B$
(b) $A - C$
(c) $-3B + C$
(d) AB and BA
(e) C^2
(f) Verify that $[A + B] - C = A + [B - C]$

0.38. Given the matrices

$$A = \begin{bmatrix} a_{11} & a_{12} & a_{13} & a_{14} \\ a_{21} & a_{22} & a_{23} & a_{24} \end{bmatrix} \quad \text{and} \quad B = \begin{bmatrix} b_{11} & b_{12} \\ b_{21} & b_{22} \\ b_{31} & b_{32} \\ b_{41} & b_{42} \end{bmatrix},$$

compute AB and BA.

0.39. Find the determinant of the following matrices:

(a) $\begin{bmatrix} 3 & 1 \\ 2 & -2 \end{bmatrix}$,

(b) $\begin{bmatrix} -1 & 3 & 5 \\ 1 & -3 & -5 \\ -1 & 3 & 5 \end{bmatrix}$,

(c) $\begin{bmatrix} c_{11} & c_{12} & c_{13} \\ c_{21} & c_{22} & c_{23} \\ c_{31} & c_{32} & c_{33} \end{bmatrix}$.

0.40. Using the method of cofactors, find the determinant of

(a) $\begin{bmatrix} 1 & 0 & -2 \\ -3 & 0 & 4 \\ 2 & -5 & -1 \end{bmatrix}$,

(b) $\begin{bmatrix} d_{11} & d_{12} & d_{13} \\ d_{21} & d_{22} & d_{23} \\ d_{31} & d_{32} & d_{33} \end{bmatrix}$.

0.41. Find the transpose of the matrices given in Problem 0.37.

0.42. Find the inverse of the matrices given in Problem 0.37.

0.43. Using Problem 0.37, verify the following:

   (a) $A^T B \neq A B^T$ (b) $A^T B^T \neq B^T A^T$.

0.44. Using Problem 0.37, show that the determinant of AC equals the determinant of A times the determinant of C, that is, that $|AC| = |A| \cdot |C|$.

0.45. Is the following matrix a singular matrix?

$$\begin{bmatrix} 1 & -3 & 1 \\ 2 & 1 & 2 \\ 1 & 5 & 3 \end{bmatrix}.$$

References

[1] Allendoerfer, C. B. and C. O. Oakley. *Principles of Mathematics*, 2nd ed., New York: McGraw-Hill Book Company, Inc., 1963.

[2] Bellman, R. *Introduction to Matrix Analysis*. New York: McGraw-Hill Book Company, Inc., 1960.

[3] Dinkines, F. *Elementary Theory of Sets*. New York: Appleton-Century-Crofts, Inc., 1964.

[4] Finkbeiner, D. T. *Introduction to Matrices and Linear Transformations*. San Francisco: W. H. Freeman and Company, 1966.

[5] Franklin, P. *Methods of Advanced Calculus*. New York: McGraw-Hill Book Company, Inc., 1944.

[6] Hall, M. *Combinatorial Theory*. Waltham, Massachusetts: Blaisdell Publishing Company, 1967.

[7] Halmos, P. R. *Naive Set Theory*. Princeton, N.J.: D. Van Nostrand Company, Inc., 1960.

[8] Hohn, F. E. *Elementary Matrix Algebra*. New York: The Macmillan Company, 1959.

[9] Kaplan, W. *Advanced Calculus*. Reading, Massachusetts: Addison-Wesley Publishing Company, Inc., 1959.

[10] Richardson, M. *College Algebra*. Englewood Cliffs: Prentice-Hall, Inc., 1961.

[11] Riordan, J. *An Introduction to Combinatorial Analysis*. New York: John Wiley and Sons, Inc., 1968.

[12] Thomas, G. B. *Calculus and Analytic Geometry*. Reading, Massachusetts: Addison-Wesley Publishing Company, Inc., 1966.

[13] Widder, V. D. *Advanced Calculus*. Englewood Cliffs, New Jersey: Prentice-Hall, Inc., 1961.

Probability

1

1.0 Introduction

Probability theory is concerned with the construction of mathematical models that enable us to make predictions about certain mass phenomena from the necessarily incomplete information derived from sampling techniques.

Probability theory had its beginnings with games of chance in the seventeenth century. The earliest mathematical thought regarding probability arose out of the collaboration of the eminent mathematicians Blaise Pascal and Pierre Fermat and a gambler, Chevalier de Méré. They were interested in what seemed to be contradictions between mathematical calculations and actual games of chance, such as throwing dice, tossing a coin, or spinning a roulette wheel. For example, in repeated throws of a die, it was observed that each number, one to six, appeared approximately equally often; that is, each number appeared with a frequency of approximately 1/6. However, if two dice were rolled, the sum of numbers showing on the two dice, that is, two to twelve, did not appear equally often. It was then recognized that, as the number of throws increased, the frequency of these possible results could be predicted by following some simple rules. Similar basic experiments were conducted using other games of chance which resulted in the establishment of various basic rules of probability. Probability theory was developed solely to be applied to games of chance until the eighteenth century, when Pierre Laplace and Karl F. Gauss applied the basic probabilistic rules to other physical problems. A complete treatment of the classical approach to probability theory is given by I. Todhunter, Reference [4]. Some of the classical concepts and definitions are discussed in Section 1.2.

The modern theory of probability was initiated by the Russian mathematician A. N. Kolmogorov in 1933. He developed the subject from an axiomatic point of view using advanced mathematics (measure theory);

37

however, it is quite possible to develop and apply the basic concepts of probability using the less difficult techniques of set theory. It is the objective of this book, using the set theory techniques, to develop probability theory by the axiomatic approach, which is the clearest and most useful way to handle both theory and applications.

In recent years, probability theory, always one of the most interesting of studies, has emerged as one of the most important mathematical disciplines. Some of the areas in which probability has been successfully applied are: statistics, engineering, operations research, physics, medicine, business, economics, accounting, education, sociology, psychology, agriculture, meteorology, linguistics, and political science.

1.1   Definitions of Probability

The development of the concept of probability from its earliest formulations to the modern approach can be studied by analyzing the various definitions of the term. It is the objective of this section to introduce these definitions and to illustrate both their uses and their limitations.

We shall discuss the following four definitions of probability:

(1)   *Probability as a measure of belief*
(2)   *Classical or a priori probability*
(3)   *Relative-frequency or a posteriori probability*
(4)   *Axiomatic definition of probability.*

1.   *Probability as a measure of belief.* The value of the probability of an event may sometimes be assessed by one's own judgment. For example, one might say concerning a woman's pregnancy, "I'm almost certain that she will have a boy." This statement may be interpreted as meaning that the probability of the woman having a son is being assessed at a high value, or the probability of the woman having a boy is greater than the probability of her having a girl. As a second example, if one says, "It is probable that we shall land on Mars," he is saying that the probability of our landing on Mars is high. In each of these examples, the high probability assigned to the events involved was not the result of an exact method of determination but was the exercising of a belief.

This approach to measuring probability is certainly not sufficient to solve the various physical problems of today, although it is often a useful approach for the layman. However, one must remember that the solutions of various open theoretical and experimental problems may owe their success to the mathematician's or scientist's *belief* that a solution is attainable.

2.   *Classical or a priori probability.*   The probability of an event S_1, written $Pr(S_1)$, may be expressed as the ratio n_{s_1}/n, where n_{s_1} is the number of ways that S_1 may occur in the particular situation considered and n is the total number of possible outcomes in the given situation. In each case, these outcomes must be equally likely.

As the name implies, n, the total number of outcomes of a given situation, and n_{s_1}, the number of outcomes favorable to S_1 of the same situation, are found *a priori*, that is, without actually conducting the experiment. The following examples will illustrate the meaning of the classical or a priori definition of probability.

Example 1.1.1   In tossing a fair die, there are six possible outcomes of the experiment, each of which is equally likely and three of which result in an odd number. Therefore, the probability of obtaining an odd number is given by

$$\frac{n_{s_1}}{n} = \frac{3}{6} = \frac{1}{2}.$$

Example 1.1.2   Consider the experiment of drawing a card from an ordinary deck of 52 playing cards. There are 52 possible outcomes in the experiment, and we assume that each card has the same chance of being chosen. Since 13 of the 52 cards are diamonds, the probability that a card drawn at random will be a diamond is

$$\frac{n_{s_1}}{n} = \frac{13}{52} = \frac{1}{4};$$

the probability that it will be a picture card is

$$\frac{n_{s_2}}{n} = \frac{12}{52} = \frac{3}{13};$$

and the probability that it will be an ace is

$$\frac{n_{s_1}}{n} = \frac{4}{52} = \frac{1}{13}.$$

It is important to note that all possible outcomes in a given situation must be equally likely: If one tossed a coin twice, desiring to obtain "tails" on both occasions, one could reason, according to the classical definition of probability, that there are three possible outcomes to the experiment; that is, two heads, one head and one tail, and two tails; and the required probability would be

$$\frac{n_{s_1}}{n} = \frac{1}{3}.$$

However, this reasoning is not correct because the above outcomes are not equally likely. There are, in fact, *four* equally likely outcomes: HH, HT, TH, and TT; and the correct probability is therefore 1/4.

If in Example 1.1.1 the die is not fair or, in other words, the appearance of each of the six faces is not equally likely, the classical definition of probability is not applicable. Moreover, the classical definition of probability cannot measure the probability of events when the total number of possible outcomes in a physical phenomenon is infinite. For this reason, we turn to a third definition of probability.

3. *Relative-frequency or a posteriori probability.* This definition was developed as the result of the work of R. Von Mises (1936), Reference [2], and is stated as follows:

$$\lim_{n \to \infty} \frac{n_{s_1}}{n} = p, \tag{1.1.1}$$

where n is the total number of *identical* trials in a given problem, n_{s_1} is the number of occurrences of the event S_1, and p is the probability of the event. ("Identical" simply means that each trial is conducted under identical conditions.)

The concept of the limit in Equation (1.1.1) suggests that its applicability to various scientific problems can not be very extensive because, in such problems, n is usually finite and the limit of the ratio n_{s_1}/n cannot be taken. But, despite this theoretical limitation, the relative-frequency definition of probability is perhaps one of the most popular definitions of probability among scientists: from a practical point of view, the limitation means that the accuracy of measuring the probability of a "true state of nature," p, increases as the number of trials becomes very large. For example, in tossing a coin which need not be fair, we are interested in obtaining the probability, p, of getting a head, which is given by

$$\lim_{n \to \infty} \frac{n_H}{n}.$$

This does not offer us a specific answer, but it does give us an approximate value of p for a particular number of trials, and this approximation will improve as n increases. If we were to use the a priori definition of probability, we would have estimated p to be equal to 1/2, but this may be only a lucky guess because we have no evidence that the coin is fair. As a matter of fact, in tossing a symmetrical coin, the probability of obtaining a head approaches that of obtaining a tail as $n \to 2000$ trials.

As the name a posteriori implies, p is calculated *after* the experiment has been performed; whereas, in the classical definition of probability, it is determined *before* conducting the experiment.

4. The axiomatic definition of probability.   This definition results from the 1933 studies of A. N. Kolmogorov, Reference [1], and is the most important definition of probability because it eliminates most of the difficulties that are encountered in using the other definitions and because it provides a solid basis for further study of probability theory. Although the original development of the axiomatic approach depended upon advanced mathematics (measure theory), we introduce it here by means of finite set operations. Section 1.2 is devoted entirely to the development of the axiomatic definition of probability.

1.2   Axiomatic Definition of Probability

We shall begin the formulation of the axiomatic definition of probability by defining certain essential basic concepts.

By an *experiment* we mean a specific procedure that we follow and at the completion of which we observe certain results. Each possible outcome of the experiment is represented by a *sample point*. The set of all possible outcomes of an experiment is represented by a *sample space* denoted by S. For example, if our experiment is to toss a fair coin once, the sample space consists of two possible outcomes, a head and a tail, so that $S = \{H, T\}$. If we were to roll a die, the total number of possible outcomes of this experiment would be six; thus,

$$S = \{x : x = 1, 2, 3, 4, 5, 6\}.$$

If the experiment were to flip a coin twice, the sample space would consist of four sample points:

$$S = \{(H, H), (H, T), (T, H), (T, T)\}.$$

We define an *event* to be a set of sample points with some specified property. Thus, in the example of tossing a coin twice, the event S_1 of getting heads on both the first and second tosses is a subset of S, and we write $S_1 = \{(H, H)\} \subset S$. An event which consists of only one sample point is called a *simple* or *elementary event*; thus $S_1 = \{(H, H)\}$ is a simple event. An event which consists of more than one sample point is called a *compound event*. In the experiment of rolling a die, the event S_2 of getting an odd number consists of the outcomes 1, 3, and 5. Therefore, $S_2 = \{x : x = 1, 3, 5\}$. We shall refer to the sample space S as a universal set and all other sets will be considered as being subsets (events) of S.

For our purposes, we shall consider the sample space S from either of two points of view—*discrete* or *continuous*.

Definition 1.2.1   *A sample space S is* discrete *if it contains a finite number of points or an infinite number of points which can be put into a one-to-one correspondence with the positive integers.*

Example 1.2.1   The sample space of positive integers 1, 2, 3, ..., 100, that is, $S = \{x: x = 1, 2, 3, \ldots, 100\}$ contains a finite number of points, and so it is a discrete sample space.

Definition 1.2.2   *A sample space S is* continuous *if it contains a continuum of points.*

Example 1.2.2   Consider an experiment in which we wish to observe the lifetime of a certain type of light bulb. Then the outcome of this experiment forms a continuous sample, that is,

$$S = \{t: 0 \leq t < \infty\}.$$

We shall now state some basic definitions of those sets that are subsets of S.

Definition 1.2.3   *Two events, S_1 and S_2, of the sample space S are said to be* equal *if every sample point of S_1 is also a sample point of S_2 and every sample point of S_2 is also a sample point of S_1. We denote this by $S_1 = S_2$.*

Definition 1.2.4   *If a subset S_1 of S contains no sample points, it is called the* impossible event *and is denoted by $\varnothing$, which designates the empty set.*

Definition 1.2.5   *The* complement *of an event S_1 of the sample space S will be the set of sample points that are in S but not in S_1; we denote this by $S - S_1$ or $\bar{S}_1$.*

Definition 1.2.6   *If S_1 and S_2 are two events of the sample space S, then the event that consists of all the sample points in S_1, S_2, or both is called the* union *of S_1 and S_2 and is denoted by $S_1 \cup S_2$.*

Definition 1.2.7   *If S_1 and S_2 are two events of the sample space S, then the event which consists of all points that are in both S_1 and S_2 is called the* intersection *of S_1 and S_2 and is denoted by $S_1 \cap S_2$ or $S_1 S_2$.*

Definition 1.2.8   *Two events, S_1 and S_2, of the sample space S are said to be* mutually exclusive *or* disjoint *events if $S_1 \cap S_2 = \varnothing$.*

Example 1.2.3   Let the sample space S be defined as $S = \{t:$ $0 \leq t < \infty\}$ and let two events of S be given as

$$S_1 = \{t: 25 < t \leq 100\} \quad \text{and} \quad S_2 = \{t: 60 < t \leq 140\}.$$

Then

(a) $S_1 \cup S_2 = \{t: 25 < t \leq 140\}$;
(b) $S_1 \cap S_2 = \{t: 60 < t \leq 100\}$;
(c) $\overline{S_1 \cap S_2} = \{t: 0 \leq t \leq 60 \text{ or } 100 < t < \infty\}$;
(d) $\overline{S_1 \cup S_2} = \{t: 0 \leq t \leq 25 \text{ or } 140 < t < \infty\}$;
(e) $\bar{S}_1 \cup \bar{S}_2 = \{t: 0 \leq t \leq 60 \text{ or } 100 < t < \infty\}$;
(f) $\bar{S}_1 \cap \bar{S}_2 = \{t: 0 \leq t \leq 25 \text{ or } 140 < t < \infty\}$.

Note that $\overline{S_1 \cap S_2} = \bar{S}_1 \cup \bar{S}_2$ and $\overline{S_1 \cup S_2} = \bar{S}_1 \cap \bar{S}_2$. These two relationships are called DeMorgan's Laws.

It should be clear that, if a sample space is finite or countably infinite, then every subset of the sample space S is an event. If the sample space consists of n sample points, then there are 2^n possible events in S. On the other hand, if the set is uncountable, then certain subsets of S cannot be events. The reason for this is beyond the scope of this book. We shall now state the axiomatic definition of probability. If, for every event S_i, $i = 1, 2, 3, \ldots, n, \ldots$ of the sample space S, there is a number, denoted by $Pr(S_i)$, that satisfies the following axioms:

Axiom 1.2.1: $0 \leq Pr(S_i)$;
Axiom 1.2.2: $Pr(S) = 1$;
Axiom 1.2.3: If $S_1, S_2, \ldots, S_n, \ldots$ is a sequence of mutually exclusive events, that is,

$$S_i \cap S_j = \varnothing \quad \text{for } i \neq j = 1, 2, 3, \ldots, n, \ldots,$$

then

$$Pr(S_1 \cup S_2 \cup S_3 \cup \cdots \cup S_n \cup \cdots) = Pr(S_1) + Pr(S_2) + \cdots + Pr(S_n) + \cdots$$

or

$$Pr\left(\bigcup_{i=1}^{\infty} S_i\right) = \sum_{i=1}^{\infty} Pr(S_i).$$

$Pr(S_i)$ is called the *probability* of the event S_i. If we can determine the probability of every event of the sample space S, then we say that S is a *probability space*. It should be emphasized that the axiomatic approach to probability in no way assigns a numerical value to the probability of any event. It is used primarily to manipulate probabilities of compound events so that they may be expressed in terms of probabilities of simple events, which in turn may be evaluated by one of the other definitions of probability already mentioned, most usually by the classical definition. For example, suppose that two balanced dice are tossed once, and we are interested in the following two probabilities:

(1) The probability that the sum showing on the two dice is less than six.
(2) The probability that the absolute difference of the values on the dice is greater than or equal to four.

For Part (1), we have

$$Pr(\text{Sum} < 6) = Pr[(\text{Sum} = 2) \cup (\text{Sum} = 3) \cup (\text{Sum} = 4) \cup (\text{Sum} = 5)]$$
$$= Pr(\text{Sum} = 2) + Pr(\text{Sum} = 3) + Pr(\text{Sum} = 4) + Pr(\text{Sum} = 5),$$

using Axiom 1.2.3.

Up to this point, we have used the axiomatic approach to probability, which does not suffice to evaluate the probabilities $Pr(\text{Sum} = 2)$, $Pr(\text{Sum} = 3)$, and so on. We must, therefore, use the classical definition of probability. The event $(\text{Sum} = 2)$ may occur in only one way out of 36 possible outcomes, thus $Pr(\text{Sum} = 2) = 1/36$. The event $(\text{Sum} = 3)$ may occur in either of two different ways, thus $Pr(\text{Sum} = 3) = 2/36$. Similarly, we obtain $Pr(\text{Sum} = 4) = 3/36$ and $Pr(\text{Sum} = 5) = 4/36$.
Therefore,

$$Pr(\text{Sum} < 6) = \frac{1}{36} + \frac{2}{36} + \frac{3}{36} + \frac{4}{36} = \frac{5}{18}.$$

In Part (2), we shall let E represent the absolute difference showing on the dice. Thus we want to determine $Pr(E \geq 4)$, which may be written as

$$Pr[(E = 4) \cup (E = 5)]$$

or, (using Axiom 1.2.3),

$$Pr(E = 4) + Pr(E = 5).$$

Again, we can go no further using the axiomatic approach; we must shift to the classical approach in order to evaluate $Pr(E = 4)$ and $Pr(E = 5)$. Since the event $E = 4$ may occur in either of four different ways, as shown in the accompanying diagram,

Die no. 1	1	2	5	6
Die no. 2	5	6	1	2

$Pr(E = 4) = 4/36$ because the total number of possible outcomes is 36. In a similar way, it can be determined that $Pr(E = 5) = 2/36$. Thus,

$$Pr(E \geq 4) = \frac{4}{36} + \frac{2}{36} = \frac{1}{6}.$$

Now we shall establish some elementary theorems of probability.

Theorem 1.2.1 If S_1 and S_2 are any two events of the sample space S, such that $S_1 \subset S_2$, then $Pr(S_1) \leq Pr(S_2)$.

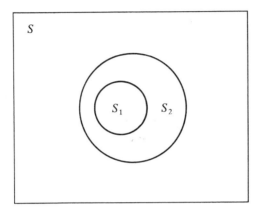

Figure 1.2.1

Proof From Figure 1.2.1, we can see that $S_2 = S_1 \cup (S_2 \cap \bar{S}_1)$. Because S_1 and $S_2 \cap \bar{S}_1$ are mutually exclusive events, we apply Axiom 1.2.3 and have

$$Pr(S_2) = Pr(S_1 \cup (S_2 \cap \bar{S}_1))$$
$$= Pr(S_1) + Pr(S_2 \cap \bar{S}_1).$$

However, from Axiom 1.2.1,

$$Pr(S_1) \leq Pr(S_1) + Pr(S_2 \cap \bar{S}_1),$$

which implies that

$$Pr(S_1) \leq Pr(S_2).$$

   Theorem 1.2.2   If S_k is any event of the sample space S, then $Pr(S_k) \leq 1$.

   Proof   From the fact that $S_k \subset S$ and from Theorem 1.2.1, we can write

$$Pr(S_k) \leq Pr(S).$$

Applying Axiom 1.2.2, we have

$$Pr(S_k) \leq 1.$$

   Theorem 1.2.3   If S_k is any event of the sample space S, then

$$Pr(\bar{S}_k) = 1 - Pr(S_k).$$

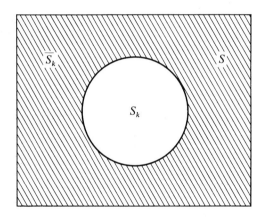

Figure 1.2.2

   Proof   From Figure 1.2.2,

$$S = S_k \cup \bar{S}_k,$$

since S_k and $\bar{S}_k$ are mutually exclusive. Applying Axiom 1.2.3, we have

$$Pr(S) = Pr(S_k) + Pr(\bar{S}_k).$$

Hence, from Axiom 1.2.2,

$$1 = Pr(S_k) + Pr(\bar{S}_k)$$

or

$$Pr(\bar{S}_k) = 1 - Pr(S_k).$$

Theorem 1.2.4   If $\varnothing$ is the impossible event of the sample space S, then $Pr(\varnothing) = 0$.

Proof   Because we know that $\varnothing \cup S = S$, where $\varnothing$ and S are mutually exclusive, we have, by applying Axioms 1.2.2 and 1.2.3,

$$Pr(\varnothing \cup S) = Pr(S)$$

or

$$Pr(\varnothing) + Pr(S) = Pr(S),$$

which implies $Pr(\varnothing) = 0$.

Theorem 1.2.5   If S_1 and S_2 are any two events of the sample space S, then

$$Pr(S_1 \cup S_2) = Pr(S_1) + Pr(S_2) - Pr(S_1 \cap S_2).$$

Proof   From Figure 1.2.3, we see that $S_1 \cup S_2 = (S_1 \cap \bar{S}_2) \cup S_2$. Since $S_1 \cap \bar{S}_2$ and S_2 are mutually exclusive events, applying Axiom 1.2.3, we have

$$Pr(S_1 \cup S_2) = Pr(S_1 \cap \bar{S}_2) + Pr(S_2). \qquad (1.2.1)$$

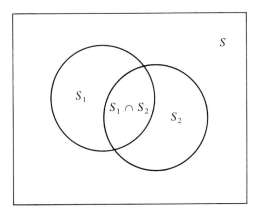

Figure 1.2.3

However, we can write the event S_1 as a pair of mutually exclusive events, that is,

$$S_1 = (S_1 \cap S_2) \cup (S_1 \cap \bar{S}_2)$$

or

$$Pr(S_1) = Pr(S_1 \cap S_2) + Pr(S_1 \cap \bar{S}_2). \tag{1.2.2}$$

Solving Equation (1.2.2) for $Pr(S_1 \cap \bar{S}_2)$ and substituting it into Equation (1.2.1), we have

$$Pr(S_1 \cup S_2) = Pr(S_1) + Pr(S_2) - Pr(S_1 \cap S_2).$$

If the events S_1 and S_2 are mutually exclusive, then, according to Axiom 1.2.3, the last expression becomes

$$Pr(S_1 \cup S_2) = Pr(S_1) + Pr(S_2).$$

In certain cases where the sample space is finite, it is sometimes useful to choose the sample points, say n of them, in such a way that the probability of each point is equal to $1/n$. This technique often facilitates the process of evaluating the probabilities of compound events, as shown in the following example.

Example 1.2.4   Consider the experiment of drawing cards from a well-shuffled deck. The sample space consists of 52 sample points corresponding to the 52 possible cards that might be drawn. We would like to find the probability of the following events:

(a) S_1 = the occurrence of a diamond in a single draw;
(b) S_2 = the occurrence of a picture card in a single draw;
(c) The event of a diamond or a picture card, or a *picture diamond*, that is, $S_1 \cup S_2$;
(d) The event of not obtaining event $S_1 \cup S_2$, that is, $\overline{S_1 \cup S_2}$.

Solution
(a) The probability of any one card being drawn is the same as that of any other card, that is, $Pr(E_1) = Pr(E_2) = \cdots = Pr(E_{52}) = 1/52$. The event S_1 consists of 13 sample points each with probability of occurrence equal to $1/52$; therefore,

$$Pr(S_1) = \sum_{i=1}^{13} Pr(E_i) = 13 \frac{1}{52} = \frac{1}{4}.$$

(b)   Similarly,

$$Pr(S_2) = \sum_{i=1}^{12} Pr(S_i) = \frac{3}{13}.$$

(c)   Applying Theorem 1.2.5,

$$Pr(S_1 \cup S_2) = Pr(S_1) + Pr(S_2) - Pr(S_1 \cap S_2),$$

where

$$Pr(S_1 \cap S_2) = Pr(\text{picture diamond}) = \frac{3}{52}$$

(the number of sample points with the attribute picture diamond over the total number of sample points in the sample space.) Hence,

$$Pr(S_1 \cup S_2) = \frac{13}{52} + \frac{12}{52} - \frac{3}{52} = \frac{11}{26}.$$

(d)   We know from Theorem 1.2.3 that

$$Pr(\overline{S_1 \cup S_2}) = 1 - Pr(S_1 \cup S_2).$$

Therefore,

$$Pr(\overline{S_1 \cup S_2}) = 1 - \frac{22}{52} = \frac{15}{26}.$$

Note also that Theorem 1.2.1 is verified from Parts (a) and (b), that is, $Pr(S_2)Pr(S_1)$.

A generalization of Theorem 1.2.5, known as the *General Law of Total Probability*, is attributed to Poincaré, Reference [3], and is given by the following theorem.

Theorem 1.2.6   If $S_1, S_2, \ldots, S_n$ is a sequence of events defined on the sample space S, then

$$Pr\left(\bigcup_{i=1}^{n} S_i\right) = \sum_{i=1}^{n} Pr(S_i) - \sum_{\substack{i,j=1 \\ i<j}}^{n} Pr(S_i \cap S_j) + \sum_{\substack{i,j,k \\ i<j<k}}^{n} Pr(S_i \cap S_j \cap S_k)$$

$$+ \cdots + (-1)^{n+1} Pr(S_1 \cap S_2 \cap \cdots \cap S_n).$$

The proof of this theorem is by mathematical induction and is given in Exercise 1.25.

The general law of total probability for mutually exclusive events reduces to

$$Pr\left(\bigcup_{i=1}^{n} S_i\right) = \sum_{i=1}^{n} Pr(S_i).$$

1.3   Conditional Probability

Let S be the sample space; let S_1 and S_2 be events of S. We define the *conditional probability* of the event S_1, given that event S_2 has occurred, denoted by $Pr(S_1|S_2)$, as the probability of $S_1 \cap S_2$ divided by the probability of S_2. That is,

$$Pr(S_1|S_2) = \frac{Pr(S_1 \cap S_2)}{Pr(S_2)}, \quad \text{where } Pr(S_2) > 0. \tag{1.3.1}$$

Similarly,

$$Pr(S_2|S_1) = \frac{Pr(S_1 \cap S_2)}{Pr(S_1)}, \quad \text{where } Pr(S_1) > 0. \tag{1.3.2}$$

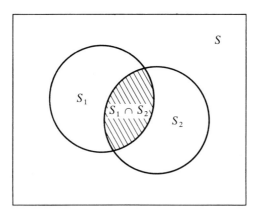

Figure 1.3.1

One can illustrate the event $S_1 \cap S_2$, as shown by the Venn diagram in Figure 1.3.1. If, for example, the sample space S consists of n elementary events, n_1 of which have the attribute associated with S_1, n_2 of which have the attribute associated with S_2, and n_{12} of which have the attribute associated with both S_1 and S_2, then

$$Pr(S_1) = \frac{n_1}{n}, \quad Pr(S_2) = \frac{n_2}{n}, \quad Pr(S_1 \cap S_2) = \frac{n_{12}}{n}$$

and

$$Pr(S_1 | S_2) = \frac{\dfrac{n_{12}}{n}}{\dfrac{n_2}{n}} = \frac{n_{12}}{n_2}$$

or

$$Pr(S_2 | S_1) = \frac{\dfrac{n_{12}}{n}}{\dfrac{n_1}{n}} = \frac{n_{12}}{n_1}.$$

Example 1.3.1   Suppose that in a deck of cards we have removed the three picture diamonds (jack, queen, and king), and from the remaining 49 cards we select one card at random. Let the event S_1 denote that the chosen card is a picture card, and let the event S_2 denote that the chosen card is a spade. Event S_1 consists of nine sample points, which implies that $Pr(S_1) = 9/49$. The event $S_1 \cap S_2$ represents the appearance of a picture spade. The number of sample points in $S_1 \cap S_2$ is therefore three; so $Pr(S_1 \cap S_2) = 3/49$. The event S_2 consists of 13 sample points, each with the probability of $1/49$ of occurring. Thus $Pr(S_2) = 13/49$. Now, suppose that we have been told that the card drawn is a spade and we are interested in finding the probability that it is a picture also.

Solution   We write

$$Pr(S_1 | S_2) = \frac{Pr(S_1 \cap S_2)}{Pr(S_2)} = \frac{\dfrac{3}{49}}{\dfrac{13}{49}} = \frac{3}{13}.$$

Furthermore, the probability of a spade, given that the chosen card is a picture, is shown by

$$Pr(S_2 | S_1) = \frac{Pr(S_1 \cap S_2)}{Pr(S_1)} = \frac{\dfrac{3}{49}}{\dfrac{9}{49}} = \frac{1}{3}.$$

Example 1.3.2   Consider the experiment of rolling a pair of fair dice. Suppose that it is observed that the sum of the two dice is seven, and we want to find the probability that at least one of the dice shows a three.

Solution   The sample space in the experiment consists of 36 sample points, We must determine the number of sample points in the sample space that constitute the event S_1 (the sum is seven):

$$S_1 = \{(1, 6), (2, 5), (3, 4), (4, 3), (5, 2), (6, 1)\},$$

and the event S_2 (a three appears on at least one die):

$$S_2 = \{(3, 1), (3, 2), (3, 3), (3, 4), (3, 5), (3, 6),$$
$$(6, 3), (5, 3), (4, 3), (2, 3), (1, 3)\}.$$

That is, there are six sample points in S_1 and 11 sample points in S_2. Hence,

$$Pr(S_1) = \frac{6}{36}, \qquad Pr(S_1 \cap S_2) = \frac{2}{36}$$

and

$$Pr(S_2 | S_1) = \frac{\dfrac{2}{36}}{\dfrac{6}{36}} = \frac{1}{3}.$$

Formulas (1.3.1) and (1.3.2) can be written as

$$Pr(S_1 \cap S_2) = Pr(S_1)Pr(S_2 | S_1) = Pr(S_2)Pr(S_1 | S_2), \qquad (1.3.3)$$

that is, the probability of the intersection of S_1 and S_2 equals the product of the probability of S_1 and the conditional probability of S_2, given that S_1 has occurred, or the probability of event S_2 times the conditional probability of S_1, given that S_2 has occurred. Furthermore,

$$Pr(S_1 | S_2) = \frac{\dfrac{2}{36}}{\dfrac{11}{36}} = \frac{2}{11},$$

the probability of obtaining a sum of seven, given that a three has appeared on at least one die.

Example 1.3.3   In Example 1.3.1, we were interested in obtaining the probability that a picture spade had occurred. If we are given enough information so that the conditional probability, $Pr(S_2|S_1)$, can be calculated, then, using Equation (1.3.3), we have the desired probability:

$$Pr(S_1 \cap S_2) = Pr(S_1)Pr(S_2|S_1)$$

$$= \frac{9}{49} \times \frac{1}{3} = \frac{3}{49}.$$

The concept of conditional probability can be extended to more than two events: if S_1, S_2, and S_3 are events of the sample space S, then

$$Pr(S_3|S_1 \cap S_2) = \frac{Pr(S_1 \cap S_2 \cap S_3)}{Pr(S_1 \cap S_2)}, \quad Pr(S_1 \cap S_2) > 0,$$

or

$$Pr(S_1 \cap S_2 \cap S_3) = Pr(S_1 \cap S_2)Pr(S_3|S_1 \cap S_2). \tag{1.3.4}$$

But

$$Pr(S_1 \cap S_2) = Pr(S_1)Pr(S_2|S_1),$$

and Equation (1.3.4) becomes

$$Pr(S_1 \cap S_2 \cap S_3) = Pr(S_1)Pr(S_2|S_1)Pr(S_3|S_1 \cap S_2). \tag{1.3.5}$$

That is, the probability of the intersection of the three events equals the probability of S_1 times the conditional probability of S_2, given that S_1 has occurred, times the probability of event S_3, given the joint occurrence of events S_1 and S_2.

A generalization of equation (1.3.5) to n events, which is known as the *General Law of Compound Probability*, is given by Theorem 1.3.1.

Theorem 1.3.1   Let S_1, S_2, S_3, ..., S_n be events of the sample space S, such that

$$Pr(S_1 \cap S_2 \cap S_3 \cap \cdots \cap S_j) > 0 \quad \text{for } 1 \leq j \leq n - 1.$$

Then

$$Pr(S_1 \cap S_2 \cap \cdots \cap S_n) = Pr(S_1)Pr(S_2|S_1)Pr(S_3|S_1 \cap S_2) \cdots$$
$$Pr(S_n|S_1 \cap S_2 \cap \cdots \cap S_{n-1}).$$

For the proof of this theorem, see Exercise 1.25.

Example 1.3.4   A lot in a certain warehouse contains 40 electrical generators of which six are known to be defective. On a particular day, five generators will be used. We are interested in the probability that all five will be operable.

Solution   Let S_1, S_2, S_3, S_4, and S_5 be the events that the first, second, third, fourth, and fifth generators are operable. Then, according to Theorem 1.3.1, we have

$$Pr(S_1 \cap S_2 \cap S_3 \cap S_4 \cap S_5) = Pr(S_1)Pr(S_2|S_1)Pr(S_3|S_1 \cap S_2) \cdots$$
$$Pr(S_5|S_1 \cap S_2 \cap S_3 \cap S_4)$$

$$= \left(\frac{34}{40}\right)\left(\frac{33}{39}\right)\left(\frac{32}{38}\right)\left(\frac{31}{37}\right)\left(\frac{30}{36}\right).$$

Here $Pr(S_1) = 34/40$ because 34 of the 40 generators are operable. $Pr(S_2|S_1)$, the probability that the second generator is operable given that the first one was, is 33/39, since there are only 33 operable of the remaining 39 generators. Similarly, $Pr(S_3|S_1 \cap S_2) = 32/38$ because there are 32 operable of the remaining 38 operable generators, and so on.

We shall now prove that the definition of conditional probability satisfies Axioms 1.2.1 to 1.2.3. Let S_1, S_2, and S_3 be events of the sample space S, such that $Pr(S_i) > 0, i = 1, 2, 3$. Then we must show that

(1) $Pr(S_1|S_2) \geq 0$;

if $(S_1|S_2)$ is the sure event,

(2) $Pr(S_1|S_2) = 1$;

if $S_1 \cap S_2 = \emptyset$,

(3) $Pr(S_1 \cup S_2|S_3) = Pr(S_1|S_3) + Pr(S_2|S_3)$.

Proof of (1): $0 \leq Pr(S_1 \cap S_2)$ implies that $0 \leq Pr(S_2)Pr(S_1|S_2)$. Dividing both sides of the last expression by $Pr(S_2) > 0$ gives $0 \leq Pr(S_1|S_2)$, which is the condition expressed by Axiom 1.2.1.

Proof of (2):   If S_1, given S_2, is the sure event, then $S_1 \subset S_2$ and

$$Pr(S_1|S_2) = \frac{Pr(S_1 \cap S_2)}{Pr(S_2)} = \frac{Pr(S_2)}{Pr(S_2)} = 1.$$

This condition is expressed by Axiom 1.2.2.

Proof of (3):

$$Pr(S_1 \cup S_2 | S_3) = \frac{Pr[(S_1 \cup S_2) \cap S_3]}{Pr(S_3)}$$

$$= \frac{Pr[(S_1 \cap S_3) \cup (S_2 \cap S_3)]}{Pr(S_3)}.$$

But, because S_1 and S_2 are mutually exclusive, so are the events $S_1 \cap S_3$ and $S_2 \cap S_3$. Thus we obtain:

$$Pr(S_1 \cup S_2 | S_3) = \frac{Pr(S_1 \cap S_3) + Pr(S_2 \cap S_3)}{Pr(S_3)}$$

$$= \frac{Pr(S_1 \cap S_3)}{Pr(S_3)} + \frac{Pr(S_2 \cap S_3)}{Pr(S_3)}$$

$$= Pr(S_1 | S_3) + Pr(S_2 | S_3).$$

By mathematical induction, this proof can be extended to $S_1, S_2, \ldots, S_n$ events of S.

From these remarks, we see that the axioms of the axiomatic definition hold for the concept of conditional probability; and, therefore, theorems similar to Theorems 1.2.1, 1.2.2, 1.2.4, and 1.2.5 can be stated for conditional probability.

1.4 Marginal Probabilities

Let S be a sample space which consists of n observations; let $G_1, G_2, \ldots,$ G_k be a sequence of pairwise mutually exclusive events, such that

$$\bigcup_{i=1}^{k} G_i = S;$$

and let $E_1, E_2, \ldots, E_t$ be another sequence of pairwise mutually exclusive events defined on S, such that

$$\bigcup_{i=1}^{t} E_i = S.$$

Thus, the sample space has been partitioned into two sequences of events $\{G_i\}$, $i = 1, 2, \ldots, k$ and $\{E_i\}$, $i = 1, 2, \ldots, t$, both of which are within themselves pairwise mutually exclusive but are not necessarily pairwise mutually exclusive between the two sequences. Such a partition of S into $kt = n$ disjoint subsets of S is shown in Table 1.4.1, where n_{11} is the number of observations that have both characteristics G_1 and E_1, n_{12} is the number of observations that have both characteristics G_1 and E_2, n_{ij} is the number of observations which have both characteristics G_i and E_j, and

$$n = \sum_{i=1}^{k} \sum_{j=1}^{t} n_{ij}.$$

Table 1.4.1

			E				
G	E_1	E_2	E_3	$\cdots$	$\cdots$	E_t	
G_1	n_{11}	n_{12}	n_{13}	$\cdots$	$\cdots$	n_{1t}	$\sum_{j=1}^{t} n_{1j}$
G_2	n_{21}	n_{22}	n_{23}	$\cdots$	$\cdots$	n_{2t}	$\sum_{j=1}^{t} n_{2j}$
G_3	n_{31}	n_{32}	n_{33}	$\cdots$	$\cdots$	n_{3t}	$\sum_{j=1}^{t} n_{3j}$
$\vdots$	$\vdots$	$\vdots$	$\vdots$	$\cdots$	$\cdots$	$\vdots$	$\vdots$
$\vdots$	$\vdots$	$\vdots$	$\vdots$	$\cdots$	$\cdots$	$\vdots$	$\vdots$
G_k	n_{k1}	n_{k2}	n_{k3}	$\cdots$	$\cdots$	n_{kt}	$\sum_{j=1}^{t} n_{kj}$
	$\sum_{i=1}^{k} n_{i1}$	$\sum_{i=1}^{k} n_{i2}$	$\sum_{i=1}^{k} n_{i3}$	$\cdots$	$\cdots$	$\sum_{i=1}^{n} n_{it}$	n

The probability of occurrence of event $G_2 \cap E_3$ (*joint probability*) is equal to the number of observations that are common to both G_2 and E_3, n_{23}, divided by the total number of observations in the sample space, n:

$$Pr(G_2 \cap E_3) = \frac{n_{23}}{n} = p_{23},$$

and, in general,

$$Pr(G_i \cap E_j) = \frac{n_{ij}}{n} = p_{ij}. \tag{1.4.1}$$

Therefore, by calculating the probabilities for every cell of Table 1.4.1, we construct a *probability sample space* as shown in Table 1.4.2, where

$$\sum_{i=1}^{k} \sum_{j=1}^{t} p_{ij} = \sum_{i=1}^{k} p_{i.} = \sum_{j=1}^{t} p_{.j} = p_{..} = 1.$$

Table 1.4.2

G	E_1	E_2	E_3	$\cdots$	$\cdots$	E_t	
			E				
G_1	p_{11}	p_{12}	p_{13}	$\cdots$	$\cdots$	p_{1t}	$\sum_{j=1}^{t} p_{1j} = p_1.$
G_2	p_{21}	p_{22}	p_{23}	$\cdots$	$\cdots$	p_{2t}	$\sum_{j=1}^{t} p_{2j} = p_2.$
G_3	p_{31}	p_{32}	p_{33}	$\cdots$	$\cdots$	p_{3t}	$\sum_{j=1}^{t} p_{3j} = p_3.$
$\vdots$	$\vdots$	$\vdots$	$\vdots$	$\cdots$	$\cdots$	$\vdots$	$\vdots$
$\vdots$	$\vdots$	$\vdots$	$\vdots$	$\cdots$	$\cdots$	$\vdots$	$\vdots$
G_k	p_{k1}	p_{k2}	p_{k3}			p_{kt}	$\sum_{j=1}^{t} p_{kj} = p_k.$
	$\sum_{i=1}^{k} p_{i1} =$	$\sum_{i=1}^{k} p_{i2} =$	$\sum_{i=1}^{k} p_{i3} = \cdots$		$\cdots$	$\sum_{i=1}^{k} p_{it} =$	1
	$p_{.1}$	$p_{.2}$	$p_{.3}$	$\cdots$	$\cdots$	$p_{.t}$	

Often in physical problems when the joint attribute of two happenings is recorded, for example $G_i \cap E_j$, we are interested in finding the probability of the event G_i alone. Now, from the manner in which we have partitioned the sample space, we can write G_i as

$$G_i = (G_i \cap E_1) \cup (G_i \cap E_2) \cup \cdots \cup (G_i \cap E_t); \qquad (1.4.2)$$

and, since $(G_i \cap E_j) \cap (G_i \cap E_{j*}) = \emptyset$ for $j \neq j^*$, applying Axiom 1.2.3 to expression (1.4.2), we have

$$Pr(G_i) = Pr(G_i \cap E_1) + Pr(G_i \cap E_2) + \cdots + Pr(G_i \cap E_t)$$

$$= \sum_{j=1}^{t} Pr(G_i \cap E_j) = \frac{1}{n} \sum_{j=1}^{t} n_{ij} = p_{i..}$$

$$(1.4.3)$$

The sum of the probabilities of the ith row, as given in Equation (1.4.3), is called the *marginal probability* of event G_i. The last column of Table 1.4.2 gives the marginal probabilities of the events G_i, $i = 1, 2, \ldots, k$. For example, the marginal probability of G_2 is given by

$$Pr(G_2) = \sum_{j=1}^{t} Pr(G_2 \cap E_j) = \frac{1}{n} \sum_{j=1}^{t} n_{2j} = p_2..$$

Similarly, the marginal probability of event E_j is given by summing all the probabilities in column j, that is,

$$Pr(E_j) = \sum_{i=1}^{k} Pr(G_i \cap E_j) = \frac{1}{n} \sum_{i=1}^{k} n_{ij} = p_{.j}. \qquad (1.4.4)$$

For example, the marginal probability E_6 is given by

$$Pr(E_6) = \sum_{i=1}^{k} Pr(G_i \cap E_6) = \frac{1}{n} \sum_{i=1}^{k} n_{i6} = p_{.6}.$$

Furthermore, the conditional probability of event G_2, given that event E_1 has occurred, is given by

$$Pr(G_2|E_1) = \frac{Pr(G_2 \cap E_1)}{Pr(E_1)} = \frac{\dfrac{n_{21}}{n}}{\dfrac{1}{n} \displaystyle\sum_{i=1}^{k} n_{i1}}$$

$$= \frac{p_{21}}{p_{.1}} = p_{2|1},$$

and, in general,

$$Pr(G_i|E_j) = \frac{Pr(G_i \cap E_j)}{Pr(E_j)} = \frac{\dfrac{n_{ij}}{n}}{\dfrac{1}{n} \displaystyle\sum_{i=1}^{k} n_{ij}}$$

$$= \frac{p_{ij}}{p_{.j}} = p_{i|j}. \qquad (1.4.5)$$

Similarly,

$$Pr(E_3|G_2) = \frac{Pr(G_2 \cap E_3)}{Pr(G_2)} = \frac{\frac{n_{23}}{n}}{\frac{1}{n}\sum_{j=1}^{t} n_{2j}}$$

$$= \frac{p_{23}}{p_{2.}} = p_{3|2};$$

and, in general,

$$Pr(E_j|G_i) = \frac{Pr(G_i \cap E_j)}{Pr(G_i)} = \frac{\frac{n_{ij}}{n}}{\frac{1}{n}\sum_{j=1}^{t} n_{ij}}$$

$$= \frac{p_{ij}}{p_{i.}} = p_{j|i}. \tag{1.4.6}$$

Example 1.4.1   An industrial firm is trying a certain electrical component, which is used in one of their systems, provided by two companies G_1 and G_2. The components have been installed into three systems E_1, E_2, and E_3, each one operating under different environmental conditions. After the systems have functioned for a period of t hours, they are inspected and the number of defective systems is given in Table 1.4.3.

Table 1.4.3

	E			
G	E_1	E_2	E_3	Total
G_1	30	20	10	60
G_2	10	15	35	60
Total	40	35	45	120

The joint probabilities of the events $G_i \cap E_j$, $i = 1, 2,$ and $j = 1, 2, 3$ are given by Equation (1.4.1) as

$$Pr(G_i \cap E_j) = \frac{n_{ij}}{n} = p_{ij}$$

Table 1.4.4

	\multicolumn{4}{c}{E}			
G	E_1	E_2	E_3	Total
G_1	$\dfrac{1}{4}$	$\dfrac{1}{6}$	$\dfrac{1}{12}$	$\dfrac{1}{2}$
G_2	$\dfrac{1}{12}$	$\dfrac{1}{8}$	$\dfrac{7}{24}$	$\dfrac{1}{2}$
Total	$\dfrac{1}{3}$	$\dfrac{7}{24}$	$\dfrac{3}{8}$	1

and have been calculated from Table 1.4.3, as shown in Table 1.4.4. For example, the probability that a component that was obtained from company G_1 and used in system E_3 is defective is $1/12$, as shown in Table 1.4.4.

If a system is chosen at random and the component is inspected and found to be defective, then what is the probability that it came from company G_1 ?

Solution   The answer to this question is given by the marginal probability of event G_1, that is,

$$Pr(G_1) = \sum_{j=1}^{3} Pr(G_1 \cap E_j) = \frac{1}{n} \sum_{j=1}^{3} n_{ij}$$

$$= \frac{30 + 20 + 10}{120} = \frac{1}{2}.$$

Therefore, the probabilities given in the column under Total are the marginal probabilities of the events G_1 and G_2.

A system was chosen at random and the component was found to be defective; what is the probability that it is installed in system E_3 ?

Solution   The answer to this question is given by the marginal probability of E_3:

$$Pr(E_3) = \sum_{i=1}^{2} Pr(G_i \cap E_3) = \frac{1}{n} \sum_{i=1}^{2} n_{12}$$

$$= \frac{10 + 35}{120} = \frac{3}{8}.$$

Therefore, the probabilities given in the last row of Table 1.4.4 are the marginal probabilities of the events E_1, E_2, and E_3.

Furthermore, we might be interested in the following probabilities:

$$Pr(G_1|E_1) = \frac{Pr(G_1 \cap E_1)}{Pr(E_1)} = \frac{\dfrac{1}{4}}{\dfrac{1}{3}} = \frac{3}{4}$$

is the probability that a defective component chosen at random from system of the type E_1 was purchased from company G_1.

$$Pr(E_1|G_2) = \frac{Pr(G_2 \cap E_1)}{Pr(G_2)} = \frac{\dfrac{1}{12}}{\dfrac{1}{2}} = \frac{1}{6}$$

is the probability that the defective component came from system E_1, given that it was purchased from company G_2.

The partition of the sample space can be extended into three sequences of events, $\{G_i\}$, $i = 1, 2, \ldots, k$, $\{E_i\}$, $i = 1, 2, \ldots, t$ and $\{F_i\}$, $i = 1, 2, \ldots, r$. In this case, the sample space will be partitioned into cells, where each cell would consist of a number, that is, n_{ijl} representing the number of observations having attribute G_i, E_j, and F_l. The probability that such an event occurs is equal to n_{ijl} divided by n, the total number of observations in the sample space S. Here

$$\sum_{l=1}^{r} \sum_{j=1}^{t} \sum_{i=1}^{k} n_{ijl} = n.$$

Also,

$$Pr(G_i \cap E_j \cap F_l) = \frac{n_{ijl}}{n}.$$

The marginal probabilities of the events E_m, $m = 1, 2, 3, \ldots, t$ and $E_m F_p$, $p = 1, 2, \ldots, r$, are given by

$$Pr(E_m) = \sum_{i=1}^{k} \sum_{l=1}^{r} Pr(G_i \cap E_m \cap F_l)$$

$$= \frac{1}{n} \sum_{i=1}^{k} \sum_{l=1}^{r} n_{iml}$$

$$= p_{.m.}.$$

and

$$Pr(E_m \cap F_p) = \sum_{i=1}^{k} Pr(G_i \cap E_m \cap F_p)$$

$$= \frac{1}{n} \sum_{i=1}^{k} n_{imp}$$

$$= p_{\cdot mp},$$

respectively.

The conditional probability of the event G_i, given that event $E_j \cap F_l$ has occurred, and $G_i \cap F_l$, given that the event E_j has occurred, are given by

$$Pr(G_i | E_j \cap F_l) = \frac{Pr(G_i \cap E_j \cap F_l)}{Pr(E_j \cap F_l)}$$

$$= \frac{\dfrac{n_{ijl}}{n}}{\dfrac{1}{n} \sum_{i=1}^{k} n_{ijl}} = \frac{p_{ijl}}{p_{\cdot jl}}$$

$$= p_{i|jl}$$

and

$$Pr(G_i \cap F_l | E_j) = \frac{Pr(G_i \cap E_j \cap F_l)}{Pr(E_j)}$$

$$= \frac{\dfrac{n_{ijl}}{n}}{\dfrac{1}{n} \sum_{i=1}^{k} \sum_{l=1}^{r} n_{ijl}} = \frac{p_{ijl}}{p_{\cdot j \cdot}}$$

$$= p_{il|j},$$

respectively. For example,

$$Pr(E_6 | G_1 \cap F_3) = \frac{Pr(G_1 \cap E_6 \cap F_3)}{Pr(G_1 \cap F_3)}$$

$$= \frac{\dfrac{n_{163}}{n}}{\dfrac{1}{n} \sum_{j=1}^{t} n_{ij3}}$$

$$= \frac{p_{163}}{p_{1 \cdot 3}} = p_{6|13},$$

and

$$Pr(E_3 \cap F_5 | G_3) = \frac{Pr(G_3 \cap E_3 \cap F_5)}{Pr(G_3)}$$

$$= \frac{\dfrac{n_{335}}{n}}{\dfrac{1}{n} \displaystyle\sum_{j=1}^{t} \sum_{l=1}^{r} n_{3jl}}$$

$$= \frac{p_{335}}{p_{3..}} = p_{35|3}.$$

This concept of partitioning the sample space can be easily generalized to m different partitions.

1.5 Bayes' Theorem

Let the sample space S be partitioned into a finite number of mutually exclusive events, $S_1, S_2, \ldots, S_n$. Also, let S^* be any other event of the sample space S. That is,

$$S^* = S \cap S^* = (S_1 \cup S_2 \cup \cdots \cup S_n) \cap S^*$$
$$= (S_1 \cap S^*) \cup (S_2 \cap S^*) \cup \cdots \cup (S_n \cap S^*). \qquad (1.5.1)$$

Since $S_i \cap S^*$, $i = 1, 2, \ldots, n$ are mutually exclusive, we can apply Axiom 1.2.3 to Equation (1.5.1); that is,

$$Pr(S^*) = Pr(S_1 \cap S^*) + Pr(S_2 \cap S^*) + \cdots + Pr(S_n \cap S^*). \qquad (1.5.2)$$

But, according to Equation (1.3.3), we obtain for every i

$$Pr(S_i \cap S^*) = Pr(S^* | S_i)Pr(S_i);$$

and Equation (1.5.2) can be written as

$$Pr(S^*) = Pr(S_1)Pr(S^* | S_1) + Pr(S_2)Pr(S^* | S_2) + \cdots + Pr(S_n)Pr(S^* | S_n)$$
$$= \sum_{i=1}^{n} Pr(S_i)Pr(S^* | S_i). \qquad (1.5.3)$$

Expression (1.5.3) is known as the theorem of *absolute probability* of event S^*.

Furthermore, the conditional probability of S_i, given S^*, is given for every i by

$$Pr(S_i|S^*) = \frac{Pr(S_i \cap S^*)}{Pr(S^*)}, \quad Pr(S^*) > 0. \tag{1.5.4}$$

Substituting Equation (1.5.3) for $Pr(S^*)$ and $Pr(S_i)Pr(S^*|S_i)$ for $Pr(S_i \cap S^*)$ in Equation (1.5.4), we obtain the Theorem 1.5.1, which results from the work of Thomas Bayes.

Theorem 1.5.1 (Bayes' Theorem)   If S_1, S_2, ..., S_n and S^* satisfy the above assumptions, that is, the theorem of absolute probability and $Pr(S^*) > 0$, then for every $i = 1, 2, \ldots, n$ we have

$$Pr(S_i|S^*) = \frac{Pr(S_i)Pr(S^*|S_i)}{Pr(S_1)Pr(S^*|S_1) + Pr(S_2)Pr(S^*|S_2) + \cdots + Pr(S_n)Pr(S^*|S_n)}$$

or

$$Pr(S_i|S^*) = \frac{Pr(S_i)Pr(S^*|S_i)}{\sum\limits_{j=1}^{n} Pr(S_j)Pr(S^*|S_j)}$$

$$= \frac{Pr(S_i)Pr(S^*|S_i)}{Pr(S^*)}. \tag{1.5.5}$$

Equation (1.5.5) is sometimes called the *formula for a posteriori probability* rather than *Bayes' formula* because the formula gives us the probability of S_i after S^* has been observed. Also, the probabilities $Pr(S_i)$ in *Bayes' formula* are called *a priori probabilities*.

The following examples illustrate some of the various applications of Bayes' Theorem.

Example 1.5.1   Consider that we have in an industrial complex two large boxes, each of which contains 30 electrical components. It is known that the first box contains 26 operable and four nonoperable components and that the second box contains 28 operable and two nonoperable components. We are interested in obtaining the probability that a component selected at random will be operable, assuming that the probability of making a selection from each of the boxes is the same.

Solution   Let S_1 and S_2 be the events of selecting the first and second boxes, respectively, and let S^* be the event that an operable component is chosen. We note that the event of selecting an operable component, S^*, can occur either with S_1 or S_2; that is,

$$S^* = (S_1 \cap S^*) \cup (S_2 \cap S^*).$$

Since $S_1 \cap S^*$ and $S_2 \cap S^*$ are mutually exclusive events, we have

$$Pr(S^*) = Pr(S_1 \cap S^*) + Pr(S_2 \cap S^*),$$

or

$$Pr(S^*) = Pr(S_1)Pr(S^*|S_1) + Pr(S_2)Pr(S^*|S_2).$$

Also,

$$Pr(S_1) = Pr(S_2) = \frac{1}{2}, \qquad Pr(S^*|S_1) = \frac{13}{15}$$

and

$$Pr(S^*|S_2) = \frac{14}{15}.$$

Therefore, the probability that the component chosen is operable is given by

$$Pr(S^*) = \left(\frac{1}{2}\right)\left(\frac{26}{30}\right) + \left(\frac{1}{2}\right)\left(\frac{28}{30}\right) = .90.$$

Furthermore, suppose the component chosen at random were operable and we wish to find the probability that the component was chosen from box S_1, $Pr(S_1|S^*)$.

Solution   By Bayes' formula,

$$Pr(S_1|S^*) = \frac{Pr(S_1)Pr(S^*|S_1)}{Pr(S_1)Pr(S^*|S_1) + Pr(S_2)Pr(S^*|S_2)}$$

$$= \frac{\left(\frac{1}{2}\right)\left(\frac{26}{30}\right)}{\left(\frac{1}{2}\right)\left(\frac{26}{30}\right) + \left(\frac{1}{2}\right)\left(\frac{28}{30}\right)} = \frac{26}{54} \approx .48.$$

Example 1.5.2   Three weapon systems are shooting at the same target. From the design point of view, each weapon has an equally likely chance of hitting the target; however, in actual practice it has been observed that the precision of these weapon systems is not the same; that is, the first weapon will usually hit the target 10 out of 12 shots, the second will hit it nine out of 12 shots, and the third will hit it eight out of 12 shots. We have observed that the target has been hit, and we are interested in finding the probability that the shot was fired by the third weapon system.

Solution   Let S_1, S_2, and S_3 be the events that the target has been hit by the first, second, and third weapon system, respectively. Also, let S^* be the event that the target has been hit. We wish to find $Pr(S_3 \mid S^*)$. Thus, according to Bayes' theorem, we have

$$Pr(S_3 \mid S^*) = \frac{Pr(S_3)Pr(S^* \mid S_3)}{Pr(S_1)Pr(S^* \mid S_1) + Pr(S_2)Pr(S^* \mid S_2) + Pr(S_3)Pr(S^* \mid S_3)}$$

$$= \frac{\left(\frac{1}{3}\right)\left(\frac{8}{12}\right)}{\left(\frac{1}{3}\right)\left(\frac{10}{12}\right) + \left(\frac{1}{3}\right)\left(\frac{9}{12}\right) + \left(\frac{1}{3}\right)\left(\frac{8}{12}\right)} = \frac{8}{27},$$

meaning that the probability that the shot was fired from the third weapon system is 8/27, assuming, of course, that $Pr(S_1) = Pr(S_2) = Pr(S_3) = 1/3$, as was specified in the design of the system.

Furthermore,

$$Pr(S_2 \mid S^*) = \frac{\left(\frac{1}{3}\right)\left(\frac{9}{12}\right)}{\left(\frac{1}{3}\right)\left(\frac{10}{12}\right) + \left(\frac{1}{3}\right)\left(\frac{9}{12}\right) + \left(\frac{1}{3}\right)\left(\frac{8}{12}\right)} = \frac{9}{27}$$

and

$$Pr(S_1 \mid S^*) = \frac{\left(\frac{1}{3}\right)\left(\frac{10}{12}\right)}{\left(\frac{1}{3}\right)\left(\frac{10}{12}\right) + \left(\frac{1}{3}\right)\left(\frac{9}{12}\right) + \left(\frac{1}{3}\right)\left(\frac{8}{12}\right)} = \frac{10}{27}.$$

1.6   Independent Events

The notion of independent events is quite basic and plays a central role in probability theory. Let S_1 and S_2 be two events of the sample space S, with positive probabilities. The event S_2 is said to be *independent* of event S_1 if

$$Pr(S_1 \cap S_2) = Pr(S_1)Pr(S_2). \tag{1.6.1}$$

Here, the probability of the intersection of the events $S_1 \cap S_2$ is equal to the product of the probabilities of S_1 and S_2. Therefore, from the definition of conditional probability (1.3.1), if S_1 and S_2 are independent events, then

$$Pr(S_2 \mid S_1) = \frac{Pr(S_1 \cap S_2)}{Pr(S_1)} = \frac{Pr(S_1)Pr(S_2)}{Pr(S_1)} = Pr(S_2). \tag{1.6.2}$$

That is, the probability that S_2 occurs is not affected by the fact that S_1 has occurred.

Note that, if S_2 is independent of S_1, then S_1 is independent of S_2. To show this independence, we write

$$Pr(S_1 \cap S_2) = Pr(S_1)Pr(S_2|S_1) = Pr(S_2)Pr(S_1|S_2) \qquad (1.6.3)$$

and

$$Pr(S_2|S_1) = Pr(S_2).$$

It follows that

$$Pr(S_1|S_2) = Pr(S_1).$$

Example 1.6.1   Consider a problem where two guns are shooting at the same target. Let S_1 and S_2 be the events that the target is hit by guns one and two, respectively. The probability that S_1 occurs is obviously unaffected by the occurrence or nonoccurrence of S_2. It has been observed that $Pr(S_1) = 1/3$ and $Pr(S_2) = 1/4$. Thus, the probability of both guns hitting the target is given by

$$Pr(S_1 \cap S_2) = Pr(S_1)Pr(S_2)$$

$$= \left(\frac{1}{3}\right)\left(\frac{1}{4}\right) = \frac{1}{12}.$$

Furthermore, if we are interested in the probability that S_1 or S_2 occurs, we use Theorem 1.2.5 and write

$$Pr(S_1 \cup S_2) = Pr(S_1) + Pr(S_2) - Pr(S_1 \cap S_2)$$
$$= Pr(S_1) + Pr(S_2) - Pr(S_1)Pr(S_2)$$

$$= \left(\frac{1}{3}\right) + \left(\frac{1}{4}\right) - \left(\frac{1}{12}\right) = \frac{1}{2}.$$

If the events S_1 and S_2 do not satisfy Equation (1.6.1), they are said to be *dependent* or *nonindependent*. Thus, the events S_1 and S_2 are dependent if and only if

$$Pr(S_1 \cap S_2) \neq Pr(S_1)Pr(S_2).$$

Example 1.6.2   Let S_1 and S_2 denote the events that a particular sports coat and a pair of trousers, respectively, are purchased on a specified day. It has been found that $Pr(S_1) = Pr(S_2) = .46$ and $Pr(S_1 \cap S_2) = .23$. Determine the conditional probabilities $Pr(S_1|S_2)$ and $Pr(S_2|S_1)$ and the total probability $Pr(S_1 \cup S_2)$. Are the events S_1 and S_2 independent ?

Solution   The conditional probabilities are obtained by

$$Pr(S_1 | S_2) = \frac{Pr(S_1 \cap S_2)}{Pr(S_2)} = \frac{.23}{.46} = .5$$

and

$$Pr(S_2 | S_1) = \frac{Pr(S_1 \cap S_2)}{Pr(S_1)} = \frac{.23}{.46} = .5.$$

The total probability is given by

$$Pr(S_1 \cup S_2) = Pr(S_1) + Pr(S_2) - Pr(S_1 \cap S_2)$$
$$= .46 + .46 - .23 = .69.$$

The two events are dependent, not independent, because $Pr(S_1 | S_2) \neq Pr(S_1)$, or, equivalently, $Pr(S_1 \cap S_2) \neq Pr(S_1)Pr(S_2)$.

The independence of two events can be generalized to a finite number of events defined on the sample space. Let $S_1, S_2, \ldots, S_n$ be a finite sequence of events of S. These events are said to be *mutually independent* or *independent* if

$$Pr(S_{j_1} \cap S_{j_2} \cap \cdots \cap S_{j_t}) = Pr(S_{j_1})Pr(S_{j_2}) \cdots Pr(S_{j_t})$$

for all integer indices $j_1, j_2, \ldots, j_t$, such that $1 \leq j_1 < j_2 < \cdots < j_t \leq n$. That is, the probability of the intersection of every combination of events equals the product of their probabilities. For example, the events S_1, S_2, and S_3 are independent if

(a) $Pr(S_1 \cap S_2) = Pr(S_1)Pr(S_2)$
(b) $Pr(S_1 \cap S_3) = Pr(S_1)Pr(S_3)$
(c) $Pr(S_2 \cap S_3) = Pr(S_2)Pr(S_3)$
(d) $Pr(S_1 \cap S_2 \cap S_3) = Pr(S_1)Pr(S_2)Pr(S_3).$

Furthermore, it follows that

$$Pr(S_1 | S_2 \cap S_3) = Pr(S_1 | S_2) = Pr(S_1 | S_3) = Pr(S_1),$$
$$Pr(S_2 | S_1 \cap S_3) = Pr(S_2 | S_1) = Pr(S_2 | S_3) = Pr(S_2),$$

and

$$Pr(S_3 | S_1 \cap S_2) = Pr(S_3 | S_1) = Pr(S_3 | S_2) = Pr(S_3),$$

assuming that the events S_1, S_2, S_3, $S_1 \cap S_2$, and $S_1 \cap S_3$ have nonzero probabilities. The total number of equations of the form (a) to (d) that are required to establish the independence of n events equals $2^n - (n + 1)$.

Keep in mind that it is possible for the events in the sequence $S_1, S_2, \ldots, S_n$ to be independent in twos, in threes, in fours, and so on; yet $S_1, S_2, \ldots, S_n$ may not be independent. The following example will illustrate.

Example 1.6.3   A sample poll of 100 voters revealed the following information concerning three party candidates, A, B, and C, who were running for three different offices:

10 in favor of both A and B,

35 in favor of A or B but not C,

25 in favor of B but not A or C,

65 in favor of B or C but not A,

25 in favor of C but not A or B,

 0 in favor of A and C but not B,

15 turned in blank ballots.

Here, A, B, and C are pairwise independent but are not three-way independent, as shown below.

$$Pr(A \cap B \cap C) = \frac{10}{100} = \frac{1}{10} \quad \text{and} \quad Pr(A)Pr(B)Pr(C) = \left(\frac{20}{100}\right)\left(\frac{50}{100}\right)\left(\frac{50}{100}\right) = \frac{1}{20}$$

$$Pr(A \cap B) = \frac{1}{10} \quad \text{and} \quad Pr(A)Pr(B) = \frac{1}{10},$$

$$Pr(A \cap C) = \frac{1}{10} \quad \text{and} \quad Pr(A)Pr(C) = \frac{1}{10},$$

$$Pr(B \cap C) = \frac{1}{4} \quad \text{and} \quad Pr(B)Pr(C) = \frac{1}{4}.$$

We shall now state some obvious properties of independent events.

(a) If S_1 and S_2 are two mutually exclusive events, then these events are independent if and only if $Pr(S_1)Pr(S_2) = 0$, and this will be so if and only if either $Pr(S_1)$ or $Pr(S_2)$ or both are equal to zero.

(b) If S_1 and S_2 are independent, then Theorem 1.2.5 can be written as

$$Pr(S_1 \cup S_2) = Pr(S_1) + Pr(S_2) - Pr(S_1)Pr(S_2).$$

(c) If S_1 and S_2 are independent events, then their complements $\bar{S}_1$ and $\bar{S}_2$ are also independent, and

$$Pr(\bar{S}_1 \cap \bar{S}_2) = Pr(\bar{S}_1)Pr(\bar{S}_2).$$

(d) If S_1, S_2, and S_3 are independent events, then S_1 is independent of $S_2 \cap S_3$ and $S_2 \cup S_3$.

1.7 Combinatorial Probability

As we have seen throughout our discussion, the number of observations in a sample space S is the basis for obtaining probabilities of various events defined on S. That is, if we know that, in a certain problem, the space consists of n equally likely observations and n_{s_1} of them are favorable to event S_1, then the probability that event S_1 will occur is given by

$$Pr(S_1) = \frac{n_{s_1}}{n}.$$

In this section, we shall discuss the manner in which we can obtain the total number of observations of the sample space under four basic sampling procedures. A review of Section 0.3 will enhance your understanding of the following material.

The initial step in many physical problems involves the concept of a *random sample*: when we say that a random sample of k objects was drawn from a population of N objects, we mean that each one of the N objects had equal probability of being selected. When a random sample of size k is taken, the sample space will consist of a certain number of k-tuples, or the total number of ways in which the random sample of size k can be selected. We shall consider the following four sampling schemes:

1. Sampling with replacement and the objects being ordered.
2. Sampling without replacement and the objects being ordered.
3. Sampling without replacement and the objects being unordered.
4. Sampling with replacement and the objects being unordered.

For the purpose of illustrating the above sampling methods, we shall consider that we have a population of N objects numbered $1, 2, 3, \ldots, N$, from which we shall take a random sample of size k according to one of the four sampling schemes listed above.

Sampling under Scheme 1.   There are N possible ways in which the first observation in the sample can be drawn. There are also N possible ways in which the second observation in the sample can be drawn. Therefore, there are N^2 possible outcomes for the first two drawings of the sample. Continuing in this manner, it is obvious that the sample space S will consist of

$$N^k \quad k\text{-tuples.} \tag{1.7.1}$$

Example 1.7.1   An urn contains nine balls numbered 1 to 9. If a random sample with replacement of size $k = 6$ be taken, then the sample space S, according to Equation (1.7.1), will consist of 9^6,   6-tuples.

Example 1.7.2   If a die is rolled five times, then the sample space S will consist of 6^5 5-tuples. That is, this experiment is equivalent to sampling with replacement where the number of times that we roll the die is equivalent to the size of the random sample and N is equivalent to the number of faces on the die.

Sampling under Scheme 2.   There are N possible ways in which the first observation of the sample can be drawn. There are $N - 1$ possible ways in which the second object in the sample can be selected. Finally, there are $N - (k - 1) = N - k + 1$ possible ways in which the kth observation may be drawn. Therefore, applying Rule 2 (Section 0.3), the total number of k-tuples that the sample space consists of is given by

$$P_k^N = N(N - 1)(N - 2) \cdots (N - k + 1)$$

$$= \frac{N!}{(N - k)!}. \tag{1.7.2}$$

If in (1.7.2) $k = N$, then $P_N^N = N(N - 1)(N - 2) \cdots (1) = N!$.

Example 1.7.3   An urn holds 11 balls that are numbered 1 to 11. A random ordered sample of size $k = 3$ is drawn. Then, according to Equation (1.7.2), the sample space S will consist of $11!/(11 - 3)! = 990$ 3-tuples.

Example 1.7.4   If 13 cards are selected from an ordinary deck of playing cards and the order in which the cards are drawn is important, then the sample space S will consist of $52!/(52 - 13)!$ 13-tuples.

Example 1.7.5   An urn contains nine balls that are numbered 1 to 9. If a random sample of size $k = 9$ is drawn and order is of importance, then there are $N! = k! = 9!$ possible ways in which this sample can be drawn.

Sampling under Scheme 3.   To obtain the total number of ways in which a random sample can be drawn under this scheme, we simply need to eliminate the order in Scheme 2. This is done by dividing $N!/(N - k)!$ by the number of different sample orderings possible. If the population is of size N and the sample is of size k, then the total number of samples is

$$\frac{P_k^N}{k!} = \frac{N!}{k!(N - k)!} = \binom{N}{k}, \qquad k = 0, 1, 2, \ldots, N. \tag{1.7.3}$$

Example 1.7.6   If a football squad consists of 72 players, how many possible selections of 11-man teams are there?

Solution   Applying Equation (1.7.3), we have

$$\binom{72}{11} = \frac{72!}{11!(72 - 11)!}.$$

That is, the sample space consists of $\binom{72}{11}$ 11-tuples.

Example 1.7.7   What is the total number of ways in which a 13-card hand can be drawn from an ordinary deck of playing cards ?

Solution   Since there is no replacement and order is irrelevant, the number of ways is

$$\binom{52}{13} = \frac{52!}{13!\,(52-13)!}.$$

Sampling under Scheme 4.   In obtaining an unordered sample of size k, with replacement, from a population of size N, $k-1$ replacements will be made before sampling ceases. Thus N is increased by $k-1$ so that sampling in this manner may be thought of as drawing an unordered sample of size k from a population of size $N+k-1$. That is, the number of samples is

$$\binom{N+k-1}{k} = \frac{(N+k-1)!}{k!\,(N-1)!}, \quad k = 0, 1, 2, \dots. \tag{1.7.4}$$

Example 1.7.8   An urn contains 15 balls numbered 1 to 15. If a random sample of size $k = 4$ is drawn with replacement but without regard for order from the urn, then, according to Equation (1.7.4), the sample space consists of

$$\binom{15+4-1}{4} = \frac{18!}{4!\,14!} \quad \text{4-tuples.}$$

We shall now derive a useful formula which concerns itself with the number of ways that a sample of size k may be partitioned into r ordered groups of unordered elements such that not only will the ith group contain k_i elements for $k = 1, 2, \dots, r$, but also

$$\sum_{i=1}^{r} k_i = k.$$

Here, the elements of the first group may be selected in $\binom{k}{k_1}$ ways, those of the second group in $\binom{k-k_1}{k_2}$ ways, those of the third group in $\binom{k-k_1-k_2}{k_3}$ ways, ..., and those of the rth group in $\binom{k-k_1-k_2-\cdots-k_{r-1}}{k_r}$ ways. Taking the product of these combinations gives

$$\frac{k!}{k_1!\,k_2!\,k_3!\cdots k_r!},$$

which is derived from

$$\frac{k!}{k_1!\,(k-k_1)!} \cdot \frac{(k-k_1)!}{k_2!\,(k-k_1-k_2)!} \cdot \frac{(k-k_1-k_2)!}{k_3!\,(k-k_1-k_2-k_3)!}$$
$$\ldots\ldots \frac{(k-k_1-k_2-\cdots-k_{r-1})!}{k_r!\,(k-k_1-k_2-\cdots-k_r)!},$$

where the second component of the denominators of each factor cancels with the numerator of each succeeding factor. This last expression reduces to

$$\frac{k!}{k_1!\,k_2!\,k_3!\cdots k_r!} = \binom{k}{k_1,\,k_2,\,k_3,\,\ldots,\,k_r}. \tag{1.7.5}$$

Example 1.7.9   A die is tossed 10 times. Find the total number of ways in which one can obtain the following: three aces, no two's, two threes, no fours, three fives, and two sixes.

Solution   This number is given by applying Equation (1.7.5); that is,

$$\binom{10}{3,\,0,\,2,\,0,\,3,\,2} = \frac{10!}{3!\,0!\,2!\,0!\,3!\,2!}.$$

Example 1.7.10   Four players in a game of bridge are dealt 13 cards each from an ordinary deck of 52 cards. The total number of ways in which we can deal the 13 cards to the four players is given by Equation (1.7.5); that is,

$$\binom{52}{13,\,13,\,13,\,13} = \frac{52!}{13!\,13!\,13!\,13!}.$$

We shall now illustrate some of the uses of the above counting techniques in solving various probability problems.

Example 1.7.11   If a five-volume set of books is placed on a book shelf at random, what is the probability that the books will be in the correct order ?

Solution   Let A be the event that the five-volume set of books is in the correct order. The sample space S consists of $P^5 = 5!/(5-5)! = 5 \cdot 4 \cdot 3 \cdot 2 \cdot 1$ 5-tuples and there is only one 5-tuple favorable to event A. Therefore,

$$Pr(A) = \frac{1}{5 \cdot 4 \cdot 3 \cdot 2 \cdot 1}.$$

Example 1.7.12   A certain lot of 26 mechanical components contains six defective items. A random sample of four components is drawn from the lot.

(a)   What is the probability that all four components drawn are operable ?
(b)   That two are operable and two defective ?

Solution   (a) Let A be the event that all four components are operable. The sample space S consists of $\binom{26}{4}$ 4-tuples because order is not relevant. The number of 4-tuples in the sample space favorable to event A is given by $\binom{20}{4}$, since there are 20 operable components in the lot. Therefore,

$$Pr(A) = \frac{\binom{20}{4}}{\binom{26}{4}}.$$

(b) Let B be the event of drawing two operable and two defective components. The sample space in this part remains the same as in (a). The number of ways of drawing two operable components out of 20 is given by $\binom{20}{2}$; the number of ways of drawing two defectives out of six is given by $\binom{6}{2}$. The total number of ways of achieving event B is given by $\binom{20}{2}\binom{6}{2}$ (applying Rule 2, Section 0.3). Therefore,

$$Pr(B) = \frac{\binom{20}{2}\binom{6}{2}}{\binom{26}{4}}.$$

Example 1.7.13   Suppose that seven cards are selected at random from an ordinary deck of 52 cards. What is the probability that two of the cards are aces, one is a nine, one is a ten, one is a jack, one is a queen, and one is a king ?

Solution   Let A be the event that seven cards are drawn—two are aces, and there is one nine, one ten, one jack, one queen, and one king. The sample space S consists of $\binom{52}{7}$ 7-tuples, because order is not relevant. The number of ways of obtaining two aces is $\binom{4}{2}$; the number of ways of obtaining one nine, one ten, one jack, one queen, or one king is $\binom{4}{1}$; and the total number of ways of achieving event A, that is, the total number of 7-tuples in the sample space favorable to event A, is given by

$$\binom{4}{2}\binom{4}{1}\binom{4}{1}\binom{4}{1}\binom{4}{1}\binom{4}{1}.$$

Therefore,

$$Pr(A) = \frac{\binom{4}{2}\binom{4}{1}^5}{\binom{52}{7}}.$$

Example 1.7.14   A lot of 45 electrical components numbered 1 to 45 is drawn at random, one by one, and is divided among five customers.
(a) Suppose that it is known that components 7, 11, 16, 21, and 36 are defective. What is the probability that each customer will receive one defective component ?

Solution   Let A represent the event desired. The sample space S according to Equation (1.7.4) consists of

$$\binom{45}{9, 9, 9, 9, 9}$$

points. The total number of sample points favorable to event A is given by

$$\binom{5}{1, 1, 1, 1, 1}\binom{40}{8, 8, 8, 8, 8}.$$

That is, the five defective components can be distributed to the five customers in 5! ways and the 40 remaining components, according to Equation (1.7.4), can be divided among the customers in $\binom{40}{8, 8, 8, 8, 8}$ ways. We obtain

$$Pr(A) = \frac{\binom{40}{8, 8, 8, 8, 8}\binom{5}{1, 1, 1, 1, 1}}{\binom{45}{9, 9, 9, 9, 9}}.$$

(b) What is the probability that one customer will have drawn five defective components ?

Solution   Let B be the desired event. The totality of sample points in S remains the same as that in part (a). The total number of sample points favorable to event B is given by

$$\binom{5}{1}\binom{5}{5}\binom{40}{4,\ 9,\ 9,\ 9,\ 9}$$

and

$$Pr(B) = \frac{\binom{5}{1}\binom{5}{5}\binom{40}{4,\ 9,\ 9,\ 9,\ 9}}{\binom{45}{9,\ 9,\ 9,\ 9,\ 9}}.$$

(c) What is the probability that two customers will receive two defective components each, two none and the other one ?

Solution   Let C be the desired event; then by reasoning similar to that above we have

$$Pr(C) = \frac{\binom{5}{2,\ 2,\ 1,\ 0,\ 0}\binom{40}{7,\ 7,\ 8,\ 9,\ 9}\binom{5}{2,\ 2,\ 1}}{\binom{45}{9,\ 9,\ 9,\ 9,\ 9}}.$$

Example 1.7.15   In choosing an unordered sample of size k with replacement from a population of size N, find the probability that r specified elements are included in the sample.

Solution   Here, let $r < k < N$. (a) The sample can be obtained in $\binom{N+k-1}{k}$ ways. (b) The r elements may be selected in $\binom{r}{r} = 1$ way. (c) After the r elements are included in the sample, there are $N - r$ other elements in the population, from which $k - r$ will be selected to be included in the sample. The number of ways this can be done is equal to

$$\binom{(N-r)+(k-r)-1}{k-r} = \binom{N+k-2r-1}{k-r}.$$

Therefore, the probability desired is

$$\frac{\binom{N+k-2r-1}{k-r}}{\binom{N+k-1}{k}}.$$

Example 1.7.16   From a population of size 10, an unordered sample of size 6 will be selected, with replacement. Find the probability that four specified elements will be included in the sample.

Solution   The probability asked for is

$$\frac{\dbinom{10 + 6 - (2 \cdot 4) - 1}{6 - 4}}{\dbinom{10 + 6 - 1}{6}}$$

$$= \frac{\dbinom{7}{2}}{\dbinom{15}{6}} = \frac{3}{715}.$$

Up until now, we have been dealing with probability problems by determining the number of points in the sample space and then dividing this number into the number of points favorable to the event whose probability we wish to find. In many instances, this procedure can become exceedingly tedious, especially if the number of sample points is large and/or difficult to determine; to escape these difficulties, set up a real valued function on the sample space, which helps us to find the probabilities we want. This function is called a *random variable* and will be discussed in detail in the next chapter. But its *probability density*, which characterizes the behavior of the random variable, is what helps us in determining probabilities.

For example, suppose a coin is tossed four times and we are interested in the number of heads that occur. In this case, we shall let the random variable X be equal to the number of heads that occur; consequently, its probability density function is

$$f(x) = Pr(X = x) = \begin{cases} \dfrac{\dbinom{4}{x}}{16}, & x = 0, 1, 2, 3, 4, \\ 0, & \text{elsewhere.} \end{cases}$$

Thus we can find, without lengthy calculations, $Pr(X = x_0)$, where x_0 is any real number from $-\infty$ to $+\infty$. That is,

$$Pr(X = 3) = \frac{\dbinom{4}{3}}{16} = \frac{4}{16}; \quad Pr(X = -2) = 0; \quad Pr(X = 7) = 0;$$

$$Pr(X = 0) = \frac{\dbinom{4}{0}}{16} = \frac{1}{16}; \quad \text{and so forth.}$$

In addition to considering in detail the concept of a random variable, we shall also study in detail in the next chapter the methods of determining the density of a random variable, the uses of the random variable, and some very important probability densities.

1.8 Summary

Four definitions of probability have been discussed, namely:

(1) *Probability as a measure of belief,*
(2) *Classical or a priori probability,*
(3) *Relative frequency or a posteriori probability,*
(4) *Axiomatic definition of probability.*

Let S_i, $i = 1, 2, \ldots, n, \ldots$ represent events of the sample space S. The number $Pr(S_i)$, which satisfies $0 \leq Pr(S_i)$, $Pr(S) = 1$, and for $S_i \cap S_j = \varnothing$, $i \neq j = 1, 2,$ $3, \ldots, n, \ldots, Pr\left(\bigcup_{i=1}^{\infty} S_i\right) = \sum_{i=1}^{\infty} Pr(S_i)$ is called the *probability* of the event S_i.

The following elementary properties of probability were studied:

(1) If S_1 and S_2 are any two events of the sample space S, such that $S_1 \subset S_2$, then $Pr(S_1) \leq Pr(S_2)$.
(2) If S_k is any event of the sample space S, then $Pr(S_k) \leq 1$ and $Pr(\bar{S}_k) = 1 - Pr(S_k)$.
(3) If $\varnothing$ is the empty set, then $Pr(\varnothing) = 0$.
(4) If S_1 and S_2 are any two events of the sample space S, then $Pr(S_1 \cup S_2) = Pr(S_1) + Pr(S_2) - Pr(S_1 \cap S_2)$. Let $S_1, S_2, \ldots, S_n$ be a sequence of events defined on S. *The General Law of Total Probability* is given by

$$Pr\left(\bigcup_{i=1}^{n} S_i\right) = \sum_{i=1}^{n} Pr(S_i) - \sum_{\substack{i,j=1 \\ i<j}}^{n} Pr(S_i \cap S_j) + \sum_{\substack{i,j,k \\ i<j<k}}^{n} Pr(S_i \cap S_j \cap S_k)$$

$$+ \cdots + (-1)^{n+1} Pr(S_1 \cap S_2 \cap \cdots \cap S_n).$$

The *conditional probability* of the event S_1, given that event S_2 has occurred, $S_1 | S_2$, is given by

$$Pr(S_1 | S_2) = \frac{Pr(S_1 \cap S_2)}{Pr(S_2)}, \qquad Pr(S_2) > 0.$$

Let $S_1, S_2, S_3, \ldots, S_n$ be events defined on S. *The General Law of Compound Probability* is given by

$$Pr(S_1 \cap S_2 \cap \cdots \cap S_n) =$$
$$Pr(S_1)Pr(S_2|S_1)Pr(S_3|S_1 \cap S_2) \ldots Pr(S_n|S_1 \cap S_2 \cap \cdots \cap S_{n-1}),$$

where

$$Pr(S_1 \cap S_2 \cap \cdots \cap S_j) > 0, \quad 1 \leq j \leq n-1.$$

The concept of *marginal probability* was studied.

Partition S into a finite number of mutually exclusive events $S_1, S_2, \ldots, S_n$ and let $S^* = (S_1 \cap S^*) \cup (S_2 \cap S^*) \cup \cdots \cup (S_n \cap S^*)$. The *absolute probability* of event S^* is

$$Pr(S^*) = \sum_{i=1}^{n} Pr(S_i)Pr(S^*|S_i).$$

If $Pr(S^*) > 0$, then for every $i = 1, 2, \ldots, n$ we have *Bayes' theorem*:

$$Pr(S_i|S^*) = \frac{Pr(S_i)Pr(S^*|S_i)}{\displaystyle\sum_{j=1}^{n} Pr(S_j)Pr(S^*|S_j)}.$$

Let $S_1, S_2, \ldots, S_n$ be a finite sequence of events of S. These events are said to be *mutually independent* or *independent* if

$$Pr(S_{j_1} \cap S_{j_2} \cap \cdots \cap S_{j_t}) = Pr(S_{j_1})Pr(S_{j_2}) \ldots Pr(S_{j_t})$$

for all integer indices $j_1, j_2, \ldots, j_t$, such that $1 \leq j_1 < j_2 < \cdots < j_t \leq n$.

Combinatorial probability was discussed by considering four sampling schemes:

(1) *Sampling with replacement and the objects being ordered,*
(2) *Sampling without replacement and the objects being ordered,*
(3) *Sampling without replacement and the objects being unordered,*
(4) *Sampling with replacement and the objects being unordered.*

Exercises

1.1. Given the following six postulates which are true for all sets contained in the sample space S:

P_1: $A, B \subset S$ implies $A \cup B, A \cap B \subset S$ (existence postulate).
P_2: $A \cup B = B \cup A$, and $A \cap B = B \cap A$ (commutative postulate).

P_3: $(A \cup B) \cup C = A \cup (B \cup C)$, and $(A \cap B) \cap C = A \cap (B \cap C)$
(associative postulate).

P_4: $A \cap (B \cup C) = (A \cap B) \cup (A \cap C)$, and $A \cup (B \cap C) = (A \cup B)$
$\cap (A \cup C)$ (distributive postulate).

P_5: $A \cap S = A \cup \varnothing = A$ (identity postulate).

P_6: $A \cap \bar{A} = \varnothing$, and $A \cup \bar{A} = S$ (complementation postulate).

Using only postulates one through six and any others you might derive, prove

(a) $A \cup S = S$ and $A \cap \varnothing = \varnothing$ (b) $A \cup A = A$ and $A \cap A = A$

(c) $\bar{S} = \varnothing$ and $\bar{\varnothing} = S$ (d) $\overline{(\bar{A})} = A$

(e) $\overline{A \cup B} = \bar{A} \cap \bar{B}$ and $\overline{A \cap B} = \bar{A} \cup \bar{B}$

(f) $A \cup (A \cap B) = A$ and $A \cap (A \cup B) = A$.

1.2. If $S_1, S_2, \ldots, S_n \subset S$, then, for $k \le n - 1$, show that

$$Pr\left[\left(\bigcup_{i=1}^{k} S_i\right) \cup S_{k+1}\right] = Pr\left(\bigcup_{i=1}^{k+1} S_i\right).$$

(See page 85).

1.3. If $Pr(B) > 0$, then show that

(a) $Pr(A|B) = Pr(A)/Pr(B)$ for $A \subset B$

(b) $Pr(A|B) = 1$ for $A \supset B$.

1.4. If $Pr(B) > 0$ and $Pr(\bar{B}) > 0$, show that $Pr(A|B) + P(\bar{A}|B) = 1$.

1.5. Show that in general the following two statements are false:

(a) $Pr(A|B) + Pr(A|\bar{B}) = 1$,   (b) $Pr(A|B) + Pr(\bar{A}|\bar{B}) = 1$.

1.6. If $Pr(B) = p$, $Pr(\bar{A}|B) = q$, and $Pr(\bar{A} \cap \bar{B}) = r$, find

(a) $Pr(A \cap \bar{B})$,   (b) $Pr(A)$,

(c) $Pr(B|A)$.

1.7. If A and B are independent events, prove that

(a) A and $\bar{B}$ are independent   (b) $\bar{A}$ and B are independent

(c) $\bar{A}$ and $\bar{B}$ are independent.

1.8. Show that, if two sets are mutually exclusive, they are not independent but that the converse does not hold.

1.9. If A and B each play the game of each tossing alternately a fair coin, the winner being the one who tosses a head first, find the probability that A wins, assuming A tosses first.

1.10. Find the same probability as in Exercise 1.9 but in this case let the probability that the coin comes up heads on any one toss be equal to p.

1.11. State when two independent events are also mutually exclusive.

1.12. State when two mutually exclusive events are also independent.

For Problems 1.13 to 1.17, assume that n, m, and k are integers, with $n > k$ and $m > k$.

1.13. Show that

(a) $(1 + t)^n = \sum_{x=0}^{n} \binom{n}{x} t^x$ (b) $(1 - t)^n = \sum_{x=0}^{n} (-1)^x \binom{n}{x} t^x$

(c) $(1 + t)^{-n} = \sum_{x=0}^{\infty} (-1)^x \binom{n - 1 + x}{x} t^x$

(d) $(1 - t)^{-n} = \sum_{x=0}^{\infty} \binom{n - 1 + x}{x} t^x.$

1.14. Show that

(a) $\sum_{x=0}^{r} \binom{n}{x} \binom{m}{r - x} = \binom{n + m}{r}$

(b) $\sum_{x=0}^{n} \binom{n}{x}^2 = \binom{2n}{n}.$

1.15. Show that

(a) $\binom{n}{k} = \binom{n - 1}{k - 1} + \binom{n - 1}{k}$

(b) $\sum_{x=0}^{n-k} \binom{n - 1 - x}{k - 1} = \binom{n}{k}$

(c) $\sum_{x=0}^{k} \binom{n - 1 - x}{k - x} = \binom{n}{k}.$

1.16. Show that

(a) $\binom{-n}{k} = (-1)^k \binom{n + k - 1}{k}$

(b) $\binom{-n}{-k} (-1)^{n+k} \binom{k - 1}{n - 1}, \; k \geq n.$

1.17. Show that

(a) $\sum_{x=0}^{n,\,2k}(-1)^x\binom{n}{x}\binom{n}{2k-x}=(-1)^k\binom{n}{k},$

where $n,\,2k=min(n,\,2k)$ and $\dfrac{n}{2}>k$

(b) $\sum_{x=0}^{2k}(-1)^x\binom{n+x}{x}\binom{n+2k-x}{2k-x}=\binom{n+k}{k}$

(c) $\sum_{x=0}^{k}(-1)^x\binom{n+k}{x}=(-1)^k\binom{n-1+k}{k}$

(d) $\sum_{x=0}^{k}(-1)^x\binom{m-1+x}{x}\binom{n}{k-x}=\binom{n-m}{k}$

(e) $\sum_{x=0}^{n,\,k}(-1)^x\binom{n}{x}\binom{m-1+k-x}{k-x}=(-1)^k\binom{n-m}{k}$

(f) $\sum_{x=k}^{n}\binom{x}{k}=\binom{n+1}{k+1}$

(g) $\sum_{x=0}^{k}(-1)^x\binom{n}{x}=(-1)^k\binom{n-1}{k}$

1.18. The Fibonacci sequence of integers is 1, 1, 2, 3, 5, 8, 13, ..., where each element in the sequence is the sum of the previous two terms. Show that the ith term may be expressed as

$$\sum_{x=0}^{\left[\frac{i-1}{2}\right]}\binom{i-1-x}{x},$$

where $[(i-1)/2]$ is the largest integer not exceeding $(i-1)/2$.

1.19. If n balls numbered 1 to n are put at random into n cells numbered 1 to n, where each cell is occupied by one ball, then the probability that exactly m matches (ball and cell each have the same number) occur is given by

$$Pr(m)=\frac{1}{m!}\sum_{k=m}^{n}(-1)^{k-m}\frac{1}{(k-m)!}.$$

Verify this formula for $n=4$ and $m=0, 1, 2, 3, 4$. Derive the formula for obtaining at least $m(m\geq1)$ matches and get

$$\frac{1}{(m-1)!}\sum_{k=m}^{n}(-1)^{k-m}\frac{1}{k(k-m)!}.$$

1.20.   ***Example***   A point divides a line segment into two unequal parts. Two other points, one on either side of the first point, are chosen at random. Find the probability that the three segments formed by the second two points make a triangle.

Solution   Let the line segment be denoted as shown in Figure (a) where lengths a and b are fixed by the location of the first point and x and y can each vary in length from 0 to a and from 0 to b, respectively.

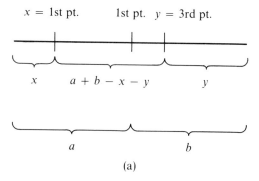

(a)

We want the lengths x, y, and $a + b - x - y$ to form a triangle, which means that any one of the lengths cannot exceed the sum of the other two lengths. Thus, we have that

$$x < \frac{a+b}{2}, \quad y < \frac{a+b}{2}, \quad \text{and} \quad x + y > \frac{a+b}{2}.$$

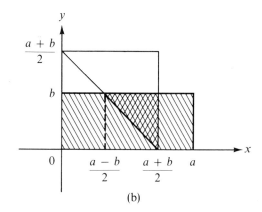

(b)

In (b), the doubly shaded area represents these three inequalities and the singly shaded area represents all possible values that x and y may take on. Therefore, the doubly shaded area divided by the singly shaded area represents the probability that we want; this reasoning is completely analogous to representing a probability as the number of favorable outcomes divided by the total number of outcomes.

Our answer comes out to be $b/2a$, which we might note is dependent on the assumption that a is greater than b. Otherwise, the result would be $a/2b$. Thus, the answer is (smaller length)/2(larger length).

We now present several exercises which should be solved in a similar manner.

1.21. A point is chosen at random on a line segment of length l. Find the probability that the two line segments thus formed, along with the distance $l/2$, will form a triangle.

1.22. Three points, X_1, X_2, and X_3, are chosen at random on a line segment of length l. Find the probability that X_3 falls between X_1 and X_2.

1.23. Two points are chosen at random on a line segment of length l. Find the probability that the three line segments thus formed make a triangle.

1.24. A different type of problem is the following: Three points are chosen at random on the circumference of a circle. Find the probability that they lie on the same semicircle.

1.25. The proof of Theorem 1.2.6 (*General Law of Total Probability*) is given by mathematical induction as follows:

Clearly, the theorem holds for $n = 2$, that is, it results in Theorem 1.2.5. Assume that the theorem is true for $n = k$; we will show that it is also true for $n = k + 1$.

We assume that

$$Pr\left(\bigcup_{i=1}^{k} S_i\right) = \sum_{i=1}^{k} Pr(S_i) - \sum_{\substack{i,j=1 \\ i<j}}^{k} Pr(S_i \cap S_j)$$
$$+ \cdots + (-1)^{k+1} Pr(S_1 \cap S_2 \cap \cdots \cap S_k) \qquad (1.9.1)$$

is true, and we want to show that

$$Pr\left(\bigcup_{i=1}^{k+1} S_i\right) = \sum_{i=1}^{k+1} Pr(S_i) - \sum_{i,j=1}^{k+1} Pr(S_i \cap S_j)$$
$$+ \cdots + (-1)^{k+1} Pr(S_1 \cap S_2 \cap \cdots \cap S_{k+1}). \qquad (1.9.2)$$

We can write

$$Pr\left[\left(\bigcup_{i=1}^{k} S_i\right) \cap S_{k+1}\right] = Pr\left(\bigcup_{i=1}^{k} S_i\right) + Pr(S_{k+1}) - Pr\left[\left(\bigcup_{i=1}^{k} S_i\right) \cap S_{k+1}\right]$$

or

$$Pr\left(\bigcup_{i=1}^{k+1} S_i\right) = Pr(S_{k+1}) + Pr\left(\bigcup_{i=1}^{k} S_i\right) - Pr\left[\bigcup_{i=1}^{k} (S_1 \cap S_{k+1})\right].$$

(1.9.3)

It can be shown (Exercise 1.2) that

$$Pr\left[\left(\bigcup_{i=1}^{k} S_i\right) \cup S_{k+1}\right] = Pr\left(\bigcup_{i=1}^{k+1} S_i\right).$$

Substituting Equation (1.9.1) for $Pr(\bigcup_{i=1}^{k} S_i)$ in Equation (1.9.3), we have

$$Pr\left(\bigcup_{i=1}^{k+1} S_i\right) = Pr(S_{k+1}) + \left[\sum_{i=1}^{k} Pr(S_i) - \sum_{\substack{i,j=1 \\ i<j}}^{k} Pr(S_i \cap S_j)\right.$$

$$+ \cdots + (-1)^{k+1} Pr(S_1 \cap S_2 \cap \cdots \cap S_k)\Big]$$

$$- Pr\left[\bigcup_{i=1}^{k} (S_i \cap S_{k+1})\right].$$

(1.9.4)

But

$$Pr\left[\bigcup_{i=1}^{k} (S_i \cap S_{k+1})\right] = \sum_{i=1}^{k} Pr(S_i \cap S_{k+1})$$

$$- \sum_{\substack{i,j=1 \\ i<j}}^{k} Pr[(S_i \cap S_{k+1}) \cap (S_j \cap S_{k+1})]$$

$$+ \cdots + (-1)^{k+1} Pr[(S_1 \cap S_{k+1}) \cap (S_2 \cap S_{k+1})$$

$$\cap \cdots \cap (S_k \cap S_{k+1})],$$

and Equation (1.9.4) becomes

$$Pr\left(\bigcup_{i=1}^{k+1} S_i\right) = Pr(S_{k+1}) + \sum_{i=1}^{k} Pr(S_i) - \sum_{\substack{i,j=1 \\ i<j}}^{k} Pr(S_i \cap S_j)$$

$$+ \cdots + (-1)^{k+1} Pr(S_1 \cap S_2 \cap \cdots \cap S_k)$$

$$- \left[\sum_{i=1}^{k} Pr(S_i \cap S_{k+1}) - \sum_{\substack{i,j=1 \\ i<j}}^{k} Pr[(S_i \cap S_{k+1})\right.$$

$$\cap (S_j \cap S_{k+1})] + \cdots + (-1)^{k+1} Pr[(S_1 \cap S_{k+1})$$

$$\cap (S_2 \cap S_{k+1}) \cap \cdots \cap (S_k \cap S_{k+1})]$$

or

$$Pr\left(\bigcup_{i=1}^{k+1} S_i\right) = \sum_{i=1}^{k+1} Pr(S_i) + \left\{-\sum_{\substack{i,j=1 \\ i<j}}^{k} Pr(S_i \cap S_j)\right.$$

$$+ \sum_{\substack{i,j,1,=1 \\ i<j<1}}^{k} Pr(S_i \cap S_j \cap S_1)$$

$$+ \cdots + (-1)^{k+1} Pr(S_1 \cap S_2 \cap \cdots \cap S_k)\bigg\}$$

$$+ \left\{-\sum_{i=1}^{k} Pr(S_i \cap S_{k+1})\right.$$

$$+ \sum_{\substack{i,j=1 \\ i<j}}^{k} Pr(S_i \cap S_j \cap S_{k+1})$$

$$+ \cdots + (-1)^{k+2} Pr(S_1 \cap S_2$$

$$\cap \cdots \cap S_k \cap S_{k+1})\bigg\}:$$

or

$$Pr\left(\bigcup_{i=1}^{k+1} S_i\right) = \sum_{i=1}^{k+1} Pr(S_i) - \sum_{\substack{i,j=1 \\ i<j}}^{k+1} Pr(S_i \cap S_j)$$

$$+ \sum_{\substack{i,j,1=1 \\ i<j<1}}^{k+1} Pr(S_i \cap S_j \cap S_1)$$

$$- \cdots - (-1)^{k+1} Pr(S_1 \cap S_2 \cap \cdots \cap S_{k+1}).$$

$$(1.9.5)$$

Therefore, Equation (1.9.5) equals Equation (1.9.2), which proves the theorem.

Having seen the proof of Theorem 1.2.6, prove Theorem 1.3.1 (*General Law of Compound Probability*).

Problems

1.1. A pair of balanced dice are tossed. If X equals the total number of spots showing on the dice, then, for $k = 2, 3, \ldots, 12$, find

(a) $Pr(X = k)$ (b) $Pr(X \le k)$ (c) $Pr(X \ge k)$

1.2. In Problem 1.1, find

    (a) $Pr(4 \le X \le 9)$ (b) $Pr(4 < X \le 9)$
    (c) $Pr(4 \le X < 9)$ (d) $Pr(4 < X < 9)$

1.3. In a freshman high school class of 400 students, 110 take math, 130 take English, 150 take history, 30 take math and English, 40 take math and history, 50 take English and history, and 280 take math or English or history. If a freshman student is picked at random from the class, then, for $k = 0,\ 1, 2, 3$, find the probability that

    (a) he takes exactly k of the named subjects
    (b) he takes at least k of the named subjects
    (c) he takes no more than k of the named subjects.

1.4. A man tosses a fair coin twice. Find the conditional probability that he gets two heads, given that he got at least one head.

1.5. Three balanced dice are tossed. Find the probability of obtaining a 9, given that

    (a) the sum is odd   (b) the sum is less than or equal to 9
    (c) none of the dice are odd   (d) at least one of the dice is odd
    (e) at least two of the dice are odd
    (f) all three of the dice are odd
    (g) all the dice are different   (h) two of the dice are the same
    (i) all three of the dice are the same

1.6. Three men, A, B, and C, fire at a target. A fires twice as often as B, who fires three times as often as C, who in turn fires once every six seconds. B's accuracy is twice that of A's, which is one third that of C's, which in turn is equal to 0.8. After one minute of shooting, firing is halted. Find the probability that the target is hit. (Is this probability any different than if the firing had been halted at the end of, say, six seconds ?)

1.7. In Problem 1.6, assume that the target was hit at least once. Find the probability that any one hit was the result of

    (a) A's firing   (b) B's firing   (c) C's firing.

1.8. Each of twelve ordered boxes contains twelve coins, consisting of pennies and dimes. The number of dimes in each box is equal to its order among the boxes, that is, box number one contains one dime and eleven pennies, box number two contains two dimes and ten pennies, etc. A pair of fair dice is tossed, and the total showing indicates which box is chosen to have a coin selected at random from it. Find the probability that the coin selected is a dime.

1.9. In Problem 1.8, assume that the coin selected is a dime. Then, for $k = 1, 2, \ldots, 12$, find the probability that it came from box k.

1.10. If a balanced coin is tossed n times, find the probability of getting at least one head.

1.11. In Problem 1.10, find the least number of times the coin need be tossed in order to ensure that, the probability of getting at least one head is greater than three quarters.

1.12. If a population consists of five different objects, find the probability that the third object is included in a sample of size three under

(a) scheme 1   (b) scheme 2   (c) scheme 3
(d) scheme 4.

1.13. Suppose six balanced dice are tossed. Find the probability that

(a) all show a different value
(b) exactly two of them show the same value
(c) at least k of them show the same value, where $k = 2, 3, 4, 5, 6$.

1.14. In tossing a pair of fair dice, find the probability that a total of k results before a total of 7 shows, where $k = 4, 5, 6, 8, 9, 10$. *Hint*: Consider the infinite geometric series

$$Pr(k) + Pr(\bar{k} \cap \bar{7})Pr(k) + [Pr(\bar{k} \cap \bar{7})]^2 Pr(k) + \cdots = \frac{Pr(k)}{Pr(k) + Pr(7)},$$

the sum of which should be derived and not just accepted.

1.15. In the game of craps, the thrower wins on the first throw if he gets a 7 or an 11. He loses on the first throw if he gets a 2, a 3, or a 12. To win on any subsequent throw, he must roll the same total he rolled on the first throw before he rolls a 7, provided, of course, that the first throw was not a 2, a 3, or 12. Otherwise, he loses. Find the probability that the thrower wins in the game of craps.

1.16. In the game of poker find the probability of being dealt

(a) a royal flush (A, K, Q, J, 10 of the same suit).
(b) a straight flush but not a royal flush (five consecutive cards of the same suit except A, K, Q, J, 10).
(c) four of a kind (four cards of the same face value and another card).
(d) a full house (three cards of the same face value and two other cards each of the same face value).

(e) a flush but not a straight flush or a royal flush (five cards of the same suit but not in consecutive order).

(f) a straight but not a flush (five cards in consecutive order, but not all from the same suit).

(g) three of a kind (three cards of the same face value and two others each of different face value with respect to each other and with respect to the first three cards).

(h) two pairs (two cards of the same face value, two more cards, each of the same face value but different from the first two, and another card different in face value from the first four).

(i) a pair (two cards of the same face value and three other cards each different in face value with respect to each other and with respect to the first two cards).

1.17. (*Chevalier de Méré's problem*) Determine which outcome in the following two situations is more likely to occur: obtaining a total of 6 at least once when tossing a die four times, or obtaining a total of 12 at least once when tossing a pair of dice 24 times.

1.18. (*Banach's problem*) A man has two boxes of matches, each of which contains n matches. He selects a box at random and uses one match from it each time he wishes to light a cigarette. Find the probability that, when he selects a box to extract a match from it, the box is empty and the other box has k matches in it, where $k = 0, 1, \ldots, n$.

1.19. A coin is tossed until the same result appears twice in a row. Find the probability that

(a) this event occurs on the nth toss
(b) 6 or fewer tosses are required for this event
(c) this event occurs on an even numbered toss.

1.20. There are s pairs of shoes in a closet. A man selects $2n$ shoes at random. Find the probability that he will find at least one pair among the $2n$ shoes selected.

1.21. An urn contains w_1 white and b_1 black balls. A second urn contains w_2 white and b_2 black balls. A ball is selected at random from the first urn and placed in the second urn. Then a ball is selected at random from the second urn. Find the probability that it is white.

1.22. In Problem 1.21, assume that the ball selected from the second urn is white. Find the probability that it came from the first urn.

1.23. If n persons each flip a balanced coin, find the probability that exactly one coin is at odds with all the rest.

References

[1] Kolmogorov, A. N. *Grundbegriffe der Wahrscheinlichkeitsrechnung*, Ergeb. Mat. und ihrer Grenzg., Vol. 2., No. 3, 1933. (Translated to: *Foundations of the Theory of Probability.* New York: Chelsea Publishing Company, 1936.)

[2] Poincaré, H. *Calcul des Probabilités.* Paris: Gauthier-Villero, 1912.

[3] Todhunter, I. *A History of the Theory of Probability from the Time of Pascal to Laplace.* New York: Chelsea Publishing Company, 1949.

[4] Von Mises, R. *Wahrscheinlichkeit, Statistik und Wahrheit.* Vienna: Springer-Verlug OHG, 1936.

Suggested Supplementary Reading

Brown, G. S. *Probability and Scientific Inference.* London: Longmans, Green, and Company, 1957.

Carnap, R. *Logical Foundations of Probability.* Chicago: University of Chicago Press, 1950.

Cramer, H. *The Elements of Probability Theory.* New York: John Wiley and Sons, Inc., 1955.

Drake, A. W. *Fundamentals of Applied Probability Theory.* New York: McGraw-Hill Book Company, Inc., 1967.

Feller, W. *An Introduction to Probability Theory and its Applications.* Vol. I, 2nd ed. New York: John Wiley and Sons, Inc., 1957.

Fisz, M. *Probability Theory and Mathematical Statistics.* New York: John Wiley and Sons, Inc., 1963.

Good, I. J. *Probability and the Weighing of Evidence.* New York: Hafner Publishing Company, 1950.

Harris, B. *Theory of Probability.* Reading, Massachusetts: Addison-Wesley Publishing Company, Inc.

Krickeberg, K. *Probability Theory.* Reading, Massachusetts: Addison-Wesley Publishing Company, Inc., 1965 (Translation of 1962 German book).

Munroe, M. E. *Theory of Probability.* New York: McGraw-Hill Book Company, Inc., 1951.

Papoulis, A. *Probability, Random Variables and Stochastic Processes.* New York: McGraw-Hill Book Company, Inc., 1965.

Parzen, E. *Modern Probability Theory and its Applications.* New York: John Wiley and Sons, Inc., 1960.

Reichenbach, H. *Theory of Probability*. 2nd ed. Berkeley, California: University of California Press, 1949.

Uspensky, J. V. *Introduction to Mathematical Probability*. New York: McGraw-Hill Book Company, Inc., 1937.

Von Mises, R. *Probability, Statistics, and Truth*. 2nd ed. New York: The Macmillan Company, 1957.

Von Wright, G. H. *A Treatise on Induction and Probability*. New York: Harcourt, Brace and Company, Inc., 1951.

Wadsworth, G. P., and J. G. Bryan. *Introduction to Probability and Random Variables*. New York: McGraw-Hill Book Company, Inc., 1960.

Discrete Random Variables and Probability Distributions

2

2.0 Introduction: The Concept of a Random Variable

A random variable is a function (rule) that assigns a number to every outcome of an experiment. That is, if, after an experiment, $s_1, s_2, s_3, \ldots, s_n$ are all of the possible outcomes that constitute the sample space S and we wish to assign a number to each of these outcomes by using a rule $X(s_i), i = 1, 2, \ldots, n$, then we call this rule a random variable.

Before we proceed to define precisely the meaning of and the role of a random variable in probability theory and applications, we shall briefly review the concept of a function, which plays a central role in scientific investigation.

In mathematics and in many of the physical sciences, we encounter very basic formulas. For example, if r is the radius of a circle, then its area is given by $A = \pi r^2$. If we wish to determine the area of a circle, we must specify its radius. Thus, the area is a "dependent variable," whose value depends on the "independent variable" r. For each value of r, then, there is a corresponding value of area; and the collection of these pairs of numbers is a *function* (or *mapping*), that is, a function is a rule or relationship between values of r and A. Therefore, we can say that the area of a circle is a function of its radius, or $A = f(r)$. The notion of a function involves three things: (1) a set D called the *domain* of the function, (2) a set R called the *range* (or *image*) of the function, and (3) a rule that assigns to each element $x \in D$ an element $y \in R$. Thus, the set of pairs

$$\{(x, y): x \in D, y \in R; \quad y = f(x)\}$$

is a function if $y = f(x)$ does not assign two values of y to a single value of x. In the above example, let the domain be the set $D = \{r: r = 1, 2, 3, 4\}$; then, applying the rule $A = f(r) = \pi r^2$ for $r \in D$, we get $f(1) = \pi$, the value of f at $r = 1$, $f(2) = 4\pi$, the value of f at $r = 2$, and so on. Thus, we obtain the images (which may be called the range) of the function $R = \{A: A = \pi, 4\pi, 9\pi, 16\pi\}$, and therefore the function itself is the set

$$\{(1, \pi), (2, 4\pi), (3, 9\pi), (4, 16\pi)\}.$$

A precise definition of the term *function* is: a collection of ordered pairs of numbers (x, y), where $x \in D$ and $y \in R$, with no two different pairs having the same first member.

Now suppose that S is the sample space of a given experiment and let $X(s)$ be a real valued function, defined on S, that transforms points of S to the set R of real numbers. Thus, S is the domain of the function and the range is the set of real numbers. For example, if we consider the experiment of flipping a pair of coins, the sample space consists of four elements:

$$S = \{(H, H), (H, T), (T, H), (T, T)\}.$$

If we let $X(s)$ be a real valued function that can assume values equal to the number of heads in s_i: $s_1 = HH$, $s_2 = HT$, $s_3 = TH$ and $s_4 = TT$, then this function may be represented by the set of ordered pairs

$$\{(s_1, X(s_1)), (s_2, X(s_2)), (s_3, X(s_3)), (s_4, X(s_4))\}$$

or

$$\{(s_1, 2), (s_2, 1), (s_3, 1), (s_4, 0)\}.$$

As another example, consider the experiment of rolling a pair of dice: the sample space will consist of 36 ordered pairs of numbers

$$S = \{(1, 1), (1, 2), (1, 3), \ldots, (6, 6)\}.$$

If we let $X(e_i, e_j) = e_i + e_j$, $i, j = 1, 2, \ldots, 6$ be a real valued function that assigns to each point (e_i, e_j) in S the sum of its members, then this function can be represented by the set of ordered pairs

$$\{[(e_1, e_1), X(e_1, e_1)], [(e_1, e_2), X(e_1, e_2)], \ldots, ([e_6, e_6), X(e_6, e_6)]\}$$

or

$$\{[(1, 1), 2], [(1, 2), 3], [(1, 3), 4], \ldots, [(6, 6), 12]\}.$$

We shall now define the concept of a random variable.

Definition 2.1.0   *Let S be a sample space and X(s) a real valued function (defined on S) that transforms the points of S into a subset of the real line, R_X (range space). Then X is called a random variable, provided the probabilities of $\{X(s) = x\}$ and $\{X(s) \leq x\}$ can be calculated, where s is any element in the sample space and x is any real number in R_X.*

For convenience, we shall denote X(s) by X and the values of the range space, R_X, by $x_1, x_2, \ldots, x_n, \ldots$. Using only the two events listed in the definition, the following events can be specified.

(1) $\{X < x_1\}, \{X \geq x_1\}, \{X > x_1\}$;

(2) $\{x_1 \leq X \leq x_2\}, \{x_1 < X \leq x_2\}, \{x_1 \leq X < x_2\}, \{x_1 < X < x_2\}$.

For example, the events

$$\{x_1 \leq X < x_2\} = \{X \leq x_2\} - \{X = x_2\} - \{X \leq x_1\} + \{X = x_1\}$$

and

$$\{x_1 \leq X \leq x_2\} = \{X \leq x_2\} - \{X \leq x_1\} + \{X = x_1\}.$$

We shall illustrate the meaning of the above definition with the following example: Consider the previous example, in which a fair pair of dice were rolled once. Here the sample space consists of 36 ordered pairs of numbers, namely,

$$S = \{(1, 1), (1, 2), (1, 3), \ldots, (6, 6)\}.$$

Let the random variable X represent the total number of spots showing on the dice. Thus, X assigns to each ordered pair in S its sum; that is, $X(1, 1) = 2$, $X(1, 2) = 3, \ldots, X(6, 6) = 12$, which values are in R_X. So far we have established that X is a real valued function, defined on S, that has a range that is a subset of R_X. Next, consider the events $\{X = x\}$ and $\{X \leq x\}$, where x may be any real number. It is clear that the probabilities of these events are defined. For example,

$$Pr(x = -38) = 0, \quad Pr(X = 5.5) = 0, \quad Pr(X = 8) = \frac{5}{36},$$

$$Pr(X \leq 0) = 0, \quad Pr(X \leq 6.4) = Pr(X \leq 6) = \frac{15}{36},$$

$$Pr(X \leq 45) = 1 \quad \text{and} \quad Pr(X \leq \infty) = 1.$$

We have further shown that the probabilities of the events $\{X = x\}, \{X \leq x\}$, $x \in R_X$, are defined. Therefore, X is a random variable.

Other synonyms for a random variable are: chance variable, variate, *and* stochastic variable. *We shall denote random variables by the capital letters, X, Y, Z, and so on; X(s) will indicate the value which has been assigned to an observation of the experiment.*

Random variables in this book will be divided into two classes:

(1)   discrete random variables
(2)   continuous random variables.

In this chapter, we shall be concerned with the one-dimensional discrete random variable. In Chapter 3, we shall discuss the one-dimensional continuous random variable; these concepts will be generalized in Chapter 5.

2.1   Discrete Probability Density Function

We shall begin by defining a one-dimensional discrete random variable.

Definition 2.1.1   *Let X be a random variable. If the number of elements in the range space, R_X, is finite or countably infinite, then X is called a one-dimensional discrete random variable.*

One of the primary objectives in developing the concept of a random variable is the calculation of the probability so that it assumes certain values. For example, we may be interested in finding the probabilities of some of the events given in the previous section. That is, $Pr(X = x_1)$, the probability that the random variable is equal to x_1; $Pr(x_1 < X < x_2)$, the probability that the random variable falls between x_1 and x_2. More precisely, if $E_1 = \{x: x_1 < x < x_2\}$, then $Pr\{x_1 < X < x_2\} = Pr(X \text{ in } E_1)$, the probability that the random variable assumes a value contained in a certain set $E_1 \subset E$. Similarly, we shall be interested in $Pr(X < x_1)$, $Pr(X \le x_2)$, $Pr(X > x_2)$, $Pr(X \ge x_2)$, and $Pr(x_1 \le X \le x_2)$.

A mathematical function will be used to determine these probabilities, and it is called the *probability density function of a random variable.* For example, if the discrete random variable X may assume the values $x_1, x_2, x_3, \dots, x_n, \dots$ we might be interested in determining a function $f(x)$ such that $f(x_1), f(x_2), \dots, f(x_n), \dots$ are the probabilities that $X = x_1$, $X = x_2, \dots, X = x_n, \dots$, respectively. Having such a function helps us to find the probability of the event $\{x_1 \le X \le x_2\}$; that is,

$$Pr(x_1 \le X \le x_2) = \sum_{x_1 \le x \le x_2} f(x).$$

We formulate such a mathematical function in Definition 2.1.2.

Definition 2.1.2   *Let X be a one-dimensional discrete random variable. A function $f(x_i)$ is called a* discrete probability density function *of the random variable X if the following conditions are satisfied:*

(1) $f(x_i) \geq 0$,   for all $x_i \in R_X$,

(2) $\sum\limits_{x_i \in R_X} f(x_i) = 1$,

where the summation is taken over all x_i in the range space. Thus, we shall call $f(x_i)$ a discrete probability density function *or* density function *of the random variable X if conditions (1) and (2) hold. Other common ways in which we can phrase this definition are "$f(x_i)$ is the distribution of the random variable X" and "the random variable X is distributed as $f(x_i)$." The distribution $f(x_i)$ is also referred to as the "mass" or "frequency" density function. The following examples will illustrate the manner in which the distribution of a random variable can be determined and applied.*

Example 2.1.1   Let an experiment consist of tossing five fair coins, and let the random variable X represent the number of heads that show. Thus, X may take on the values 0, 1, 2, 3, 4, or 5; we wish to construct its probability density function.

Solution: Since each toss of a coin has two possible outcomes, the sample space of this experiment contains 2^5 5-tuples, and the event of of getting x heads can occur in $\binom{5}{x}$ ways. Therefore,

$$f(x) = \begin{cases} \dfrac{\binom{5}{x}}{2^5}, & x = 0, 1, \ldots, 5, \\ 0, & \text{elsewhere.} \end{cases}$$

We can verify that $f(x)$ is the probability distribution function of the random variable X by showing that conditions (1) and (2) are satisfied:

$$\sum\limits_{\text{all } x} f(x) = \sum\limits_{x=0}^{5} \frac{\binom{5}{x}}{2^5} = 1 \quad \text{and} \quad f(x) \geq 0, \quad \text{for} \quad x = 0, 1, 2, \ldots, 5.$$

Now we can use the discrete probability density function $f(x)$ to calculate the following probabilities, for example, concerning the random variable X.

(a) $Pr(X = 3) = f(3) = \dfrac{\binom{5}{3}}{2^5} = \dfrac{5}{16}$, the probability of obtaining *exactly* three heads in the tossing of five coins;

(b) $Pr(X \le 4) = \sum_{x=0}^{4} \dfrac{\dbinom{5}{x}}{2^5}$

$\qquad\qquad = 1 - Pr(x > 4) = 1 - Pr(X = 5)$

$\qquad\qquad = 1 - \dfrac{\dbinom{5}{5}}{2^5} = \dfrac{31}{32},$

the probability that the random variable X is *at most* equal to four heads;

(c) $Pr(X \ge 3) = \sum_{x=3}^{5} \dfrac{\dbinom{5}{x}}{2^5}$

$\qquad\qquad\qquad = 1 - Pr(x < 3) = 1 - \sum_{x=0}^{2} \dfrac{\dbinom{5}{x}}{2^5} = \dfrac{1}{2},$

the probability that the random variable X is *at least* equal to three heads;

(d) $Pr(2 \le X \le 4) = \sum_{x=2}^{4} \dfrac{\dbinom{5}{x}}{2^5} = \dfrac{25}{32},$

the probability that the random variable X (the number of heads) assumes a value in the closed interval [2, 4];

(e) $Pr(X = 2 \mid X \le 3) = \dfrac{\dfrac{\dbinom{5}{2}}{2^5}}{\displaystyle\sum_{x=0}^{3} \dfrac{\dbinom{5}{x}}{2^5}} = \dfrac{\dbinom{5}{2}}{\displaystyle\sum_{x=0}^{3} \dbinom{5}{x}} = \dfrac{5}{13},$

the probability that the random variable X equals two, given that the number of heads is less than or equal to three;

(f) $Pr(X \le 2 \mid X < 4) = \dfrac{\displaystyle\sum_{x=0}^{2} \dfrac{\dbinom{5}{x}}{2^5}}{\displaystyle\sum_{x=0}^{3} \dfrac{\dbinom{5}{x}}{2^5}} = \dfrac{\displaystyle\sum_{x=0}^{2} \dbinom{5}{x}}{\displaystyle\sum_{x=0}^{3} \dbinom{5}{x}} = \dfrac{8}{13},$

the probability that the number of heads is less than or equal to two when it is known that less than four heads occurred.

Figure 2.1.1 shows the graph of the density function $f(x)$ as vertical lines, the lengths of which indicate the probabilities for all possible values that the random variable can assume.

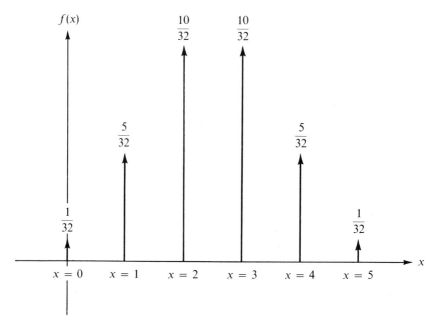

Figure 2.1.1

Notice that the function is symmetrical: the probability that the random variable $X = 0$, no heads, is equal to the probability that $X = 5$, all heads; also $Pr(X = 1) = Pr(X = 4) = 5/32$, and so on. Furthermore, the graph indicates that the probability of getting two heads is the same probability as that of getting three heads, due to the fact that the probability of obtaining a head on a single toss is the same as that of obtaining a tail.

Example 2.1.2   Consider the experiment of throwing a pair of fair dice once. Let the random variable X be equal to the sum of the spots resulting; and we wish to find its density, $f(x)$, where X may take on the values $2, 3, \ldots, 12$.

Solution: Here, $f(2) = f(12) = 1/36$, $f(3) = f(11) = 2/36$, $f(4) = f(10) = 3/36$, $f(5) = f(9) = 4/36$, $f(6) = f(8) = 5/36$, and $f(7) = 6/36$. With a little algebraic manipulation, we obtain

$$f(x) = \begin{cases} \dfrac{6 - |7 - x|}{36}, & x = 2, 3, \ldots, 12, \\ 0, & \text{elsewhere.} \end{cases}$$

Using this density function, we can obtain the following probabilities, for example:

(a) $Pr(5 < X \le 7) = \sum_{x=6}^{7} (6 - |7 - x|/36) = 11/36$, the probability that the sum is greater than five but less than eight.

(b) $Pr(X > 9) = \sum_{x=10}^{12} (6 - |7 - x|/36) = 6/36$, the probability that the observed sum is greater than nine.

Figure 2.1.2 shows the graph of $f(x)$; the vertical lines indicate the probabilities for the values of x which the random variable assumes.

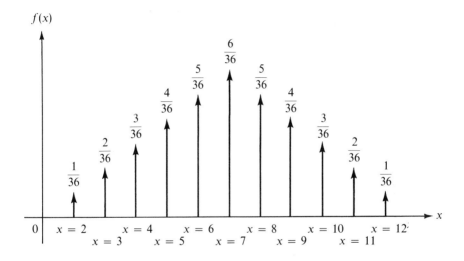

Figure 2.1.2

It is clear that $f(x) \ge 0$ for all x, and one can verify that

$$\sum_{x=2}^{12} \frac{6 - |7 - x|}{36} = 1.$$

Example 2.1.3   In the experiment of Example 2.1.2, suppose that the random variable X were equal to the difference of the spots resulting. Then X could take on the values $-5, -4, \ldots, 0, \ldots, 4, 5$; and $f(-5) = f(5) = 1/36$, $f(-4) = f(4) = 2/36$, $f(-3) = f(3) = 3/36$, $f(-2) = f(2) = 4/36$, $f(-1) = f(1) = 5/36$, and $f(0) = 6/36$. Combining these results gives

$$f(x) = \begin{cases} \dfrac{6 - |x|}{36}, & x = -5, -4, \ldots, 5, \\ 0, & \text{elsewhere.} \end{cases}$$

(a)   The probability that the random variable assumes a value between -3 and 4 exclusively is given by

$$Pr(-3 < X < 4) = \sum_{x=-2}^{3} \frac{6 - |x|}{36} = \frac{27}{36}.$$

(b)   The probability that the observed difference of the spots is either -4 or 0 is

$$Pr(X = -4) + Pr(X = 0) = f(-4) + f(0) = \frac{2}{36} + \frac{6}{36} = \frac{2}{9}.$$

Example 2.1.4   Find c so that the function given by

$$f(x) = c2^{-|x|}, \qquad x = 0, \pm 1, \pm 2, \ldots$$

is a probability density function.

Solution: Here, we must find c such that

$$\sum_{x=-\infty}^{\infty} c2^{-|x|} = 1.$$

Thus,

$$\sum_{x=-\infty}^{\infty} c2^{-|x|} = c \sum_{x=-\infty}^{-1} 2^{-x} + c2^0 + \sum_{x=1}^{\infty} 2^{-x}$$

$$= c \sum_{x=1}^{\infty} 2^{-x} + c + c \sum_{x=1}^{\infty} 2^{-x}$$

$$= c + c + c = 1,$$

and

$$3c = 1 \quad \text{or} \quad c = \frac{1}{3}.$$

Therefore,

$$f(x) = \frac{1}{3} 2^{-|x|}, \quad x = 0, \pm 1, \pm 2, \ldots$$

is a probability density function.

Another way of graphing a discrete probability density function is by a *probability histogram*, as shown in Figure 2.1.3 for Example 2.1.4. In the probability histogram, the rectangles are customarily made of equal width

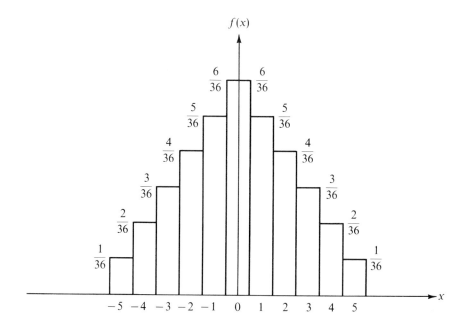

$f(x)$

Figure 2.1.3

so that the areas of the rectangles are proportional to their heights. Furthermore, the base of each rectangle extends from one half of a unit below to one half of a unit above the value that the random variable can assume.

2.2 Cumulative Distribution Function

We have seen that, given a discrete random variable, X, it is often necessary to determine various probabilities concerning the behavior of X. For example, we might be interested in calculating the probability that the random variable X takes on a value contained in the set $E_1 = \{x: x_1 \le x \le x_2\}$ or in the set $E_j = \{x: x \le x_j\}$. The probability that X assumes a value in E_j can be obtained by writing

$$Pr(X \le x_j) = \sum_{x_i \le x_j} f(x_i), \qquad (2.2.1)$$

where $f(x_i)$ is the probability density function of the random variable X. We shall denote such a function by $F(x)$ and define it in Definition 2.2.1.

Definition 2.2.1   *The function $F(x)$, defined by*

$$F(x) = Pr(X \leq x) = \sum_{x_i \leq x} f(x_i),$$ (2.2.2)

where the summation is extended over all points x_i for which $x_i \leq x$, is called the cumulative distribution function *of the discrete random variable X, having a probability density function $f(x_i)$.*

As the name implies, the cumulative distribution function $F(x)$ accumulates the values of $f(x_i)$ as x_i goes from $-\infty$ to x. Also, its graph is a " step function" that is continuous from the right.

Example 2.2.1   The cumulative distribution function of the random variable X, whose density function was given in Example 2.1.1, is obtained by

$$F(x) = Pr(X \leq x) = \begin{cases} 0, & x < 0, \\ \sum_{x_i \leq [x]^*} \dfrac{\binom{5}{x_i}}{2^5}, & 0 \leq x \leq 5, \\ 1, & x > 5. \end{cases}$$

Table 2.2.1

x	0	1	2	3	4	5
$F(x)$	$\dfrac{1}{32}$	$\dfrac{6}{32}$	$\dfrac{16}{32}$	$\dfrac{26}{32}$	$\dfrac{31}{32}$	$\dfrac{32}{32}$

Table 2.2.1 gives the cumulative probabilities for all the possible values that the random variable can assume and provides data for the graphical representation of $F(x)$, as shown in Figure 2.2.1.

Theorem 2.2.1 states the properties of the cumulative distribution function of a discrete random variable.

* $[x]$ denotes the greatest integer not exceeding x.

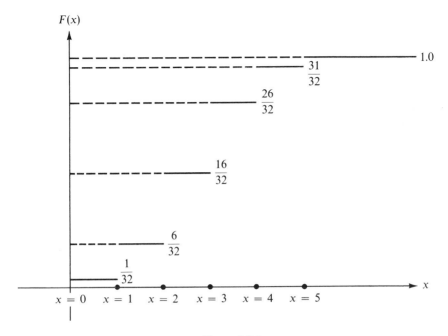

Figure 2.2.1

Theorem 2.2.1   If $F(x)$ is the cumulative distribution function of the discrete random variable X, then $F(x)$ has the following properties:

(1) $F(\infty) = 1$;
(2) $F(-\infty) = 0$;
(3) $F(x)$ is a nondecreasing function of x;
(4) $F(x)$ is continuous from the right.

Proof   Properties (1) and (2) follow from the definition of a probability density function of the random variable X. To show property (3), that is, $F(x_2) \geq F(x_1)$ for x_1 and x_2, two points on the real axis, such that $x_1 < x_2$, we let the set $E_1 = \{x: x \leq x_1\}$ be a subset of the set $E_2 = \{x: x \leq x_2\}$. Thus,

$$E_1 \subset E_2 \quad \text{or} \quad \{x: x \leq x_1\} \subset \{x: x \leq x_2\}. \tag{2.2.3}$$

Applying Theorem 1.2.1 to expression (2.2.3), we have $Pr(E_1) \leq Pr(E_2)$, which is equivalent to

$$Pr(X \leq x_1) \leq Pr(X \leq x_2)$$

or

$$F(x_1) \leq F(x_2).$$

Thus, $F(x)$ is nondecreasing. To show that the distribution function is continuous from the right, we shall need Definition 2.2.2.

Definition 2.2.2   *A sequence of events $\{E_i\}$, $i = 1, 2, 3, \ldots$ is nonincreasing if*

$$E_i \supset E_{i+1}$$

for all i. The intersection of the events of the nonincreasing sequence is called the limit of this sequence, that is,

$$\lim_{i \to \infty} E_i = \bigcap_{i=1}^{\infty} E_i = E^*.$$

Let $x_1 > x_2 > \cdots > x^*$ be a decreasing sequence of points which converge to x^* from the right, and let E_i, $i = 1, 2, \ldots$ be the event that the random variable X assumes a value from the interval $(x^*, x_i]$. That is,

$$E_i = \{x : x \in (x^*, x_i]\}.$$

Observe that, if $i_1 < i_2$, the occurrence of event E_{i_2} implies the occurrence of the event E_{i_1}. Thus, the sequence of events $\{E_i\}$ is a nonincreasing sequence. The point x^* is not included in any of the intervals considered, which implies the intersection of the events E_i, $i = 1, 2, \ldots$ is the impossible event; that is, $Pr(E^*) = 0$, where $E^* = \bigcap_{i=1}^{\infty} E_i$. Therefore,

$$\lim_{i \to \infty} Pr(E_i) = \lim_{i \to \infty} Pr[x^* < X \leq x_i]$$

$$= \lim_{i \to \infty} \{Pr[X \leq x_i] - Pr[X \leq x^*]\}$$

$$= \lim_{i \to \infty} [F(x_i) - F(x^*)]$$

$$= \lim_{i \to \infty} F(x_i) - F(x^*)$$

$$= 0$$

or

$$F(x^*) = \lim_{i \to \infty} F(x_i) = \lim_{x_i \to x_i^*} F(x_i).$$

Thus, we have continuity at the point x^* from the right.

Example 2.2.2 The cumulative distribution function of the probability density of the experiment, as stated in Example 2.1.2, is given by

$$F(x) = Pr(X \le x) = \begin{cases} 0, & x < 2, \\ \displaystyle\sum_{x_i \le [x]} \frac{6 - |7 - x_i|}{36}, & 2 \le x \le 12, \\ 1, & x > 12. \end{cases}$$

Figure 2.2.2 shows the fact that $F(x)$ is a step function and continuous from the right.

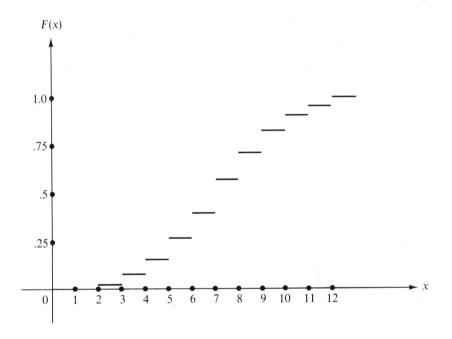

Figure 2.2.2

2.3 Discrete Probability Distributions

In this section, we shall study some special discrete probability distributions that are applicable to various physical problems.

2.3.1 The Point Binomial Distribution Consider an experiment entailing a single observation, the result of which will be one of two possible outcomes, for example, success or failure, operable or nonoperable, or yes or no. Whatever the event, if the probability of a success is p, the probability of a failure is $q = 1 - p$, where $p + q = 1$. We shall denote a failure by 0 and a success by 1, and we shall formulate the distribution of the experiment as follows:

Definition 2.3.1   *A random variable X is said to be distributed as a* point binomial *if its probability density function is*

$$f(x; p) = \begin{cases} p^x q^{1-x}, & x = 0, 1, \quad 0 < p < 1, \\ 0, & elsewhere. \end{cases} \tag{2.3.1}$$

It is easy to show that the conditions of a probability density function are satisfied. Equation (2.3.1) *is a one-parameter distribution, where the parameter is p. In general, the word* parameter *means a constant that characterizes a probability density function. A* statistic *is a parameter-free function of a random variable, which is based on the observed values of a given experiment. Usually a parameter is estimated by a statistic.*

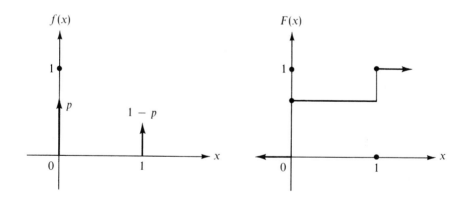

Figure 2.3.1

Figure 2.3.1 *shows the graph of f(x) and F(x).*

Example 2.3.1   Consider the experiment of firing a missile that has been observed to fire successfully with a probability of $p = .88$. The density of the random variable X is

$$f(x; .88) = \begin{cases} (.88)^x (.12)^{1-x}, & x = 0, 1, \\ 0, & elsewhere. \end{cases}$$

The probability that the missile will fire successfully is

$$Pr(X = 1) = f(1) = .88,$$

and the probability of a failure is

$$Pr(X = 0) = f(0) = .12.$$

2.3.2   The Binomial Distribution   The binomial or Bernoulli distribution, named after James Bernoulli, (1654–1705), is one of the more widely used discrete probability distributions. It applies to problems that involve independent repeated trials, the outcomes of which have been classified into two categories, for example, success and failure, where the probability of a success is the same for each trial. The binomial distribution is thus a generalization of the point binomial. The random variable of interest in such a problem is the number of times in which the experiment results in a success.

More precisely, consider an experiment consisting of n independent trials; the outcome of each trial is either a success or a failure, with probabilities p and $1 - p$, respectively. Let 0 denote a failure and 1 denote a success. If X denotes the number of successes among the n independent trials, the value that it takes on will be equal to the number of 1's appearing. For example, in a sequence such as {0, 1, 1, 0, 1, 1, 1, 0, 0, 0}, we have a failure on the first trial, a success on the second and third trials, a failure on the fourth trial, and so on. Therefore, the possible values that X can assume are 0, 1, 2, 3, $\ldots$, n. In order to obtain the probability that $X = r$ successes, we proceed as follows: the r 1's and $n - r$ 0's can occur in any one of

$$\binom{n}{r} = \frac{n!}{r!(n-r)!}$$

distinct orderings of the n trials. The probability of each such ordering is equal to the product of r p's and $n - r$ $(1 - p)$'s because all trials are independent. Adding these $\binom{n}{r}$ probabilities, we obtain

$$Pr(X = r) = \binom{n}{r} p^r (1 - p)^{n-r}.$$

Thus, we state Definition 2.3.2.

Definition 2.3.2   *A random variable X is said to have a* binomial or Bernoulli distribution *if its probability density function is given by*

$$f(x; n, p) = \begin{cases} \binom{n}{x} p^x (1 - p)^{n-x}, & x = 0, 1, 2, \ldots, n, \\ 0 < p < 1, \\ 0, & elsewhere. \end{cases} \qquad (2.3.2)$$

The binomial distribution has two parameters, n and p. The parameter n is a discrete parameter because it can only have values 1, 2, 3, ..., and p is a continuous parameter, because it can assume any value between 0 and 1. In any particular problem, n and p must have specific numerical values. The parameter p is usually estimated from given data in various physical problems. The maximum value of the binomial density function is obtained if we use the integral part of $(n + 1)p$ for x. For example, if the experiment consists of 10 trials and $p = .75$, then $f(x; 10, .75)$ will attain a maximum value when x is put equal to 8, which is the integral part of $(10 + 1)(.75)$. This value of x, which maximizes $f(x; n, p)$, is called the mode *or* modal value.

It is clear that $f(x; n, p)$ is a density function because $f(x; n, p) \geq 0$ for $x = 0$, $1, 2, ..., n$ and

$$\sum_{x=0}^{n} f(x; n, p) = \sum_{x=0}^{n} \binom{n}{x} p^x (1 - p)^{n-x} = [p + (1 - p)]^n = 1.$$

The cumulative distribution function is given by

$$F(x) = Pr(X \leq x) = \begin{cases} 0, & x < 0 \\ \sum_{i=0}^{[x]} \binom{n}{i} p^i (1 - p)^{n-1}, & 0 \leq x \leq n \\ 1, & x > n \end{cases}$$

The binomial distribution has been tabulated for various values of x, n, and p. Some of the more useful tables are [1], [2], *and* [3]. *Tables of Individual Terms, Binomial Distributions, and Cumulative Terms, Binomial Distributions on page 585 ff contain probabilities for selected values of x, n, and p.*

The following examples illustrate some of the many applications of the binomial distribution.

Example 2.3.2   A fair coin is tossed 10 times. We shall consider heads a success and tails a failure. It is clear that $p = 1/2$, $n = 10$, and the assumptions that underlie the binomial distribution are satisfied. Therefore,

(a)   the probability of exactly seven successes is

$$Pr(X = 7) = f\left(7; 10, \frac{1}{2}\right) = \binom{10}{7}\left(\frac{1}{2}\right)^7\left(\frac{1}{2}\right)^3 = \frac{15}{128};$$

(b)   the probability of at least seven successes is

$$Pr(X \geq 7) = \sum_{x=7}^{10} \binom{10}{x}\left(\frac{1}{2}\right)^x\left(\frac{1}{2}\right)^{10-x} = \frac{11}{64};$$

(c)   the probability of at most seven successes is

$$Pr(X \le 7) = \sum_{x=0}^{7} \binom{10}{x} \left(\frac{1}{2}\right)^x \left(\frac{1}{2}\right)^{10-x}$$

$$= 1 - Pr(X > 7) = \frac{53}{64};$$

(d)   the probability of no successes is

$$Pr(X = 0) = f\left(0; 10, \frac{1}{2}\right) = \left(\frac{1}{2}\right)^{10} = \frac{1}{1024},$$

which is the same as the probability of exactly 10 successes.

The cumulative distribution of this example is given by

$$F(x) = \begin{cases} 0, & x < 0, \\ \sum_{i=0}^{[x]} \binom{10}{i} \left(\frac{1}{2}\right)^i \left(\frac{1}{2}\right)^{10-i}, & 0 \le x \le 10, \\ 1, & x > 10. \end{cases}$$

Example 2.3.3   A quarterback on a football team has a pass completion average of .62. If, in a given game, he attempts 16 passes, what is the probability that he will complete (a) 12 passes and (b) more than half of his passes?

Solution:

(a) $Pr(X = 12) = \binom{16}{12}(.62)^{12}(.38)^4 = 0.1224;$

(b) $Pr(X > 8) = \sum_{x=9}^{16} \binom{16}{x}(.62)^x(.38)^{16-x} = 0.7701.$

Example 2.3.4   A man fires at a target six times; the probability of his hitting it is equal to .40. (a) What is the probability that he will hit the target at least once? (b) How many times must he fire at the target so that the probability of hitting it at least once is greater than .77?

Solution:

(a) $Pr(X \ge 1) = Pr(\overline{X < 1}) = 1 - Pr(X = 0) = 1 - \binom{6}{0}(.4)^0(.6)^6$

$$= 1 - (.6)^6.$$

(b)   Here we must find n such that

$$1 - (.6)^n > .77. \tag{2.3.3}$$

Inequality (2.3.3) may be written as $(.6)^n < .23$, which implies that

$$n \log .6 < \log .23 \quad \text{or} \quad n > \frac{\log .23}{\log .6} = \frac{-.6383}{-.2219} = 2.9.$$

Therefore the man must fire at the target three or more times in order to maintain a probability greater than .77 of hitting it at least once.

If the probability of a success in the binomial distribution varies from trial to trial, we have what is known as the *generalized binomial distribution*. Consider an experiment which consists of n independent trials. On the rth trial, $r = 1, 2, \ldots, n$, a success may occur with probability p_r or a failure with probability $1 - p_r = q_r$. The random variable X, the number of successes in n trials, can assume the values 1, 2, 3, $\ldots$, n, and it has a *generalized binomial distribution*. X may be represented as the sum

$$X = X_1 + X_2 + \cdots + X_n,$$

where the random variables X_i, $i = 1, 2, \ldots, n$ are independent and distributed as follows:

$$p_r = Pr(X_r = 1) \quad \text{and} \quad 1 - p_r = Pr(X_r = 0).$$

The probability that $X = r$ is obtained by summing the probabilities of each possible combination of r successes and $(n - r)$ failures. The following example will illustrate the above distribution.

Example 2.3.5   An electronics store has received two shipments of an electronic component. It is known that the fraction of defective components in the first shipment is $q_1 = 1 - p_1 = .01$; in the second, the fraction is $q_2 = 1 - p_2 = .02$. We draw a component at random from each shipment and assign the value of 1 to the random variable X_i, $i = 1, 2$, if the component is operable and the value 0 if it is defective. Hence, the random variable $X = X_1 + X_2$ can assume the values 0, 1, 2, that is, that none, one, or both of the components is operable, where

$$p_1 = Pr(X_1 = 1) = .99 \quad \text{and} \quad p_2 = Pr(X_2 = 1) = .98.$$

To find the density of X, we proceed as follows:

$$Pr(X = 0) = Pr(X_1 = 0)Pr(X_2 = 0) = q_1 \cdot q_2 = (.01)(.02) = .0002,$$

$$Pr(X = 1) = Pr(X_1 = 1)Pr(X_2 = 0) + Pr(X_1 = 0)Pr(X_2 = 1)$$

$$= p_1 \cdot q_2 + q_1 \cdot p_2 = (.99)(.02) + (.98)(.01) = .0296$$

$$Pr(X = 2) = Pr(X_1 = 1)Pr(X_2 = 1) = p_1 \cdot p_2 = (.99)(.98) = .9702$$

Notice that the conditions of a density function are satisfied; that is, $Pr[X = x] \geq 0$ for $x = 0, 1, 2$, and

$$Pr(X = 0) + Pr(X = 1) + Pr(X = 2) = 1.$$

2.3.3 The Poisson Distribution The Poisson distribution is a limiting form of the binomial, in which $p \to 0$ and $n \to \infty$ in such a way that np remains constant. It is used in many cases to approximate the binomial distribution when the number of trials n is comparatively large, p is small, and the product $\lambda = np$ is of moderate magnitude.

We shall derive the Poisson distribution by proving the following theorem, which is credited to the French mathematician S. Poisson, who announced it in 1837.

Theorem 2.3.1 Let the random variable X be distributed according to the binomial density:

$$f(x; n, p) = \begin{cases} \binom{n}{x} p^x (1 - p)^{n-x}, & x = 0, 1, 2, \ldots, n, \\ 0, & \text{elsewhere.} \end{cases}$$

If for $n = 1, 2, 3, \ldots$ the relation $p = \lambda/n$, where λ is a constant greater than zero, holds, then

$$\lim_{n \to \infty} f(x; n, p) = \begin{cases} \dfrac{e^{-\lambda} \lambda^x}{x!}, & x = 0, 1, 2, \ldots, \\ 0, & \text{elsewhere.} \end{cases}$$

Proof Substituting $p = \lambda/n$ into the binomial density and taking the limit as $n \to \infty$ gives

$$\lim_{n \to \infty} \left\{ \binom{n}{x} \left(\frac{\lambda}{n} \right)^x \left(1 - \frac{\lambda}{n} \right)^{n-x} \right\} = \lim_{n \to \infty} \left\{ \frac{n!}{x!(n-x)!} \frac{\lambda^x}{n^x} \cdot \left(1 - \frac{\lambda}{n} \right)^n \cdot \frac{1}{\left(1 - \frac{\lambda}{n} \right)^x} \right\}$$

$$= \frac{\lambda^x}{x!} \lim_{n \to \infty} \left\{ \frac{n(n-1)(n-2) \cdots (n - x + 1)}{n^x} \right\}$$

$$\cdot \lim_{n \to \infty} \left(1 - \frac{\lambda}{n} \right)^n \lim_{n \to \infty} \frac{1}{\left(1 - \frac{\lambda}{n} \right)^x} \cdot$$

Dividing n into each factor of $n(n + 1)(n - 2) \cdots (n - x + 1)$, we have

$$\lim_{n \to \infty} \left\{ 1 \left(1 - \frac{1}{n} \right) \left(1 - \frac{2}{n} \right) \cdots \left(1 - \frac{x - 1}{n} \right) \right\} = 1$$

Using the facts that

$$\lim_{n \to \infty} \left(1 - \frac{\lambda}{n}\right)^n = e^{-\lambda}$$

and

$$\lim_{n \to \infty} \frac{1}{\left(1 - \frac{\lambda}{n}\right)^x} = 1$$

we obtain the desired result:

$$\lim_{n \to \infty} \binom{n}{x} p^x (1 - p)^{n-x} = \frac{e^{-\lambda} \lambda^x}{x!}, \quad x = 0, 1, 2, \dots.$$

Hence, we have Definition 2.3.3.

Definition 2.3.3   *A random variable X is said to have a* Poisson *distribution if its probability density function is given by*

$$f(x; \lambda) = \begin{cases} \dfrac{e^{-\lambda} \lambda^x}{x!}, & x = 0, 1, 2, \dots, \\[2mm] & \lambda = np > 0, \\[2mm] 0, & elsewhere. \end{cases} \qquad (2.3.4)$$

It is easy to see that the definition of a density function is satisfied: $f(x; \lambda) \geq 0$ *and*

$$\sum_{x=0}^{\infty} \frac{e^{-\lambda} \lambda^x}{x!} = e^{-\lambda} \sum_{x=0}^{\infty} \frac{\lambda^x}{x!} = e^{-\lambda} e^{\lambda} = 1$$

because

$$1 + \frac{\lambda^2}{2!} + \frac{\lambda^3}{3!} + \cdots + \frac{\lambda^k}{k!} + \cdots$$

converges for all real λ to e^{λ}.

The cumulative distribution of the Poisson density is given by

$$F(x) = Pr(X \leq x) = \begin{cases} 0, & x < 0, \\[2mm] \displaystyle\sum_{x_i \leq [x]} \frac{e^{-\lambda} \lambda^{x_i}}{x_i!}, & x \geq 0. \end{cases}$$

Tables of Individual Terms, Poisson Distributions and Cumulative Terms, Binomial Distributions, on page 585 ff , contain cumulative probabilities of the Poisson distribution for selected values of λ.

There are many interesting random phenomena in the sciences that satisfy the conditions of the Poisson density function. Typical problems in which the probability p that the event occurs is comparatively small and the number of observations n is large are those problems that are concerned with rare occurrences of events in a fixed time interval. Some problems of this type are:

(1)   the frequency of certain " peaks " per minute at a telephone switchboard;
(2)   the number of misprints per page in a dictionary;
(3)   the number of traffic accidents which occur per day on a certain turnpike;
(4)   the number of α-particles emitted per hour by a radioactive source;
(5)   the number of babies born with a heart defect in a large city during a one-year period;
(6)   the number of " no-hitters " pitched by a Hall of Famer during his baseball career;
(7)   the number of live viruses remaining after the production process of a certain vaccine.

The Poisson distribution is characterized by the single parameter λ, which represents the average number of occurrences of the event in a given number of trials. Furthermore, it is easier to compute probabilities using the Poisson density than using the binomial probability function. The following recursive formulas are very useful in calculating successive probabilities of Equation (2.3.4):

$$f(x; \lambda) \frac{\lambda}{x+1} = \frac{e^{-\lambda}\lambda^{x+1}}{(x+1)!} = f(x+1; \lambda) \qquad (2.3.5)$$

and

$$f(x; \lambda) \frac{x}{\lambda} = \frac{e^{-\lambda}\lambda^{x-1}}{(x-1)!} = f(x-1; \lambda). \qquad (2.3.6)$$

For example, if $\lambda = 2.5$, we evaluate $f(0; 2.5)$ using Equation (2.3.4),

$$f(0; 2.5) = e^{-2.5} = .08208$$

Applying the recursion formula (2.3.5), we have

$$f(1; 2.5) = f(0; 2.5)\frac{2.5}{1} = (.08208)(2.5) = .2052;$$

$$f(2; 2.5) = f(1; 2.5)\frac{2.5}{2} = (.2052)\frac{2.5}{2} = .2565.$$

E. C. Molina, Reference [3], has prepared excellent tables for the Poisson function for values of $\lambda = .001(.001)\ .01(.01)\ .3(.1)\ 15(1)\ 100$. T. Kitazawa, Reference [1], also has tabulated the Poisson distribution for $\lambda = .001(.001)$ 1.00, 1.01(.01) 5.00 and 5.01(.01) 10.00.

Figure 2.3.2 illustrates the behavior of the Poisson density as we vary the size of λ. Observe that, for small values of λ $(\lambda \leq 1)$, the line diagram of the density is skewed to the right; as λ increases, the function becomes symmetrical.

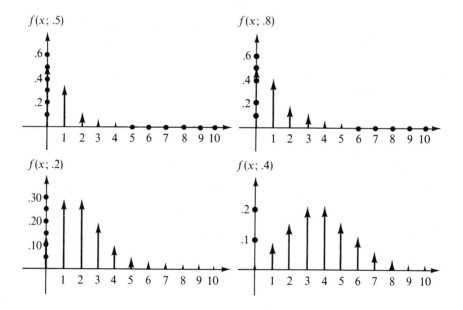

Figure 2.3.2

Table 2.3.1 shows that, for comparatively small x and n, the Poisson distribution gives a good approximation of the binomial distribution.

There is no set rule for the size of p and n in approximating the binomial with the Poisson distribution. In practice, if $p \leq .1$ and n is fairly large $(n \geq 40)$, the approximation will be quite good.

Table 2.3.1

$$n = 45, \quad p = .02, \quad \lambda = .9$$

x	0	1	2	3	4	5	6	7
Binomial	.4028	.3699	.1661	.0485	.0104	.0017	.0002	.0000
Poisson	.4065	.3659	.1646	.0493	.0111	.0020	.0003	.0000

The following examples illustrate some of the problems to which the Poisson distribution may be applied.

Example 2.3.6   A certain electronics company produces a particular type of vacuum tube. It has been observed that, on the average, three tubes out of 100 are defective. The company packs the tubes in boxes of 400. What is the probability that a box of 400 tubes will contain (a) r defective tubes; (b) at least k defectives; and (c), at most, one defective?

Solution: Since n is large and p small, these probabilities can be approximated by using the Poisson density with $\lambda = np = (400)(.03) = 12$ as follows:

(a) $Pr(X = r) = \dfrac{e^{-12}(12)^r}{r!}, \quad r \leq 400;$

(b) $Pr(X \geq k) = \displaystyle\sum_{x=k}^{400} \dfrac{e^{-12}(12)^k}{k!};$

(c) $Pr(X \leq 1) = \displaystyle\sum_{x=0}^{1} \dfrac{e^{-12}(12)^x}{x!} = 13e^{-12}.$

Example 2.3.7   Suppose it is known that a mathematics textbook of 400 pages contains 200 misprints, which are randomly distributed throughout the text. We are interested in the probability that a given page will contain (a) no misprints (b) three or more misprints.

Solution: Because the probability that a misprint will appear on a given page is $p = .0025$ and $n = 200$, it is justifiable to use the Poisson distribution and to obtain the necessary probabilities with $\lambda = 0.5$. Thus,

(a) $Pr(X = 0) = e^{-0.5} = .6065;$

(b) $Pr(X \geq 3) = \displaystyle\sum_{x=3}^{200} \dfrac{e^{-0.5}(.5)^x}{x!}$

$\qquad = 1 - \displaystyle\sum_{x=0}^{2} \dfrac{e^{-0.5}(.5)^x}{x!} = 1 - 1.625e^{-.5}.$

Example 2.3.8 (Rutherford and Geiger).   In Table 2.3.2, we give the results of the famous physics experiment, conducted by Rutherford and Geiger, regarding the α-particles emitted by a radioactive substance in 2608 periods of 7.5 seconds each.

Table 2.3.2

x	0	1	2	3	4	5	6	7	8	9	10
n_x	57	203	383	525	532	408	273	139	45	27	16
$f(x; 3.87)$	54.4	210.5	407.4	525.5	508.4	393.5	253.8	140.3	67.9	29.2	17.1

In this experiment, $n = 2608$ and p is quite small, and the distribution of the random variable X can be approximated by the Poisson density. The average number λ of α-particles emitted during a period of 7.5 seconds is

$$\lambda = \frac{1}{2608} \sum_{x=0}^{10} x n_x = 3.87,$$

and

$$f(x; 3.87) = \frac{e^{-3.87}(3.87)^x}{x!}, \qquad x = 0, 1, 2, \ldots, 10.$$

In fact, the third row of Table 2.3.2 shows that the Poisson density gives a good approximation of the problem. Now we can calculate the following probabilities:

(a)   what is the probability that in a given period of 7.5 seconds we shall observe five particles?

$$Pr(X = 5) = \frac{e^{-3.87}(3.87)^5}{5!};$$

(b)   what is the probability that we will observe at most three particles?

$$Pr(X \leq 3) = \sum_{x=0}^{3} \frac{e^{-3.87}(3.87)^x}{x!}.$$

We see that the Poisson distribution was developed as a limiting form of the binomial density; however, the Poisson function can be derived independently of the binomial distribution. We shall develop it by considering the following problem. Let $f(x; t)$ be the probability of getting x successes in a time interval of length t under the following conditions:

(1)   the probability of a success during a very small time interval Δt is $\alpha \Delta t, \alpha > 0$;

(2) the probability that more than one success occurs during such a time interval Δt is negligible;

(3) the probability of having a certain number of successes in a time interval of length t depends only on t and not on when the time interval begins or ends.

Then we can write

$$
\begin{aligned}
f(x; t + \Delta t) &= Pr\{[(x \text{ successes in } t) \cap (0 \text{ successes in } \Delta t)] \\
&\quad \cup [(x - 1 \text{ successes in } t) \cap (1 \text{ success in } \Delta t)]\} \\[4pt]
&= Pr[(x \text{ successes in } t) \cap (0 \text{ success in } \Delta t)] \\
&\quad + Pr[x - 1 \text{ successes in } t) \cap (1 \text{ success in } \Delta t)] \\[4pt]
&= Pr(x \text{ successes in } t)Pr(0 \text{ successes in } \Delta t) \\
&\quad + Pr(x - 1 \text{ successes in } t)Pr(1 \text{ success in } \Delta t) \\[4pt]
&= f(x; t)[1 - \alpha \Delta t] + f(x - 1; t)[\alpha \Delta t]. \tag{2.3.7}
\end{aligned}
$$

Subtracting $f(x; t)$ from both sides of Equation (2.3.7) and dividing by Δt gives

$$
\frac{f(x; t + \Delta t) - f(x; t)}{\Delta t} = \frac{\{f(x; t)[1 - \alpha \Delta t] + f(x - 1; t)[\alpha \Delta t]\} - f(x, t)}{\Delta t}.
$$

$$\tag{2.3.8}$$

Taking the limit of both sides of Equation (2.3.8) as $\Delta t \to 0$ and simplifying, the result is

$$
\lim_{\Delta t \to 0} \frac{f(x; t + \Delta t) - f(x; t)}{\Delta t} = \lim_{\Delta t \to 0} \frac{\alpha \Delta t[f(x - 1; t) - f(x; t)]}{\Delta t}
$$

$$
= \alpha[f(x - 1; t) - f(x; t)].
$$

Therefore,

$$
\frac{df(x; t)}{dt} = \alpha[f(x - 1; t) - f(x; t)]. \tag{2.3.9}
$$

For $x = 0, f(0 - 1, t) = 0$, and Equation (2.3.9) becomes

$$
\frac{df(0; t)}{dt} = -\alpha f(0; t)
$$

or

$$
\frac{df(0; t)}{f(0; t)} = -\alpha \, dt. \tag{2.3.10}
$$

Integrating both sides of Equation (2.3.10),

$$\int \frac{df(0;t)}{f(0;t)} = -\alpha \int dt$$

or

$$\ln f(0;t) = -\alpha t + c \qquad (2.3.11)$$

For $t = 0, f(0;0) = 1$, which implies $c = 0$. Thus,

$$\ln f(0;t) = -\alpha t$$

or

$$f(0;t) = e^{-\alpha t}.$$

Also, for $x = 1$, Equation (2.3.9) becomes

$$\frac{df(1;t)}{dt} + \alpha f(1;t) = \alpha e^{-\alpha t}. \qquad (2.3.12)$$

Solving this nonhomogeneous differential equation with the initial condition $f(1;0) = 0$, we have

$$f(1;t) = \frac{e^{-\alpha t}(\alpha t)^1}{1!}. \qquad (2.3.13)$$

Similarly, for $x = 2$ and $f(2, 0) = 0$, Equation (2.3.9) becomes

$$\frac{df(2;t)}{dt} + \alpha f(2;t) = \alpha f(1;t)$$

or

$$\frac{df(2;t)}{dt} + \alpha f(2;t) = \alpha^2 t e^{-\alpha t}. \qquad (2.3.14)$$

The solution of Equation (2.3.14) is given by

$$f(2;t) = \frac{(\alpha t)^2 e^{-\alpha t}}{2!}.$$

Continuing with this recursive approach, we conclude that, for any x, as long as $f(x; 0) = 0$, we have

$$f(x, t) = \frac{e^{-\alpha t}(\alpha t)^x}{x!}, \quad x = 0, 1, 2, \ldots, n, \ldots \tag{2.3.15}$$

Therefore, if $\lambda = \alpha t$, the average number of occurrences of successes in the time period t, Equation (2.3.15) is identical to the Poisson density function. A rigorous proof of the above development can be achieved by induction.

Example 2.3.9   Find the probability that, during a three-minute interval, there will be exactly five telephone calls if it is known that the probability of an incoming call to the switchboard during Δt seconds is $1/45 \, \Delta t$.

Solution: Here, $\lambda = \alpha \, \Delta t = 1/45 \, (180 \text{ seconds}) = 4$, and

$$Pr(X = 5) = \frac{e^{-4}(4)^5}{5!} = .1563.$$

What is the probability that during a two-minute interval there will be more than three calls but less than six? Here, $\Delta t = 120$; so $\lambda = 2.67$ and

$$Pr(3 < X < 6) = \sum_{x=4}^{5} \frac{e^{-2.67}(2.67)^x}{x!}.$$

2.3.4   The Hypergeometric Distribution   One of the discrete distributions that is useful in industrial engineering problems (quality inspection) and in other physical problems of the combinatorial type is the hypergeometric distribution. Consider the following experiment: We are given a population of n elements of which n_1 are successes and $n_2 = n - n_1$ are failures. A random sample of size r is drawn from n, and we seek the probability that the group so chosen will contain x successes. Thus, the random variable X can assume values from zero up to and equal to r or n_1, whichever is smaller. To find the probability that there are exactly x successes in the random sample, we proceed as follows: The total number of ways in which r elements can be selected out of n (disregarding order) is $\binom{n}{r}$; thus, each element in the sample space has a probability $1/\binom{n}{r}$ of being chosen. The total number of ways in which x successes can be selected from n_1 is $\binom{n_1}{x}$, and the remaining $(r - x)$ elements can be selected in $\binom{n_2}{r - x}$ ways. Therefore, the total number of ways in which we can achieve x successes and $r - x$ failures is $\binom{n_1}{x}\binom{n_2}{r - x}$, and the probability of this selection is given by $\binom{n_1}{x}\binom{n_2}{r - x} \big/ \binom{n}{r}$.

Definition 2.3.4   *A random variable X has the* hypergeometric distribution *if it has the following function for its probability density:*

$$
f(x; r, n_1, n_2) = \begin{cases} \dfrac{\dbinom{n_1}{x}\dbinom{n_2}{r-x}}{\dbinom{n_1+n_2}{r}}, & \begin{array}{l} x = 0, 1, 2, \ldots, r \le n_1 \\ \text{or} \\ x = 0, 1, 2, \ldots, n_1 \le r, \end{array} \qquad (2.3.16) \\[2em] 0, \quad \text{elsewhere.} \end{cases}
$$

The hypergeometric distribution depends on the three parameters r, n_1, *and* n_2. *It is easy to show that it satisfies the conditions of a density function,* $f(x; r, n_1, n_2)$ ≥ 0 *for* $x = 0, 1, 2, \ldots, r \le n_1$ *or* $n_1 \le r$, *and*

$$
\sum_{x=0}^{r} \frac{\dbinom{n_1}{x}\dbinom{n_2}{r-x}}{\dbinom{n_1+n_2}{r}} = \frac{1}{\dbinom{n_1+n_2}{r}} \sum_{x=0}^{r} \dbinom{n_1}{x}\dbinom{n_2}{r-x}. \qquad (2.3.17)
$$

From Exercise 1.14 *we saw that*

$$
\sum_{x=0}^{r} \binom{n_1}{x}\binom{n_2}{r-x} = \binom{n_1+n_2}{r},
$$

and Equation (2.3.17) *thus becomes*

$$
\frac{\dbinom{n_1+n_2}{r}}{\dbinom{n_1+n_2}{r}} = 1.
$$

We shall show some applications of the hypergeometric distribution in the problems below.

Example 2.3.10   A lot of 60 electrical components was subjected to a quality inspection. It was found that 48 of the components were nondefective and the remaining components were defective. If a random sample of 15 components is chosen from this lot, what is the probability that (a) exactly 11 of them will be operable, (b) at most nine will be operable?

Solution: Applying the hypergeometric distribution, we have

(a) $Pr(X = 11) = \dfrac{\dbinom{48}{11}\dbinom{12}{4}}{\dbinom{60}{15}}$;

(b) $Pr(x \le 9) = \displaystyle\sum_{x=0}^{9} \dfrac{\dbinom{48}{x}\dbinom{12}{15-x}}{\dbinom{60}{15}} = \displaystyle\sum_{x=3}^{9} \dfrac{\dbinom{48}{x}\dbinom{12}{15-x}}{\dbinom{60}{15}}$

Example 2.3.11   The faculty senate of a certain college consists of 66 senators, 38 of whom are from the sciences, 28 of whom are from the arts. A committee of 16 senators was chosen at random. What is the probability that the committee will have no more than six senators from the arts?

Solution: From Equation (2.3.17),

$$Pr(X \le 6) = \sum_{x=0}^{6} \frac{\dbinom{28}{x}\dbinom{38}{16-x}}{\dbinom{66}{16}}.$$

Calculating probabilities using the hypergeometric distribution becomes laborious when n is large. The work, however, is simplified by first calculating $f(0; r, n_1, n_2)$ and then applying the following recursion formulas, which are derived directly from the hypergeometric density.

$$f(x-1; r, n_1, n_2) = \frac{(r-x)(n_1-x)}{(x+1)(n-n_1-r+x+1)} f(x; r, n_1, n_2) \quad (2.3.18)$$

and

$$f(x+1; r, n_1, n_2) = \frac{x(n-n_1-r+x)}{(r-x+1)(n_1-x+1)} f(x; r, n_1, n_2). \quad (2.3.19)$$

The recursion formula (2.3.19) was used to obtain the results in Example 2.3.12, which are given in Table 2.3.3. In Reference [1], tables have been calculated for the hypergeometric distribution for $n = n_1 + n_2(1)100$ and $r = 1(1)50$; $r = 1(1)50$ means that the values of r begin with the value one and increase by jumps of one until the value 50 is reached.

Example 2.3.12   A wholesaler who specializes in rebuilding automobile engines has in stock 30 engines of a specific make. Only 20 of the engines were completely overhauled: the others were only partially rebuilt. A local mechanic purchased seven of the engines. What is the probability that (a) all seven engines were completely overhauled; (b) at least four were completely overhauled; and (c) at most r were completely overhauled, where $r \le 7$?

Solution:

(a) $\quad Pr(X = 7) = \dfrac{\dbinom{20}{7}\dbinom{10}{0}}{\dbinom{30}{7}}$;

(b) $\quad Pr(X \geq 4) = \displaystyle\sum_{x=4}^{7} \dfrac{\dbinom{20}{x}\dbinom{10}{7-x}}{\dbinom{30}{7}}$;

(c) $\quad Pr(X \leq r) = \displaystyle\sum_{x=0}^{r} \dfrac{\dbinom{20}{x}\dbinom{10}{7-x}}{\dbinom{30}{7}}$.

Table 2.3.3

x	0	1	2	3	4	5	6	7
$f(x)$	.0001	.0021	.0235	.1176	.2855	.3427	.1904	.03821
$F(x)$	.0001	.0022	.02564	.1432	.4288	.7714	.9618	1.000

The graph of $f(x)$ and $F(x)$ for Example 2.3.12 is given in Figure 2.3.3.

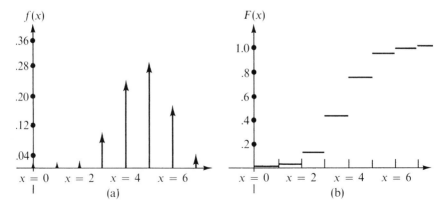

Figure 2.3.3

It has been left as an exercise (Problem 3) to show that, if we were to purchase an engine from the local mechanic, the probability of the engine's having been completely overhauled is the same as if we had purchased the engine from the wholesaler.

The hypergeometric distribution approaches that of the binomial as n becomes large. That is, if p is the original proportion of successes in the population, the probability of obtaining x successes and $r - x$ failures in r trials, without replacement, is given according to Equation (2.3.16) by

$$f(x; r, p, n) = \begin{cases} \dfrac{\dbinom{np}{x}\dbinom{n - np}{r - x}}{\dbinom{n}{r}}, & \begin{array}{l} x = 0, 1, 2, \ldots, r \le n_1, \\ \qquad\qquad \text{or} \\ x = 0, 1, 2, \ldots, n_1 \le r, \end{array} \\[12pt] 0, \quad elsewhere, \end{cases} \qquad (2.3.20)$$

where $n = n_1 + n_2$ is the total number of successes and failures, as before. Equation (2.3.20) can be written as

$$f(x; r, p, n) = \frac{(np)!\,(n - np)!\,r!\,(n - r)!}{x!\,(np - x)!\,(r - x)!\,(n - np - r + x)!\,n!}. \qquad (2.3.21)$$

Approximating $n!$ in Equation (2.3.21) by using Stirling's formula and taking the limit as $n \to \infty$, we get

$$\lim_{n \to \infty} f(x; r, p, n) = \binom{r}{x} p^x (1 - p)^{r - x}, \qquad x = 0, 1, \ldots, r.$$

The details of the proof are left as an exercise (see Problem 3).

2.3.5 The Geometric Distribution   Consider an experiment that meets the assumptions underlying the binomial situation, except that the number of trials is not fixed. The trials are independent and identical, and each of them can result in one of two possible outcomes, a success or a failure, with probability p and $1 - p$ respectively. In the binomial distribution, the random variable X, the number of successes, can assume values $0, 1, 2, \ldots, n$. However, in this case, we are interested in the number of trials required for the first success. Thus, the discrete random variable X can assume any one of an infinite number of positive integral values $1, 2, 3, \ldots$. Trial x can yield the first success only if we have observed an unbroken run of $x - 1$ failures during the first $x - 1$ trials. The probability that this run of $x - 1$ failures occurs is $(1 - p)^{x-1}$. Thus, the probability of $x - 1$ failures followed by a success is $(1 - p)^{x-1}p$. We state the distribution of such a random variable in Definition 2.3.5.

Definition 2.3.5   *A random variable X has the* geometric distribution *if it has the following function for its probability density:*

$$f(x;p) = \begin{cases} p(1-p)^{x-1}, & x = 1, 2, 3, \ldots, \quad 0 < p < 1, \\ 0, & elsewhere. \end{cases} \qquad (2.3.22)$$

This one-parameter distribution is called the geometric distribution because its successive terms constitute a geometric progression. The conditions of a density function are satisfied, that is, $f(x) \geq 0$ for all x, and from the formula for the sum of an infinite geometric series, we have

$$\sum_{x=1}^{\infty} p(1-p)^{x-1} = 1.$$

The cumulative distribution of the geometric density is given by

$$F(x) = Pr(X \leq x) = \begin{cases} 0, & x < 1 \\ \sum_{x_i \leq [x]} p(1-p)^{x_i-1}, & x \geq 1 \end{cases}$$

The following problems will illustrate some of the uses of the geometric distribution:

Example 2.3.13   In a game of billiards, a player continues to play until he misses a shot. If a particular player misses any of his shots with probability $p = 1/4$, what is the probability that this player's turn will last (a) exactly six shots? (b) at most five shots? (c) at least four shots?

Solution: Assuming that the shots are independent and $p = 1/4$ remains the same for every shot, we can apply the geometric distribution:

(a) $Pr(X = 6) = \left(\frac{1}{4}\right)\left(\frac{3}{4}\right)^5;$

(b) $Pr(x \leq 5) = \sum_{x=1}^{5} \left(\frac{1}{4}\right)\left(\frac{3}{4}\right)^{x-1};$

(c) $Pr(X \geq 4) = \sum_{x=4}^{\infty} \left(\frac{1}{4}\right)\left(\frac{3}{4}\right)^{x-1} = 1 - \sum_{x=1}^{3} \left(\frac{1}{4}\right)\left(\frac{3}{4}\right)^{x-1}.$

Example 2.3.14   What is the probability that we shall need six or fewer tosses of a fair pair of dice to throw a sum of five?

Solution: The probability of throwing a five on any throw is 1/9, and the desired probability is

$$Pr(x \le 6) = \sum_{x=1}^{6} \left(\frac{1}{9}\right)\left(\frac{8}{9}\right)^{x-1}.$$

The probability that it will take more than four throws of the pair of dice to obtain a sum of five:

$$Pr(X > 4) = 1 - Pr(X \le 4) = 1 - \sum_{x=1}^{4} \left(\frac{1}{9}\right)\left(\frac{8}{9}\right)^{x-1}.$$

Example 2.3.15 Suppose that a student can take a certain standard examination in French as many times as he wishes. The number of times a student takes this examination is a random variable closely approximated by the geometric distribution. If the probability of his passing the examination any time is $p = .66$, what is the probability that (a) he passes the examination on the third try and (b) he fails to pass the examination on the first five tries?

Solution: Applying Equation (2.3.2), we have

(a) $Pr(X = 3) = (.66)(.34)^2$;

(b) $1 - F(5) = 1 - Pr(X \le 5) = 1 - \sum_{x=1}^{5} (.66)(.34)^{x-1}.$

2.3.6 The Negative Binomial Distribution Consider an experiment which meets the assumptions underlying the binomial density function. Whereas in the binomial we are interested in the number of successes achieved in n trials, in the negative binomial we are interested in the number of trials required to achieve r successes. Thus, if we let the random variable X be the number of trials required to achieve r successes, X may take on the values $r, r + 1, r + 2, \ldots$. If we achieve r successes in x trials, then we have obtained $x - r$ failures, and the probability that this event occurs in a particular order is $p^r(1 - p)^{x-r}$. But since the last trial resulted in a success, there are $r - 1$ other successes which occurred in $x - 1$ trials, and this can happen in $\binom{x-1}{r-1}$ ways. The probability of achieving r successes in x trials is thus

$$\binom{x - 1}{r - 1} p^r(1 - p)^{x-r}, \qquad x = r, r + 1, \ldots.$$

We define the distribution of the random variable in Definition 2.3.6.

Definition 2.3.6 *A random variable X has the negative binomial distribution if it has the following function for its probability density:*

$$f(x; p, r) = \begin{cases} \binom{x - 1}{r - 1} p^r(1 - p)^{x-r}, & x = r, \ r + 1, \ldots, \\ & 0 < p < 1, \\ 0, & elsewhere. \end{cases} \qquad (2.3.23)$$

It is clear that this two-parameter distribution is greater than or equal to zero for all values of x, where r > 0. We must also show that

$$\sum_{x=r}^{\infty} f(x; p, r) = 1.$$

$$\sum_{x=r}^{\infty} \binom{x-1}{r-1} p^r (1-p)^{x-r} = p^r \sum_{x=r}^{\infty} \binom{x-1}{x-r} (1-p)^{x-r}. \qquad (2.3.24)$$

Let y = x − r; and, applying the result of Problem 3 to (2.3.24), we have

$$p^r \sum_{x=r}^{\infty} \binom{x-1}{x-r} (1-p)^{x-r} = p^r \sum_{y=0}^{\infty} (-1)^y \binom{-r}{y} (1-p)^y \qquad (2.3.25)$$

$$= p^r [1 - (1-p)]^{-r}$$

$$= p^r p^{-r} = 1.$$

Therefore, f(x; p, r) satisfies the conditions of a probability density function. Note that the negative binomial density gets its name from $\binom{-r}{y}$ *in Equation (2.3.25).*

We shall now consider the following applications of the negative binomial distribution:

Example 2.3.16   In order to pass a certain marksmanship test, an individual is required to shoot at a target until he scores six bulls-eyes. He is judged on the number of trials that are necessary to achieve this score. If the probability of his hitting a bulls-eye on any trial is .25, what is the probability that: (a) he requires nine shots, (b) he requires more than nine but less than 12 shots?

Solution:

(a)   Here

$$p = \frac{1}{4}, \quad r = 6$$

and

$$Pr(X = 9) = \binom{9-1}{6-1} \left(\frac{1}{4}\right)^6 \left(\frac{3}{4}\right)^{9-6} = \binom{8}{5} \left(\frac{1}{4}\right)^6 \left(\frac{3}{4}\right)^3.$$

(b)   In this case, p and r are the same as in (a), but we want

$$Pr(9 < X < 12) = \sum_{x=10}^{11} \binom{x-1}{5} \left(\frac{1}{4}\right)^6 \left(\frac{3}{4}\right)^{x-6}$$

$$= \binom{9}{5} \left(\frac{1}{4}\right)^6 \left(\frac{3}{4}\right)^4 + \binom{10}{5} \left(\frac{1}{4}\right)^6 \left(\frac{3}{4}\right)^5.$$

Example 2.3.17   Find the probability that a person flipping a fair coin will get the sixth head on the eleventh trial.

Solution: Here

$$d = \frac{1}{2}, \quad r = 6,$$

$$Pr(X = 11) = \binom{11 - 1}{6 - 1}\left(\frac{1}{2}\right)^6 \left(\frac{1}{2}\right)^{11-6} = \binom{10}{5}\left(\frac{1}{2}\right)^{11}.$$

Example 2.3.18   What is the probability that seven draws are required to get three aces from an ordinary deck of 52 cards, with replacement?

Solution: In this case,

$$r = 3, \quad p = \frac{4}{52}$$

and

$$Pr(X = 7) = \binom{7 - 1}{3 - 1}\left(\frac{1}{13}\right)^3 \left(\frac{12}{13}\right)^{7-3} = \binom{6}{2}\left(\frac{1}{13}\right)^3 \left(\frac{12}{13}\right)^4.$$

In this chapter, we have studied the concept of a one-dimensional discrete random variable, developed a number of discrete probability distributions, and illustrated some of their uses. There are, however, many physical situations that must be characterized by a continuous random variable. That is, a continuous random variable may assume a nondenumerable (noncountable) number of values. Chapter 3 is devoted to studying the one-dimensional continuous random variable and to examining some useful continuous probability distributions.

2.4 Summary

A *random variable* is a function (rule) which assigns a number to every outcome of an experiment. More precisely, let S be a sample space and $X(s)$ a real valued function (defined on S), which transforms the points of S into a subset of the real line, R_X, that is, the *range space*. Then $X = X(s)$ is called a *random variable*, provided the probabilities of $\{X(s) = x\}$ and $\{X(s) \le x\}$ can be calculated, where s is any element in the sample space and x any real number in the range space.

Let X be a random variable. If the number of elements in the range space, R_X, is finite or countably infinite, then X is called a *one-dimensional discrete random variable*.

Let X be a one-dimensional discrete random variable. A function $f(x_i)$ is called a *discrete probability density function* of the random variable X if the following conditions are satisfied:

(1) $f(x_i) \geq 0$ for all $x_i \in R_X$

(2) $\displaystyle\sum_{x_i \in R_x} f(x_i) = 1,$

where the summation is taken over all x_i in the range space.

The *cumulative distribution function* of the discrete random variable X is

$$F(x) = Pr(X \leq x) = \sum_{x_i \leq [x]} f(x_i),$$

where the summation is extended over all points x_i, for which $x_i \leq [x]$. $F(x)$ possesses the following properties: (1) $F(\infty) = 1$; (2) $F(-\infty) = 0$; (3) $F(x)$ is a nondecreasing function of x; and (4) $F(x)$ is continuous from the right.

The following important discrete probability distributions have been developed:

(1) *The point binomial distribution* is applicable to experiments with a single observation, the results of which will be one of two possible outcomes.

(2) *The binomial or Bernoulli distribution* is a generalization of the point binomial distribution because it applies to problems that involve independent trials whose outcomes have been classified into two categories, say, success and failure, with the probability of success being the same for each trial.

(3) *The Poisson distribution*, developed as a limiting form of the binomial distribution, is used in many cases to approximate the binomial distribution when the number of trials is comparatively large and the probability of success fairly small. The Poisson distribution, commonly known as the distribution of rare events, is also developed as the solution of a differential equation.

(4) *The hypergeometric distribution* is used to find the probability that there are exactly x successes in a random sample of size r from a population of n elements, of which n_1 are successes and $n_2 = n - n_1$ are failures.

(5) *The geometric distribution* was developed to obtain the probability that a success will occur at a particular trial in an experiment that meets the assumptions underlying the binomial probability density function.

(6) *The negative binomial distribution* was developed to obtain the probability that we need a particular number of trials to achieve a certain number of successes in an experiment that meets the assumptions underlying the binomial distribution.

Exercises

2.1. Seven cards are dealt from an ordinary deck of playing cards.

   (a) Determine the probability density function for the number of hearts dealt.
   (b) Write the cumulative distribution function. Be sure to include the admissible values of the random variable.

2.2. An experiment consists of tossing six fair coins. Determine the probability density and cumulative distribution function for the number of heads that will appear in the experiment.

2.3. A symmetrical coin is tossed until a tail appears.

   (a) Determine the probability density for the number of tosses required.
   (b) Obtain the cumulative distribution function.

2.4. A company received a shipment of a certain type of electronic component. The lot consists of r_1 operable and r_2 defective components. A sample of m components are drawn from the lot without replacement.

   (a) What is the probability density function of the number of operable components?
   (b) What is the probability that at least k of the m components to be inspected will be operable?

2.5. A fair die is rolled until a six appears. Let X be the number of rolls required in the experiment. Find $f(x)$ and $F(x)$. Sketch the graphs of $f(x)$ and $F(x)$.

2.6. An urn contains eight white balls and twelve black ones. Ten balls are drawn at random from the urn. Find the probability density function for the number of white balls drawn in the following two situations:

   (a) If there is replacement.
   (b) If there is no replacement.

2.7. Find k so that the function given by

$$f(x) = \frac{k}{x+1}, \quad x = 1, 2, 3, 4$$

is a probability density function. Graph the density and cumulative distribution functions. Show that the properties of the cumulative distribution function are satisfied.

2.8.   Find c so that the discrete function given by

$$f(x) = \frac{1}{c} 4^{-|x|}, \quad x = 0, \pm 1, \pm 2, \ldots,$$

is a probability density function. What is the cumulative distribution function of the random variable X?

2.9.   Let

$$f(x) = \begin{cases} \dfrac{k}{x^2}, & x = \pm 1, \pm 2, \pm 3, \ldots, \\ 0, & \text{elsewhere.} \end{cases}$$

(a)   Find k so that $f(x)$ is a probability density function.
(b)   Determine the cumulative distribution function of the random variable X.

2.10. Show that the function given by

$$f(x) = \begin{cases} \dfrac{1}{2^{1+|x|}}, & x = \pm 1, \pm 2, \ldots, \\ 0, & \text{elsewhere} \end{cases}$$

is a probability density function of the discrete random variable X.

2.11. Show that the binomial probability density function $f(x; n, p)$ given by Equation (2.3.2) can be written as

$$f(n - x; n, 1 - p) = \begin{cases} \dbinom{n}{n-x}(1-p)^{n-x}p^{n-(n-x)}, & x = 0, 1, 2, \ldots, n, \\ & 0 < p < 1, \\ 0, & \text{elsewhere.} \end{cases}$$

2.12. A simple way to calculate binomial probabilities is as follows: For a given n and p, evaluate $f(0; n, p)$ and then apply the recursive relationship

$$f(x + 1; n, p) = f(x; n, p) \frac{p(n - x)}{(1 - p)(x + 1)}$$

to obtain other binomial probabilities. Derive this recursion formula.

2.13. Show that for $x = 0, 1, 2, \ldots, 4 \leq n_1$,

$$\sum_{x=0}^{n_1, r} \binom{n_1}{x} \binom{n_2}{r-x} = \binom{n_1 + n_2}{r},$$

where n_1, r means $min(n_1, r)$.

2.14. A simple recursive formula for calculating hypergeometric probabilities is

$$f(x+1; r, n_1, n_2) = \left\{ \frac{(r-x)(n_1-x)}{(x+1)(n_2-r+x+1)} \right\} f(x; r, n_1, n_2).$$

Derive this recursive relationship and then apply it to calculate the hypergeometric probabilities for $r = 6$, $n_1 = 7$, and $n_2 = 8$.

2.15. Show that the hypergeometric distribution is asymptotically a binomial distribution, that is,

$$\lim_{n \to \infty} \frac{\binom{pn}{x}\binom{n-np}{r-x}}{\binom{n}{r}} = \binom{n}{x} p^x (1-p)^{n-x},$$

where $n = n_1 + n_2$, $pn = n_1$, $x = 0, 1, 2, \ldots, r \leq np$ or $x = 0, 1, 2, \ldots$, $np < r$.

2.16. Show that the geometric distribution function given by (2.3.2) satisfies the conditions of a probability density function.

2.17. Show that

$$\sum_{y=0}^{\infty} \binom{y+r-1}{y}(1-p)^y = \sum_{y=0}^{\infty} (-1)^y \binom{-r}{y}(1-p)^y,$$

where $0 \leq p \leq 1$.

2.18. n cards are drawn from an ordinary deck of cards with or without replacement, where $n \leq 52$. If exactly k spades are contained in the n drawn cards, show that the probability that the jth card was a spade is k/n.

Problems

2.1. In Exercise 2.1, find the probability that

(a) exactly five hearts are dealt
(b) the number of hearts dealt falls between two and five, inclusive.

2.2. In Exercise 2.2,

    (a) what is the probability of at most four heads appearing?

    (b) what is the probability that the number of heads will be between two and five, inclusive?

2.3. In Exercise 2.3,

    (a) what is the probability of obtaining the first tail at the fourth trial?

    (b) what is the probability that the first tail will appear in at most three trials?

2.4. In Exercise 2.6, find the probability that

    (a) at least five white balls are drawn

    (b) at most five white balls are drawn

2.5. In Exercise 2.7, find

    (a) $Pr[X > 2]$ (b) $Pr[2.5 \leq X \leq 7.3]$.

2.6. *Discrete uniform distribution.* Let X be a discrete random variable which may assume the values $x_1, x_2, \ldots, x_n$ with equal probability. The probability density function of X is given by

$$(x) = \begin{cases} \dfrac{1}{n}, & x = x_1, x_2, \ldots, x_n, \\ 0, & \text{otherwise.} \end{cases}$$

Thus, if the range of the random variable is $x = 2, 3, \ldots, 9$, then the discrete uniform distribution of X is

$$f(x) = \begin{cases} \dfrac{1}{8}, & x = 2, 3, \ldots, 9, \\ 0, & \text{otherwise.} \end{cases}$$

What is the probability that

    (a) the value which the random variable assumes is greater than six?

    (b) the value which the random variable assumes is greater than four but less than or equal to seven?

    (c) the value which the random variable assumes is greater than or equal to eight?

2.7. In the general population, the probability that an infant is a male is 0.52. Assuming that the sexes of fraternal twins are independent, what is the probability that fraternal twins will have the same sex?

2.8.   If a die is rolled 120 times, find the probability that 35 or more sixes will appear.

2.9.   Two fair dice are rolled many times. Find the probability that

   (a)   in the first seven rolls four sevens appear
   (b)   the first seven appears on the seventh roll
   (c)   the fourth seven appears on the seventh roll.

2.10.   Consider the experiment of rolling a die. Assume that a success occurs whenever a one or a five appears and a failure occurs if another number appears. If the die is rolled five times,

   (a)   find the probability that three successes will occur
   (b)   find the probability that at most two successes occur
   (c)   write and graph the cumulative distribution function of the random variable that characterizes the experiment.

2.11.   Suppose that a radio tube inserted into a certain type of a system has a probability of 0.2 of functioning more than 500 hours. If 20 such tubes are tested,

   (a)   find the probability that exactly k of these tubes will function more than 500 hours
   (b)   find the probability that the number of tubes that will be operable more than 500 hours falls between twelve and seventeen, exclusively
   (c)   sketch the cumulative distribution function of the random variable that describes the random phenomenon.

2.12.   A basketball team is playing an opposing team, and both of the teams have the same ability.

   (a)   Which of the following two events is more likely to occur: one team winning two basketball games out of five or the same team winning three games out of four?
   (b)   Which of the following two events is more likely to occur: a team winning at least two games out of five or the same team wins at most three games out of four?

2.13.   From a standard deck of 52 playing cards, seven cards are dealt at random without replacement. What is the probability that

   (a)   exactly two of them will be aces?
   (b)   at least three will be aces?
   (c)   at most one will be an ace?

2.14.   A distributor of a certain high-precision component determines that 5% of his product will not meet the required standards of the consumer.

He sells the components in packages of 300 and guarantees that 90% of them will pass the required standards. Find the probability that a package violates the distributor's guarantee.

2.15. White mice are used to evaluate the effectiveness of a certain drug. If only 50% of the mice react to the drug, how many mice should be used to ensure that at least one of the mice will give an observable reaction. with a probability of at least 0.95?

2.16. Suppose that, during the course of a basketball game, a certain player is fouled three times and that each time he is allowed to make one penalty shot. Because it is his first time at the foul line, the probability that he makes his first shot is 0.3. However, he is not a bad shooter; the probability that he makes his second shot is 0.8. The third shot is taken during the last few seconds of the game and may win the game for his team. The player is extremely nervous, and the opposing team has already called time out in order to rattle him. The probability of his making the third shot is reduced to 0.1. What is the probability that he makes exactly two shots out of the three?

2.17. The proportion of mice which convulse when exercised after receiving a standard dose of insulin increases as the time since the last feeding increases. The first group has been without food for four hours, and the probability of their convulsing is 0.5. A second group has been without food for five hours, and the probability that a mouse in this group will convulse is 0.6. A third group has been without food for five and one-half hours, and the probability that a mouse in this group will convulse is 0.65. If one mouse is selected from each of the three groups and this sample of size three is tested, what is the probability that

(a) fewer than two mice will convulse?
(b) at most two mice will convulse?

2.18. A store receives three shipments of flashlight batteries. It is known that the fraction of defective batteries in the first, second, and third shipment is .015, .01, and .05, respectively. If a battery is selected at random from each of the three shipments, what is the probability that

(a) at most two of the batteries are defective?
(b) none of the batteries are defective?

2.19. A pharmaceutical company produces a certain type of vaccine. It has been determined that, on the average, two out of one hundred viruses remain alive after application of the vaccine. What is the probability that a batch of 500 viruses, after application of the vaccine, will contain

(a) exactly ten live viruses?
(b) at most six live viruses?
(c) no live viruses?

2.20. It has been observed that the probability of the birth of a "phantom" poodle (black with white feet) is 0.01. If 50 poodles are born in the kennel of a certain poodle breeder in a given year, what is the probability that

(a) none of them will be of the "phantom" variety?
(b) at least three of them will be of the "phantom" variety?

2.21. A drug manufacturer receives a shipment of 20,000 calibrated "eye-droppers" for administering Salvin Poliovirus Vaccine. If the calibration marks are missing on 400 of the droppers and these defective droppers are scattered randomly throughout the shipment, what is the probability that

(a) at least one defective dropper will be detected in a random sample of 30?
(b) at most five defective droppers will be detected in a random sample of 50?

2.22. Suppose that, in a certain production process, it is found that two defective items are produced for every 100 items. These items are sold in lots of 100. Company A has ordered two lots with the agreement that, if there are more than four defectives, the remaining items will be returned for a refund of the entire purchase price. What is the probability that the purchase price will be refunded?

2.23. The probability that a swimmer can break the world record in the butterfly event is 0.05. If he competes in 12 meets during the course of a year, what is the probability that he will break the record at least once? Construct a table comparing the binomial probabilities with those of the Poisson distribution for all possible values that the random variable can assume.

2.24. In geophysics, the age of a zeicon may be determined by counting the number of uranium fission tracks on a polished surface that has been etched with hydroflouric acid both before and after neutron bombardment. Each track represents the fission of one atom. The probability that any atom decays by fission is very small (half-life is equal to 8×10^{15} years), but there is a very large number of atoms in a sample. If, for a given sample, there should be five tracks, on the average, in the area of the surface examined, what is the probability of finding fewer than three tracks in this area and thus greatly underestimating the age of the material?

2.25. Five cards are dealt from an ordinary deck of playing cards. What is the probability that the hand will contain

(a) no aces?　　(b) at least two aces?　　(c) at most one ace?

2.26. A men's store purchased a lot of 100 shirts from a certain manufacturer. It was observed that 88 of the shirts were not damaged but that the remaining shirts were not suitable to sell. If a random sample of 40 shirts is chosen from this lot, what is the probability that

    (a)   exactly 36 shirts have not been damaged?
    (b)   at most 22 shirts were not damaged?

2.27. Five cards are drawn, without replacement, from a deck of cards containing only four spades and six clubs. What is the probability that the spades outnumber the clubs?

2.28. Solve Problem 2.21 using the hypergeometric and binomial probability density functions, and compare your answers. Is n large enough to accept the answers given by the binomial distribution?

2.29. A lazy fisherman decides to cast until he has caught a single fish. If the stream is so well stocked that on the average a person catches a fish every tenth try, what is the probability that the fisherman will catch a fish after exactly five tries?

2.30. A volleyball team has a 70% chance of winning each point while it is the serving team. As soon as the serving team fails to score, it must give up service. What is the probability that the score will be five to nothing before the serve is lost by this team for the first time?

2.31. A bridge player has a probability 0.25 of being dealt a biddable hand on each deal. What is the probability that he must be dealt three hands in order to get a biddable hand?

2.32. A chemist is working on a new theory, but he needs to confirm it with laboratory experiments. Each trial is considered a success if a certain electronic device that is used to trigger the reaction functions successfully. The chemist has only enough chemicals to perform the experiment five times, but four of these trials must be "successes" in order to give him sufficient information about his new theory. The electronic device is built in such a way that if it breaks down it cannot be repaired, and the chemist has neither the time nor the money to order a new one. What should the device's probability of failure be on each trial if the chemist wishes to be 93% certain that the first failure occurs after the fourth trial?

2.33. A carnival worker operates a "throw-until-you-win" game, that is, each person is allowed all the throws he needs to be successful. To increase the number of persons playing the game (and consequently the profit), the worker wants to design the game so that 95% of the patrons win in seven throws or less. What should the probability of success be on a single throw so that the carnival worker can achieve his objective?

2.34. A golf tournament is arranged in such a way that, in order to qualify, a golfer must win two other tournaments of a similar nature during the year. Assume that the probability of winning each tournament remains constant for each golfer. At the beginning of the golfing season, a man wishes to bet that a particular golfer either will not qualify for the tournament or will actually win the tournament. He wants to be 90% certain that one of these two events actually will occur before he places his bet. What must the golfer's probability of winning be before the man is willing to bet?

2.35. The probability of winning the local gas station's "Tigerama" game is 0.001. A man is determined to win. What is the probability of his winning if he goes to the gas station exactly 100 times?

2.36. A man is playing Russian roulette. Before each pull of the trigger, he spins the cylinder, which contains a bullet in one of the six chambers. What is the probability that he will shoot himself on the third try?

2.37. A certain type of vaccine is packaged with five vials to the box. To package the vaccine in this way, the packer picks a vial off a moving belt, checks it for defects, puts it in the box if it is satisfactory, and sets it aside if it is not. If, on the average, 98% of the vials are satisfactory,

    (a)   what percentage of boxes will be filled after inspecting only six vials?

    (b)   for what percentage of boxes will it be necessary to inspect seven vials?

2.38. A card player draws *n* cards from an ordinary deck and lays them aside, unnoticed. Then he draws another card. Find the probability that this last card is a spade.

References

[1]   Kitogowa, T. *Tables of Poisson Distribution*, Tokyo: Baifukan Press, 1952.

[2]   Lieberman, G. J. and D. B. Owen. *Tables of the Hypergeometric Probability Distribution*. Stanford, California: Stanford University Press, 1961.

[3]   Molina, E. C. *Poissons Exponential Binomial Limit*. Princeton, New York: D. Van Nostrand Company, 1942.

[4]   Roming, H. G. 50–100 *Binomial Tables*, New York: John Wiley and Sons, Inc., 1953.

[5]   *The Tables of the Binomial Probability Distribution*. Washington: National Bureau of Standards, Applied Mathematics Series 6, 1950.

[6]   *Tables of the Cumulative Binomial Probability Distribution*. Cambridge: Harvard University Press, 1955.

Suggested Supplementary Reading

Cramer, H. *The Elements of Probability Theory and Some of its Applications*. New York: John Wiley and Sons, Inc., 1955. Stockholm: Almqvist and Wiksell, 1954.

Drake, A. W. *Fundamentals of Applied Probability Theory*. New York: McGraw-Hill Book Company, Inc., 1967.

Feller, W. *An Introduction to Probability Theory and Its Applications*. Vol. 1. 2nd ed. New York: John Wiley and Sons, Inc., 1960.

Fisz, M. *Probability Theory and Mathematical Statistics*. 3rd ed. New York: John Wiley and Sons, Inc., 1962.

Goldberg, S. *Probability: An Introduction*. New Jersey: Prentice-Hall, Inc., 1960.

Harris, B. *Theory of Probability*. Reading, Massachusetts: Addison-Wesley Publishing Company, Inc., 1966.

Lindgren, B. W. and McElrath, G. W. *Introduction to Probability and Statistics*. 2nd ed. New York: The Macmillan Company, 1966.

Mendenhall, W. *Introduction to Probability and Statistics*. 3rd ed. Belmont, California: Wadsworth Publishing Company, Inc., 1971.

Meyer, P. L. *Introduction to Probability and Statistical Applications*. Reading, Massachusetts: Addison-Wesley Publishing Company, Inc., 1965.

Monroe, M. E. *Theory of Probability*. New York: McGraw-Hill Book Company, Inc., 1951.

Papoulis, A. *Probability Random Variables and Stochastic Processes*. New York: McGraw-Hill Book Company, Inc., 1965.

Parzen, E. *Modern Probability Theory and Its Applications*. New York: John Wiley and Sons, Inc., 1960.

Continuous Random Variables and Probability Distributions

3

3.0 Introduction

In Chapter 2, we introduced the concept of a random variable and discussed in detail the behavior of a discrete random variable. The aim in this chapter is to study the continuous random variable, to derive most of the *important continuous probability density functions*, and to illustrate some of their uses with physical applications.

3.1 Continuous Random Variable and Probability Density Function

A continuous random variable may assume a nondenumerable (non-countable) number of values, whereas a discrete random variable is restricted to taking on isolated values. Typical examples of a continuous random variable are: the operational life of a certain electrical system, $0 \leq x < \infty$; the temperature fluctuation in the Sea of Tranquillity on the moon, $-273°C \leq x < \infty$; the length of time of a telephone conversation, $t_1 \leq x \leq t_2$; the power output of a certain machine operating in a changing environment, $0 \leq x < \infty$; there are many other examples with similar characteristics. Here the random variable may assume values from a certain interval or from a collection of intervals from the range of the random variable.

We study the continuous random variable so that we may calculate the probabilities that the variate will assume values from a certain interval on the real axis. To obtain such probabilities, one must be able to derive the probability density function of the continuous random variable. One of the prime tasks in probability is the formulation of the distribution of a random variable; then, once we know its distribution, we know the laws governing it.

We shall begin the development of the probability density function of a continuous random variable with a discussion of a physical phenomenon. Consider the example of putting an electrical system into operation at time $t = 0$, thinking of the time that elapses until its failure as a random variable X, which assumes values from the interval $[0, T]$. Here the random variable can assume a noncountable number of values. Let us assume that we have observed n such systems and have recorded the elapsed times until failure. One could interpret X as a discrete random variable and calculate probabilities that the random variable X can assume certain individual values. However, from a realistic point of view, one must deal with intervals rather than with individual points. Let us divide the time interval $(0, T]$ into r subintervals, each of equal length: $(t_0, t_1], (t_1, t_2], \ldots, (t_{r-1}, t_r]$, such that

$$0 < t \leq t_1 \leq t_2 \leq \cdots \leq T;$$

and let $x_i, i = 1, 2, 3, \ldots, r$ represent the number of systems which failed in the ith subinterval such that

$$\sum_{i=1}^{r} x_i = n.$$

The number of systems that have failed in the ith subinterval, divided by n, will be the relative frequency that a system will fail between t_{i-1} and t_i.

Thus, we can construct a probability histogram, as shown in Figure 3.1.1, with p as the empirical probability, such that $\sum_{i=1}^{r} p_i = 1$, where $p_i = x_i/n$, $i = 1, 2, \ldots, r$.

The rectangles of the histogram are of equal width; thus, their areas are proportional to their heights. Furthermore, the sum of the areas of all the rectangles is equal to one.

Therefore, we can estimate the probability that a system will fall in the interval $(t_0, t_3]$ by adding the areas of the three rectangles over this interval: If X is the random variable representing the number of failures, then

$$Pr(x_0 \leq X \leq x_3) = Pr[(X = x_1) \cup (X = x_2) \cup (X = X_3)]$$

$$= Pr(X = x_1) + Pr(X = x_2) + Pr(X = x_3)$$

$$= p_1 + p_2 + p_3.$$

Using this approach, one is able to obtain estimates of the probabilities that a continuous random variable is contained in an interval in terms of areas. These estimates can be improved by decreasing the widths of the intervals, which increases the number of such intervals so that we can approximate the area under the rectangles by a continuous function, as shown in Figure 3.1.2.

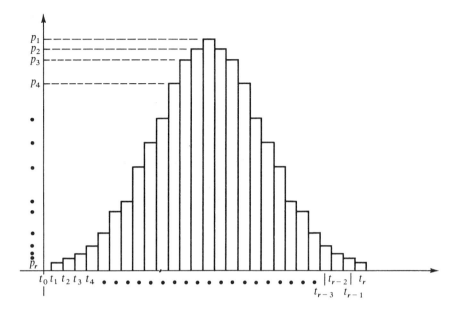

Figure 3.1.1

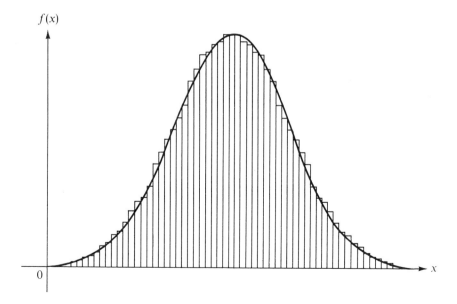

Figure 3.1.2

In fact, what we have described above is the definition of a definite (Reimann) integral. Suppose the interval $(0, T]$ has been subdivided into m intervals. If the kth subinterval is of width $(\Delta x)_k$ and height $f(x_k)$, and x_k is any point in this subinterval, then

$$\lim_{m \to \infty} \sum_{k=0}^{m} f(x_k)(\Delta x)_k = \int_0^T f(x)\, dx. \tag{3.1.1}$$

Accordingly, there is a function, $f(x)$, which will give the correct probability for any interval in the range of the random variable in terms of the area under the smooth curve. Of course, such a function becomes meaningless when we speak of its ith value; the probabilities are given by areas under the curve, not by evaluating the function at a particular value. Thus, the probability that a continuous random variable is equal to a specific value is equal to zero. That is,

$$Pr(X = x_0) = 0.$$

We shall now proceed to formulate the concepts developed in the above discussion, as follows:

Definition 3.1.1   *Let X be a random variable. If the range space, R_X, is an interval or the union of two or more nonoverlapping intervals, then X is called a* one-dimensional continuous random variable.

Definition 3.1.2   *Let X be a one-dimensional continuous random variable. A function $f(x)$ is called a* continuous probability density function *of the random variable X if the following conditions are satisfied:*

(1) $f(x) \geq 0,$ *for all $x \in R_X$*
(2) $\int_{R_X} f(x)\, dx = 1,$

where the integration is performed over those x's which are contained only in the intervals of the range space. Furthermore, it must be true that for any real numbers α and β such that $\alpha < \beta$,

$$Pr(\alpha \leq X \leq \beta) = \int_\alpha^\beta f(x)\, dx.$$

We shall call $f(x)$ a *probability density function* or *density function* of the continuous random variable X if the above conditions hold. As in the discrete case, other common ways in which we can phrase the definition are "the random variable X is distributed as $f(x)$" and "$f(x)$ is the distribution of the random variable X."

In order for the integral (3.1.1) to exist in a given interval, it is necessary that the function $f(x)$ be continuous almost everywhere on the interval. Thus, we shall assume that the density function of a continuous variate is continuous except, at most, for a finite number of points.

Given the probability density function $f(x)$ of a continuous random variable X and letting $E_1 = \{x: a \le x \le b\}$, we can define

$$Pr(E_1) = Pr(a \le X \le b) = \int_{E_1} f(x)\,dx = \int_a^b f(x)\,dx.$$

The probability is represented by the shaded area under the graph in Figure 3.1.3.

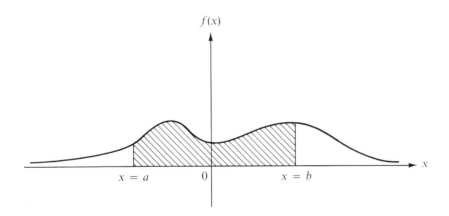

Figure 3.1.3

The probability density function of a continuous variate may be obtained by some mathematical reasoning of the problem or by fitting the function to the data at hand and forcing it to satisfy the conditions of a probability density function. Thus, if we are given a continuous function, say $g(x)$, $-\infty < x < \infty$, we can evaluate $\int_{-\infty}^{\infty} g(x)\,dx = c$, where $c > 0$ is some real number not necessarily equal to one. Next, we can obtain a new function

$$f(x) = \frac{g(x)}{c}, \quad -\infty < x < \infty,$$

so that, if $f(x) \ge 0$ for all x, then $f(x)$ is a density function.

Finally, we must emphasize again that $f(x)$ does not give the probability of anything when evaluated at a particular value of x. However, when this function is integrated between two limits, it yields a probability.

Example 3.1.1   The length of time in minutes that an individual talks on a long-distance telephone call has been found to be of a random nature. Let x be the length of the talk; assume it to be a continuous random variable with probability density function given by

$$f(x) = \begin{cases} \alpha e^{-(1/4)x}, & x > 0, \\ 0, & \text{elsewhere.} \end{cases}$$

Find
(a)   the value of α that makes $f(x)$ a probability density function;
(b)   the probability that this individual will talk (i) between 7 and 12 minutes, (ii) less than 7 minutes, (iii) more than 12 minutes;
(c) $Pr(x \le 7 | 5 \le X \le 10)$.

Solution:
(a)   Applying the definition of a probability density function, we can integrate

$$\int_0^\infty \alpha e^{-(1/4)x}\, dx = 1$$

and obtain $\alpha = \dfrac{1}{4}$.

(b)   (i) $Pr(7 \le X \le 12) = \displaystyle\int_7^{12} \frac{1}{4} e^{-(1/4)x}\, dx = e^{-7/4} - e^{-3}$

(ii) $Pr(X \le 7) = \displaystyle\int_0^7 \frac{1}{4} e^{-(1/4)x}\, dx = 1 - e^{-7/4}$

(iii) $Pr(X \ge 12) = \displaystyle\int_{12}^\infty \frac{1}{4} e^{-(1/4)x}\, dx = e^{-3}$.

(c)   The concept of conditional probability discussed in Section 1.3 can be meaningfully applied here.

$$Pr(X \le 7 | 5 \le X \le 10) = \frac{Pr(5 \le X \le 7)}{Pr(5 \le X \le 10)}$$

$$= \frac{\displaystyle\int_5^7 \frac{1}{4} e^{-(1/4)x}\, dx}{\displaystyle\int_5^{10} \frac{1}{4} e^{-(1/4)x}\, dx} = \frac{1 - e^{-1/2}}{1 - e^{-5/4}},$$

is the probability that the telephone conversation lasted less than 7 minutes, given the fact that it lasted between 5 and 10 minutes.

Figure 3.1.4 shows the graph of the density function and the probability of part (b) as areas under $f(x)$.

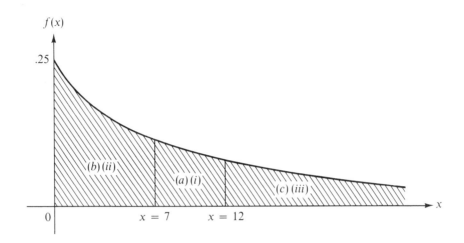

Figure 3.1.4

Example 3.1.2 The number of automobiles that a certain dealer sells per day can be considered a random variable of the continuous type, with the following function for its probability density:

$$f(x) = \begin{cases} \beta(x + 1), & 0 \le x \le 12, \\ \dfrac{-10(6\beta - 1)}{x^2}, & 12 < x \le 20, \\ 0, & \text{elsewhere.} \end{cases}$$

Note that the continuity of such a physical phenomenon can be justified by a manner similar to that used in the above discussion (see Section 3.1).
Find the value of β that makes $f(x)$ a density function and the probability that the dealer will sell between 8 and 14 cars in a given day.

Solution: To determine the value of β, we must integrate $f(x)$ over all admissible values of x,

$$\int_{-\infty}^{\infty} f(x)\, dx = \int_0^{12} \beta(x + 1)\, dx + \int_{12}^{20} \frac{-10(6\beta - 1)}{x^2}\, dx = 1,$$

and we obtain $\beta = 1/123$. Now

$$Pr(8 \le X \le 14) = \int_8^{14} f(x)\, dx$$

$$= \int_8^{12} \frac{1}{123}(x+1)\, dx + \int_{12}^{14} \frac{1170\, dx}{123x^2}$$

$$= \frac{811}{1722} = .47.$$

Figure 3.1.5 shows the graph of the above probability density function, and it also shows the desired probability in terms of the shaded area under the curve.

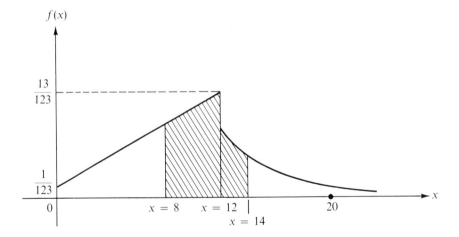

Figure 3.1.5

3.2 Cumulative Distribution Function of a Continuous Random Variable

Once the probability density function of a continuous random variable is known, we can determine various probabilities concerning its behavior. For example, as we have already seen, we might be interested in the probability that the value of the random variable X lies in a certain set $S_1 = \{x: x \le x_1\}$; that is,

$$Pr(X \text{ in } S_1) = Pr(X \le x_1) = \int_{-\infty}^{x_1} f(x)\, dx. \tag{3.2.1}$$

We denote such a function (3.2.1) by $F(x)$; it is defined in Definition 3.2.1.

Definition 3.2.1   *The function defined by*

$$F(x) = Pr(X \le x) = \int_{-\infty}^{x} f(s)\, ds \qquad (3.2.2)$$

is called the cumulative distribution function of the continuous random variable X, *having probability density function* $f(x)$.

Example 3.2.1   Find the cumulative distribution function of the continuous random variable X, having foi its probability density the function

$$f(x) = \begin{cases} \dfrac{3}{8}(x^2 - x + 1), & 0 \le x \le 2, \\[2mm] 0, & \text{elsewhere.} \end{cases}$$

Solution: Applying Equation (3.2.2), we have
for $x < 0$:

$$F(x) = P(X \le x) = \int_{-\infty}^{x} f(x)\, dx = \int_{-\infty}^{x} 0 \cdot dx = 0;$$

for $0 \le x \le 2$:

$$F(x) = P(X \le x) = \int_{-\infty}^{0} f(x)\, dx + \int_{0}^{x} f(x)\, dx$$

$$= F(0) + \int_{0}^{x} \frac{3}{8}(x^2 - x + 1)\, dx = 0 + \frac{3}{8}\left[\frac{x^3}{3} - \frac{x^2}{2} + x\right]_{0}^{x}$$

$$= \frac{3(2x^3 - 3x^2 + 6x)}{8 \cdot 6} = \frac{x(2x^2 - 3x + 6)}{16};$$

for $x > 2$:

$$F(x) = P(X \le x) = \int_{-\infty}^{2} f(x)\, dx + \int_{2}^{x} f(x)\, dx$$

$$= F(2) + \int_{2}^{x} 0 \cdot dx = 1.$$

Therefore,

$$F(x) = \begin{cases} 0, & x < 0, \\[2mm] \dfrac{x(2x^2 - 3x + 6)}{16}, & 0 \le x \le 2, \\[2mm] 1, & x > 2. \end{cases} \qquad (3.2.3)$$

Thus, if we wish to find the probability that the random variable can assume a value between zero and some value of x less than 2, we need only evaluate Equation (3.2.3) at that point. A graphical representation of Equation (3.2.3) is shown in Figure 3.2.1.

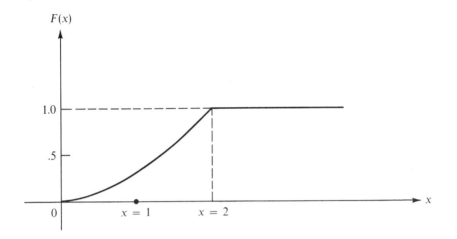

Figure 3.2.1

The cumulative distribution function of the continuous type has some interesting properties that are similar to those of the discrete case. We state these properties in the following theorem.

Theorem 3.2.1   If $F(x)$ is the cumulative distribution function of the continuous random variable X, then $F(x)$ has the following properties:

(1) $F(\infty) = 1$;

(2) $F(-\infty) = 0$;

(3) $F(x)$ is a nondecreasing function;

(4) $F(x)$ is continuous from the right;

(5) $\dfrac{dF(x)}{dx} = f(x)$, for all x, at which $F(x)$ is differentiable.

Proof   Properties (1) to (4) are identical to those of Theorem 2.2.1, and the proof will be omitted. By definition, we can write

$$F(x) = Pr(X \le x) = \int_{-\infty}^{x} f(t)\, dt.$$

Applying the fundamental theorem of calculus, we obtain property (5), that is, $F'(x) = f(x)$.

Example 3.2.2   If a continuous random variable X has for its probability density the function

$$f(x) = \begin{cases} \dfrac{1}{4} x e^{-x/2}, & x \geq 0, \\ 0, & \text{elsewhere.} \end{cases}$$

then, for $x \geq 0$,

$$F(x) = Pr(X \leq x) = \frac{1}{4} \int_0^x t e^{-t/2} \, dt = 1 - e^{-x/2}\left(1 + \frac{x}{2}\right).$$

Therefore,

$$F(x) = \begin{cases} 0, & x < 0 \\ 1 - e^{-x/2}\left(1 + \dfrac{x}{2}\right), & x \geq 0. \end{cases}$$

The probability that the random variable assumes a value in the interval $[3,6]$ is

$$Pr(3 \leq X \leq 6) = \frac{1}{4} \int_3^6 x \, e^{-x/2} \, dx = F(6) - F(3) = \frac{5}{2} e^{-3/2} - 4e^{-3}.$$

Figure 3.2.2 shows the graph of Example 3.2.2, which illustrates the properties of the cumulative distribution function.

Example 3.2.3   The life length, T, of a mechanical system can be interpreted as behaving like a random variable of the continuous type, with probability density function $f(t)$. If the cumulative distribution of such a system is

$$F(t) = \begin{cases} 0, & t < 0, \\ 1 - \exp - \dfrac{(t - \gamma)^\beta}{\alpha}, & \alpha > 0, \beta, \gamma \geq 0, t \geq 0, \end{cases}$$

find the probability density function that describes the failure behavior of such a system.

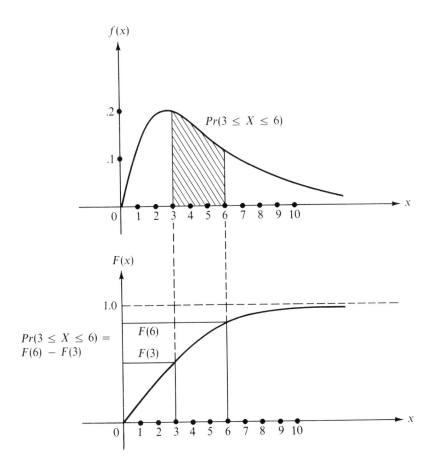

Figure 3.2.2

Solution: Applying condition (5) of Theorem 3.2.1, we have, for $t \geq 0$,

$$\frac{dF(t)}{dt} = \frac{\beta}{\alpha}(t - \gamma)^{\beta - 1} \exp{} - \frac{(t - \gamma)^{\beta}}{\alpha} = f(t).$$

It is easy to show that $f(t)$ satisfies the conditions of a density function.

The terminology used in this book is quite standard; however, you should keep in mind that, when we speak of a *probability distribution* of a random variable, we refer to its *probability density function*. When we speak of the *distribution function*, we always mean its *cumulative distribution function*.

3.3 Continuous Probability Distributions

In this section, we shall study a number of continuous probability distributions that are applicable to a number of physical phenomena.

3.3.1 The Uniform Distribution   The simplest probability density function of a random variable X of the continuous type is the uniform distribution.

Definition 3.3.1   *A random variable X has a* uniform *or* rectangular *distribution if its probability density function is given by*

$$f(x) = \begin{cases} \dfrac{1}{\beta - \alpha}, & \alpha < x < \beta, \quad 0 < \alpha < \beta < \infty, \\ 0, & \text{elsewhere.} \end{cases} \tag{3.3.1}$$

Clearly, the conditions of a density function hold.
The cumulative distribution function of the random variable X is given by

$$F(x) = Pr(X \le x) = \int_{-\infty}^{x} \frac{1}{\beta - \alpha} \, dx.$$

Hence,

$$F(x) = \begin{cases} 0, & x \le \alpha, \\ \dfrac{x - \alpha}{\beta - \alpha}, & \alpha < x < \beta, \\ 1, & x \ge \beta. \end{cases}$$

Figure 3.3.1 *shows the graphs of $f(x)$ and $F(x)$.*

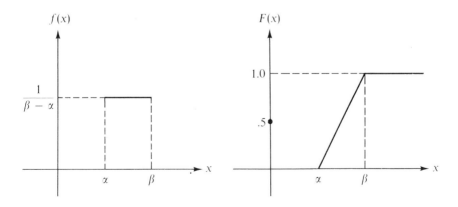

Figure 3.3.1

Applying to Equation (3.3.1) the linear transformation

$$y = \frac{x - \alpha}{\beta - \alpha},$$

we obtain the distribution of the random variable Y, which is uniform over the interval [0, 1]; *that is,*

$$f(y) = \begin{cases} 1, & 0 < y < 1, \\ 0, & \text{elsewhere.} \end{cases}$$

Example 3.3.1   The melting point, X, of a certain specimen may be assumed to be a continuous random variable that is uniformly distributed over the interval [110, 120]. Then

$$f(x) = \begin{cases} \dfrac{1}{10}, & 110 \leq x \leq 120, \\ 0, & \text{elsewhere.} \end{cases}$$

The probability that such a specimen will melt between 112° and 115° is

$$Pr(112 \leq X \leq 115) = \int_{112}^{115} \frac{1}{10} \, dx = \frac{3}{10}.$$

Example 3.3.2   The efficiency, X, of a certain electrical component may be assumed to be a random variable that is distributed uniformly between 0 and 100 units. What is the probability that X is
(a)   between 60 and 80 units and
(b)   greater than 90 units?

Solution: From Equation (3.3.1), we have

(a) $Pr(60 \leq X \leq 80) = \int_{60}^{80} f(x) \, dx = \dfrac{1}{100} \int_{60}^{80} dx = .20,$

(b) $Pr(X \geq 90) = \dfrac{1}{100} \int_{90}^{100} dx = 1 - \dfrac{1}{100} \int_{0}^{90} dx = 1 - .9 = .10.$

Thus, 20% of the electrical components will have an efficiency between 60 and 80 units and only 10% will have an efficiency that is more than 90 units.

3.3.2   The Gaussian or Normal Distribution   The normal density function is the most important probability function because it has unique mathematical properties and because it can be applied to practically any physical problem. It constitutes the basis for the development of many of the methods of statistical theory.

The normal density function was discovered by De Moivre in 1733 as a limiting form of the binomial distribution. In 1774, Pierre Laplace studied the mathematical properties of the normal density. Through an historical error, the discovery of the normal distribution was attributed to Gauss (1777–1855), who, in a paper in 1809, first referred to it. The function was studied in the nineteenth century by scientists who noted that errors of measurements followed a pattern that was closely approximated by a function they called the "normal curve of error." The density function is stated in Definition 3.3.2.

Definition 3.3.2   *A random variable X is said to be* Gaussian *or normally distributed if it has the following as its probability density function:*

$$f(x; \mu, \sigma^2) = \frac{1}{\sqrt{2\pi}\,\sigma} \exp\left(-\frac{1}{2}\left(\frac{x-\mu}{\sigma}\right)^2\right), \quad \begin{matrix} -\infty < x < \infty, \\ -\infty < \mu < \infty, \sigma > 0. \end{matrix}$$

$$(3.3.2)$$

The two parameters μ and σ, which completely describe the normal density function, are of significant importance and will be discussed in Chapter 4. The density function $f(x; \mu, \sigma^2)$ has one mode at $x = \mu$ and two inflection points located $\pm\sigma$ from the modal point. The function is symmetrical about μ. Figures 3.3.2 and 3.3.3 show a graphical representation of the normal distribution for a fixed value of σ, with μ varying, and for a fixed value of μ, with

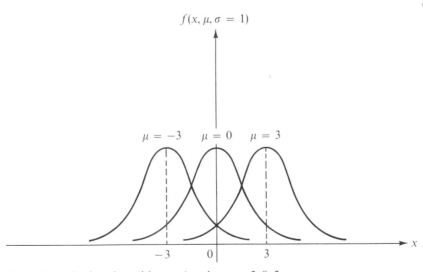

Normal density function with $\sigma = 1$ and $\mu = -3, 0, 3$.

Figure 3.3.2

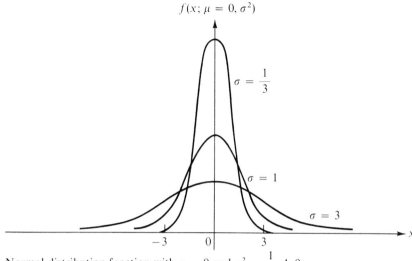

Normal distribution function with $\mu = 0$ and $\sigma^2 = \dfrac{1}{9}, 1, 9$.

Figure 3.3.3

σ *varying, respectively. Thus, the parameter* μ *is a " location parameter," that is, it shifts the mode of the function on the x-axis;* σ *is a " shape parameter," that is, it alters the shape of the density with respect to a fixed scale. For small values of* σ, *the distribution is closely compact to the mode; as* σ *increases, the density deviates farther from* μ.

We shall now proceed to show that Equation (3.3.2) is a probability density function. It is clear that $f(x; \mu, \sigma^2)$ *is greater than zero for* $-\infty < x < \infty$, $-\infty < \mu < \infty$, *and* $\sigma > 0$. *To show that*

$$\int_{-\infty}^{\infty} f(x; \mu, \sigma^2) \, dx = 1,$$

we proceed as follows: Let I *represent the value of the integral,*

$$I = \frac{1}{\sqrt{2\pi}\,\sigma} \int_{-\infty}^{\infty} \exp\left(-\frac{1}{2}\left(\frac{x-\mu}{\sigma}\right)^2\right) dx. \qquad (3.3.3)$$

Applying the linear transformation $y = (x - \mu)/\sigma$, *which implies* $\sigma dy = dx$, *to Equation (3.3.3), we have*

$$I = \frac{1}{\sqrt{2\pi}} \int_{-\infty}^{\infty} e^{-(1/2)y^2} \, dy,$$

which, for the sake of symmetry, may be written as

$$I = \frac{2}{\sqrt{2\pi}} \int_0^\infty e^{-y^2/2} \, dy. \tag{3.3.4}$$

We shall show that $I^2 = 1$; since $f(x; \mu, \sigma^2) \geq 0$, it follows that $I = 1$. Consider

$$I^2 = \frac{2}{\sqrt{2\pi}} \int_0^\infty e^{-(1/2)y^2} \, dy \cdot \frac{2}{\sqrt{2\pi}} \int_0^\infty e^{-(1/2)z^2} \, dz$$

$$= \frac{4}{2\pi} \int_0^\infty \int_0^\infty e^{-(1/2)(y^2 + z^2)} \, dy \, dz. \tag{3.3.5}$$

Changing the double integral (3.3.5) from rectangular to polar coordinates by letting $y = r \sin \theta$, $z = r \cos \theta$ and changing the limits accordingly, we have

$$I^2 = \frac{4}{2\pi} \int_0^\infty \int_0^{\pi/2} |J| e^{-(1/2)r^2} \, d\theta \, dr. \tag{3.3.6}$$

It was shown in Section (0.5) that the absolute value of the Jacobian is r, and Equation (3.3.6) becomes

$$I^2 = \frac{4}{2\pi} \int_0^\infty \int_0^{\pi/2} r e^{-(1/2)r^2} \, d\theta \, dr$$

$$= \int_0^\infty r e^{-(1/2)r^2} \, dr = 1.$$

Therefore, $I = 1$, and it has been verified that Equation (3.3.2) is a probability density function.

Applying the linear transformation $y = (x - \mu)/\sigma$ to Equation (3.3.2), as seen above, results in

$$f(y; \mu = 0, \sigma^2 = 1) = \frac{1}{\sqrt{2\pi}} e^{-(1/2)y^2}, \quad -\infty < y < \infty. \tag{3.3.7}$$

Equation (3.3.7) is known as the unit or standard normal distribution *of the random variable Y. This transformation simply locates the mean of the variate Y at $y = 0$, and the parameter σ becomes unity.*

The cumulative distribution function of the normal density function is given by

$$F(x) = Pr(X \leq x)$$

$$= \frac{1}{\sqrt{2\pi} \, \sigma} \int_{-\infty}^x \exp\left(-\frac{1}{2}\left(\frac{t - \mu}{\sigma}\right)^2\right) dt, \quad -\infty < x < \infty, \; -\infty < \mu < \infty,$$
$$\sigma > 0. \tag{3.3.8}$$

A graph of F(x) is shown in Figure 3.3.4.

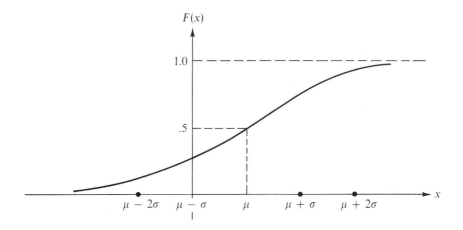

Figure 3.3.4

If we let $y = (t - \mu)/\sigma$ *in Equation* (3.3.8), *we have*

$$F\left(\frac{x - \mu}{\sigma}\right) = \frac{1}{\sqrt{2\pi}} \int_{-\infty}^{\frac{x-\mu}{\sigma}} e^{-(1/2)y^2}\, dy. \tag{3.3.9}$$

The above function cannot be integrated explicitly, and the probabilities are calculated numerically. The normal density and its cumulative form, Equation (3.3.9), *have been tabulated extensively. The table of Normal Distribution, page* 626, *has the normal density function* $f(x, \mu = 0, \sigma^2 = 1)$ *for various values of x. Table* 8, *on page* 624 *has values of* $F(x)$ *for various values of* $(x - \mu)/\sigma$. *In using the tables, one must keep in mind that* $f(x; \mu = 0, \sigma^2 = 1) = f(-x; \mu = 0, \sigma^2 = 1)$ *and* $F(x) = 1 - F(-x)$. *That is, because of the symmetrical property of Equation* (3.3.2), *we need only have probabilities for positive values of x. For example,*

$$Pr(X \le -x) = \frac{1}{\sqrt{2\pi}\,\sigma} \int_{-\infty}^{-x} \exp\left(-\frac{1}{2}\left(\frac{t - \mu}{\sigma}\right)^2\right) dt$$

$$= \frac{1}{\sqrt{2\pi}} \int_{-\infty}^{\frac{-x-\mu}{\sigma}} e^{-(1/2)y^2}\, dy$$

$$= F\left(\frac{-x - \mu}{\sigma}\right) = 1 - F\left(\frac{x + \mu}{\sigma}\right),$$

and

$$Pr(\alpha \le X \le \beta) = \frac{1}{\sqrt{2\pi}\,\sigma} \int_{\alpha}^{\beta} \exp\left(-\frac{1}{2}\left(\frac{x-\mu}{\sigma}\right)^2\right) dx$$

$$= \frac{1}{\sqrt{2\pi}} \int_{\frac{\alpha-\mu}{\sigma}}^{\frac{\beta-\mu}{\sigma}} e^{-(1/2)y^2}\, dy$$

$$= Pr\left(Y \le \frac{\beta-\mu}{\sigma}\right) - Pr\left(Y \le \frac{\alpha-\mu}{\sigma}\right)$$

$$= F\left(\frac{\beta-\mu}{\sigma}\right) - F\left(\frac{\alpha-\mu}{\sigma}\right).$$

Also,

$$Pr(X \ge \gamma) = \frac{1}{\sqrt{2\pi}\,\sigma} \int_{\gamma}^{\infty} \exp\left(-\frac{1}{2}\left(\frac{x-\mu}{\sigma}\right)^2\right) dy$$

$$= \frac{1}{\sqrt{2\pi}} \int_{\frac{\gamma-\mu}{\sigma}}^{\infty} e^{-(1/2)y^2}\, dy$$

$$= 1 - Pr\left(X \le \frac{\gamma-\mu}{\sigma}\right)$$

$$= 1 - F\left(\frac{\gamma-\mu}{\sigma}\right).$$

Although the parameters μ and σ will be studied later, we can define them as follows: μ is the mean or average of the information and σ^2 the variance of the random variable X, which is normally distributed. The σ or standard deviation indicates the amount of dispersion from μ of the values that X can assume. In actual applications of the normal distribution, the domain of X is finite and μ and σ^2 are estimated by statistical methods.

We shall illustrate some of the applications of the normal distribution with Examples 3.3.3 through 3.3.5.

Example 3.3.3   The scores, say X, of an examination may be assumed to be a continuous random variable normally distributed with $\mu = 75$ and $\sigma^2 = 64$. What is the probability that
(a)   a score chosen at random will be between 80 and 85,
(b)   a score will be greater than 85%, and
(c)   a score will be less than 90%?

Solution: Here the distribution of the scores, X, is

$$f(x; \mu = 75, \sigma^2 = 64) = \frac{1}{8\sqrt{2\pi}} \exp\left(-\frac{1}{2}\left(\frac{x-75}{8}\right)^2\right), \quad -\infty < x < \infty.$$

Thus,

(a) $Pr(80 \leq X \leq 85) = \dfrac{1}{\sqrt{2\pi}\, 8} \displaystyle\int_{80}^{85} \exp\left(-\dfrac{1}{2}\left(\dfrac{x-75}{8}\right)^2\right) dx.$

Let $y = (x - 75)/8$, implying $8dy = dx$; and, changing the limits accordingly, we have

$$Pr(80 \leq X \leq 85) = \dfrac{1}{\sqrt{2\pi}} \int_{\frac{80-75}{8}}^{\frac{85-75}{8}} e^{-(1/2)y^2}\, dy = \dfrac{1}{\sqrt{2\pi}} \int_{.625}^{1.25} e^{-(1/2)y^2}\, dy$$

$$= F(1.25) - F(.625).$$

From Table 8 we obtain

$$Pr(80 \leq X \leq 85) = .8944 - .7340 = .1604.$$

Therefore, there is about a 16% chance that the score will be a grade between 80 and 85.

(b) $Pr(X > 85) = 1 - Pr(X \leq 85)$

$$= 1 - \dfrac{1}{8\sqrt{2\pi}} \int_{-\infty}^{85} \exp\left(-\dfrac{1}{2}\left(\dfrac{x-75}{8}\right)^2\right) dx$$

$$= 1 - \dfrac{1}{\sqrt{2\pi}} \int_{-\infty}^{\frac{85-75}{8}} e^{-(1/2)y^2}\, dy$$

$$= 1 - F(1.25)$$

$$= 1 - .8944$$

$$= .1056.$$

(c)   Similarly, we can calculate

$$Pr(X \leq 90) = \dfrac{1}{8\sqrt{2\pi}} \int_{-\infty}^{90} \exp\left(-\dfrac{1}{2}\left(\dfrac{x-75}{80}\right)^2\right) dx$$

$$= \dfrac{1}{\sqrt{2\pi}} \int_{-\infty}^{\frac{90-75}{8}} e^{-(1/2)y^2}\, dy$$

$$= F(1.875)$$

$$= .9696.$$

Example 3.3.4   A noise voltage, X, which assumes values of x volts, is normally distributed with $\mu = 1$v and $\sigma = .80$v. Find the probability that
(a) $|X|$ will not exceed 2.0v and
(b)   the noise voltage level is exceeded 95% of the time.

Solution:

(a) $Pr(|X| \le 2\text{v}) = Pr(-2\text{v} \le X \le 2\text{v})$

$$= \frac{1}{\sqrt{2\pi}\,.8\text{v}} \int_{-2\text{v}}^{2\text{v}} \exp\left(-\frac{1}{2}\left(\frac{x\text{v} - 1\text{v}}{.8\text{v}}\right)^2\right) dx$$

$$= \frac{1}{\sqrt{2\pi}} \int_{\frac{-2\text{v}-1\text{v}}{.8\text{v}}}^{\frac{2\text{v}-1\text{v}}{.8\text{v}}} e^{-(1/2)y^2}\, dy$$

$$= F(1.25) - [1 - F(3.75)] = .8943.$$

(b) $Pr(X > x\text{v}) = 1 - Pr(X \le x\text{v})$

$$= 1 - \frac{1}{\sqrt{2\pi}\,.8\text{v}} \int_{-\infty}^{x\text{v}} \exp\left(-\frac{1}{2}\left(\frac{x\text{v} - 1\text{v}}{.8\text{v}}\right)^2\right) dx$$

$$= 1 - \frac{1}{\sqrt{2\pi}} \int_{-\infty}^{\frac{x\text{v}-1\text{v}}{.8\text{v}}} e^{-(1/2)y^2}\, dy$$

$$= 1 - F\left(\frac{x\text{v} - 1\text{v}}{.8\text{v}}\right) = .05.$$

Thus,

$$F\left(\frac{x\text{v} - 1\text{v}}{.8\text{v}}\right) = .05,$$

and, from tables, we have

$$\frac{x\text{v} - 1\text{v}}{.8\text{v}} = -1.64 \quad \text{or} \quad x = -.312.$$

Hence,

$$Pr(X > -.312\text{v}) = .95.$$

Example 3.3.5   Suppose that the diameters of golf balls manufactured by a certain company are normally distributed with $\mu = 1.96$ in. and $\sigma = .04$ in. A golf ball will be considered defective if its diameter is less than 1.90 in. or greater than 2.02 in. What is the percentage of defective balls manufactured by the company?

Solution: Here we want

$$Pr[(X < 1.90) \cup (X > 2.02)] = 1 - Pr(1.90 \le X \le 2.02)$$

$$= 1 - \frac{1}{.04\sqrt{2\pi}} \int_{1.90}^{2.02} \exp\left(-\frac{1}{2}\left(\frac{x - 1.96}{.04}\right)^2\right) dx$$

$$= 1 - \frac{1}{\sqrt{2\pi}} \int_{\frac{1.90 - 1.96}{.04}}^{\frac{2.02 - 1.96}{.04}} e^{-(1/2)y^2} \, dy$$

$$= 1 - \left[F\left(\frac{2.02 - 1.96}{.04}\right) - F\left(\frac{1.90 - 1.96}{.04}\right) \right]$$

$$= 1 - [F(1.5) - F(-1.5)]$$

$$= 1 - \{F(1.5) - [1 - F(1.5)]\}$$

$$= 1 - [2F(1.5) - 1]$$

$$= 2 \cdot [1 - F(1.5)]$$

$$= 2 \cdot (1 - .9332)$$

$$= 2(.0668)$$

$$= .1336.$$

Therefore, the company manufactures about 13.4% defective golf balls.

Although very few random phenomena precisely obey a normal probability law, the laws that they do obey can, under certain conditions, be closely approximated by the normal probability law. In this sense, the normal distribution is of paramount importance. Some of the densities that may be approximated by the normal distribution under certain conditions are the *binomial*, the *hypergeometric*, the *Poisson*, and the *gamma*. But it is of particular importance that, under certain conditions, as the size of a sample becomes large, the distribution of the sample mean,

$$\bar{x} = \frac{1}{n}\sum x_i,$$

may be justifiably approximated by a normal distribution. The last fact, called the *Central Limit Theorem*, will be discussed in greater detail later.

3.3.3 The Gamma Distribution   We shall now define another density function that plays an important role in various physical phenomena.

Definition 3.3.3   *A random variable X is said to be distributed as the* gamma distribution *if it has the following function for its probability density:*

$$f(x; \alpha, \beta) \begin{cases} \dfrac{1}{\Gamma(\alpha)\beta^\alpha} x^{\alpha-1} e^{-x/\beta}, & x > 0, \quad \alpha, \beta > 0, \\ \\ 0, & elsewhere. \end{cases} \qquad (3.3.10)$$

We proceed by showing that this two-parameter function satisfies the conditions of a probability density. It is clear that $f(x; \alpha, \beta) \geq 0$ because

$$\Gamma(\alpha) = \int_0^\infty y^{\alpha-1} e^{-y} \, dy \quad for \quad \alpha > 0$$

is a positive function. To show that

$$\int_0^\infty f(x; \alpha, \beta) \, dx = \int_0^\infty \frac{1}{\Gamma(\alpha)\beta^\alpha} x^{\alpha-1} e^{-x/\beta} \, dx = 1, \qquad (3.3.11)$$

let $y = x/\beta$, $\beta dy = dx$ in Equation (3.3.11). We then have

$$\int_0^\infty f(x; \alpha, \beta) \, dx = \frac{1}{\Gamma(\alpha)} \int_0^\infty y^{\alpha-1} e^{-y} \, dy$$

$$= \frac{\Gamma(\alpha)}{\Gamma(\alpha)} = 1,$$

and the conditions of a probability density have been verified.

The parameters α and β determine the shape of the density function, which is skewed to the right for all values of α and β; however, the skewness decreases as α increases. Figure 3.3.5 shows the graph of the gamma density for a fixed $\beta = 1$ and $\alpha = 1, 2, 3$.

Figure 3.3.6 shows the graph of the gamma density for a fixed $\alpha = 2$ and $\beta = 1/2, 1, 2$.

We can obtain the value of x at which the density attains its mode by differentiating $f(x; \alpha, \beta)$ and setting it equal to zero,

$$f'(x; \alpha, \beta) = \frac{1}{(\alpha-1)!\beta^\alpha} \left\{ (\alpha-1)x^{\alpha-2} e^{-(x/\beta)} - \frac{1}{\beta} x^{\alpha-1} e^{-(x/\beta)} \right\} = 0,$$

which implies that $x = (\alpha - 1)\beta$. Therefore, we can obtain a family of gamma densities by varying α and β, with each density attaining its maximum at the same value of x. Furthermore, as $x \to \infty$, $f(x; \alpha, \beta) \to 0$ for $\alpha, \beta > 0$. If $\alpha \geq 1$, then the gamma density curve starts at the origin. For $0 < \alpha < 1$, which implies that $\Gamma(\alpha) = (\alpha - 1)!$ in Equation (3.3.10) is negative, $f(x; \alpha, \beta)$ becomes infinite as x approaches zero; that is, it has the $f(x; \alpha, \beta)$ axis as an asymptote.

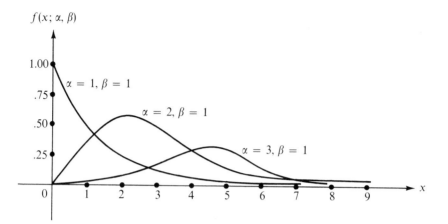

Figure 3.3.5

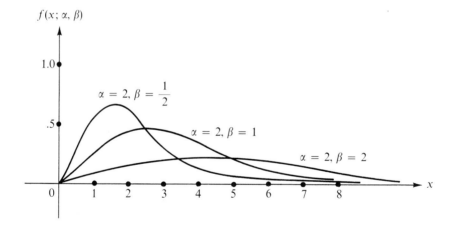

Figure 3.3.6

When $\alpha = 1$ in the gamma probability density, we obtain an important density function, defined in Definition 3.3.4.

Definition 3.3.4   *A random variable X is said to have an* exponential *distribution if it has the following function as its probability density:*

$$f(x; \beta) = \begin{cases} \dfrac{1}{\beta}\, e^{-(x/\beta)}, & x \geq 0, \quad \beta > 0, \\[2mm] 0, & elsewhere. \end{cases} \qquad (3.3.12)$$

It is not very difficult to verify that the one-parameter function (3.3.12) satisfies the conditions of a probability density. The exponential density is a decaying type of function, whose rate of decay depends on the parameter β. Figure 3.3.7 illustrates the exponential distribution for β = 1/2, 1, 2.

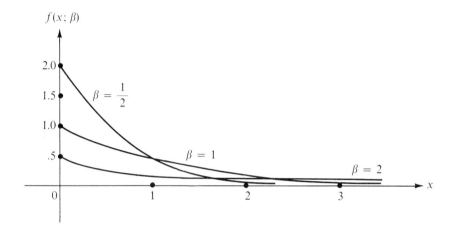

Figure 3.3.7

The cumulative distribution function of the gamma density is

$$F(x) = Pr(X \le x) = \begin{cases} 0, & x \le 0, \\ \dfrac{1}{\Gamma(\alpha)\beta^\alpha} \displaystyle\int_0^x t^{\alpha-1} e^{-(t/\beta)}\, dt, & x > 0. \end{cases} \qquad (3.3.13)$$

The function F(x) can be integrated exactly if (α − 1) is a positive integer or zero; numerical integration is necessary if it is not an integer. Equation (3.3.13), which is known as the incomplete gamma function, *has been tabulated, in Reference [3], for various values of α and β.*

Example 3.3.6   The daily consumption of fuel in millions of gallons at a certain airport can be treated as a random variable having a gamma density with α = 3 and β = 1. Suppose that the airport can store 2 million gallons of fuel; find the probability that this fuel supply will be inadequate on any given day.

Solution: Here the gamma distribution with α = 3, β = 1 is

$$f(x; \alpha = 3, \beta = 1) = \begin{cases} \dfrac{1}{2!}\, x^2 e^{-x}, & x \ge 0, \\ 0, & \text{elsewhere,} \end{cases}$$

and

$$Pr(X > 2) = \frac{1}{2} \int_2^\infty x^2 e^{-x} \, dx = 5e^{-2}$$

$$= .6767.$$

Example 3.3.7   The time in hours during which an electrical generator is operational is a random variable that follows the exponential distribution with $\beta = 160$. What is the probability that a generator of this type will be operational for
(a)   less than 40 hours,
(b)   between 60 and 160 hours, and
(c)   more than 200 hours?

   Solution: Here the exponential density function is

$$f(x; 160) = \begin{cases} \dfrac{1}{160} e^{-(x/160)}, & x \geq 0, \\ 0, & \text{elsewhere.} \end{cases}$$

The cumulative distribution function of $f(x; 160)$ for $x \geq 0$ is given by

$$F(x) = Pr(x \leq x) = \int_0^x \frac{1}{160} e^{-(t/160)} \, dt$$

$$= 1 - e^{-(x/160)}.$$

Therefore,

$$F(x) = \begin{cases} 0, & x < 0, \\ 1 - e^{-(x/160)}, & x \geq 0. \end{cases}$$

Thus,

(a) $Pr(X \leq 40) = 1 - e^{-.25} = .22119;$
(b) $Pr(60 \leq X \leq 160) = F(160) - F(60) = e^{-.375} - e^{-1} = .3194;$
(c) $Pr(X > 200) = 1 - F(200) = e^{-1.25} = .2865.$

   Students commonly ask "When do we know that the gamma density is applicable in a given physical problem?" There is no direct answer to this question; however, you proceed to determine the answer by constructing a probability histogram from the information at hand; from the shape of this histogram, you decide whether the random variable follows the gamma density. Also, the parameters α and β must be statistically estimated. In Chapter 4, we shall discuss some additional properties of the gamma distribution.

3.3.4 The Beta Distribution   A frequently employed distribution, used, for example, when the random variable assumes values that are percentages or when concern is with physical phenomena of the continuous type, which have values lying between 0 and 1, is the beta distribution.

Definition 3.3.5   *A random variable X is said to have a* beta distribution *if it has the following function for its probability density:*

$$f(x; \alpha, \beta) = \begin{cases} \dfrac{\Gamma(\alpha + \beta)}{\Gamma(\alpha)\Gamma(\beta)} \, x^{\alpha-1}(1-x)^{\beta-1}, & 0 < x \le 1, \quad \alpha, \beta > 0 \\ 0, & elsewhere. \end{cases} \tag{3.3.14}$$

To verify that function (3.3.14) *is a density function, we must show that* $f(x; \alpha, \beta) \ge 0$ *for* $0 \le x \le 1$ *and* $\alpha, \beta > 0$ *and that the function integrates to one over the whole domain of X. The first condition can be easily shown, but, for the second condition, we proceed as follows: We can write*

$$(\alpha - 1)!(\beta - 1)! = \Gamma(\alpha)\Gamma(\beta) \tag{3.3.15}$$

$$= \left(\int_0^\infty x^{\alpha-1} e^{-x} \, dx \right) \left(\int_0^\infty y^{\beta-1} e^{-y} \, dy \right)$$

$$= \int_0^\infty \int_0^\infty x^{\alpha-1} y^{\beta-1} e^{-(x+y)} \, dxdy.$$

Applying the transformation $z = x/(x + y)$ *or* $x = zy/(1 - z)$ *to Equation* (3.3.15), *with* $dx = \{y/(1 - z)^2\} \, dz$ *with* $0 \le z \le 1$, *we have*

$$\Gamma(\alpha)\Gamma(\beta) = \int_0^\infty \int_0^1 \left(\frac{zy}{1-z} \right)^{\alpha-1} y^{\beta-1} e^{-\{y/(1-z)\}} \frac{y}{(1-z)^2} \, dzdy. \tag{3.3.16}$$

Let $t = y/1 - z$ *and* $(1 - z) \, dt = dy$ *in Equation* (3.3.16). *Thus,*

$$\Gamma(\alpha)\Gamma(\beta) = \int_0^\infty \int_0^1 z^{\alpha-1}(1-z)^{\beta-1} t^{\alpha+\beta-1} e^{-t} \, dzdt$$

$$= \left(\int_0^\infty t^{\alpha+\beta-1} e^{-t} \, dt \right) \left(\int_0^1 z^{\alpha-1}(1-z)^{\beta-1} \, dz \right)$$

$$= \Gamma(\alpha + \beta) \int_0^1 z^{\alpha-1}(1-z)^{\beta-1} \, dz. \tag{3.3.17}$$

This implies that

$$\frac{\Gamma(\alpha + \beta)}{\Gamma(\alpha) \, (\beta)} \int_0^1 z^{d-1}(1-z)^{\beta-1} \, dz = 1,$$

which must be shown.

The two parameters α and β determine the shape of the beta distribution.
Figure 3.3.8 shows the graph of the density for a fixed value of β, while α varies.

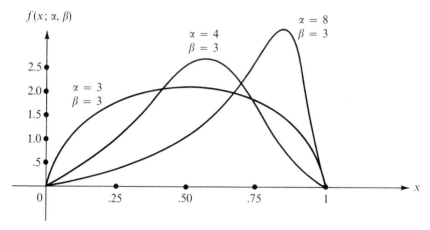

Figure 3.3.8

In Figure 3.3.9, we show the graph of the beta density for a fixed value of α,
while β varies.

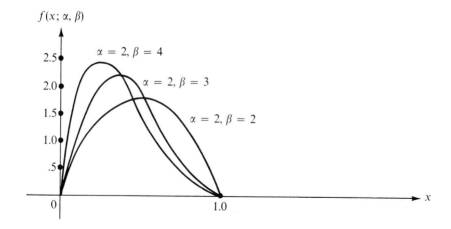

Figure 3.3.9

Observe that, when $\alpha < \beta$, the density is skewed to the right and, when $\beta < \alpha$, it is skewed to the left. The beta distribution is symmetrical when $\alpha = \beta$. The graph of the distribution is U-shaped when $(\alpha - 1)$ and $(\beta - 1)$ are negative and J-shaped if only one of them is negative. The density function attains its mode at $x = (\alpha - 1)/(\alpha + \beta - 2)$ when $(\alpha - 1)$ and $(\beta - 1)$ are positive; the same point is its minimum when they are negative. It is possible to generate a family of beta density functions, all of which will have the same mode, by selecting the values of the parameters α and β properly.

Some special cases of the beta distribution are:

(1) When $\alpha = \beta = 1$, we have the rectangular distribution,

$$f(x) = \begin{cases} 1, & 0 \le x \le 1, \\ 0, & elsewhere. \end{cases}$$

(2) When $\alpha = 1, \beta = 2$, and $\alpha = 2, \beta = 1$, we have the triangular distributions,

$$f(x; \alpha = 1, \beta = 2) = \begin{cases} 2(1 - x), & 0 \le x \le 1, \\ 0, & elsewhere. \end{cases}$$

and

$$f(x; \alpha = 2, \beta = 1) = \begin{cases} 2x, & 0 \le x \le 1, \\ 0, & elsewhere. \end{cases}$$

The cumulative distribution of the beta density is

$$F(x) = Pr(X \le x) = \begin{cases} 0, & x \le 0, \\ \dfrac{\Gamma(\alpha + \beta)}{\Gamma(\alpha)\Gamma(\beta)} \displaystyle\int_0^x t^{\alpha - 1}(1 - t)^{\beta - 1} \, dt, & 0 < x < 1, \\ 1, & x \ge 1. \end{cases}$$

$$(3.3.18)$$

This $F(x)$ is known as the incomplete beta function, which cannot be directly computed if α and β are large. Tables in Reference [2] have been compiled for various values of α and β. It can be shown that the incomplete beta function and the cumulative binomial function are related as follows:

$$\sum_{x=\alpha}^{N} \binom{N}{x} p^x (1 - p)^{N - x} = \frac{\Gamma(N + 1)}{\Gamma(\alpha)\Gamma(N - \alpha + 1)}$$

$$\times \int_0^x x^{\alpha - 1}(1 - x)^{N - \alpha} \, dx, \quad 0 \le x < N.$$

Example 3.3.8   The proportion of students who pass a standard examination may be treated as a continuous random variable, say X, having a beta distribution with $\alpha = 15$ and $\beta = 3$. Find the probability that, in a certain school, less than 80% of the students pass the test.

Here,

$$f(x; \alpha = 15, \beta = 3) = \begin{cases} \dfrac{\Gamma(18)}{\Gamma(15)\Gamma(3)} x^{14}(1-x)^2, & 0 < x < 1, \\ 0, & \text{elsewhere,} \end{cases}$$

and

$$Pr(X < .8) = \frac{17 \cdot 16 \cdot 15}{2} \int_0^{.8} x^{14}(1-x)^2 \, dx$$

$$= 17 \cdot 15 \cdot 8 \int_0^{.8} x^{14}(1 - 2x + x^2) \, dx$$

$$= .30962.$$

Thus, we are 31% certain that less than 80% of the students will pass this examination.

Example 3.3.9   The daily proportion of major automobile accidents across the United States can be treated as a random variable having a beta distribution with $\alpha = 6$ and $\beta = 4$. Find the probability that, on a certain day, the percentage of major accidents is less than 80% but greater than 60%.

Solution: Applying Equation (3.3.14), we have

$$Pr(.60 \le X \le .80) = \frac{\Gamma(10)}{\Gamma(6)\Gamma(4)} \int_{.5}^{.8} x^5(1-x)^3 \, dx$$

$$= .4317.$$

3.3.5 The Cauchy Distribution   A classical distribution of minor importance is the Cauchy density, defined in Definition 3.3.6.

Definition 3.3.6   *A random variable X is said to have a* Cauchy *distribution if it has the following function as its density:*

$$f(x; \alpha, \mu) = \frac{1}{\pi} \frac{\alpha}{\alpha^2 + (x - \mu)^2}, \quad -\infty < x < \infty, \tag{3.3.19}$$

$$-\infty < \mu < \infty, \alpha > 0.$$

Verifying that function (3.3.19) is a probability density: by inspection, the first condition is satisfied; by letting $y = (x - \mu)/\alpha$ and $\alpha dy = dx$, $f(x; \alpha, \mu)$ becomes

$$\frac{1}{\pi} \int_{-\infty}^{\infty} \frac{dy}{1 + y^2} = \frac{1}{\pi} \tan^{-1} y \bigg|_{-\infty}^{\infty} = \frac{1}{\pi} \left\{ \frac{\pi}{2} - \left(-\frac{\pi}{2} \right) \right\} = 1.$$

The parameter μ locates the center of symmetry of the Cauchy density, and α is a shape parameter. Under the linear transformation $z = x - \mu$, μ becomes zero and Equation (3.3.19) becomes

$$f(z; \alpha) = \frac{1}{\pi} \frac{\alpha}{(\alpha^2 + z^2)}. \tag{3.3.20}$$

The cumulative distribution function of Equation (3.3.19) is

$$F(x) = Pr(X \le x) = \frac{1}{\pi \alpha} \int_{-\infty}^{x} \frac{1}{1 + \left(\dfrac{t - \mu}{\alpha} \right)^2} \, dt = \frac{1}{\pi} \int_{-\infty}^{\frac{x-\mu}{\alpha}} \frac{1}{1 + y^2} \, dy$$

$$= \frac{1}{\pi} \left[\tan^{-1} y \right]_{-\infty}^{(x-\mu)/\alpha} = \frac{1}{2} + \frac{1}{\pi} \tan^{-1} \left(\frac{x - \mu}{\alpha} \right), \quad \alpha > 0.$$

Figure 3.3.10 shows the graph of $f(x, \alpha, \mu)$ for $\mu = 0$ and $\alpha = 1, 2, 3$ and the corresponding graph of $F(x)$.

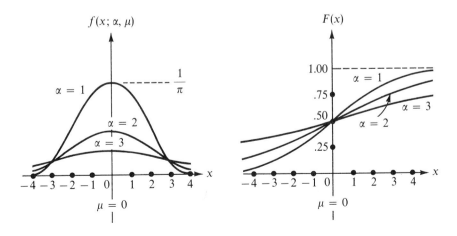

Figure 3.3.10

The development of the Cauchy density, Equation (3.3.19), is as follows: In Figure 3.3.11, assume that a randomly chosen straight line is drawn through the point (μ, α). It hits the x-axis at the point $(x, 0)$, making an angle of θ with the α-axis. Assume that θ varies from $-(\pi/2)$ to $+(\pi/2)$. Then

$$f(\theta) = \begin{cases} \dfrac{1}{\pi}, & \dfrac{\pi}{2} \le \theta \le \dfrac{\pi}{2}, \\ 0, & elsewhere. \end{cases}$$

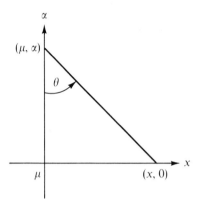

Fig. 3.3.11

We wish to find the density of the random variable X, where $x - \mu = \alpha \tan \theta$, and we proceed as follows:

$$h(x) = f(\theta) \left| \frac{d\theta}{dx} \right|,$$

where

$$\frac{d\theta}{dx} = \frac{1}{\dfrac{dx}{d\theta}} = \frac{1}{\alpha \sec^2 \theta} = \frac{1}{\dfrac{\alpha^2 + (x - \mu)^2}{\alpha_2}} = \frac{\alpha}{\alpha^2 + (x - \mu)^2}.$$

When $\theta = -(\pi/2)$, $x = -\infty$;   and, when $\theta = \pi/2$, $x = +\infty$. Therefore,

$$h(x) = \frac{1}{\pi} \frac{\alpha}{\alpha^2 + (x - \mu)^2}, \quad -\infty < x < \infty.$$

Example 3.3.10 A BB gun is mounted at the point $(0, \alpha)$ on a bench so that it can freely swing $180°$. The gun fires BB's on a straight line marked on a board directly in front of the bench. If all angular positions of the gun are equally likely, what is the probability that a shot will hit the line between b_1 and b_2?

Solution: The physical description of this problem is similar to the development of the Cauchy density; and, if we assume that $\alpha = .5$ and $\mu = 0$, we can use Equation 3.3.19 to calculate the desired probability. Thus,

$$Pr(b_1 \leq X \leq b_2) = \frac{1}{\pi} \int_{b_2}^{b_1} \frac{5}{(.5)^2 + (x)^2)^2} \, dx$$

$$= \frac{1}{\pi} \left[\tan^{-1} \frac{b_2}{.5} - \tan^{-1} \frac{b_1}{.5} \right].$$

The probability that a shot is k ft or more away to the right of vertical is

$$Pr(X > k) = 1 - Pr(X \leq k) = 1 - F(k)$$

$$= \frac{1}{2} - \frac{1}{\pi} \tan^{-1} \frac{k}{.5}.$$

We shall discuss this distribution again in a later chapter.

3.3.6 The Laplace Distribution

A distribution of some importance to engineering problems is defined in Definition 3.3.7.

Definition 3.3.7 A random variable X is said to have a Laplace Distribution *if it has the following function for its density:*

$$f(x; \mu, \sigma) = \frac{1}{2\sigma} e^{-(|x - \mu|/\sigma)}, \quad -\infty < x < \infty, \quad -\infty < \mu < \infty,$$

$$\sigma > 0. \tag{3.3.21}$$

The parameter μ locates the mode of $f(x; \mu, \sigma)$, and σ serves as shape parameter. The density is symmetrical with respect to μ. It is clear that $f(x; \mu, \sigma)$ is greater than zero for all μ, x, and $\sigma > 0$. Next, let $y = (x - \mu)/\sigma$, $dx = \sigma dy$, and

$$\frac{1}{2\sigma} \int_{-\infty}^{\infty} e^{(|x - \mu|/\sigma)} \, dx = \frac{1}{2\sigma} \int_{-\infty}^{\mu} e^{(x - \mu)/\sigma} \, dx + \frac{1}{2\sigma} \int_{\mu}^{\infty} e^{\{(x - \mu)/\sigma\}} \, dx$$

$$= \frac{1}{2} \int_{-\infty}^{0} e^y \, dy + \frac{1}{2} \int_{0}^{\infty} e^{-y} \, dy$$

$$= \frac{1}{2} + \frac{1}{2} = 1.$$

Thus, expression (3.3.21) is a probability density function. The cumulative distribution function is

$$F(x) = Pr(X \le x) = \frac{1}{2\sigma} \int_{-\infty}^{x} e^{-(|t-\mu|/\sigma)} \, dt. \qquad (3.3.22)$$

For $x \le \mu$, expression (3.3.22) becomes

$$F(x) = \frac{1}{2} e^{(x-\mu)/\sigma};$$

and, for $x > \mu$, it becomes

$$F(x) = 1 - \frac{1}{2} e^{-(x-\mu)/\sigma}.$$

Therefore,

$$F(x) = \begin{cases} \dfrac{1}{2} e^{(x-\mu)/\sigma}, & x < \mu, \\[2mm] 1 - \dfrac{1}{2} e^{-(x-\mu)/\sigma}, & x \ge \mu. \end{cases}$$

Figure 3.3.12 shows the graph of the Laplace density for $\mu = 1$ and $\sigma = 1/2, 1, 2$ and also the Laplace cumulative distribution function.

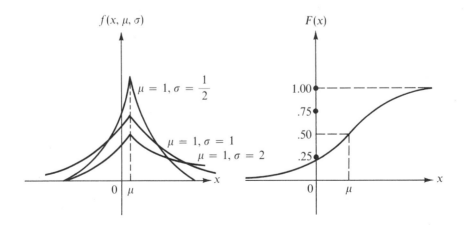

Figure 3.3.12

Example 3.3.11   A company produces ball bearings, the diameters of which may vary. Let X be a variate that assumes for values the diameters of the bearings, and let it be distributed according to Laplace's density with $\mu = 4$ units and $\sigma = .008$. Customer specification requires that the bearing diameter lie in the interval $4.00 \pm .016$. Bearings outside this interval are considered defective. What fraction of the total production of the ball bearings will be acceptable to the customer?

Solution: Here, Laplace's distribution for $\mu = 4$ and $\sigma = .004$ is

$$f(x; 4, .004) = \frac{1}{(.008)2} e^{(|x-\mu|/.008)}, \quad -\infty < x < \infty,$$

$$Pr(4.000 - .016 \le X \le 4.000 + .016)$$

$$= \frac{1}{.016} \int_{3.984}^{4.016} e^{(|x-4|/.008)} \, dx$$

$$= F(4.016) - F(3.984)$$

$$= 1 - \frac{1}{2} e^{-(4.016-4.000)/.008} - \frac{1}{2} e^{(3.984-4.0)/.008}$$

$$= 1 - \frac{1}{2} (e^{-2} + e^{-2})$$

$$= .864665.$$

Thus, 86.47% of the produced bearings will be acceptable to the customer.

Example 3.3.12   What should the limits be on the diameter of the ball bearing in Example 3.3.11 so that the proportion of acceptable bearings will be 90%? Here we want to find x so that

$$Pr(4 - x \le X \le 4 + x) = \frac{1}{(.008)2} \int_{4-x}^{4+x} e^{(|x-4|/.008)} \, dx = .90.$$

Thus,

$$F(4 + x) - F(4 - x) = .9,$$

which implies

$$1 - \frac{1}{2} e^{-(x/.008)} - \frac{1}{2} e^{-(x/.008)} = .9$$

or

$$e^{-(x/.008)} = .1,$$

which implies

$$\frac{-x}{.008} = \ln .1,$$

or

$$x = .0184.$$

Therefore, the limits on the diameter of the ball bearings should be $\pm.0184$ to make the unacceptable number of bearings equal to 10%.

3.3.7 The Log-Normal Distribution

The log-normal distribution in its simplest form may be defined as the distribution of a random variable whose logarithm obeys the normal probability density. Let Y be a random variable that is normally distributed, with parameters μ_y and σ_y. If $Y = \ln X$ or $X = e^Y$, then X is said to have a log-normal distribution. This distribution arises in physical problems when the domain of the variate, X, is greater than zero and its histogram is markedly skewed. This skewing occurs when X is affected by random causes that produce small effects that are proportional to the variate X. The outcome of these random causes, each producing a small constant effect, is normally distributed. The log-normal distribution has been used in economics, sociology, biology, and anthropometry, and in various physical and industrial processes.

The distribution of the variate X is defined in Definition 3.3.8.

Definition 3.3.8   *A random variable X is distributed as a* log normal *if it has the following function for its probability density:*

$$f(x) = \begin{cases} \dfrac{1}{x\sigma_y\sqrt{2\pi}}\exp\left\{-\dfrac{1}{2\sigma_y^2}(\ln x - \mu_y)^2\right\}, & \begin{aligned} &x > 0, \\ &\sigma_y > 0, \ -\infty < \mu_y < \infty, \end{aligned} \\ 0, \quad elsewhere. \end{cases}$$

$$(3.3.23)$$

The two parameters which define the density completely, μ_y and σ_y, play the roles of locating the relative position of the mean and the amount of dispersion of the information with respect to μ_y, respectively. These parameters are related to the parameters of the random variable X as follows:

$$\mu_y = \ln\left(\sqrt{\frac{\mu_x^4}{\mu_x^2 + \sigma_x^2}}\right), \quad \sigma_y = \ln\left(\sqrt{\frac{\mu_x^2 + \sigma_x^2}{\mu_x^2}}\right). \qquad (3.3.24)$$

(See Problem 3.29).

To verify that function (3.3.23) is a probability density, it is sufficient to show that $f(x; \mu_x, \sigma_x)$ integrates into one. Let

$$z = \frac{1}{\sigma_y}(\ln x - \mu_y), \quad \sigma_y xd = dx.$$

Then

$$\frac{1}{\sigma_y\sqrt{2\pi}} \int_0^\infty \frac{1}{x} \exp\left\{-\frac{1}{2\sigma_y^2}(\ln x - \mu_y)^2\right\} dx = \frac{1}{2\pi} \int_{-\infty}^\infty e^{-(1/2)z^2} dz = 1.$$

The cumulative distribution of the log normal is

$$F(x) = Pr(X \le x) = \frac{1}{\sqrt{2\pi}\,\sigma_y} \int_0^x \frac{1}{t} \exp\left\{-\frac{1}{2\sigma_y^2} \ln t - \mu_y)^2\right\} dt.$$

$$(3.3.25)$$

Let

$$z = \frac{\ln t - \mu_y}{\sigma_y}, \quad \sigma_y t dz = dt,$$

and Equation (3.3.25) becomes

$$F(x) = \frac{1}{\sqrt{2\pi}} \int_{-\infty}^{\frac{\ln x - \mu_y}{\sigma_y}} e^{-(1/2)z^2} dz$$

$$= F\left(\frac{\ln x - \mu_y}{\sigma_y}\right).$$

Thus, the probability that the random variable X assumes its value from an interval greater than zero and less than x can be obtained from the normal tables, page 624 ff. Similarly, if X is log normally distributed with parameters, as given in Equation (3.3.24), and $0 < \alpha < \beta$, then

$$Pr(\alpha \le X \le \beta) = Pr(\alpha \le e^Y \le \beta)$$

$$= Pr(\ln \alpha \le Y \le \ln \beta)$$

$$= Pr\left(\frac{\ln \alpha - \mu_y}{\sigma_y} \le \frac{Y - \mu_y}{\sigma_y} \le \frac{\ln \beta - \mu_y}{\sigma_y}\right)$$

$$= F\left(\frac{\ln \beta - \mu_y}{\sigma_y}\right) - F\left(\frac{\ln \alpha - \mu_y}{\sigma_y}\right).$$

Figures 3.3.13 and 3.3.14 show the graph of the log-normal density for fixed μ_y and varying σ_y^2, and for fixed σ_y^2 and varying μ_y, respectively. Figures 3.3.13 and 3.3.14 illustrate that the distribution is positively skewed and that, the greater the value of the parameter σ_y, the greater the skewness.

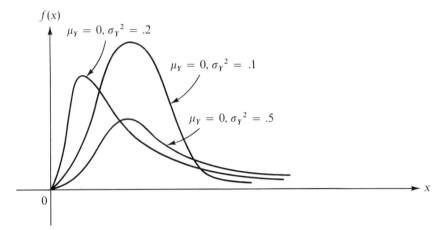

Figure 3.3.13

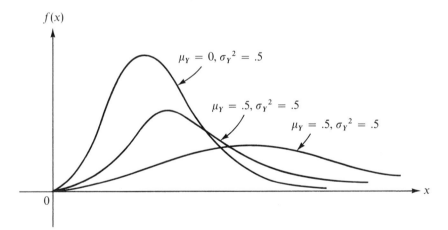

Figure 3.3.14

The median of the log normal is at $x = e^{\mu_Y}$. The relative positions of the mean, median, *and* mode *are at $e^{\mu_Y + (1/2)\sigma_Y^2}$, e^{μ_Y}, and $e^{\mu_Y - \sigma_Y^2}$, respectively, where the mean is the average value of X,*

$$\int_{-\infty}^{\infty} xf(x) \, dx,$$

the median is that value of m which satisfies the equation

$$\int_{-\infty}^{m} f(x)\, dx = \frac{1}{2} = \int_{m}^{\infty} f(x)\, dx,$$

and the mode is the value of x at which the probability density function attains its maximum.

The log-normal distribution possesses a number of interesting properties, most of which are immediate consequences of the normal distribution and will be discussed in a later chapter.

The question of when the log-normal distribution is applicable in a given physical problem when a certain amount of data has been obtained can be answered by plotting the cumulative distribution of ln *X on normal probability paper; if the resulting curve is nearly a straight line, then X has a log-normal distribution. In such a problem, the parameters* μ_y *and* σ_y *are estimated from the given information.*

Example 3.3.13   In an effort to establish a suitable height for the controls of a moving vehicle, information was gathered about X, the amount that the heights of the operators vary from 60 inches, which is the minimum height of the operators. It was verified that the data that were collected followed the log-normal distribution by plotting the distribution of ln X on normal probability paper. If we assume that $\mu_x = 6$ in. and $\sigma_x = 2$ in. what percentage of operators would have a height less than 65.5 in.? Here,

$$X = 65.5 - 60 = 5.5$$

$$Pr(X \le 5.5) = Pr(e^Y \le 5.5) = Pr(Y \le \ln 5.5)$$

$$= Pr\left(Z \le \frac{\ln 5.5 - \mu_y}{\sigma_y}\right) = F\left(\frac{\ln 5.5 - \mu_y}{\sigma_y}\right).$$

But

$$\mu_y = \ln \sqrt{\frac{6^4}{6^2 + 2^2}} = \ln \frac{36}{\sqrt{40}}$$

$$= \ln \left(\frac{36}{6.32}\right) = \ln 5.69 = 1.74,$$

$$\sigma_y = \ln \sqrt{\frac{6^2 + 2^2}{6^2}} = \ln \sqrt{\frac{40}{36}}$$

$$= \ln \sqrt{1.11} = \ln 1.054 = .053.$$

Thus,

$$F\left(\frac{\ln 5.5 - \mu_y}{\sigma_y}\right) = F\left(\frac{1.70 - 1.74}{.053}\right)$$

$$= F\left(\frac{-.04}{.053}\right) = F(-.75)$$

$$= 1 - F(.75) = 1 - .7734$$

$$= .2266.$$

If an operator is chosen at random, what is the probability that his height will be between 64 and 66 in.?

$$X_1 = 64 - 60 = 4,$$

$$X_2 = 66 - 60 = 6.$$

Here we want

$$Pr(4 \le X \le 6) = Pr(4 \le e^Y \le 6) = Pr(\ln 4 \le Y \le \ln 6)$$

$$= Pr\left[\left(\frac{\ln 6 - \mu_y}{\sigma_y}\right) \le Z \le \left(\frac{\ln 4 - \mu_y}{\sigma_y}\right)\right]$$

$$= F\left(\frac{1.79 - 1.74}{.053}\right) - F\left(\frac{1.39 - 1.74}{.053}\right)$$

$$= F\left(\frac{.05}{.053}\right) - F\left(\frac{-.33}{.053}\right)$$

$$= F(.94) - F(-6.60)$$

$$= F(.94) - [1 - F(6.60)]$$

$$= F(.94) - 1 + F(6.60)$$

$$= .8264 - 1 + 1 = .8264.$$

For additional information, the book of J. Aitchison and J. A. C. Brown, Reference [1], is entirely devoted to the importance and usefulness of the log-normal distribution.

3.3.8   The Weibull Distribution   In 1951, W. Weibull, Reference [3], introduced a probability density function that is applicable to many physical phenomena. It is extremely useful in studies of failure models.

Definition 3.3.10   *A random variable X is said to be distributed as the* Weibull distribution *if it has function 3.3.26 for its probability density:*

$$f(x; \alpha, \beta, \gamma) = \begin{cases} \dfrac{\beta}{\alpha}(x - \gamma)^{\beta - 1} e^{-\{(x - \gamma)^{\beta}/\alpha\}}, & x > \gamma, \quad \alpha, \beta, \gamma > 0, \\ \\ 0, & elsewhere. \end{cases}$$

$$(3.3.26)$$

The three parameters α, β, and γ, which completely describe the Weibull density, are of significant importance. Here α is a scale parameter, β is a shape parameter, and γ is the location or threshold parameter. The density function attains its maximum point when

$$x = \gamma + \frac{\gamma(\beta - 1)^{1/\beta}}{\beta}.$$

Figure 3.3.15 shows a graphical representation of the Weibull density for $\alpha = 1$, $\gamma = 0$, and varying β, $\beta = 1/2, 1, 2, 5$.

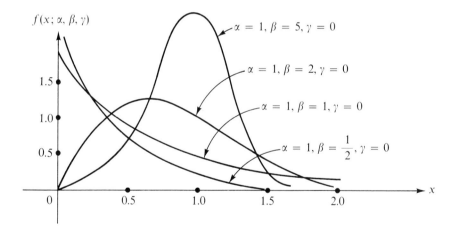

Figure 3.3.15

We notice that the density is skewed to the right for all values of the parameters. However, the skewness decreases as the shape parameter β increases.
   It is clear that $f(x; \alpha, \beta, \gamma) \geq 0$ for $x > \gamma$ and $\alpha, \beta, \gamma > 0$. Now if we let

$$y = \frac{(x - \gamma)^{\beta}}{\alpha}, \quad \frac{\alpha}{\beta} \frac{1}{(x - \gamma)^{\beta - 1}} \, dy = dx,$$

we have

$$\frac{\beta}{\alpha} \int_{\gamma}^{\infty} (x - \gamma)^{\beta - 1} e^{-\{(x-\gamma)^\beta/\alpha\}} \, dx = \int_{0}^{\infty} e^{-y} \, dy = 1.$$

Thus, Equation (3.3.26) satisfies the conditions of a probability density function. The cumulative distribution of the Weibull for $x > \gamma$ is given by

$$F(x) = Pr(X \leq x) = \frac{\beta}{\alpha} \int_{0}^{x} (t - \gamma)^{\beta - 1} e^{-\{(t-\gamma)^\beta/\alpha\}} \, dt,$$

which reduces to

$$1 - e^{-\{(x-\alpha)^\beta/\alpha\}}.$$

Thus

$$F(x) = \begin{cases} 0, & x \leq 0, \\ 1 - e^{-\{(x-\gamma)^\beta/\alpha\}}, & x > \gamma, \quad \alpha, \beta > 0, \gamma \geq 0. \end{cases}$$

The Weibull density function is flexible enough to be applicable to a number of problems. This flexibility can be displayed by deriving the following distributions as special cases of the Weibull:
(1) *When $\beta = 1$ and $\gamma = 0$ in the Weibull density, we obtain the* exponential distribution,

$$f(x; \alpha) = \begin{cases} \dfrac{1}{\alpha} e^{-(x/\alpha)}, & x \geq 0, \quad \alpha > 0, \\ 0, & \textit{elsewhere.} \end{cases}$$

which we discussed in Section 3.3.3.
(2) *When we let $\beta = 2$ and $\gamma = 0$ in Equation (3.3.26), we obtain an important probability distribution, which is defined in Definition 3.3.11.*

Definition 3.3.11   *A random variable X is said to have a* Rayleigh *distribution if it has the following function for its probability density:*

$$f(x) = \begin{cases} \dfrac{2}{\alpha} x e^{-(x^2/\alpha)}, & x \geq 0, \quad \alpha > 0, \\ 0, & \textit{elsewhere.} \end{cases} \tag{3.3.27}$$

This distribution is of significant importance in the theory of sound. Its meaning and derivation can be obtained by considering the following problem: In trying to locate an object on the $x - y$ plane, we determine its distance from the origin by measuring the distance along the x and y axes and applying the Pythagorean formula: $r^2 = x^2 + y^2$. If the measurements are subject to random error with X and Y representing errors in measurement that are assumed to be independent and normally distributed with $\mu = 0$ and $\sigma^2 = \alpha/2$, then the distribution of $R = \sqrt{X^2 + Y^2}$ is known as the Rayleigh *distribution.*

Figure 3.3.16 *shows a graphical representation of the behavior of the shape parameter* α *in* (3.3.27).

(3)   *The Weibull distribution offers a very close approximation to the normal distribution for certain values of the parameters. It was found in a particular problem that, for* α = 1, β = 3.2589, *and* γ = 0 *of the Weibull density and for* μ = 0.8964 *and* σ² = .0924 *of the Gaussian density, the two are practically identical. This comparison is shown by Figure* 3.3.17.

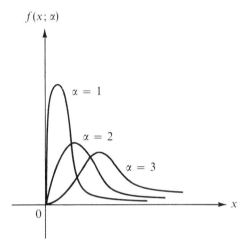

Figure 3.3.16

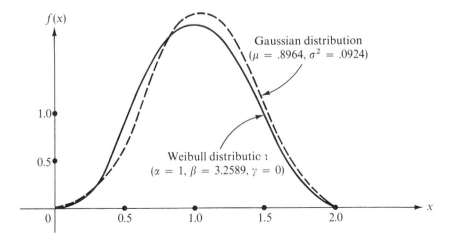

Figure 3.3.17

In Chapter 4, we shall discuss some additional properties of the Weibull and Rayleigh distributions.

Example 3.3.14   The amplitude of a signal generated by a certain source is usually assumed to be a random variable of the continuous type that is Rayleigh distributed. Given that the receiver can detect a signal of specified minimum amplitude x_0, find the probability that the receiver will be processing a signal.

Solution: Applying Equation (3.3.27), we have

$$Pr(X \geq x_0) = \frac{2}{\alpha} \int_{x_0}^{\infty} xe^{-(x^2/\alpha)}dx = e^{-(x_0^2/\alpha)}.$$

The shaded area of Figure 3.3.18 represents this probability.

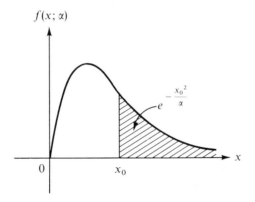

Figure 3.3.18

3.3.9 Other Continuous Probability Distributions   The following probability density functions are of importance in various physical phenomena. We shall define the functions here and study their properties in the forthcoming chapters.

Definition 3.3.12   *A random variable X is said to be distributed as* Maxwell's distribution *if it has the following function for its density:*

$$f(x; \sigma) = \begin{cases} \dfrac{2\sigma^3}{\sqrt{2\pi}} x^2 e^{-(x^2\sigma^2/2)} & x \geq 0, \quad \sigma > 0, \\ 0, & elsewhere. \end{cases}$$

$$(3.3.28)$$

Definition 3.3.13   *A random variable X is said to be distributed as the extreme-value distribution if it has the following function for its probability density:*

$$f(x) = e^{-x - e^{-x}}, \quad -\infty < x < \infty. \tag{3.3.29}$$

Definition 3.3.14   *A random variable X is said to be distributed as the arc sine distribution if it has the following function for its probability density:*

$$f(x) = \begin{cases} \dfrac{1}{\pi} \{x(1-x)\}^{-(1/2)}, & 0 < x < 1, \\ 0, & elsewhere. \end{cases} \tag{3.3.30}$$

Definition 3.3.15   *A random variable X is distributed as* Pareto's *distribution if it has the following function for its probability density:*

$$f(x) = \begin{cases} rA^r(x^{r+1})^{-1}, & 0 \le A \le x, \quad r \ge 0, \\ 0, & elsewhere. \end{cases} \tag{3.3.31}$$

The Maxwell's distribution, sometimes referred to as Maxwell's velocity distribution, is applicable to problems in physics. The extreme-value density has been used in the areas of hydrology, failure models, and meteorology. Pareto's and the arc sine distributions have been applied, respectively, to various problems in econometrics and electrical engineering.

3.4   Applications to Reliability

In this section, we shall introduce some of the basic aspects of the notion of reliability and apply some of the preceding continuous distributions to various failure models. The widely accepted definition of reliability in its simplest and most general form reads: "Reliability is the probability that a system (or component) performs its purpose adequately for the period of time intended under the operating conditions encountered." Thus, this definition implies that reliability is the probability that a certain system will not fail to perform its function for a definite interval of time.

Let $t = 0$ be the time at which a system is put into operation and T be the *life length* or *time to failure* of the system. The time T, as was discussed previously, may be considered as a continuous random variable with probability density function $f(t)$. We shall refer to $f(t)$ as the *failure density* of the system. The concept of reliability is defined more precisely in Definition 3.4.1.

Definition 3.4.1   *The* reliability function *of a system at time t, denoted by R(t), is given by*

$$R(t) = Pr(T \geq t),$$

where T is the time to failure of the system. Hence,

$$R(t) = 1 - Pr(T < t) = 1 - \int_0^t f(x) \, dx$$

$$= 1 - F(t). \tag{3.4.1}$$

Definition 3.4.2   *Another important concept in reliability is the* failure rate *of a system. We can define failure rate mathematically as "the integral of the failure density taken from some time t to t + Δt divided by the integral of the failure density from t to infinity." Thus,*

$$Pr(t \leq T \leq t + \Delta t \,|\, T > t) = \frac{Pr(t \leq T \leq t + \Delta t)}{Pr(T > t)}$$

$$= \frac{\int_t^{t+\Delta t} f(x) \, dx}{\int_t^{\infty} f(x) \, dx} = \frac{f(t)}{1 - \int_0^t f(x) \, dx}$$

$$= \frac{f(t)}{1 - F(t)}, \quad F(t) < 1.$$

Note that

$$F'(t) = \lim_{\Delta \to 0} \frac{F(t + \Delta t) - F(t)}{\Delta t}$$

$$= \lim_{\Delta t \to 0} \frac{1}{\Delta t} \int_t^{t+\Delta t} f(x) \, dx$$

$$= \lim_{\Delta t \to 0} \frac{1}{\Delta t} f(c) \, t, \quad < t \leq c \leq t + \Delta t$$

$$= \lim_{c \to t} f(c) \quad (\text{as } \Delta t \to 0 \; c \to t)$$

$$= f(t).$$

The failure or hazard rate function, *denoted by ρ(t), is given by*

$$\rho(t) = \frac{f(t)}{1 - F(t)} = \frac{f(t)}{R(t)}, \tag{3.4.2}$$

for $F(t) < 1$. Hence, if the probability desnity function of T, the time to failure of the system, is known, we can determine the failure rate. Furthermore, if the failure rate is known, we can obtain the density function of T as follows: Differentiating Equation (3.4.1) with respect to t, we have

$$R'(t) = -F'(t).$$

But $F'(t) = f(t)$, and Equation (3.4.2) becomes

$$\rho(t) = \frac{-R'(t)}{R(t)}. \tag{3.4.3}$$

If we let $R(0) = 1$, that is, if the system is functioning at $t = 0$, and we integrate both sides of Equation (3.4.3) from 0 to t, we have

$$\int_0^t \rho(x)\, dx = -\int_0^t \frac{R'(x)}{R(x)}\, dx$$

$$= -\ln R(t) + \ln R(0)$$

$$= -\ln R(t).$$

Therefore,

$$R(t) = \exp\left(-\int_0^t \rho(x)\, dx\right)$$

and

$$(t) = F'(t) = -R'(t) = \rho(t)R(t)$$

$$= \rho(t) \exp\left(-\int_0^t \rho(x)\, dx\right). \tag{3.4.4}$$

When one speaks of a system, one may refer to a very complex system that is made up of various subsystems that are delineated into components. In predicting the probability of survival of such a complex system, it is necessary to know the reliability behavior of each one of the components that constitute the system. However, in this section, we intend to consider only very simple systems, that is, systems which consist of a single component.

In initiating the reliability study of a certain system, one must begin by asking the question: What is the probability density function that best describes the behavior of the random times at which such systems fail? There are statistical tests available that one can use to determine the fitness of a failure density. However, we can intuitively obtain a fairly good approximation of a failure density from the use of probability histograms.

The failure distribution of a system varies according to the cause of the failure. For example, we might be concerned with an electrical system, the failure rate of which may be quite different from that of a mechanical system. Or the cause of failure may be due to the structure of the system, which is an even more complicated problem. Furthermore, system failure is subject to the effects of the environment in which it functions.

We shall now present various failure density functions, indicate the type of failures these probability functions are applicable to, and illustrate them with examples.

(1)   The Exponential   One of the best known, most useful, and most thoroughly explored failure distributions is the *exponential*, Equation 3.3.12. This failure density function, which has a number of desirable mathematical properties, is applicable to many types of component failures, especially in electrical systems.

Thus, if the time to failure of a system is given by

$$f(t) = \frac{1}{\beta} e^{-(t/\beta)}, \qquad \beta > 0, t \geq 0, \tag{3.4.5}$$

the reliability function becomes

$$R(t) = 1 - F(t) = 1 - \frac{1}{\beta} \int_0^t e^{-(x/\beta)} \, dx$$

$$= e^{-(t/\beta)}, \quad \beta > 0, \quad t \geq 0.$$

Applying formula (3.4.2), we obtain a constant failure rate. That is,

$$\rho(t) = \frac{\dfrac{1}{\beta} e^{-(t/\beta)}}{1 - \dfrac{1}{\beta} \int_0^t e^{-(x/\beta)} \, dx} = \frac{1}{\beta}.$$

Therefore, if we are studying a system whose failure rate is constant, we can calculate by using Equation (3.4.4) the failure density function of the system.

Example 3.4.1   An electrical component was studied in the laboratory, and it was determined that its failure rate was approximately equal to $1/\beta = .05$. What is the reliability of such a component at 10 hours? Here we are given that $\rho(t) = .05$, and, thus

$$R(10) = 1 - F(10) = e^{-10(.05)} = e^{-1/2}$$

$$= .6065.$$

Figure 3.4.1 shows the graph of $f(t)$, $F(t)$, $\rho(t)$, and $R(t)$ of this example, with the shaded area representing $R(10)$.

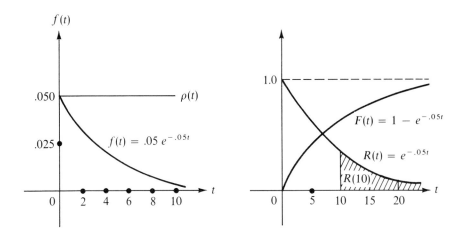

Figure 3.4.1

(2) The Gamma   The gamma density is used quite often as a failure probability function for components whose distribution is skewed. The failure density, as defined in Equation (3.3.10), is

$$f(t; \alpha, \beta) = \frac{1}{\Gamma(\alpha)\beta^{\alpha}} t^{\alpha-1} e^{-(x/\beta)}, \quad \alpha, \beta > 0, \quad t \geq 0. \qquad (3.4.6)$$

The failure rate of this density function is constant for $\alpha = 1$, increasing for $\alpha > 1$, and decreasing for $\alpha < 1$. This is illustrated in Figure 3.4.2 for $\beta = 1$ and $\alpha = 1/2, 1, 2$.

For $\beta = 1$, the reliability function of Equation (3.4.6) is

$$R(t) = 1 - \frac{1}{\Gamma(\alpha)} \int_{0}^{t} x^{\alpha-1} e^{-x} \, dx.$$

This function is graphed for $\alpha = 1/2$, 1, and 2, as shown in Figure 3.4.3.

(3) The Weibull   The Weibull density is applicable as a failure function whenever the system we are studying consists of more than one component and whenever failure is due to the most serious defect of a large number of defects that may be present in the system. It has been shown that fatigue failures, ball-bearing failures, and vacuum tube failures follow the Weibull

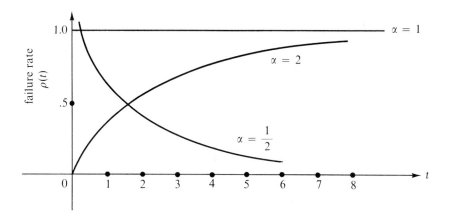

Figure 3.4.2

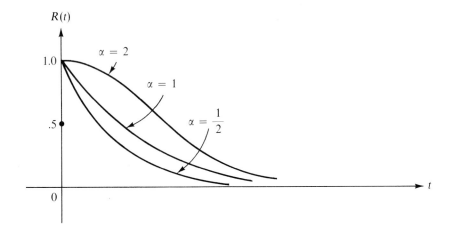

Figure 3.4.3

failure density function. It is possible to study the reliability of complex systems whose failure functions may be increasing, decreasing, or remaining constant by the appropriate choices of the parameters that describe the Weibull function.

The reliability function for the Weibull failure rate, as defined by Equation (3.3.26), is

$$R(t) = 1 - \frac{\beta}{\alpha} \int_{\gamma}^{t} (x - \gamma)^{\beta - 1} \exp\left(-\frac{(x - \gamma)^{\beta}}{\alpha}\right) dx = \exp\left(-\frac{(t - \gamma)^{\beta}}{\alpha}\right),$$

$$\alpha, \beta > 0, \quad \gamma \geq 0, \quad t \geq \gamma. \quad (3.4.7)$$

The failure rate function is

$$\rho(t) = \frac{f(t)}{R(t)} = \frac{\beta}{\alpha}(t-\gamma)^{\beta-1}, \quad \alpha, \beta > 0, \quad \gamma \geq 0,$$

which implies that it is proportional to powers of t. The $\rho(t)$ is increasing for $\beta > 1$; it is decreasing for $0 < \beta < 1$; and it remains constant for $\beta = 1$, as shown in Figure 3.4.4.

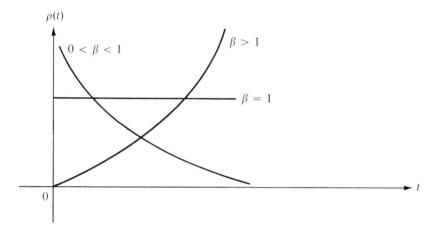

Figure 3.4.4

Example 3.4.2   Suppose that the time to failure of a certain system follows the Weibull function as its failure density. If the reliability of the system is specified, $R(t) = .90$, and the parameters α, β, and γ are given the values 5, 1/3, and 4, respectively, find the time of operation of the system.

Substituting the given values into Equation (3.4.7), we have

$$.90 = \exp\left(-\frac{(t-4)^{1/4}}{5}\right),$$

which gives

$$t \approx 4.1462.$$

Therefore, the probability is .90 that such a system will not fail up to $t = 4.1462$.

(4)　The Normal　　There are many systems whose failure behavior follows the normal distribution, particularly mechanical systems and systems that fail because of some "wearing" effects. The density of the life length of such systems is given by

$$f(t) = \frac{1}{\sqrt{2\pi}\,\sigma}\,\exp\left\{-\frac{1}{2}\left(\frac{t-\mu}{\sigma}\right)^2\right\}, \quad \mu \ge 0, \ \sigma > 0, \ t \ge 0.$$

Here, we are not defining the normal failure function for $t < 0$ because the life length of a system is certainly greater than zero. The parameters μ and σ in $f(t)$ respectively represent the expected failure time of the system and the amount of dispersion of the failure times. Thus, since $f(t)$ is symmetrical with respect to μ, the reliability of a system at a time $t > \mu$ is the same for $t < \mu$.

The reliability function is given by

$$R(t) = 1 - Pr(T \le t)$$

$$= 1 - \frac{1}{\sqrt{2\pi}\,\sigma}\int_0^t \exp\left\{-\frac{1}{2}\left(\frac{x-\mu}{\sigma}\right)^2\right\} dx$$

$$= 2 - F\left(\frac{t-\mu}{\sigma}\right) - F\left(\frac{\mu}{\sigma}\right). \tag{3.4.8}$$

Example 3.4.3　　Suppose that the life length of a mechanical component is normally distributed.
(a)　If $\sigma = 3$ and $\mu = 100$, find the reliability of such a system at 105 hours.
(b)　What should be the expected life of the component if it has reliability of .90 for 120 hours?

Solution:
(a)　Applying (3.4.8), we have

$$R(105) = 2 - F\left(\frac{105 - 100}{3}\right) - F\left(\frac{100}{3}\right)$$

$$= 2 - F\left(\frac{5}{3}\right) - F(33.3)$$

$$= .0475.$$

Therefore, if 100 such components are put into operation, approximately .95 will fail during the time period 0 hours to 105 hours.
(b)　Here Equation (3.4.8) becomes

$$.90 = 2 - F\left(\frac{120 - \mu}{3}\right) - F\left(\frac{\mu}{3}\right),$$

or

$$F\left(\frac{120 - \mu}{3}\right) + F\left(\frac{\mu}{3}\right) = 1.1.$$

But, because μ must be greater than 120, $F(\mu/3) = 1$, and we thus have

$$F\left(\frac{120 - \mu}{3}\right) = .1.$$

Using Table 8 of the normal distribution, we obtain

$$\frac{120 - \mu}{3} = -1.28.$$

Thus, the expected life of the component μ is about 116 hours.

In this chapter, we have studied the concept of a one-dimensional continuous random variable, discussed a number of continuous probability distributions, and illustrated some of their uses. However, there are many physical phenomena that must be characterized by a two-dimensional random variable; this characterization will be the aim of Chapter 6. One important aid to our study of random variables is the study of functional forms of random variables, forms which arise in many practical situations and which will be considered in the following chapter.

3.5 *Summary*

Let X be a random variable. If the range space, R_X, is an interval or the union of two or more nonoverlapping intervals, then X is called a *one-dimensional continuous random variable*.

Let X be a one-dimensional continuous random variable. A function $f(x)$ is called a *continuous probability density function* of the random variable X if the following conditions are satisfied:

(1) $f(x) \geq 0$ for all $x \in R_X$

(2) $\int_{R_X} f(x) \, dx = 1,$

where the integration is performed over those x's which are contained only in the intervals of the range.

The *cumulative distribution function* of the continuous random variable x is

$$F(x) = Pr(X \leq x) = \int_{-\infty}^{x} f(s)\, ds.$$

$F(x)$ possesses the following properties: (1) $F(\infty) = 1$; (2) $F(-\infty) = 0$; (3) $F(x)$ is a nondecreasing function; (4) $F(x)$ is continuous from the right; and (5) $\{dF(x)/dx\} = f(x)$ for all x for which $F(x)$ is differentiable.

The following important continuous probability distributions have been studied: *Uniform, Gaussian or Normal, Gamma, exponential, Beta, rectangular, triangular, Cauchy, Laplace, Log Normal, Weibull, Rayleigh, Maxwell's, extreme value, arc sine, and Pareto's.*

The basic concepts of reliability have been discussed. Reliability is the probability that a system (or component) performs its purpose adequately for the period of time intended under the operating conditions encountered. The following failure density functions have been studied:

(1) The *exponential*, which has a number of desirable mathematical properties and is applicable to many types of component failures, especially in electrical systems;

(2) The *gamma*, which is used quite often as a failure probability function for components that have a skewed distribution;

(3) The *Weibull*, which is applicable as a failure function whenever the system we are studying consists of more than one component and failure is due to the most serious defect of a large number of defects that may be present in the system. It is mainly used as a model for fatigue failures, ball-bearing failures, and vacuum-tube failures.

Exercises

3.1. If $f(x) = k \sin x, 0 < x < \pi$, (a) evaluate k so that $f(x)$ will be the probability density function of the random variable X, (b) find $F(x)$, (c) graph $f(x)$ and $F(x)$.

3.2. A continuous random variable X assumes its values from the set $S_X = \{x: 1 \leq x \leq 4\}$ and has on this set a probability density function $f(x)$, which is proportional to x.

(a) Determine the probability density function $f(x)$.
(b) Determine $Pr[X < x]$.
(c) Sketch $f(x)$ and $F(x)$.

3.3. The probability density function of the random variable X is given by

$$f(x) = \begin{cases} \frac{3}{2}x^2, & -1 \le x \le 1, \\ 0, & \text{elsewhere.} \end{cases}$$

(a) Find the cumulative distribution function of the random variable X.

(b) Sketch $f(x)$ and $F(x)$ on the same graph.

3.4. The cumulative distribution function of the random variable Y is given by

$$F(y) = \begin{cases} 0, & y < 0, \\ \frac{1}{2}, & y = 0, \\ \frac{1}{2} + \frac{y}{4}, & 0 < y < 2, \\ 1, & y \ge 2. \end{cases}$$

Find the probability density function of the random variable Y.

3.5. The cumulative distribution function of the random variable X is given by

$$F(x) = \begin{cases} 0, & x \le 0, \\ x, & 0 < x \le \frac{1}{2}, \\ \frac{1}{2}, & \frac{1}{2} < x \le \frac{3}{4}, \\ 2x - 1, & \frac{3}{4} < x \le 1, \\ 1, & x > 1. \end{cases}$$

(a) Find $f(x)$, being sure to include any points at which $f(x)$ is undefined.

(b) Show that the properties of a cumulative distribution are satisfied by $F(x)$.

3.6. Let the cumulative distribution function of the random variable Y be given by

$$F(y) = \begin{cases} 0, & y \le 0, \\ y(3 - 2\sqrt{y}), & 0 < y < 1, \\ 1, & y \ge 1. \end{cases}$$

Find the probability density function of the random variable Y. Sketch $f(y)$.

3.7. The cumulative distribution function of the random variable Z is given by

$$F(z) = \begin{cases} 1 - (1 + z)e^{-z}, & z \ge 0, \\ 0, & \text{elsewhere.} \end{cases}$$

Show that the properties of a cumulative distribution are satisfied.

3.8. The probability density function of the random variable X is given by

$$f(x) = \begin{cases} x^{11}, & 0 < x < 1, \\ \dfrac{1}{12}, & x = 1, 4, 5, 9.5, 10 < x < 11, \\ \dfrac{1}{4}(3 - x)(x - 1), & 2 < x < 3, \\ \dfrac{5}{3x^2}, & 4 < x < 5, \\ \dfrac{1}{12}\sin x, & 2\pi < x < 3\pi, \\ \dfrac{\sqrt{2}}{6}\cos 2x, & 4\pi < x < \dfrac{33\pi}{8}, \\ 0, & \text{elsewhere.} \end{cases}$$

(a) Graph $f(x)$.   (b) Derive $F(x)$.   (c) Graph $F(x)$.

3.9. In the following functions, evaluate c so that $f(x)$ will be a probability density function:

(a) $f(x) = \dfrac{c}{x^4}, \quad x \ge 1;$

(b) $f(x; \theta) = c(\ln \theta)\theta^{-x}, \quad x \ge 0, \quad \theta > 1;$

(c) $f(x; \theta) = \dfrac{c}{3}(\theta + 1)x^\theta, \quad 0 \le x \le 1, \quad \theta \ge 0;$

(d) $f(x; \theta) = 2c(1 + 2\theta x - 3\theta x^2), \quad 0 \le x \le 1;$

(e) $f(x) = ce^{-(x/\theta)}, \quad x \ge 0;$

(f) $f(x) = \dfrac{c}{1 + x^2}, \quad -\infty < x < \infty;$

(g)
$$f(x) = \begin{cases} \dfrac{c}{2}, & 0 \le x < \dfrac{1}{3}, \\[2mm] \dfrac{3c}{2}, & \dfrac{1}{3} \le x < \dfrac{2}{3}, \\[2mm] \dfrac{c}{2}, & \dfrac{2}{3} \le x < 1, \\[2mm] 0, & \text{elsewhere}; \end{cases}$$

(h) $f(x) = c(1 - x^2), \quad -1 < x \le 1;$

(i)
$$f(z) = \begin{cases} \dfrac{c}{2}z^2, & 0 \le z < 1, \\[2mm] c\left(-z^2 + 3z - \dfrac{3}{2}\right), & 1 \le z < 2, \\[2mm] \dfrac{c}{2}(z^2 - 6z + 9), & 2 \le z \le 3, \\[2mm] 0, & \text{elsewhere}; \end{cases}$$

(j) $f(r) = c(1 - e^r)^{n-2}e^{-r}, \quad -\infty < r < \infty, \quad n \ge 0;$

(k) $f(x) = \dfrac{c}{\theta^2}xe^{-(2x/\theta)}, \quad x > 0, \quad \theta > 0;$

(l) $f(x) = c(9 - 2x), \quad 2 < x \le 4;$

(m)
$$f(x) = \begin{cases} \dfrac{1}{20x^2}, & -\infty < x \le -1, \\[2mm] \dfrac{3}{25}(2x^2 + x + 1), & -1 < x \le 1, \\[2mm] c, & 1 < x \le 3, \\[2mm] \dfrac{1}{20}(6 - x), & 3 < x \le 5, \\[2mm] c(10x - x^2 - 21), & 5 < x \le 7, \\[2mm] 0, & \text{elsewhere}; \end{cases}$$

(n) $f(x) = \dfrac{ce^{-x}}{1 - e^{-1}}, \quad 0 < x \le 1;$

(o) $f(x) = c\theta^{-(3/2)}x^2 e^{x^2/2\theta}, \quad x > 0, \quad \theta > 0;$

(p) $f(x) = \dfrac{c}{\theta^2}(\theta - x), \quad 0 < x < \theta;$

(q) $f(x) = \dfrac{c(1 + \theta)}{(x + \theta)^2}, \quad x \ge 1, \quad \theta \ge -1;$

(r) $f(x) = \dfrac{c\theta}{\alpha}\left(\dfrac{\alpha}{x}\right)^{1+\theta}, \quad x > \alpha, \quad \alpha > 0, \quad \theta > 0;$

(s) $f(x) = \dfrac{cx^3}{\theta^4}e^{-(x/\theta)}, \quad x > 0, \quad \theta > 0.$

3.10. (a) Find the cumulative distribution functions of the variables whose probability density functions are given in Exercise 3.9.
 (b) Sketch $f(x)$ and $F(x)$.

3.11. Show that (a) *Maxwell's distribution*, given by Equation (3.3.28), (b) *extreme value distribution*, given by Equation (3.3.29), (c) *arc sine distribution*, given by (3.3.30), and (d) *Pareto's distribution*, given by (3.3.31), satisfy the conditions of a probability density function and determine the cumulative distribution for each density.

3.12. The probability that the random variable X will assume a value between α and β, inclusive, with $1 \le \alpha \le \beta$, is given by

$$Pr(\alpha \le X \le \beta) = \frac{\beta - \alpha}{\alpha\beta}.$$

 (a) What is the probability density function of the random variable X?
 (b) Determine and sketch the cumulative distribution function $F(x)$.

3.13. Suppose that the probability density function of the random variable X is the *gamma distribution* with parameters α and β. Show that for $0 < a < b < \infty$

$$Pr(a \le X \le b) = \frac{1}{\Gamma(n)}\left[\sum_{i=0}^{n-1}\frac{d^i}{dy^i}(y^{n-1})\right]_{\frac{a}{\alpha}}^{\frac{b}{\beta}},$$

where

$$\frac{d^0}{dy^0}(y^{n-1}) = y^{n-1},$$

and if $a = 0$, then for $c > 0$ we have

$$Pr(X \le c) = 1 - \frac{1}{\Gamma(n)} \left[\sum_{i=0}^{n-1} \frac{d^i}{dy^i}(y^{n-1}) \right]^{\frac{c}{\beta}}.$$

3.14. A certain vacuum tube has been observed to fail uniformly over the time interval $[t_1, t_2]$.

    (a) Determine the reliability function for such a tube at time t, $t_1 \le t \le t_2$.

    (b) Calculate the failure rate of the tube.

    (c) If $180 \le t \le 220$, what is the reliability of such a tube at 200 hours?

3.15. An electrical component was studied in the laboratory, and it was determined that the time to failure of the component was characterized by the following failure density:

$$f(t; n, p) = \binom{n}{t} p^t (1 - p)^{n-t}, \quad 0 \le p \le 1$$

and

$$t = 0, 1, 2, \ldots, n.$$

    (a) Determine the reliability function of the component at time t.

    (b) Calculate the failure rate of the electrical component.

3.16. A needle of length a is tossed onto a flat surface ruled with equidistant parallel lines, the distance between each of which is d, where $d > a$. Find the probability that the needle intersects one of the ruled lines. This problem is known as *Buffon's Needle Problem*.

Solution: Assume the needle to be positioned as in (a). Let X be the perpendicular distance from the midpoint of the needle to the nearest parallel line, and let θ be the angle that the needle makes with this perpendicular line. Thus, X takes on some value x from 0 to $d/2$, and θ takes on some value θ from $-(\pi/2)$ to $\pi/2$. From (a) we see that if $x < a/2 \cos \theta$, then the needle intersects one of the lines; otherwise,

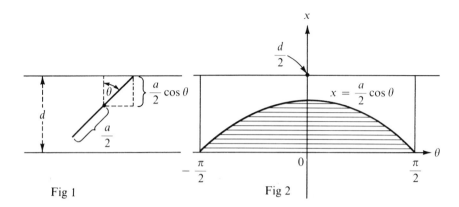

Fig 1   Fig 2

there is no intersection. Figure (6) depicts the situation: The rectangle with base π and height $d/2$ represents the total probability involved in this situation, and the shaded area represents that portion of the total probability where intersection of a parallel line with the needle occurs. Thus, our desired probability will be equal to the shaded area divided by the total area. Show that the result is $2a/\pi d$.

3.17. In Exercise 3.16, show that, if $a > d$, the probability that the needle intersects a parallel line is

$$\frac{2}{\pi}\left[\frac{(a - \sin \phi)}{d + \phi}\right], \quad \text{where} \quad \phi = \cos^{-1}\left(\frac{d}{a}\right).$$

3.18. The base, X, and the height, Y, of a triangle are obtained by picking points x and y at random on two line segments of length a and b respectively, where x is the distance from the left-hand end of the segment a to x, and similarly for y. Find the probability that the area of the triangle is less than $ab/4$.

3.19. The numbers a and b are chosen at random between 1 and 2 and -1 and 1, respectively, all values being equally likely. Find the probability that the solution to $ax + b = 0$ is less than $1/4$.

3.20. The base of a triangle is 2 units long. The length of one of its sides is X, where X was chosen at random between 0 and 4, all numbers being equally likely. The angle between the base and x is θ, where θ is chosen at random from 0 to π, all values being equally likely. Find the probability that the area of the triangle is less than 2.

Problems

3.1. Let X be a random variable, the probability density function of which is given by

$$f(x) = \begin{cases} x, & 0 \le x \le 1, \\ 2 - x, & 1 < x \le 2, \\ 0, & \text{elsewhere.} \end{cases}$$

We define the following events:

$$S_1 = \left\{x: -4 < x \le \frac{1}{2}\right\},$$

$$S_2 = \{x: 0 < x \le 1\},$$

$$S_3 = \left\{x: \frac{1}{2} \le x \le \frac{3}{2}\right\},$$

$$S_4 = \left\{x: \frac{1}{2} \le x < \infty\right\}.$$

Evaluate the probability of the following:
(a) $S_1 \cup S_2$,   (b) $S_1 \cap S_3$,
(c) $\bar{S}_1 \cup S_4$,   (d) $\bar{S}_4 \cap S_3$,
(e) $(S_1 \cap S_2) \cup S_3$,   (f) $(\bar{S}_1 \cup S_2) \cap \bar{S}_4$,
(g) $(S_1 \cap S_3) \cup (S_2 \cap S_4)$,   (h) $(S_1 \cup S_2) \cap (S_3 \cup S_4)$,
(i) $(\bar{S}_1 \cup \bar{S}_3) \cup S_2$,   (j) $(S_1 \cup S_3) \cap S_4$.

3.2. Determine the cumulative distribution function of the random variable X whose density is given in Problem 3.1. Sketch $F(x)$.

3.3. The probability density function of the random variable X is given by

$$f(x) = \begin{cases} 3x^2, & 0 \le x \le 1, \\ 0, & \text{elsewhere.} \end{cases}$$

What is the probability that neither of two independent observations that the random variable X may assume falls in the interval $[1/3, 2/3]$?

3.4. In Exercise 3.1, what is the probability that the random variable X will assume a value from $\pi/6$ to $\pi/3$, exclusively?

3.5. The probability density function of the random variable Y is given by

$$f(y) = \begin{cases} y, & 0 \le y \le 1, \\ 2 - y, & 1 < y < 2, \\ 0, & \text{elsewhere.} \end{cases}$$

What is the probability that the random variable Y will assume a value

(a) greater than 1/2?
(b) less than 3/2?
(c) between 1/2 and 3/2?

3.6. In Exercise 3.2, what is the probability that X assumes a value from the set $S_X^* \cap S_X$, $S_X = \{x: 3/2 \le x \le 3\}$?

3.7. The amount of lamb meat in hundreds of pounds that a certain slaughter house is able to sell in a day is found to be a numerical-valued random phenomenon described by the function

$$f(x) = \begin{cases} cx, & 0 \le x < 2, \\ c(10 - x), & 0 \le x \le 7. \end{cases}$$

(a) Find c so that $f(x)$ will be a probability density function.
(b) What is the probability that the number of pounds of lamb that will be sold the day before Easter will be between 150 and 550 pounds?

3.8. In Exercise 3.4, evaluate the following probabilities.

(1) $Pr\left(Y > \dfrac{1}{2}\right)$ (2) $Pr\left(\dfrac{3}{4} \le Y \le 1\right)$.

3.9. Let the probability density function of the random variable X be given by

$$f(x) = \begin{cases} \dfrac{1}{\pi - 2} x^2 \sin x, & 0 < x < \dfrac{\pi}{2}, \\ 0, & \text{elsewhere.} \end{cases}$$

(a) Find the cumulative distribution function of the random variable X.
(b) Evaluate $Pr(X \ge \pi/3)$ and $Pr(|X| \le \pi/6)$.

3.10. The graph of the cumulative distribution function of the random variable X is shown in the accompanying diagram.

(a) Find the probability density function and cumulative distribution function of the random variable X. Be sure to include all the points at which $f(x)$ is undefined.

(b) Evaluate $Pr(X \geq 5/2)$ and $Pr(1/2 \leq X \leq 5/2)$.

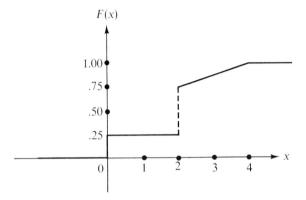

3.11. In Exercise 3.7, find the probability that the random variable Z will assume a value from $[1/2, 10]$, and $[16, \infty)$.

3.12. In Exercise 3.8, evaluate the following probabilities:

(1) $Pr\left(\dfrac{3\pi}{2} \leq X \leq 10.5\right)$, (2) $Pr(1 \leq X \leq 4.5)$,

(3) $Pr(X \geq 11.5)$, (4) $Pr(|X| \leq 3)$.

3.13. The hardness of a piece of ceramic is proportional to the firing time. Assume that a rating system has been devised to rate the hardness of a ceramic piece and that this measure of hardness is a random variable that is *distributed uniformly* between 0 and 10. If a hardness in $[5, 9]$ is desirable for kitchen ware, what is the probability that a piece chosen at random will be suitable for kitchen use?

3.14. A geologist defines granite as a rock containing quartz, feldspar, and small amounts of other minerals, provided that it contains not more than 75% quartz. If all the percentages are equally likely, what proportion of granite samples that the geologist collects during his lifetime will contain from 50% to 65% quartz?

3.15. A life insurance company has insured a group of 1000 persons who are 28 years of age. Their insurance went into effect on August 31; the fiscal year ended December 31. From the mortality table, it was found that the probability of dying at the age of 28 is approximately 0.15. If the company pays $5,000.00 benefits per claim on this group, assuming that the deaths are *uniformly distributed* throughout the year, how much reserve should the company hold for claims for this group for the rest of the fiscal year?

3.16. The thickness of the nickels minted in the Denver mint varies. We shall assume that the random variable which describes such a phenomenon is *normally distributed* with mean 1/16 in. and variance 1/40 in. A nickel will activate a candy machine if its thickness is between 1/32 in. and 3/32 in. What is the probability that if a person randomly selects a nickel from his pocket and puts it into a machine, he will be able to get candy?

3.17. A company annually uses many thousands of electric lamps, which burn continuously day and night. Assume that, under such conditions, the life of a lamp may be regarded as a variable *normally distributed* about a mean of 60 days with a standard deviation of 20 days. On January 1st, the company put 10,000 new lamps into service. Approximately how many lamps would be expected to need replacement by February 1st of the same year?

3.18. In the "time-term" method of refraction seismology, the depths from the surface to a refracting layer is estimated using the time of arrival of vibrations from a distant explosion. Suppose that, for a particular survey, the estimate of depth at each point is subject to a random error, which is assumed to be *normally distributed* with mean zero and standard deviation of 3 ft. If, at a certain point, the true depth is 2 ft, what is the probability that the estimated "depth" will be negative?

3.19. If the grades received by a class of students on an examination are *normally distributed* with a mean of 75 and a standard deviation of 10 and if the highest 10% of these grades are to be A's, find the lowest A.

3.20. A certain industrial process yields a large number of steel cylinders whose lengths are approximately *normally distributed* with mean 3.25 in. and variance 0.008 sq. in. If two cylinders are chosen at random and placed end to end, what is the probability that their combined length is less than 6.55 in.?

3.21. In order to etch an aluminum tray successfully, the pH of the acid solution used must be between 1 and 4. This acid solution is made by mixing a fixed quantity of etching compound in powder form with a given volume of water. The actual pH of the solution obtained by this method is affected by the potency of the etching compound, by slight variations in the volume of water used, and perhaps by the pH of the water. Thus, the pH of the solution varies. Assume that the random variable that describes the random phenomenon is *gamma distributed* with $\alpha = 2$ and $\beta = 1$. (a) What is the probability that an acid solution made by the above procedure will satisfactorily etch a tray? (b) What would the answer to part (a) be if $\alpha = 1$ and $\beta = 2$?

3.22. In a certain country, the distribution of incomes in thousands of dollars is described by a *gamma distribution* with $\alpha = 2$ and $\beta = 8$. What is the probability that a man chosen at random will have an income of (a) over \$14,000? (b) at least \$12,000?

3.23. A cement mixing company has only facilities for a limited amount of storage space for the sand it uses in making ready-mix cement. The demand for sand varies from day to day. Suppose that the random variable that characterizes the problem follows the *gamma distribution* with $\alpha = 2$ and $\beta = 3$. If the storage space holds only 6,000 tons of sand, what is the probability than on any given day the company will not run out of sand?

3.24. A climber is stranded on the side of a mountain and is signaling steadily with his flashlight in hope of attracting a rescue team. If the time in hours that his flashlight is capable of sending out a beam which can be observed from below is a random variable following the *exponential distribution* with $\beta = 6$, (a) what is the probability (assuming other conditions are favorable) that his signal could be seen for at least three hours? (b) construct a table showing the answer to part (a) as beta varies: $\beta = 1, 2, 3, 4, 5,$ and 6.

3.25. Telephone conversation time follows an *exponential distribution* with $\beta = 5$. If you are in a hurry to make a phone call and someone else reaches the phone booth and starts to dial first before you arrive, what is the probability that you will have to wait less than three minutes before he completes his call? Show how your answer will vary as we vary β.

3.26. The life of light bulbs used in traffic lights in a certain town is *exponentially distributed* with a mean of 500 hours. The lights are in operation 24 hours per day and it is assumed for practical purposes that the red and green signals are on for equal intervals of time. On July 25, the maintenance crew installed new bulbs in a traffic light at a major intersection. If Labor Day is September 5th and it is known that the bulbs are all burning properly on September 1st, what is the probability one of the bulbs will burn out during the holiday weekend of September 2 through September 5th?

3.27. Assume that the daily proportion of trailers and "wheeled campers" seeking accommodations in the Smoky Mountain National Park can be treated as a random variable, X, having a *beta distribution* with $\alpha = 5$ and $\beta = 7$. Find the probability that on a given day at least half of the campers seeking accommodations will have this type of equipment.

3.28. The percentage of marketable oysters which are collected on any one day from a large oyster bed varies from day to day. Assume that the random variable which describes this phenomenon follows the beta distribution with $\alpha = 3$ and $\beta = 2$. What is the probability that on any given day the percentage of marketable oysters is between 50% and 70%?

3.29. A spotlight is mounted 100 ft high on a wall, and it is placed in such a way that it can swing freely in a 180° arc. Its purpose is to illuminate another wall that is directly opposite and 173 ft away from the one on which it is mounted. The light also is capable of illuminating a portion of the wall 10 ft to either side of the center spot. Assume that all angular positions of the light are equally likely. If a man is standing 100 ft to the right of center along the wall opposite the light, what is the probability that, when the light is turned on, he will be within the lighted portion of the wall?

3.30. In nineteenth century thermodynamics, a "Maxwell's Demon" was a hypothetical creature that could observe individual molecules in a gas and could operate a shutter over a pinhole in a partition to permit or prevent the molecules from entering an evacuated chamber. In the chamber was a screen, which was parallel to the partition and whose center is five inches from the pin hole and directly opposite it. The molecules behind the shutter have random direction, but the Demon had been instructed only to allow molecules having no vertical component of velocity through the hole. What is the probability that the next molecule will hit the screen between 5 in. and 6 in. from the center?

3.31. The telescopes on the west side of the observation deck of the Empire State Building are so mounted that they swing freely in 180° arcs, aimed along the New Jersey bank of the Hudson River, which lies due west. For a dime, an observer receives 10 seconds of viewing, obviously not enough time to see from the south to the north end of the telescope's arc. Assume that Palisades Amusement Park lies two miles north of the point, directly opposite the Empire State Building, which is approximately one mile from New Jersey. Also assume that the observer can see Palisades Park if the telescope is aimed within a quarter mile on either side of it. What is the probability that an observer will see the park in any given observation, assuming that each portion of the shore is equally likely to be observed?

3.32. A physical fitness test was given to a large number of college freshmen. In part of the test, each student was asked to run as far as he could in ten minutes and the distance each student ran in miles was recorded and can be considered to be a random variable, say X. The data showed that the random variable X followed the *log-normal distribution* with $\mu_Y = 0.25$ and $\sigma_Y = 0.5$. A student is considered physically fit if he is able to run at least 1.5 miles in the time allowed. What percentage of the college freshmen would be considered physically fit if you consider only this part of the test?

3.33. An experimenter is designing an experiment to test tetanus toxoid in guinea pigs. The survival of the animal following the dose of the toxoid is a random phenomenon. Past experience has shown that the random variable that describes such a situation follows the *log-normal distribution* with $\mu_Y = 0$ and $\sigma_Y = 0.70$. As a requirement of good design the experimenter must choose doses at which the probability of surviving is 20%, 50%, and 80%. What three doses should he choose?

3.34. A potter produces plates using a potter's wheel. Since this is a hand process, there is a possibility of considerable variation in the diameters of the plates produced. A plate is considered to be satisfactory for sale if its diameter lies between 10 and 10.25 in. Assume that the random variable X represents the diameters of the plates and that X follows a *Laplace distribution* with $\mu = 10.125$ and $\sigma = 0.1$. What percentage of the potter's output will be salable? If the potter cannot make a profit unless at least 85% of his articles can be sold, what value must σ assume in order to allow a profit?

3.35. A company manufacturing seat belts for automobiles must keep the breaking strength above 2000 psi for the belts to be acceptable by automobile manufacturers. The breaking strength of the belts varies enough to be considered a random phenomenon characterized by X. If the probability distribution of the random variable X is Laplacian with $\mu = 2004$ psi and $\sigma^2 = 4$, what percentage of the belts will be rejected by the automobile manufacturers for having the breaking strength too low?

3.36. A geologist has collected a sample of a certain kind of soil and, by sifting it through a screen has determined that the diameters of soil particles are *log-normally* distributed with mean 0.060 and variance 0.0016. If his sample consists of 5 cu ft, from which he extracts one cubic foot at random to conduct a test, what is the probability that the diameter of the soil particles will be between 0.050 and 0.070 in.?

3.37. The amount of salt in kilograms that can be extracted from a given volume of water drawn from Salt Lake, Utah can be considered to be a random variable, X. Assume that X follows the *Weibull distribution* with $\alpha = 1$, $\beta = 2$, and $\gamma = 0$. In order to make it profitable to obtain salt by this particular extraction process, the yield per sample must be at least one-half kilogram. What is the probability that a given water sample will produce a satisfactory yield?

3.38. The time in seconds that the wheels in a slot machine are allowed to spin after a coin is dropped in is randomly distributed with a *Weibull distribution*, having a threshold of $\gamma = 5$ seconds, a scale parameter of 100, and a shape parameter of $\beta = 3$. What is the probability that, on a given trial, the wheels will spin for more than 10 seconds?

3.39. The time to failure of a certain component within a mechanical system is characterized by the *Poisson probability density function*,

$$f(t; \lambda) = \frac{e^{-\lambda}t^{\lambda}}{t!}, \quad \lambda > 0, t = 0, 1, 2, \ldots.$$

(a) Find the reliability and failure rate functions of the component at time t.
(b) If $\lambda = 5$, what is the reliability of such a component at 200 hours?

3.40. Suppose that the failure of a certain system is characterized by the following function:

$$f(t) = \frac{1}{\theta} e^{\{(e^t - 1)/\theta\} + t}, \quad \theta > 0, \quad t \geq 0.$$

(a) Find the reliability function and failure rate for such a system.
(b) If $\theta = 1$, what is the reliability of such a system at 150 hours?

3.41. Suppose that the time to failure of a certain mechanical system follows the *Weibull function* as its failure density with parameter $\alpha = 5$, $\beta = 1/3$, and $\gamma = 4$. What is the reliability of such a component at 15 hours?

3.42. The reliability function of a certain system is given by

$$R(t) = 1 - \frac{1}{a\sigma\sqrt{2\pi}} \int_0^t \exp\left\{-\left(\frac{x-\mu}{\sqrt{2}\sigma}\right)^2\right\} dx, \quad \sigma > 0, \ -\infty < \mu < \infty,$$

where a is a normalizing constant. Determine the failure rate of such a system.

References

[1] Aitchison, J. and J. R. C. Brown. "The Log Normal Distribution." London: Cambridge University Press.

[2] Pearson, K. "Tables of the Incomplete Gamma Function." London: *Biometrika*, 1922.

[3] Weibull, W. "A Statistical Distribution Function of Wide Applicability." *J. Appl. Mech.* 18, pp. 293–297.

Suggested Supplementary Reading

Cramer, H. *The Elements of Probability Theory and Some of Its Applications.* New York: John Wiley and Sons, Inc., 1955. Stockholm: Almqvist and Wiksell, 1954.

Drake, A. W. *Fundamentals of Applied Probability Theory.* New York: McGraw-Hill Book Company, Inc., 1967.

Feller, W. *An Introduction to Probability Theory and Its Applications.* Vol. 1. 2nd ed. New York: John Wiley and Sons, Inc., 1960.

Fisz, M. *Probability Theory and Mathematical Statistics.* 3rd ed. New York: John Wiley and Sons, Inc., 1962.

Goldberg, S. *Probability: An Introduction.* New Jersey: Prentice-Hall, Inc., 1960.

Harris, B. *Theory of Probability.* Reading, Massachusetts: Addison-Wesley Publishing Company, Inc., 1966.

Lindgren, B. W. and McElrath, G. W. *Introduction to Probability and Statistics.* 2nd ed. New York: The Macmillan Company, 1966.

Mendenhall, W. *Introduction to Probability and Statistics.* 3rd ed. Belmont, California: Wadsworth Publishing Company, Inc., 1971.

Meyer, P. L. *Introduction to Probability and Statistical Applications.* Reading, Massachusetts: Addison-Wesley Publishing Company, Inc., 1965.

Monroe, M. E. *Theory of Probability*. New York: McGraw-Hill Book Company, Inc., 1951.

Papoulis, A. *Probability Random Variables and Stochastic Processes*. New York: McGraw-Hill Book Company, Inc., 1965.

Parzen, E. *Modern Probability Theory and Its Applications*. New York: John Wiley and Sons, Inc., 1960.

Functions of a Random Variable

4

4.0 Introduction

We have seen that, basically, a *random variable* is a function (rule) which assigns a number to every outcome of an experiment; once we know the probability density function of the variable, we know the laws governing it. An important deductive problem in the study of random variables is the derivation of the probability density function of a functional form of the initial variate. That is, we are given the probability density function, $f(x)$, of a random variable X, and we wish to find the probability distribution of a functional form of this variate, $Y = g(X)$.

There are many physical problems in which the derivation of the probability density of the functional form of the given variate is extremely important. For example, the velocity V of a gas molecule (Maxwell-Boltzmann law) behaves as a random variable that is gamma distributed. We would like to derive the distribution of $E = mV^2$, the kinetic energy of the gas molecule. It is clear that, since the value of the velocity is the outcome of a random experiment, so is the value of E. Thus, the functional form of a random variable is a random variable.

In this chapter, we shall study the problem, beginning with a function of a single variate; in Chapter 6, we shall extend our investigation to multivariate functional forms of the random variable.

4.1   Distribution of a Continuous Function of a Discrete Random Variable

Let X be a discrete random variable that can assume the values $x_1, x_2, x_3,$ $\ldots, x_n$, with probabilities $f(x_1), f(x_2), f(x_3), \ldots, f(x_n)$ such that

$$\sum_{i=1}^{n} f(x_i) = 1.$$

Suppose the random variable Y is a function of X: $Y = g(X)$ and we wish to determine the probability density of Y. To do this, we proceed as follows:

(1)   determine the possible values that the variate Y can assume by substituting all the values which the random variable X can take on into $g(X)$, thus obtaining $y_1, y_2, y_3, \ldots, y_n$; and

(2)   obtain the probability that the variate Y assumes these values; that is,

$h(y_1), h(y_2), h(y_3), \ldots, h(y_n)$ such that $\sum_{i=1}^{n} h(y_i) = 1.$

The probability $h(y_i)$ is obtained by summing $f(x)$ over all values of x for which $g(x) = y_i$. We must keep in mind that several different values of x may give rise to the same value of y. This situation will occur when the function g is not a one-to-one function, that is, when there exist points x_1 and x_2, which belong to the domain of g such that $x_1 \neq x_2$ and $g(x_1) = g(x_2)$.

We shall illustrate the procedure by considering the following examples.

Example 4.1.1   Suppose that the random variable X can assume the values $0, 1, 2, 3, 4$, with the following probabilities: $Pr(X = 0) = p_0$, $Pr(X = 1) = p_1$, $Pr(X = 2) = p_2$, $Pr(X = 3) = p_3$, and $Pr(X = 4) = p_4$. Find the probability density of the variate $Y = g(X) = X^2 - 2X + 1$. Here, Y can assume the values $0, 1, 4, 9$, and its density is given by Table 4.1.1.

Table 4.1.1

y	0	1	4	9
$h(y)$	p_1	$p_0 + p_2$	p_3	p_4

Note that, in this example, the values 0 and 2 of x give rise to the value 1 for y; and, thus, $h(1) = Pr(X = 0) + Pr(X = 2) = p_0 + p_2$.

Now let us assume that the function $Y = g(X)$ is a strictly monotonic function in the interval over which X can assume its values; that is, $g(X)$ is either a strictly monotonically increasing or decreasing function of X, as shown in Figure 4.1.1. Recall that such a function guarantees that the mapping of $g^{-1}(y)$ on the set of images of $g(x)$ to the domain of $g(x)$ is a one-to-one function.

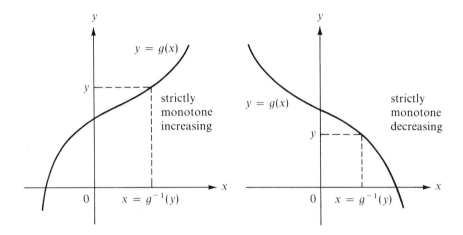

Figure 4.1.1

Thus, when the random variable X assumes the value x, Y will assume the value $y = g(x)$; and the inverse function, $x = g^{-1}(y)$, will also be strictly monotonic. In the discrete case, let $f(x)$ be the probability density function of the variate X. Whenever X assumes a particular value x with probability $f(x)$, then the variate Y assumes the corresponding value of $y = g(x)$, also with the same probability $f(x)$. Therefore,

$$h(y) = f(g^{-1}(y)).$$

More precisely, the inverse of a function is derived by expressing the independent variable as a function of the dependent variable; that is, the inverse of $y = g(x)$ is $x = g^{-1}(y)$. For example, suppose that $y = g(x) = (x + 3)/(2 - x)$; then $x = g^{-1}(y) = (2y - 3)/(y + 1)$.

Example 4.1.2   Suppose that the probability density function of the random variable X is given by

$$f(x) = \begin{cases} \dfrac{x}{8} |x - 3|, & x = 0, 1, 2, 3, 4, \\ 0, & \text{elsewhere.} \end{cases}$$

We want to find the probability density of the random variable $Y = g(X) = (1/2)X + 1$.

Solution: Here, the function $y = g(x) = (1/2)x + 1$ is an increasing function, $g^{-1}(y) = 2(y - 1)$, and

$$h(y) = f(g^{-1}(y)) = \begin{cases} \dfrac{y-1}{4} \, |2y - 5|, & y = 1, \dfrac{3}{2}, 2, \dfrac{5}{2}, 3, \\ 0, & \text{elsewhere.} \end{cases}$$

It is easy to verify that $h(y)$ is a probability density by showing that $\sum h(y) = 1$ and $h(y) \geq 0$ for all y.

To illustrate the above remarks, note that the probability that the random variable X assumes the value 4 is

$$Pr[X = 4] = f(4) = \frac{1}{2}$$

and the corresponding value of $y = (1/2)(4) + 1 = 3$, which gives the same probability, is

$$Pr[Y = 3] = h(3) = \frac{1}{2}.$$

Figure 4.1.2 shows the probability density function of the variate X and that of the derived density of the variate Y.

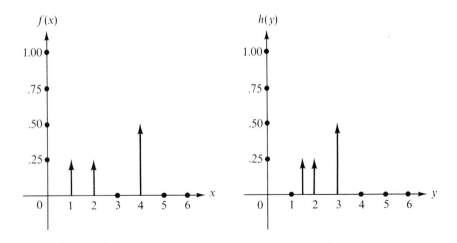

Figure 4.1.2

Example 4.1.3 Suppose that the random variable X has a Poisson distribution:

$$f(x; \lambda) = \begin{cases} \dfrac{e^{-\lambda}\lambda^x}{x!}, & x = 0, 1, 2, \ldots, \\ 0, & \text{elsewhere.} \end{cases}$$

Find the probability density function of the random variable Y, where
(a) $Y = aX + b$ (b) $Y = aX^2$ (c) $Y = \sqrt{X}$.

Solution: (a)   Since $y = g(x) = ax + b$ is a strictly monotonic function over the positive integers and $g^{-1}(y) = (y - b)/a$, we have

$$h(y; \lambda) = f(g^{-1}(y); \lambda) = \begin{cases} \dfrac{e^{-\lambda}\lambda^{\{(y-b)/a\}}}{\left(\dfrac{y-b}{a}\right)!}, & \dfrac{y-b}{a} = 0, 1, 2, \ldots, \\ & \text{or}\quad y = b, a + b, 2a + b, \ldots, \\ 0, & \text{elsewhere.} \end{cases}$$

(b)   Here, $g^{-1}(y) = \sqrt{y*/a}$, and the probability density of the variate Y is

$$h(y; \lambda) = f(g^{-1}(y); \lambda) = \begin{cases} \dfrac{e^{-\lambda}\lambda^{\sqrt{y/a}}}{\left(\sqrt{\dfrac{y}{a}}\right)!}, & \sqrt{\dfrac{y}{a}} = 0, 1, 2, \ldots, \\ & \text{or}\quad y = 0, a, 4a, 9a, \ldots, \\ 0, & \text{elsewhere.} \end{cases}$$

(c)   Similarly, $g^{-1}(y) = y^2$ and

$$h(y; \lambda) = f(g^{-1}(y); \lambda) = \begin{cases} \dfrac{e^{-\lambda}\lambda^{y^2}}{(y^2)!}, & y^2 = 0, 1, 2, \ldots, n, \ldots, \\ & y = 0, \sqrt{1}, \sqrt{2}, \ldots, \sqrt{n}, \ldots, \\ 0, & \text{elsewhere.} \end{cases}$$

Example 4.1.4 Let the random variable X have the binomial distribution

$$f(x; n, p) = \begin{cases} \dbinom{n}{x} p^x(1-p)^{n-x}, & x = 0, 1, 2, \ldots, n, \\ & 0 \le p \le 1, \\ 0, & \text{elsewhere.} \end{cases}$$

If $Y = g(X) = (X - np)^2$, find the probability density function of the random variable Y.

---

* We choose the plus sign in all cases because $x = g^{-1}(y)$ can never be negative.

Solution: Here

$$g^{-1}(y) = np \pm \sqrt{y}$$

and

$$h(y) = f(g^{-1}(y)) = \begin{cases} \binom{n}{np - \sqrt{y}} p^{np - \sqrt{y}}(1 - p)^{n(1-p) + \sqrt{y}}, \\[4pt] \qquad \begin{aligned} &y = g(x) \\ &\text{where} \quad x = 0, 1, 2, \cdots, [np]; \end{aligned} \\[10pt] \binom{n}{np + \sqrt{y}} p^{np + \sqrt{y}}(1 - p)^{n(1-p) - \sqrt{y}}, \\[4pt] \qquad \begin{aligned} &y = g(x) \\ &\text{where} \quad x = [np] + 1, [np] + 2, \cdots, n; \end{aligned} \\[10pt] 0, \quad \text{elsewhere}, \end{cases}$$

where $[np]$ denotes the largest integer not exceeding np.

The cumulative distribution function of a random variable $Y = g(X)$ of the discrete type can be derived from the discrete probability density or by directly applying the definition of $F(y)$. For example, if we want to find the cumulative distribution function of $Y = aX + b$, where the random variable X has a Poisson distribution, we proceed as follows: For

$$x \le \left[\frac{y - b}{a}\right],$$

$$F(y) = Pr(Y \le y) = Pr(aX + b \le y) = Pr\left(X \le \frac{y - b}{a}\right) = \sum_{x=0}^{\left[\frac{y-b}{a}\right]} \frac{e^{-\lambda}\lambda^x}{x!}.$$

Therefore,

$$F(y) = \begin{cases} 0, \quad y < b \\[6pt] \displaystyle\sum_{x=0}^{\left[\frac{y-b}{a}\right]} \frac{e^{-\lambda}\lambda^x}{x!}, \quad y \ge b. \end{cases}$$

The cumulative distribution function of the variate X is

$$F(x) = Pr(X \le x) = \begin{cases} 0, \quad x < 0, \\[6pt] \displaystyle\sum_{0 \le x_i \le [x]} \frac{e^{-\lambda}\lambda^{x_i}}{x_i!}, \quad x \ge 0. \end{cases}$$

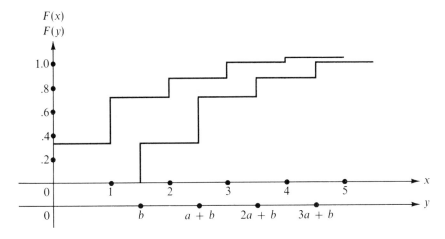

Figure 4.1.3

We conclude the discrete cases by summarizing the preceding developments as follows:

Let X be a discrete random variable having the probability density function

$$P(X = x) = \begin{cases} f(x), & x = x_1, x_2, \ldots, \\ 0, & \text{elsewhere,} \end{cases}$$

and let the random variable Y be a function of X: $Y = g(X)$. Then the probability density of the variate Y is

$$h(y) = \begin{cases} f(g_{x_i}^{-1}(y)), & y = g(x_i), \quad i = 1, 2, 3, \ldots, \\ 0, & \text{elsewhere,} \end{cases}$$

where $g_{x_i}^{-1}(y)$ is the inverse functional form of $g(x)$ that maps y back to x_i. *Note:* It may be the case that one $g(x_i)$ is equal to another. If so, add the density parts corresponding to those functions that are equal. For example, if $g(x_{j_1}) = g(x_{j_2}) = \cdots = g(x_{j_n}) = g(x_t)$, then the density part of $y = g(x_t)$ is

$$\sum_{i=1}^{n} f(g_{x_{j_i}}^{-1}(y)).$$

4.2   *Distribution of a Continuous Function of a Continuous Random Variable*

Let X be a continuous random variable with probability density function $f(x)$. We shall be concerned in this section with deriving the density of the continuous variate $Y = g(X)$. In actual practice, this situation arises quite frequently in engineering problems. The general procedure for deriving such distributions is given by Theorems 4.2.1 and 4.2.2.

Theorem 4.2.1   Let X be a random variable of the continuous type with probability density $f(x)$. If $Y = g(X)$ is a *strictly monotone increasing function* (its inverse exists for all values within the range of X) and if it is differentiable for all x, then the probability density function of the random variable $Y = g(X)$ is given by

$$h(y) = f[g^{-1}(y)] \frac{dg^{-1}(y)}{dy}.$$ (4.2.1)

Proof   From the definition of the cumulative distribution function, we have

$$H(y) = Pr(Y \le y) = Pr(g(X) \le y)$$
$$= Pr(X \le g^{-1}(y)) = F(g^{-1}(y)).$$ (4.2.2)

Differentiating equation (4.2.2) with respect to y, we obtain by using the chain rule

$$\frac{dH(y)}{dy} = \frac{dF(g^{-1}(y))}{dg^{-1}(y)} \frac{dg^{-1}(y)}{dy}$$

or

$$\frac{dH(y)}{dy} = f(g^{-1}(y)) \frac{dg^{-1}(y)}{dy}.$$

Thus, the density of the variate Y is given by Equation (4.2.1).

Example 4.2.1   Let X be a continuous random variable whose probability density is given by

$$f(x) = \begin{cases} \dfrac{1}{12}(x^2 + 1), & 0 \le x \le 3, \\ 0, & \text{elsewhere.} \end{cases}$$

If $Y = g(X) = 2X^2 - 1$, find the probability density of the variate Y.

Solution: Here we see that $g(X)$ is a strictly monotone increasing and differentiable function for $0 \le x \le 3$. Thus,

$$g^{-1}(y) = \sqrt{\frac{y+1}{2}}, \quad \frac{dg^{-1}(y)}{dy} = \frac{\sqrt{2}}{4\sqrt{y+1}};$$

and, applying Equation (4.2.1), we have

$$h(y) = \begin{cases} \dfrac{\sqrt{2}}{96}\dfrac{y+3}{\sqrt{y+1}}, & -1 \le y \le 17, \\ 0, & \text{elsewhere.} \end{cases}$$

It is easy to show that the conditions for a probability function have been met, that is, $h(y) \ge 0$ for all y in the interval $[-1, 17]$ and

$$\frac{\sqrt{2}}{96}\int_{-1}^{17}\frac{y+3}{\sqrt{y+1}}\,dy = 1.$$

Figure 4.2.1 shows a graphical comparison of $f(x)$, $g(x)$, and $h(y)$.

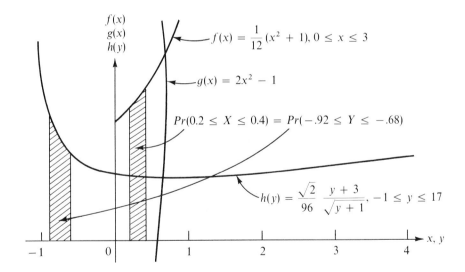

Figure 4.2.1

Example 4.2.2   Let X be a continuous random variable whose probability density function is given by

$$f(x) = \begin{cases} e^{-x}, & x \ge 0, \\ 0, & \text{elsewhere.} \end{cases}$$

If $Y = g(X) = e^{X}$, find the probability density of the variate Y.

Solution: It can be easily shown that the conditions of Theorem 4.2.1 are satisfied. Hence,

$$g^{-1}(y) = \ln y, \qquad \frac{dg^{-1}(y)}{dy} = \frac{1}{y};$$

and, applying Equation (4.2.1), we obtain

$$h(y) = \begin{cases} \dfrac{1}{y} e^{-\ln y}, & y \geq 1, \\ 0, & \text{elsewhere.} \end{cases}$$

To verify that $h(y)$ is a density function, we show that substituting $u = \ln y$, $y\,du = dy$ into

$$\int_1^\infty \frac{1}{y} e^{-\ln y}\,dy$$

gives

$$\int_0^\infty e^{-u}\,du,$$

which equals 1, and $h(y) \geq 0$ for $y \geq 1$.
The cumulative distribution of $Y = e^X$ for $y \geq 1$ is given by

$$H(y) = Pr(Y \leq y) = \int_1^y \frac{1}{t} e^{-\ln t}\,dt = 1 - e^{-\ln y}$$

so that

$$H(y) = \begin{cases} 0, & y < 1, \\ 1 - e^{-\ln y}, & y \geq 1. \end{cases}$$

Figures 4.2.2 and 4.2.3 show the graph of $g(x)$, $f(x)$, $h(y)$, and $F(x)$, $H(y)$, respectively.

Example 4.2.3   The probability density of the velocity, V, of a gas molecule, according to the Maxwell–Boltzmann law, is given by

$$f(v; \beta) = \begin{cases} cv^2 e^{-\beta v^2}, & v > 0, \\ 0, & \text{elsewhere,} \end{cases}$$

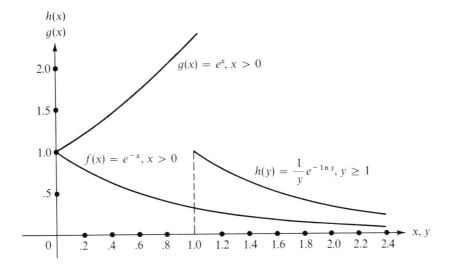

Figure 4.2.2

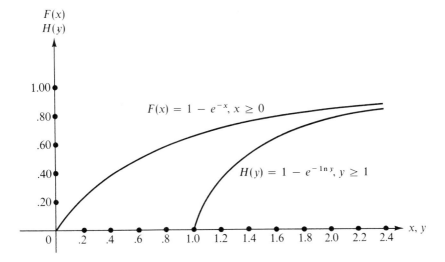

Figure 4.2.3

where c is an appropriate constant and β depends on the mass of the molecule and the absolute temperature. We shall find the density function of the kinetic energy E, which is related to V by $E = g(v) = (1/2)mv^2$.

Solution: For $v > 0$, the function $g(v)$ is a strictly monotone increasing and differentiable function. Thus,

$$g^{-1}(\varepsilon) = \sqrt{\frac{2\varepsilon}{m}}, \quad \frac{dg^{-1}(\varepsilon)}{d\varepsilon} = \frac{1}{m\sqrt{\frac{2\varepsilon}{m}}} = \frac{1}{\sqrt{2m\varepsilon}}$$

and

$$h(\varepsilon; m, \beta) = \begin{cases} \dfrac{c\sqrt{2\varepsilon}}{(m)^{3/2}} e^{-\frac{2\beta\varepsilon}{m}}, & \varepsilon > 0, \\ 0, & \text{elsewhere.} \end{cases}$$

Observe that the probability density of the kinetic energy $h(\varepsilon; m, \beta)$ is a gamma probability density function for a properly chosen c.

Example 4.2.4   Let the random variable X be normally distributed with parameters μ_x and σ_x. If $Y = g(X) = e^X$, find the probability density function of the variate Y.

Solution: Here $g(X)$ is a strictly monotone increasing and differentiable function. Thus, replacing x with $g^{-1}(y) = \ln y$ in

$$f(x; \mu_x, \sigma_x) = \frac{1}{\sqrt{2\pi}\sigma_x} \exp\left\{-\frac{1}{2}\left(\frac{x - \mu_x}{\sigma_x}\right)^2\right\}, \quad \begin{array}{c} -\infty < x < \infty \\ -\infty < \mu_x < \infty \\ \sigma_x > 0 \end{array}$$

and multiplying it by

$$\frac{dg^{-1}(y)}{dy} = \frac{1}{y},$$

we obtain

$$h(y; \mu_x, \sigma_x) = \begin{cases} \dfrac{1}{\sqrt{2\pi}\sigma_x y} \exp\left\{-\frac{1}{2}\left(\frac{\ln y - \mu_x}{\sigma_x}\right)^2\right\}, & y > 0, \\ 0, & \text{elsewhere.} \end{cases}$$

This is the log-normal probability density function, which was developed in Section 3.3.7.

Example 4.2.5 The temperature recording equipment used to determine the melting point, T, of a given substance in degrees centigrade, has an error that can be treated as a random variable having a normal distribution with parameters μ and σ. The temperature F, measured in degrees Fahrenheit, is related to T by $F = g(T) = (9/5)T + 32$. Find the probability density function which describes the behavior of F.

Solution: It is clear that the conditions of Theorem 4.2.1 hold. Thus,

$$g^{-1}(f) = \frac{5}{9}(F - 32), \quad -\infty < f < \infty,$$

$$\frac{dg^{-1}(f)}{df} = \frac{5}{9},$$

and

$$h(f) = \frac{5}{\sqrt{2\pi}9\sigma} \exp\left\{ -\frac{1}{2}\left[\frac{f - (32 + (9/5)\mu)}{9\sigma/5} \right] \right\}, \quad \begin{array}{c} -\infty < f < \infty \\ -\infty < \mu < \infty \\ \sigma > 0. \end{array}$$

Therefore, the temperature F is also normally distributed with mean $(32 + (9/5)\mu)$ and standard deviation $(9/5)\sigma$.

Theorem 4.2.2 Let X be a random variable of the continuous type, with probability density $f(x)$. If $Y = g(X)$ is a *strictly monotone decreasing function* (its inverse exists for all values within the range of X) and if it is differentiable for all x, then the probability density function of the variate $Y = g(X)$ is given by

$$h(y) = f(g^{-1}(y))\left| \frac{dg^{-1}(y)}{dy} \right|. \tag{4.2.3}$$

Proof Since $g(X)$ is a decreasing function, we have

$$\begin{aligned} H(y) = Pr(Y \le y) &= Pr(g(X) \le y) \\ &= Pr(X > g^{-1}(y)) \\ &= 1 - Pr(X \le g^{-1}(y)) \\ &= 1 - F(g^{-1}(y)). \end{aligned} \tag{4.2.4}$$

Differentiating Equation (4.2.4) with respect to y, we obtain

$$\frac{dH(y)}{dy} = \frac{dH(y)}{dg^{-1}(y)} \cdot \frac{dg^{-1}(y)}{d} = \frac{d}{dg^{-1}(y)}[1 - F(g^{-1}(y))]\frac{dg^{-1}(y)}{dy}$$

or

$$h(y) = -f(g^{-1}(y)) \frac{dg^{-1}(y)}{dy}.$$

Since $y = g(x)$ is a strictly monotone decreasing function,

$$\frac{dg^{-1}(y)}{dy} < 0.$$

Therefore,

$$-f(g^{-1}(y)) \frac{dg^{-1}(y)}{dy} = f(g^{-1}(y)) \left| \frac{dg^{-1}(y)}{dy} \right|,$$

giving Equation (4.2.3).

Example 4.2.6   Let X be a continuous random variable whose probability density function is given by

$$f(x) = \begin{cases} \dfrac{1}{4} xe^{-(x/2)}, & x \geq 0, \\ 0, & \text{elsewhere,} \end{cases} \qquad (4.2.5)$$

If $Y = g(X) = -(1/2)X + 2$, find the probability density function of the variate Y.

Solution: Here, $g(X)$ is a decreasing and differentiable function, and the above theorem is applicable. Thus,

$$g^{-1}(y) = 4 - 2y, \qquad \left| \frac{dg^{-1}(y)}{dy} \right| = |-2| = 2.$$

Applying Equation (4.2.3), we have

$$h(y) = \begin{cases} (2 - y)e^{y-2}, & y \leq 2, \\ 0, & \text{elsewhere,} \end{cases} \qquad (4.2.6)$$

and it can be shown that the conditions of a probability density function are satisfied. In Figure 4.2.4, we show a graphical comparison of $g(x)$, $f(x)$, and $h(y)$.

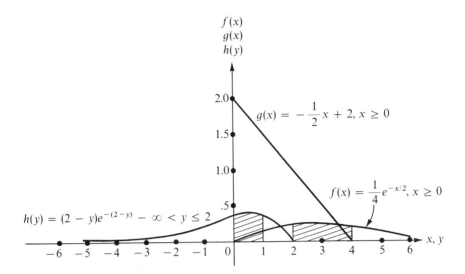

Figure 4.2.4

One can use Equation (4.2.5) to calculate $Pr(2 \le X \le 4)$ or, correspondingly, $Pr[0 \le Y \le 1]$, which can be obtained from Equation (4.2.6). These two probabilities are shown as areas under their respective probability density functions in Figure 4.2.4.

Example 4.2.7 Let $Y = g(\theta) = A \cos \theta$, where the amplitude A is a known positive value and the phase θ is a random variable whose probability density is given by

$$f(\theta) = \begin{cases} \dfrac{2}{\pi}, & 0 \le \theta \le \dfrac{\pi}{2}, \\ 0, & \text{elsewhere.} \end{cases}$$

Find the distribution function of the random variable Y.

Solution: The functional form of θ is a decreasing and differentiable function for all θ, such that $0 \le \theta \le \pi/2$. Hence,

$$g^{-1}(y) = \cos^{-1}\left(\frac{y}{A}\right)$$

and

$$\left| \frac{dg^{-1}(y)}{dy} \right| = \left| \frac{d}{dy} \cos^{-1}\left(\frac{y}{A}\right) \right| = \left| -\frac{1}{A\sqrt{1 - \dfrac{y^2}{A^2}}} \right| = (A^2 - y^2)^{-1/2}.$$

Applying Theorem 4.2.2, we have

$$h(y) = \begin{cases} \dfrac{2}{\pi}(A^2 - y^2)^{-1/2}, & 0 \le y \le A, \\ \\ 0, & \text{elsewhere.} \end{cases}$$

To verify that $h(y)$ is a probability density, we must show that

$$\frac{2}{\pi}\int_0^A \frac{1}{\sqrt{A^2 - y^2}}\,dy = \frac{2}{\pi A}\int_0^A \frac{1}{\sqrt{1 - \left(\dfrac{y}{A}\right)^2}}\,dy = 1. \qquad (4.2.7)$$

Let $u = y/A$ and $A\,du = dy$ in Equation (4.2.7), and we have

$$\frac{2}{\pi A}\int_0^A \frac{1}{\sqrt{1 - \left(\dfrac{y}{A}\right)^2}}\,dy = \frac{2}{\pi}\int_0^1 \frac{1}{\sqrt{1 - u^2}}\,du$$

$$= \frac{2}{\pi}[\sin^{-1}u]_0^1$$

$$= 1.$$

And, because $h(y) \ge 0$ for all y such that $0 \le y \le A$, the conditions of a probability density have been verified.

The cumulative distribution function of the variate Y is

$$H(y) = Pr(Y \le y) = \begin{cases} 0, & y < 0, \\ \dfrac{2}{\pi}\sin^{-1}\left(\dfrac{y}{A}\right), & 0 \le y \le A, \\ 1, & y > A. \end{cases}$$

Example 4.2.8   Let the random variable X have the following function for its probability density

$$f(x) = \begin{cases} \dfrac{1}{\beta - \alpha}, & \alpha \le x \le \beta, \\ \\ 0, & \text{elsewhere.} \end{cases}$$

Find

(a) $Pr(x_1 \le -aX + \beta \le x_2)$, $a > 0$, $b - \alpha\beta \le x_1 \le x_2 \le b - a\alpha$;
(b) $Pr(-x_3 \le -X^2 \le -x_4)$, $\alpha^2 < x_4 < x_3 < \beta^2$.

Solution: In order to obtain the above probabilities, we must first determine the probability densities of the functions $Y = g(X) = -aX + b$ and $Y = g(X) = -X^2$. Both function are differentiable and monotone decreasing in the range of x. Thus, for part (a),

$$g^{-1}(y) = \frac{b - y}{a}, \quad \left| \frac{dg^{-1}(y)}{dy} \right| = \left| -\frac{1}{a} \right| = \frac{1}{a};$$

and, applying Equation (4.2.3), we have

$$h(y) = \begin{cases} \dfrac{1}{a}\dfrac{1}{\beta - \alpha}, & b - a\beta \le y \le b - a\alpha, \\ 0, & \text{elsewhere.} \end{cases}$$

Therefore,

$$Pr(x_1 \le -aX + b \le x_2) = Pr(x_1 \le Y \le x_2) = \int_{x_1}^{x_2} \frac{1}{a} \frac{1}{\beta - \alpha} \, dy$$

$$= \frac{1}{a} \frac{1}{\beta - \alpha} (x_2 - x_1).$$

Note that the same result can be obtained by writing (a) as

$$Pr\left(\frac{b - x_2}{a} \le X \le \frac{b - x_1}{a} \right) = \int_{\frac{b - x_2}{a}}^{\frac{b - x_1}{a}} \frac{1}{\beta - \alpha} \, dy.$$

For part (b), $g^{-1}(y) = \sqrt{-y}$ and

$$\left| \frac{d}{dy} g^{-1}(y) \right| = \left| -\frac{1}{2\sqrt{-y}} \right| = \frac{1}{2\sqrt{-y}}.$$

Substituting these results into Equation (4.2.1) gives

$$h(y) = \begin{cases} \dfrac{1}{2(\beta - \alpha)\sqrt{-y}}, & -\beta^2 < y < -\alpha^2, \\ 0, & \text{elsewhere.} \end{cases}$$

Here

$$Pr(-x_3 \le -X^2 \le -x_4) = Pr(-x_3 \le Y \le -x_4) = \int_{-x_3}^{-x_4} \frac{1}{2(\beta - \alpha)\sqrt{-y}} \, dy$$

$$= \frac{1}{\beta - \alpha} (\sqrt{x_3} - \sqrt{x_4}).$$

We can obtain the same results by writing

$$Pr(-x_3 \leq -X^2 \leq -x_4) = Pr(x_4 \leq X^2 \leq x_3)$$

$$= Pr(\sqrt{x_4} \leq X \leq \sqrt{x_3})$$

$$= \int_{\sqrt{x_4}}^{\sqrt{x_3}} \frac{1}{\beta - \alpha} \, dy$$

$$= \frac{1}{\beta - \alpha} (\sqrt{x_3} - \sqrt{x_4}).$$

There are a number of cases encountered where the function of a random variable, the probability density function of which we know, is not a *one-to-one function*; that is, it is not a *strictly monotone function*. To obtain the distribution of such a function (which includes the preceding two cases) we formulate the procedure as follows:

We shall assume that the random variable X is of the continuous type and that throughout the range of X the function g: $Y = g(X)$ is differentiable. In addition, we shall assume that nowhere in the range of $f(x)$ does g equal a constant over some interval.

Let X have the density function $f(x)$ for $x_0 \leq x \leq x_n$, and 0 elsewhere; let g be the function $Y = g(X)$; and suppose we wish to find the density function of Y. When Y is not monotone in the interval $[x_0, x_n]$, the inverse of g is multiple-valued in places. To deal with this situation, we partition the interval $[x_0, x_n]$ into subintervals in such a way that $Y = g(X)$ is strictly monotone in each of these subintervals. When this is done, we say that $[x_0, x_n]$ has been partitioned so that $Y = g(X)$ is piecewise strictly monotone, thus guaranteeing that in each subinterval the inverse of g is unique. It follows that a part of the density function of Y can be determined for each subinterval. With this accomplished, we add those density parts having the same ranges to get the density function of the random variable Y.

We illustrate the above procedure as follows: Let the variate X have the continuous density function $f(x)$ for $x_0 \leq x \leq x_4$, and 0 elsewhere. Let $Y = g(X)$ be as shown in Figure (4.2.5). We partition the interval $[x_0, x_4]$ into four subintervals, as indicated, so that, in each one, g is strictly monotone, differentiable, and nowhere over an interval equals a constant. Therefore, we can write

$$y = g(x) = \begin{cases} g_1(x), & x_0 \leq x \leq x_1, \\ g_2(x), & x_1 < x \leq x_2, \\ g_3(x), & x_2 < x \leq x_3, \\ g_4(x), & x_3 < x \leq x_4, \end{cases}$$

and

$$x = g^{-1}(y) = \begin{cases} g_1^{-1}(y), & g(x_0) \leq y \leq g(x_1), \\ g_2^{-1}(y), & g(x_2) \leq y < g(x_1), \\ g_3^{-1}(y), & g(x_2) < y \leq g(x_3), \\ g_4^{-1}(y), & g(x_4) \leq y < g(x_3). \end{cases}$$

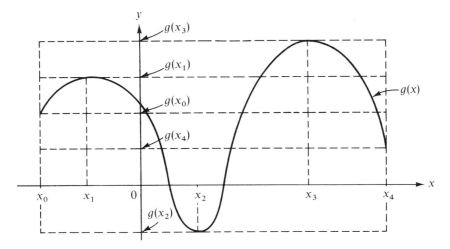

Figure 4.2.5

Next, we partition the $y = g(x)$ axis into subintervals by drawing horizontal lines at $g(x_i)$, $i = 0, 1, 2, 3, 4$. It is easy to see now that, in order to construct the density function of Y for $g(x_2) \leq y < g(x_4)$, we need only consider the parts contributed by $g_2(x)$ and $g_3(x)$; for $g(x_4) \leq y < g(x_0)$, we need parts contributed by $g_2(x)$, $g_3(x)$, and $g_4(x)$, and so on. We can now derive the density function of Y by writing:

$$h(y) = \begin{cases} f(g_2^{-1}(y)) \left| \dfrac{dg_2^{-1}(y)}{dy} \right| \\ \qquad + f(g_3^{-1}(y)) \left| \dfrac{dg_3^{-1}(y)}{dy} \right|, \quad g(x_2) \leq y < g(x_4), \\[2mm] f(g_2^{-1}(y)) \left| \dfrac{dg_2^{-1}(y)}{dy} \right| + f(g_3^{-1}(y)) \left| \dfrac{dg_3^{-1}(y)}{dy} \right| \\ \qquad + f(g_4^{-1}(y)) \left| \dfrac{dg_4^{-1}(y)}{dy} \right|, \quad g(x_4) \leq y < g(x_0), \\[2mm] f(g_1^{-1}(y)) \left| \dfrac{dg_1^{-1}(y)}{dy} \right| + f(g_2^{-1}(y)) \left| \dfrac{dg_2^{-1}(y)}{dy} \right| \\ \qquad + f(g_3^{-1}(y)) \left| \dfrac{dg_3^{-1}(y)}{dy} \right| \\ \qquad + f(g_4^{-1}(y)) \left| \dfrac{dg_4^{-1}(y)}{dy} \right|, \quad g(x_0) \leq y < g(x_1), \\[2mm] f(g_3^{-1}(y)) \left| \dfrac{dg_3^{-1}(y)}{dy} \right| \\ \qquad + f(g_4^{-1}(y)) \left| \dfrac{dg_4^{-1}(y)}{dy} \right|, \quad g(x_1) \leq y \leq g(x_3). \end{cases}$$

We follow with some illustrative examples.

Example 4.2.9   Let the continuous random variable X have the following function for its probability density:

$$f(x) = \begin{cases} \dfrac{1}{18}(x + 2), & -2 \le x \le 4, \\[2mm] 0, & \text{elsewhere.} \end{cases}$$

Find the density function of the random variable $Y = g(X) = X^2$.

Solution: Here we partition the interval $[-2, 4]$ into two subintervals, $[-2, 0]$ and $[0, 4]$, giving us

$$y = g(x) = \begin{cases} g_1(x) = x^2, & -2 \le x \le 0, \\ g_2(x) = x^2, & 0 < x \le 4. \end{cases}$$

(See Figure 4.2.6.)

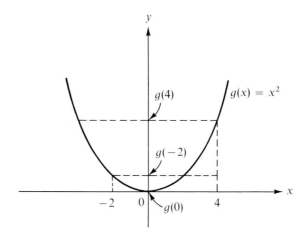

Figure 4.2.6

Also,

$$x = g^{-1}(y) = \begin{cases} g_1^{-1}(y) = -\sqrt{y}, & 0 \le y \le 4, \\ g_2^{-1}(y) = \sqrt{y}, & 4 < y \le 16, \end{cases}$$

and

$$\left| \frac{dg_2^{-1}(y)}{dy} \right| = \left| \frac{1}{2\sqrt{y}} \right| = \frac{1}{2\sqrt{y}} = \frac{dg_2^{-1}(y)}{dy}.$$

Therefore,

$$
h(y) = \begin{cases} \left| f(g_1^{-1}(y)) \left| \dfrac{dg_1^{-1}(y)}{dy} \right| + f(g_2^{-1}(y)) \left| \dfrac{dg_2^{-1}(y)}{dy} \right|, & g(0) \le y \le g(-2), \\[3ex] \left| f(g_2^{-1}(y)) \left| \dfrac{dg_2^{-1}(y)}{dy} \right|, & g(-2) < y \le g(4), \end{cases}
$$

and

$$
h(y) = \begin{cases} \dfrac{1}{9\sqrt{y}}, & 0 \le y \le 4, \\[3ex] \dfrac{1}{36\sqrt{y}}(2 + \sqrt{y}), & 4 < y \le 16, \\[3ex] 0, & \text{elsewhere.} \end{cases}
$$

The function $h(y)$ is nonnegative, and

$$
\int_4^{16} \frac{1}{36\sqrt{y}}(2 + \sqrt{y})dy + \int_0^4 \frac{1}{9\sqrt{y}}\,dy = 1.
$$

Example 4.2.10   Let the random variable θ be distributed uniformly:

$$
f(\theta) = \begin{cases} \dfrac{1}{\pi}, & -\dfrac{\pi}{2} \le \theta \le \dfrac{\pi}{2}, \\[3ex] 0, & \text{elsewhere.} \end{cases}
$$

Find the probability density function of the variate $\phi = g(\theta) = A \cos \theta$.

Solution: The function $g(\theta)$ is not a single-valued function; but, by partitioning the interval $[-(\pi/2), \pi/2]$ into the two intervals $[-(\pi/2), 0]$ and $[0, \pi/2]$, we get

$$
\phi = g(\theta) = \begin{cases} g_1(\theta) = A \cos \theta, & -\dfrac{\pi}{2} \le \theta < 0, \\[3ex] g_2(\theta) = A \cos \theta, & 0 \le \theta \le \dfrac{\pi}{2}, \end{cases}
$$

and

$$
h(\phi) = f(g_1^{-1}(\phi)) \left| \frac{dg_1^{-1}(\phi)}{d\phi} \right| + f(g_2^{-1}(\phi)) \left| \frac{d_2^{-1}(\phi)}{d\phi} \right|, \quad 0 \le \phi \le A.
$$

Also,

$$\left| \frac{dg_1^{-1}(\phi)}{d\phi} \right| = \left| \frac{dg_2^{-1}(\phi)}{d\phi} \right| = \frac{1}{A} \frac{1}{\sqrt{1 - \left(\frac{\phi}{A}\right)^2}} = (A^2 - \phi^2)^{-(1/2)}.$$

Hence,

$$h(\phi) = \begin{cases} \dfrac{2}{\pi}(A^2 - \phi^2)^{-(1/2)}, & 0 \le \phi \le A, \\[2mm] 0, & \text{elsewhere.} \end{cases}$$

The function $h(\phi)$ is nonnegative, and

$$\frac{2}{A\pi} \int_0^A \frac{1}{\sqrt{1 - \left(\frac{\phi}{A}\right)^2}} \, d\phi = \frac{2}{\pi} \int_0^1 \frac{1}{\sqrt{1 - u^2}} \, du = 1.$$

Example 4.2.11   If the random variable X is normally distributed with parameters μ and σ^2,

$$f(x; \mu, \sigma) = \frac{1}{\sqrt{2\pi}\,\sigma} \exp\left\{ -\frac{1}{2}\left(\frac{x - \mu}{\sigma}\right)^2 \right\}, \qquad \begin{aligned} &-\infty < x < \infty \\ &-\infty < \mu < \infty \\ &\sigma > 0, \end{aligned}$$

find the probability density function of the variate

$$Y = g(X) = \left(\frac{X - \mu}{\sigma}\right)^2.$$

Solution: Here we partition the real axis into two subintervals by dividing it at the point $x = \mu$. This gives us that

$$y = g(x) = \begin{cases} g_1(x) = \left(\dfrac{x - \mu}{\sigma}\right)^2, & x < \mu, \\[3mm] g_2(x) = \left(\dfrac{x - \mu}{\sigma}\right)^2, & x \ge \mu, \end{cases}$$

and

$$h(y) = f(g_1^{-1}(y)) \left| \frac{dg_1^{-1}(y)}{dy} \right| + f(g_2^{-1}(y)) \left| \frac{dg_2^{-1}(y)}{dy} \right|, \qquad y > 0.$$

Also,

$$\left| \frac{dg_1^{-1}(y)}{dy} \right| = \left| \frac{dg_2^{-1}(y)}{dy} \right| = \frac{\sigma}{2\sqrt{y}} .$$

Therefore,

$$h(y) = \begin{cases} \dfrac{y^{-(1/2)}}{\sqrt{2\pi}} \, e^{-(1/2)y}, & y > 0, \\[2mm] 0, & \text{elsewhere.} \end{cases} \tag{4.2.8}$$

The probability density (4.2.8) is a gamma distribution, where $\alpha = 1/2$ and $\beta = 2$, which is known as a *chi-square distribution* with one degree of freedom. To show that Equation (4.2.8) is a density function, recall that

$$\int_0^\infty y^{-(1/2)} e^{-(1/2)y} = \left(-\frac{1}{2} \right)! \sqrt{2} = \sqrt{2\pi},$$

which implies that $h(y) = 1$.

4.3   *Other Types of Derived Distributions*

Another case that arises is one in which the random variable X is continuous and its functional form $Y = g(X)$ is piecewise uniformly continuous. For example, let X be a continuous variate with probability density $f(x)$. If

$$Y = g(X) = \begin{cases} \alpha, & X > k, \\ -\alpha, & X \le k, \end{cases}$$

then we want to find the distribution of Y. Here Y can assume only two values, $+\alpha$ and $-\alpha$, and

$$Pr(Y = -\alpha) = Pr(X \le k) = \int_{-\infty}^{k} f(x) \, dx = F(k)$$

$$Pr(Y = \alpha) = Pr(X > k) = 1 - Pr(X \le k)$$

$$= 1 - \int_{-\infty}^{k} f(x) \, dx = 1 - F(k).$$

Thus,

$$F(y) = \begin{cases} 0, & y < -\alpha, \\ F_x(k), & -\alpha \le y < \alpha, \\ 1, & y \ge \alpha \end{cases} \quad \text{and} \quad f(y) = \begin{cases} F_x(\mu), & y = -\alpha, \\ 1 - F_x(\mu), & y = \alpha, \\ 0, & \text{elsewhere.} \end{cases}$$

Example 4.3.1   Let the random variable X have the following function for its density:

$$f(x) = \begin{cases} e^{-(x-1)}, & x \geq 1, \\ 0, & \text{elsewhere.} \end{cases}$$

Find the distribution of the variate $Y = g(X)$, which is the step function,

$$y = g(x) = \begin{cases} 1, & X > 2 \\ -1, & X \leq 2. \end{cases}$$

Solution: Thus,

$$Pr(Y = -1) = Pr(X \leq 2) = \int_1^2 e^{-(x-1)} \, dx$$

$$= \int_0^1 e^{-u} \, du = .632$$

and

$$Pr(Y = 1) = Pr(X > 2) = 1 - Pr(X \leq 2)$$

$$= 1 - \int_1^2 e^{-(x-1)} \, dx = .368.$$

Figure 4.3.1 illustrates $g(X)$, $F(x)$, and $F(y)$.

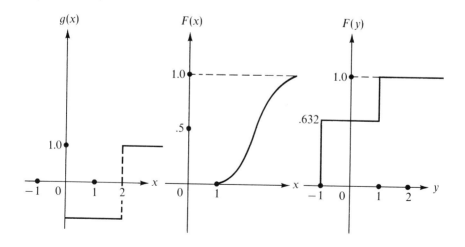

Figure 4.3.1

Thus,

$$h(y) = \begin{cases} .632, & y = -1, \\ .368, & y = 1, \\ 0, & \text{elsewhere.} \end{cases}$$

and

$$H(y) = \begin{cases} 0, & y < -1, \\ .632, & -1 \le y < 1, \\ 1, & y \ge 1. \end{cases}$$

Consider also the case in which the random variable X is of the continuous type and $Y = g(X)$ is discrete. For example, let X be exponentially distributed with parameter β,

$$f(x; \beta) = \begin{cases} \beta e^{-\beta x}, & x \ge 0, \quad \beta > 0, \\ 0, & \text{elsewhere,} \end{cases}$$

and $Y = g(X) = [X]$, where $[X]$ is the greatest integer function. $Y = 0$, $0 \le x < 1$, $Y = 1$, $1 \le x < 2$, $\ldots$, $Y = n$, $n \le x < n+1$, $\ldots$, and so on. The probability density of Y is given by

$$Pr(Y = n) = Pr(n \le X < n + 1) = \int_n^{n+1} \beta e^{-\beta x} \, dx$$

$$= e^{-\beta n} - e^{-\beta(n+1)}.$$

Thus,

$$h(y; \beta) = \begin{cases} e^{-y\beta}(1 - e^{-\beta}), & y = 0, 1, 2, \ldots, \quad \beta > 0, \\ 0, & \text{elsewhere.} \end{cases}$$

It is clear that

$$\sum_{y=0}^{\infty} h(y) = \sum_{y=0}^{\infty} (1 - e^{-\beta})e^{-y\beta} = (1 - e^{-\beta}) \sum_{y=0}^{\infty} (e^{-\beta})^y$$

$$= (1 - e^{-\beta}) \frac{1}{(1 - e^{-\beta})} = 1$$

because $e^{-\beta} < 1$ ($\beta > 0$) is a geometric series.

In this chapter, we have studied functional forms of a single random variable. More precisely, we have discussed the manner in which we can derive the probability distribution of a function of a given variate. In Chapter 6, we shall extend our investigation to multivariate functional forms of a random variable. In the study of probability theory and its applications, the *expected value* or *mean* of a random variable is perhaps the most important single parameter. It will be the aim of the next chapter to analyze the expected value and higher moments of a variate along with *moment generating* and *characteristic functions* of a probability density function of a random variable.

4.4 Summary

The following cases were studied for deriving the probability density of a functional form of a single random variable:

(1) *Distribution of a continuous function of a discrete random variable:* Let X be a discrete variate that can assume the values x_1, x_2, x_3, ..., x_n, with probabilities $f(x_1), f(x_2), \ldots, f(x_n)$, respectively, such that

$$\sum_{i=1}^{n} f(x_i) = 1.$$

To obtain the probability density of $Y = g(X)$, we determine the possible values that Y can assume, by substituting all the values which the random variable X can take on into $g(X)$, thus obtaining y_1, y_2, y_3, ..., y_n; and we obtain the probability that the variate Y assumes these values.

(2) *Distribution of a continuous function of a continuous random variable:* Let X be a random variable of the continuous type with probability density $f(x)$. If $Y = g(X)$ in *strictly monotone increasing function* and if it is differentiable for all x, then the probability density function of the variate Y is

$$h(y) = f(g^{-1}(y)) \frac{dg^{-1}(y)}{dy}.$$

The case in which the functional form of the variate is not a strictly monotone function was studied by partitioning the interval of interest into subintervals in such a way that $Y = g(X)$ is strictly monotone in each of these subintervals.

(3) *Distribution of a piecewise uniformly continuous function of a continuous variate.*

(4) *Distribution of a discrete function of a continuous random variable.*

Exercises

4.1. Let X be a discrete random variable that can assume the values -1, 0, 1, 2, 3, and 4 with probabilities 1/6, 1/12, 1/6, 1/4, 1/12, and 1/4. Find the probability densities of the following random variables:

(a) $Y = \dfrac{1}{2} X - 1,$ (b) $Z = X^2 + 1.$

4.2. The random variable X can assume the values 1, 2, 3, 4, 5, and 6 with probabilities $p_1, p_2, p_3, p_4, p_5,$ and p_6. Find the probability density function of the following random variables:

(a) $Y = (X - 1)^2,$ (b) $Z = \log X,$

(c) $W = e^{-X},$ (d) $Y = \dfrac{1}{X}.$

4.3. If the random variable X is Poisson distributed, find the density functions of the following variates:

(a) $Y = -X,$ (b) $Z = \sqrt{X},$
(c) $W = 2X - 1,$ (d) $Y = X^\alpha$ (α an integer).

4.4. If the random variable X assumes the values 1, 2, 3, and 4, with equal probability, find the density functions of the following variates:

(a) $Y = 1 - 2X,$ (b) $Z = \dfrac{X}{X + 1},$

(c) $W = \cos 2\pi X,$ (d) $Y = X^2 - X - 2.$

4.5. Let the random variable X have the binomial distribution. Find the probability density functions of the following variates:

(a) $Y = aX^2,$ (b) $Y = e^X.$

4.6. Suppose that the random variable X is uniformly distributed over the interval (α, β). Find and sketch the probability density function of the following variates:

(a) $Z = X^2 + 2,$ (b) $W = \dfrac{1}{X - 1},$

  $0 \le \alpha \le \beta < \infty,$ $2 < \alpha \le \beta < \infty,$

(c) $Y = aX + b, \quad \alpha \ne 0,$ (d) $T = \cos X, \quad 0 \le X \le \pi,$

(e) Compare graphically the densities $f(x)$, $h(z)$, and $h(w)$.

4.7.   The probability density of the variate X is given by

$$f(x) = \begin{cases} e^{-(x-6)}, & x \geq 6 \\ 0, & \text{elsewhere.} \end{cases}$$

Find the cumulative distribution function of the random variable $Y = X^2$. Compare graphically $F(x)$ and $F(y)$.

4.8.   The cumulative distribution function of the random variable X is given by

$$F(x) = \begin{cases} 0, & x < 0, \\ 1 - e^{\dfrac{-(x-\alpha)^\beta}{\alpha}}, & x \geq 0, \quad \beta > 0, \quad \alpha \geq 0. \end{cases}$$

Find the probability density function of the following variates

(a) $Y = X^2$,   (b) $Z = \ln X$.

4.9.   The density of the variate X is given by

$$f(x) = \begin{cases} \dfrac{1}{4} xe^{-(x/2)}, & x > 0, \\ 0, & \text{elsewhere.} \end{cases}$$

Find the probability distribution function of the following random variables:

(a) $Y = \alpha X + \beta, \quad \alpha > 0,$ (b) $Z = e^X,$

(c) $Y = \dfrac{1}{X},$ (d) $Z = \sqrt{X}.$

4.10. Suppose that the density of the random variable X is given by

$$f(x) = \begin{cases} \dfrac{2}{15}(x + 2), & -1 < x < 2 \\ 0, & \text{elsewhere.} \end{cases}$$

Find the probability density function of the variate $Y = X^2$. Compare graphically $f(x)$ and $h(y)$.

4.11. Let the random variable θ be uniformly distributed over the interval $(-(\pi/2), \pi/2)$. Show that the variate $X = \mu + \alpha \tan \theta$, has a Cauchy distribution whose density function is given by Equation (3.3.19) where $\alpha = 1$.

4.12. Let the random variable X have the normal distribution with parameters μ and σ^2. Find the probability density of the variate $Y = aX^2 + bX + c$.

4.13. Let the variate X be normally distributed with parameters $\mu = 0$ and $\sigma = 1$. Find and sketch the probability density functions of the following random variables:

  (a) $Y = 2X + 1$, (b) $Z = 2X^2 - 1$,
  (c) $Y = \sqrt{|X|}$.

4.14. Let the probability density function of the random variable X be given by

$$f(x) = \begin{cases} \dfrac{x^{(n-2)/2}}{2^{n/2}\,\Gamma\!\left(\dfrac{n}{2}\right)}\, e^{-(x/2)}, & x > 0,\ n = 1, 2, 3, \ldots, \\ 0, & \text{elsewhere}, \end{cases}$$

which is known as the *chi-square distribution*, with n degrees of freedom. If $S^2 = (\sigma^2/n)X$, $\sigma > 0$, then find the distribution of S^2. For what value of α and β does the new density $h(s^2)$ become a gamma probability density function?

4.15. Let the variate X be gamma distributed with parameters $\alpha = 1$ and $\beta = 2$. If

$$Y = \begin{cases} 2, & X \geq 3, \\ -2, & X < 3, \end{cases}$$

find the cumulative distribution of the random variable Y.

4.16. In a sequence of Bernoulli trials, let X be a random variable representing the number of trials required to achieve k successes. Then the probability density function of X is

$$f(x) = \begin{cases} \dbinom{x-1}{k-1} p^k (1-p)^{x-k}, & x = k, k+1, \ldots, \\ 0, & \text{elsewhere}, \end{cases}$$

where p is the probability of a success on any given trial. Show that the probability density function of $Y = X - k$ is

$$f(y) = \begin{cases} (-1)^y \dbinom{-k}{y} (1-p)^y p^k, & y = 0, 1, 2, \ldots, \\ 0, & \text{elsewhere}. \end{cases}$$

4.17. Let the random variable X have a continuous probability density function, $f(x)$. Find the probability density function of $Y = F(x)$.

4.18. If the probability density function of the random variable X is given by

$$f(x) = \begin{cases} \dfrac{3}{32}(2+x)(2-x), & -2 \le x \le 2, \\ 0, & \text{elsewhere,} \end{cases}$$

find the probability density function of the variate $Y = X(X+1)(X-1)$.

4.19. If the probability density function of the variate T is given by

$$f(x) = \frac{\Gamma\left(\dfrac{n+1}{2}\right)}{\sqrt{n}\,\Gamma\left(\dfrac{n}{2}\right)\Gamma\left(\dfrac{1}{2}\right)\left(1+\dfrac{t^2}{n}\right)^{(n+1)/2}}, \quad -\infty < t < \infty$$

find the probability density function of the random variable $Y = T^2$.

4.20. If the probability density function of the variate X is given by

$$f(x) = \begin{cases} \dfrac{1}{2\pi}, & -\pi \le x \le \pi, \\ 0, & \text{elsewhere,} \end{cases}$$

find the probability density function of the random variable $Y = 2 \sin X$.

Problems

4.1. In Exercise 4.6, find the probability that (a) the random variable Z assumes a value between $1/3$ and $2/3$, inclusive, (b) the variate Y assumes a value less than four, (c) the random variable W assumes a value greater than three, and (d) the variate T assumes a value between zero and $\pi/2$, inclusive.

4.2. In Exercise 4.8, evaluate the following probabilities:

(a) $Pr(1 \le Y \le 3.4)$,   (b) $Pr(|X| \le 4)$,   (c) $Pr(1 < Z \le 2)$.

4.3. In Exercise 4.14, for $n = 4$ and $\sigma^2 = 1$, find the probability that the random variable S^2 assumes a value which is (a) less than or equal to one, (b) between three and four, and (c) greater than six.

4.4. In Example 4.2.3, find c so that the probability density function of the kinetic energy of a gas molecule is actually a gamma probability density.

4.5. The temperature recording equipment used to determine the melting point, T, of a given substance in degrees Fahrenheit has an error which can be treated as a random variable having a normal distribution with parameters μ and σ. The temperature C, measured in degrees centigrade, is related to T by $C = g(T) = (5/9)T - 32(5/9)$. Find the probability density function which describes the behavior of C. Give a graphical comparison of this distribution with that of Example 4.2.5.

4.6. If X is normally distributed with $\mu = 0$ and $\sigma = 1$, then find the following probabilities:

    (a) $Pr[0 \le \sin \pi X \le .2]$,   (b) $Pr[-.25 \le \sin \pi X \le .25]$.

4.7. In an electrical circuit, the voltage source V is a random variable uniformly distributed between 10 and 20 volts. Find the probability density function of the power which is related to V and resistance R by $P = V^2/R$.

4.8. If a random sine wave is given by $X = A \sin \Phi$ where the amplitude A is a known positive constant and the argument Φ behaves as a random variable that is uniformly distributed on the interval $-(\pi/2)$ to $\pi/2$, then find the probability density and cumulative distribution functions of the variate X.

4.9. In Exercise 4.18, evaluate the following probabilities:

    (a) $Pr(-2 \le Y \le .2)$,   (b) $Pr(.2 \le Y \le 2)$.

4.10. In Exercise 4.20, find the probability that the random variable Y assumes a value between (a) 1/4 and 3/4, and (b) $-3/2$ and 1/4, inclusive.

Suggested Supplementary Reading

Feller, W. *An Introduction to Probability Theory and its Applications.* Vol. 1. 2nd ed. New York: John Wiley and Sons, Inc., 1960.

Fisz, M. *Probability Theory and Mathematical Statistics.* New York: John Wiley and Sons, Inc., 1963.

Harris, B. *Theory of Probability*. New York, Reading, Massachusetts: Addison-Wesley Company, 1966.

Papoulis, A. *Probability, Random Variables and Stochastic Processes*. New York: McGraw-Hill Book Company, Inc., 1965.

Parzen, E. *Modern Probability Theory and its Applications*. New York: John Wiley and Sons, Inc., 1960.

Expected Values, Moments, Moment Generating and Characteristic Functions

5

5.0   Introduction

In the study of the theory and applications of probability, the "expected value" or "mean" of a random variable is the most important single parameter. The phrase "expected value" dates back to the development of probability theory in relation to games of chance. Consider a specific example:

A gambler tosses a fair die. If the numbers one, three, or five appear, he will be paid two dollars; if a two or a four turns up, he will lose two dollars; and, if a six occurs, he will receive four dollars. Naturally, the gambler wants to know his "average" or "expected" winnings. Here the payoffs are -2, 2, and 4, and their respective probabilities are $1/3$, $1/2$, and $1/6$. The expected value is obtained by multiplying each payoff by its chance of occurrence and adding the results; thus:

$$-2\left(\frac{1}{3}\right) + 2\left(\frac{1}{2}\right) + 4\left(\frac{1}{6}\right) = 1 .$$

This is the "expected value" of the game. In other words, if the player plays this game a great number of times, his average winnings will be one dollar per toss.

When we speak of the expected value of a random variable X, we refer to an ideal or a theoretical average. However, if a given experiment is repeated many times, we would expect the average value of the random variable involved to be near its expected value.

In this chapter, in addition to studying the expected value of a random variable, we shall also study the following important concepts: moments, moment generating functions, and characteristic functions of a probability density function of a random variable.

5.1   Mathematical Expectation

In this section, we shall give a precise definition of the mathematical expectation of a distribution function and illustrate the calculations by various examples.

Definition 5.1.1   *Let X be a random variable of the discrete type, with probability density function p(x). The series*

$$E(X) = \sum_i x_i p(x_i) \tag{5.1.1}$$

is called the expected value *of the random variable X if the following inequality is satisfied:*

$$\sum_i p(x_i)|x_i| < \infty. \tag{5.1.2}$$

Example 5.1.1   Let X be a discrete random variable whose probability density function is given by Table 5.1.1.

Table 5.1.1

x	-1	0	1	2	3	4	5
$P(x)$	$\dfrac{1}{7}$	$\dfrac{1}{7}$	$\dfrac{1}{14}$	$\dfrac{2}{7}$	$\dfrac{1}{14}$	$\dfrac{1}{7}$	$\dfrac{1}{7}$

The expected value of the random variable X is given by

$$E(X) = \sum_{x=-1}^{5} xp(x) = -1\left(\frac{1}{7}\right) + 0\left(\frac{1}{7}\right) + \cdots + 5\left(\frac{1}{7}\right) = 2.$$

It is clear that, in this example, condition (5.1.2) is satisfied.

Example 5.1.2   Let the random variable X be binomially distributed with parameters n and p. The expected value of the variate X is computed as follows:

$$E(X) = \sum_{x=0}^{n} x \binom{n}{x} p^x (1-p)^{n-x}$$

$$= \sum_{x=0}^{n} \frac{xn(n-1)!}{(n-x)!\, x(x-1)!}\, p^x (1-p)^{n-x}$$

$$= n \sum_{x=1}^{n} \frac{(n-1)!}{(n-x)!\,(x-1)!}\, pp^{x-1}(1-p)^{n-x}$$

$$= np \sum_{x=1}^{n} \binom{n-1}{x-1} p^{x-1}(1-p)^{n-x}$$

$$= np,$$

where the sum is over all possible values that the random variable can assume. Arriving at the last step, we write

$$\sum_{x=1}^{n} \binom{n-1}{x-1} p^{x-1}(1-p)^{n-x} = \sum_{y=0}^{m} \binom{m}{y} p^y (1-p)^{m-y} = 1,$$

which follows by replacing $x-1$ by y and $n-1$ by m. One interpretation of the foregoing could be that, if we inspect n components of a system where each has probability p of being operable, we could "expect" that the total number of operable components would be close to np.

Example 5.1.3   Let the variate X be Poisson distributed with parameter λ. Find the expected value of the random variable X.

Solution: Here

$$p(x) = \begin{cases} \dfrac{e^{-\lambda}\lambda^x}{x!}, & x = 0, 1, 2, \ldots, \\[2mm] 0, & \text{elsewhere,} \end{cases}$$

and

$$E(X) = \sum_{x=0}^{\infty} \frac{xe^{-\lambda}\lambda^x}{x!} = e^{-\lambda} \sum_{x=0}^{\infty} \frac{x\lambda^x}{x(x-1)!}$$

$$= \lambda e^{-\lambda} \sum_{x=1}^{\infty} \frac{\lambda^{x-1}}{(x-1)!} = \lambda e^{-\lambda} \sum_{k=0}^{\infty} \frac{\lambda^k}{k!}$$

$$= \lambda e^{-\lambda} e^{\lambda} = \lambda.$$

Note that, since $E(X) = np$ for the binomial probability density function, we expect that $E(X)$ will equal λ for the Poisson probability density function because, in the derivation of the Poisson distribution, we set λ equal to np.

Definition 5.1.2 *Let X be a random variable of the continuous type with probability density function f(x). The integral*

$$E(X) = \int_{-\infty}^{\infty} xf(x)\, dx \qquad (5.1.3)$$

is called the expected value *of the random variable X, if the following inequality is satisfied*

$$\int_{-\infty}^{\infty} f(x)|x|\, dx < \infty. \qquad (5.1.4)$$

Example 5.1.4 If the random variable X is uniformly distributed over the interval (α, β), find its expected value.

Solution: Here

$$E(X) = \int_{-\infty}^{\infty} xf(x)\, dx = \frac{1}{\beta - \alpha} \int_{\alpha}^{\beta} x\, dx$$

$$= \frac{\beta^2 - \alpha^2}{2} \cdot \frac{1}{\beta - \alpha} = \frac{\beta + \alpha}{2}.$$

Example 5.1.5 Let X be a continuous random variable whose probability density function is given by

$$f(x) = \begin{cases} e^{-(x-4)}, & x > 4, \\ 0, & \text{elsewhere.} \end{cases}$$

Find the expected value of X.

Solution: Applying Equation (5.1.3), we obtain the expected value of the random variable X:

$$E(X) = \int_{4}^{\infty} xe^{-(x-4)}\, dx$$

$$= \int_{0}^{\infty} (u + 4)e^{-u}\, du = 5.$$

Example 5.1.6 Let X be normally distributed with parameters μ and σ^2. Show that the expected value of the random variable x is μ.

Solution:

$$E(X) = \int_{-\infty}^{\infty} xf(x)\, dx = \frac{1}{\sqrt{2\pi}\,\sigma} \int_{-\infty}^{\infty} x \exp\left(-\frac{1}{2}\left(\frac{x - \mu}{\sigma}\right)^2\right) dx.$$

Let $t = \dfrac{x - \mu}{\sigma,}$, $\quad \sigma t + \mu = x$, $\sigma\, dt = dx$, and

$$E(X) = \frac{1}{\sqrt{2\pi}} \int_{-\infty}^{\infty} (\sigma t + \mu) e^{-(1/2)t^2}\, dt$$

$$= \frac{1}{\sqrt{2\pi}} \int_{-\infty}^{\infty} \sigma t e^{-(1/2)t^2}\, dt + \frac{\mu}{\sqrt{2\pi}} \int_{-\infty}^{\infty} e^{-(1/2)t^2}\, dt$$

$$= 0 + \mu = \mu.$$

The expected value of a random variable, $E(X)$, is sometimes called the *mathematical expectation*, the *expectation*, or the *mean value* of the variate. The expected value of a random variable does not always exist. In fact, if the right side of Equation (5.1.1) or (5.1.3) exists but the inequality (5.1.2) or (5.1.4) is not satisfied, then the expected value of the variate does not exist. Thus, if the series (5.1.2) or the integral (5.1.4) is absolutely convergent, then the mathematical expectation of the random variable exists.

We demonstrate the above remarks with Examples 5.1.7 and 5.1.8.

Example 5.1.7   Let X be a random variable of the discrete type whose probability density function is given by

$$f(x) = \begin{cases} \dfrac{6}{\pi^2} \dfrac{1}{x^2}, & x = 1, -2, 3, -4, \ldots, \\ 0, & \text{elsewhere.} \end{cases}$$

Here, if the expected value of X exists, then we would have

$$E[X] = \sum_i x_i f(x_i) = \frac{6}{\pi^2} \left[\frac{1}{1} - \frac{1}{2} + \frac{3}{9} - \frac{4}{16} + \frac{5}{25} - \cdots \right]$$

$$= \frac{6}{\pi^2} \sum_{x=1}^{\infty} \frac{(-1)^{x-1} x}{x^2} = \frac{6}{\pi^2} \sum_{x=1}^{\infty} \frac{(-1)^{x-1}}{x}.$$

Note: it can be shown that $\sum 1/x^2 = \pi^2/6$, $x = 1, -2, 3, -4, \ldots$. Recall that

$$\log_e(1 + x) = x - \frac{x^2}{2} + \frac{x^3}{3} - \frac{x^4}{4} + \cdots + (-1)^{n-1} \frac{x^n}{n} + \cdots$$

for $-1 < x < 1$, which implies that

$$1 - \frac{1}{2} + \frac{1}{3} - \frac{1}{4} + \cdots + (-1)^{x-1} \frac{1}{x} + \cdots = \log_e(2).$$

Hence,

$$E[X] = \frac{6}{\pi^2} \log_e 2 < \infty .$$

However,

$$E[|X|] = \frac{6}{\pi^2} \sum_{x=1}^{\infty} \frac{|(-1)^{x-1}x|}{x^2} = \frac{6}{\pi^2} \sum_{x=1}^{\infty} \frac{x}{x^2}$$

$$= \frac{6}{\pi^2} \sum_{x=1}^{\infty} \frac{1}{x} = \infty .$$

Thus, even though $E[X]$ is calculated to be finite, we must conclude that the expectation of X does not exist because $E[|X|]$ is not finite.

Example 5.1.8   Let X be a continuous random variable whose probability density function is given by

$$f(x) = \frac{1}{\pi} \frac{1}{1+x^2}, \quad -\infty < x < \infty .$$

Find the expected value of X.

Applying Equation (5.1.3), we have

$$E[X] = \int_{-\infty}^{\infty} f(x) \, dx = \frac{1}{\pi} \int_{-\infty}^{\infty} \frac{x}{1+x^2} \, dx$$

$$= \lim_{h \to \infty} \left[\frac{1}{2\pi} \int_{-h}^{h} \frac{2x}{1+x^2} \, dx \right]$$

$$= \lim_{h \to \infty} \left[\frac{1}{2\pi} \log(1+x^2) \Big|_{-h}^{h} \right]$$

$$\lim_{h \to \infty} \left\{ \frac{1}{2\pi} [\log(1+h^2) - \log(1+(-h)^2)] \right\}$$

$$= \lim_{h \to \infty} \left\{ \frac{1}{2\pi} \cdot 0 \right\} = 0.$$

However,

$$E[|X|] = \int_{-\infty}^{\infty} |x| f(x) \, dx = \frac{1}{\pi} \int_{-\infty}^{\infty} \frac{|x|}{(1+x^2)} \, dx$$

$$= \frac{1}{\pi} \left[\int_{-\infty}^{0} \frac{-x}{1+x^2} \, dx + \int_{0}^{\infty} \frac{x \, dx}{1+x^2} \right]$$

$$= \frac{2}{\pi} \int_0^\infty \frac{x}{1+x^2} \, dx = \frac{1}{\pi} \int_0^\infty \frac{2x \, dx}{1+x^2}$$

$$= \lim_{h \to \infty} \frac{1}{\pi} \int_0^h \frac{2x}{1+x^2} \, dx = \lim_{h \to \infty} \left[\log(1+x^2) \Big|_0^h \right]$$

$$= \lim_{h \to \infty} \frac{1}{\pi} [\log(1+h^2) - \log 1]$$

$$= \frac{1}{\pi} \lim_{h \to \infty} [\log(1+h^2)] = \infty.$$

Therefore, although the value of integral (5.1.3) is finite, condition (5.1.4) of Definition 5.1.2 is not satisfied. Thus, the expected value of the above distribution does not exist. This example is actually the Cauchy distribution, with $a = 1$ and $\mu = 0$ (Definition 3.3.5).

5.2   Properties of Expectation

We shall now state some useful theorems regarding expectation.

Theorem 5.2.1   Let X be a random variable with probability density function $f(x)$. If $X = c$, where c is a constant, then $E(X) = c$.

Proof   If the variate X is of the continuous type, then

$$E(c) = \int_{-\infty}^\infty cf(x) \, dx = c \int_{-\infty}^\infty f(x) \, dx = c,$$

and similarly for the discrete case. Note that $X = c$ means that

$$F(x) = Pr(X \le x) = \begin{cases} 0, & x < c, \\ 1, & x \ge c. \end{cases}$$

Theorem 5.2.2   Let X be a random variable with probability density $f(x)$. If $g(X)$ is a one-to-one functional form of the variate X, then the expected value of $g(X)$ is

$$E[g(X)] = \sum_{i=1}^\infty g(x_i)f(x_i) \tag{5.2.1}$$

if X is discrete, and

$$E[g(X)] = \int_{-\infty}^\infty g(x)f(x) \, dx \tag{5.2.2}$$

if X is continuous. Note that, in order for the expected value of $g(X)$ to exist, Equations (5.2.1) and (5.2.2) must be absolutely convergent:

$$\sum_{i=1}^{\infty} |g(x_i)| f(x_i) < \infty \quad \text{and} \quad \int_{-\infty}^{\infty} |g(x)| f(x)\, dx < \infty.$$

Proof   We shall prove the theorem for the discrete case. From the functional form, we have $y_i = g(x_i)$ or $x_i = g^{-1}(y_i)$. Applying the method of deriving distributions (Section 4.1), we can write the probability density of the random variable Y as $h(y_i) = f(g^{-1}(y_i))$. Thus, by definition,

$$E(Y) = \sum_{y_i} y_i h(y_i)$$

$$= \sum_{y_i} y_i f(g^{-1}(y_i)).$$

But $y_i = g(x_i)$, and

$$E(Y) = E(g(X)) = \sum_{x_i} g(x_i) f(x_i).$$

For example, the expected value of the discrete functional form given in Example 4.1.1 is:

$$E(Y) = \sum_{i=1}^{4} y_i h(y_i)$$

$$= y_1 h(y_1) + y_2 h(y_2) + y_3 h(y_3) + y_4 h(y_4)$$

$$= y_1 f(x_1) + y_2\{f(x_0) + f(x_2)\} + y_3 f(x_3) + y_4 f(x_4)$$

$$= g(x_1)f(x_1) + g(x_0)f(x_0) + g(x_2)f(x_2) + g(x_3)f(x_3) + g(x_4)f(x_4)$$

$$= \sum_{i=0}^{5} g(x_i)f(x_i) = E[g(X)].$$

Example 5.2.1   Let X be a discrete random variable that can assume the values 0, 1, 2, 3, with probabilities 1/6, 1/3, 1/6, and 1/3, respectively. Find the expected value of $g(X) = (X - 2)^2$.

Solution: Applying Equation (5.2.1), we have

$$E[g(X)] = \sum_{x=0}^{3} p(x)(x - 2)^2$$

$$= \frac{1}{6}(-2)^2 + \frac{1}{3}(-1)^2 + \frac{1}{6}(0)^2 + \frac{1}{3}(1)^2$$

$$= \frac{4}{3}.$$

Example 5.2.2   Let the random variable X be uniformly distributed over the interval (α, β). Find the expected value of $g(X) = e^{-(x/2)} + 1$.

Solution: Here,

$$E[g(X)] = \int_{-\infty}^{\infty} g(x)f(x) = \frac{1}{\beta - \alpha} \int_{\alpha}^{\beta} (e^{-(x/2)} + 1) \, dx$$

$$= \frac{1}{\beta - \alpha} [x - 2e^{-(x/2)}]_{\alpha}^{\beta} = 1 - \frac{2}{\beta - \alpha} (e^{-\beta/2} e^{-\alpha/2}).$$

Example 5.2.3   If the random variable X has for its probability density the function

$$f(x) = \begin{cases} \dfrac{1}{2} e^{-(x-2)}, & x > 2, \\[2mm] \dfrac{1}{2} e^{x-2}, & x \leq 2, \end{cases}$$

find $E[g(X)]$, where $g(X) = |x - 2|$.

Solution: By definition,

$$E[g(X)] = \int_{-\infty}^{\infty} |x - 2| f(x) \, dx$$

$$= \frac{1}{2} \int_{-\infty}^{2} -(x - 2)e^{x-2} \, dx + \frac{1}{2} \int_{2}^{\infty} (x - 2)e^{-(x-2)} \, dx$$

$$= 1.$$

Examples 5.2.4 and 5.2.5 illustrate the fact that the expected value of a functional form of a random variable exists if and only if $E(|g(X)|)$ converges.

Example 5.2.4   Let the discrete random variable have for its probability density:

$$f(x) = \begin{cases} \dfrac{1}{2} 2^{-|x|}, & x = \pm 1, \pm 2, \ldots, \\[2mm] 0, & \text{elsewhere.} \end{cases}$$

We shall show that the expected value of the functional form,

$$g(X) = (-1)^{|X|-1} \frac{2^{|X|}}{2|X| - 1},$$

does not exist, although its $E[g(X)]$ is finite. Here

$$
\begin{aligned}
E[g(X)] &= \frac{1}{2} \sum_{x=-1}^{-\infty} (-1)^{|x|-1} \frac{2^{|x|}}{2|x|-1} 2^{-|x|} \\
&\quad + \frac{1}{2} \sum_{x=1}^{\infty} (-1)^{x-1} \frac{2^x}{2x-1} 2^{-x} \\
&= \frac{1}{2} \sum_{x=1}^{\infty} (-1)^{x-1} \frac{1}{2x-1} + \frac{1}{2} \sum_{x=1}^{\infty} (-1)^{x-1} \frac{1}{2x-1} \\
&= \sum_{x=1}^{\infty} (-1)^{x-1} \frac{1}{2x-1} = 1 - \frac{1}{3} + \frac{1}{5} - \frac{1}{7} + \cdots = \frac{\pi}{4} < \infty.
\end{aligned}
$$

However,

$$
\begin{aligned}
E[|g(X)|] &= \frac{1}{2} \sum_{x=-1}^{-\infty} \left| (-1)^{|x|-1} \frac{2^{|x|}}{2|x|-1} \right| 2^{-|x|} \\
&\quad + \frac{1}{2} \sum_{x=1}^{\infty} \left| (-1)^{|x|-1} \frac{2^{|x|}}{2|x|-1} \right| 2^{-|x|} \\
&= \frac{1}{2} \sum_{x=1}^{\infty} \left| (-1)^{x-1} \frac{2^x}{2x-1} \right| 2^{-x} + \frac{1}{2} \sum_{x=1}^{\infty} \left| (-1)^{x-1} \frac{2^x}{2x-1} \right| 2^{-x} \\
&= \frac{1}{2} \sum_{x=1}^{\infty} \frac{1}{2x-1} + \frac{1}{2} \sum_{x=1}^{\infty} \frac{1}{2x-1} \\
&= \sum_{x=1}^{\infty} \frac{1}{2x-1} = 1 + \frac{1}{3} + \frac{1}{5} + \frac{1}{7} + \cdots.
\end{aligned}
$$

Note that

$$
1 + \frac{1}{3} + \frac{1}{5} + \frac{1}{7} + \cdots > \frac{1}{3} + \frac{1}{6} + \frac{1}{9} + \frac{1}{12} + \cdots
$$

$$
= \sum_{x=1}^{\infty} \frac{1}{3x}
$$

$$
= \infty.
$$

Therefore,

$$
E[|g(X)|] = \sum_{x=1}^{\infty} \frac{1}{2x-1} = \infty,
$$

and the expected value of $g(X) = (-1)^{|X|-1} 2^{|X|}/(2|X|-1)$ does not exist.

Example 5.2.5 The probability density function of the continuous random variable is given by

$$f(x) = \frac{1}{2} e^{-|x|}, \quad -\infty < x < \infty.$$

As in the previous example, we shall show that the expectation of the functional form of the continuous variate $Y = g(X) = Xe^{|X|}$ does not exist.

$$E[Y] = E[g(X)] = \int_{-\infty}^{\infty} g(x)f(x)\, dx$$

$$= \frac{1}{2} \int_{-\infty}^{\infty} xe^{|x|}e^{-|x|}\, dx = \frac{1}{2} \int_{-\infty}^{\infty} x\, dx = 0 \quad \text{(odd function).}$$

But

$$E[|Y|] = E[|g(X)|] \quad \int_{-\infty}^{\infty} |g(x)|\, f(x)\, dx$$

$$= -\frac{1}{2} \int_{-\infty}^{0} x\, dx + \frac{1}{2} \int_{0}^{\infty} x\, dx = \int_{0}^{\infty} x\, dx = \infty \quad \text{(even function).}$$

Therefore, the expected value of $g(X) = Xe^{|X|}$ does not exist.

Theorem 5.2.3 Let X be a random variable with probability density function $f(x)$. If $g(X) = \alpha X + \beta$, then

$$E[g(X)] = \alpha E(X) + \beta.$$

Proof For the continuous case, we have

$$E[g(X)] = \int_{-\infty}^{\infty} g(x)f(x)\, dx$$

$$= \int_{-\infty}^{\infty} (\alpha x + \beta)f(x)\, dx$$

$$= \alpha \int_{-\infty}^{\infty} xf(x)\, dx + \beta \int_{-\infty}^{\infty} f(x)\, dx$$

$$= \alpha E(X) + \beta.$$

Example 5.2.6 Let X be a continuous random variable whose probability density function is given by

$$f(x) = \begin{cases} e^{-\{x-(1/2)\}}, & x > \frac{1}{2}, \\ 0, & \text{elsewhere.} \end{cases}$$

Find the expected value of the variate $Y = (1/2)X - 2$. Here

$$E(Y) = E\left(\frac{1}{2}X - 2\right) = \int_{1/2}^{\infty} \left(\frac{1}{2}X - 2\right)e^{-\{x - (1/2)\}} \, dx$$

$$= \frac{1}{2}\int_{1/2}^{\infty} xe^{-\{x - (1/2)\}} \, dx - 2\int_{1/2}^{\infty} e^{-\{x - (1/2)\}} \, dx$$

$$= \frac{3}{4} - 2 = -\frac{5}{4}.$$

Example 5.2.7   Let X be normally distributed with parameters μ and σ. Find the expected value of the variate $g(X) = (1/2)X - 3$.

Solution: In Example 5.1.6, we have shown that $E(X) = \mu$. Thus, applying Theorem 5.2.3, we have

$$E[g(X)] = E\left(\frac{1}{2}X - 3\right) = \frac{1}{2}E(X) - 3 = \frac{1}{2}\mu - 3.$$

Theorem 5.2.4   Let X be a random variable, with probability density function $f(x)$. If $f(x)$ is symmetric about the point $x = a$, $f(a - x) = f(a + x)$ for all x, then

$$E(X) = a,$$

provided $E(X)$ exists.

Proof   If X is a continuous random variable, then

$$E(a - X) = \int_{-\infty}^{\infty} (a - t)f(t) \, dt. \tag{5.2.3}$$

In Equation (5.2.3), let $t = a - x$ and $dx = -dt$. Then

$$\int_{-\infty}^{\infty} (a - t)f(t) \, dt = \int_{\infty}^{-\infty} xf(a - x)(-dx) = \int_{-\infty}^{\infty} xf(a - x) \, dx.$$

Thus,

$$E(a - X) = \int_{-\infty}^{\infty} xf(a - x) \, dx. \tag{5.2.4}$$

In Equation (5.2.3), let $t = a + x$ and $dx = dt$. Then

$$\int_{-\infty}^{\infty} (a - t)f(t) \, dt = \int_{-\infty}^{\infty} -xf(a + x) \, dx.$$

Thus,

$$E(a - X) = \int_{-\infty}^{\infty} -xf(a + x)\, dx. \qquad (5.2.5)$$

Substituting $f(a + x) = f(a - x)$ into Equation (5.2.5), we have

$$E(a - X) = \int_{-\infty}^{\infty} -xf(a - x)\, dx. \qquad (5.2.6)$$

Equating Equations (5.2.4) and (5.2.6) gives

$$E(a - X) = \int_{-\infty}^{\infty} xf(a - x)\, dx = -\int_{-\infty}^{\infty} xf(a - x)\, dx,$$

which implies $2 \int_{-\infty}^{\infty} xf(a - x)\, dx = 0$, or

$$E(a - X) = 0.$$

But

$$E(a - X) = 0 = \int_{-\infty}^{\infty} (a - x)f(x)\, dx$$

$$= a \int_{-\infty}^{\infty} f(x)\, dx - \int_{-\infty}^{\infty} xf(x)\, dx,$$

which implies that

$$0 = a - E(X),$$

or

$$E(X) = a.$$

Note that, if we let $a = 0$ in the theorem, we get $E(X) = 0$. Also, $f(x) = f(-x)$. In this case, we say that $f(x)$ is *even*; and, if we wish, we may write

$$\int_{-\infty}^{\infty} f(x)\, dx = 2 \int_{0}^{\infty} f(x)\, dx.$$

Example 5.2.8   Show that, if the variate X is distributed according to the standard normal distribution, $E(X) = 0$.

Solution: Here $a = 0$ and the density function is even, $f(x) = f(-x)$. Thus,

$$E(X) = \frac{1}{\sqrt{2\pi}} \int_{-\infty}^{\infty} xe^{-(1/2)x^2}\, dx$$

$$= -\frac{1}{\sqrt{2\pi}} \left[e^{-(x^2/2)}\right]_{-\infty}^{\infty} = 0.$$

Theorem 5.2.5   Let X be a random variable with probability density function $f(x)$. If $g(X) = g_1(X) + g_2(X)$, the sum of the two functional forms of the variate X, then

$$E[g(X)] = E[g_1(X)] + E[g_2(X)].$$

Proof   If the variate X is continuous, then

$$E[g(X)] = E[g_1(X) + g_2(X)]$$

$$= \int_{-\infty}^{\infty} [g_1(X) + g_2(X)]f(x)\, dx$$

$$= \int_{-\infty}^{\infty} g_1(X)f(x)\, dx + \int_{-\infty}^{\infty} g_2(X)f(x)\, dx$$

$$= E[g_1(X)] + E[g_2(X)].$$

Example 5.2.9   Let X be Rayleigh distributed with $\alpha = 2$. Find the expected value of the random variable

$$g(X) = \frac{1}{X} + e^{-(1/3)X^2}.$$

Solution: Applying Theorem 5.2.5, we have

$$E[g(X)] = E(X^{-1}) + E(e^{-(1/3)X^2}),$$

$$= \int_{-\infty}^{\infty} \frac{1}{x} f(x)\, dx + \int_{-\infty}^{\infty} e^{-(1/3)x^2} f(x)\, dx$$

$$= \int_{0}^{\infty} \frac{1}{x} \cdot xe^{-x^2/2}\, dx + \int_{0}^{\infty} e^{-(1/3)x^2} xe^{-(1/2)x^2}\, dx$$

$$= \frac{\sqrt{2\pi}}{2} \cdot \frac{2}{\sqrt{2\pi}} \int_{0}^{\infty} e^{-(1/2)x^2}\, dx + \int_{0}^{\infty} xe^{-(5/6)x^2}\, dx$$

$$= \frac{\sqrt{2\pi}}{2} - \frac{3}{5} \int_0^\infty e^{-(5/6)x^2} \left(-\frac{5}{3} x\right) dx$$

$$= \frac{\sqrt{2\pi}}{2} - \frac{3}{5} \left[e^{-(5/6)x^2}\right]_0^\infty$$

$$= \sqrt{\frac{\pi}{2}} + \frac{3}{5}.$$

Theorem 5.2.6 Let X be a random variable, with probability density function $f(x)$. If $g_1(X) \le g_2(X)$ for all possible values which the variate X can assume, then

(1) $E[g_1(X)] \le E[g_2(X)]$

and

(2) $|E[g_1(X)]| \le E[|g_1(X)|]$.

Proof

(1) $E[g_1(X)] = \int_{-\infty}^\infty g_1(x)f(x) \le \int_{-\infty}^\infty g_2(x)f(x)\, dx$

$= E[g_2(X)]$.

(2) $|E[g_1(X)]| = \left| \int_{-\infty}^\infty g_1(x)f(x)\, dx \right.$

$\le \int_{-\infty}^\infty |g_1(x)f(x)|\, dx$

$= \int_{-\infty}^\infty |g_1(x)| f(x)\, dx$

$= E[|g_1(x)|]$.

The discrete case can be handled similarly.

5.3 *Moments*

The moments of a distribution are a collection of descriptive constants that can be used for measuring its properties and, under some conditions, for specifying it.

The kth moment of the distribution of a random variable is the expected value of the variate involved raised to the kth power.

Definition 5.3.1   *Let X be a random variable with density function f(x).*
The kth moment or kth ordinary moment of the distribution of the variate X
is given by

$$\mu_k = E(X^k) = \sum_{i=1}^{\infty} x_i^k f(x_i) \tag{5.3.1}$$

if X is discrete, and by

$$\mu_k = E(X^k) = \int_{-\infty}^{\infty} x^k f(x)\, dx \tag{5.3.2}$$

if X is continuous.

Of course, the series (5.3.1) and the integral (5.3.2) must be absolutely
convergent for μ_k to exist. It is also clear that, if $k = 1$, we obtain the mean of
the random variable, which we will denote by μ.

Example 5.3.1   Let X be gamma distributed with parameters α and β.
Compute the rth moment of this gamma density.

   Solution: Here,

$$\mu_r = E(X^r) = \int_{-\infty}^{\infty} x^r f(x)\, dx$$

$$= \frac{1}{\Gamma(\alpha)\beta^\alpha} \int_0^{\infty} x^r x^{\alpha-1} e^{-x/\beta}\, dx$$

$$= \frac{1}{\Gamma(\alpha)\beta^\alpha} \int_0^{\infty} x^{\alpha+r-1} e^{-x/\beta}\, dx$$

$$= \frac{\Gamma(\alpha+r)\beta^{\alpha+r}}{\Gamma(\alpha)\beta^\alpha} = \frac{\Gamma(\alpha+r)\beta^r}{\Gamma(\alpha)}.$$

It is clear that, when $r = 1$, we obtain the mean of the gamma distribution,
$E(X) = \alpha\beta$.

Theorem 5.3.1   Let X have $f(x)$ for its probability density function. If
a is some constant, then

$$E[(aX)^k] = a^k E(X^k).$$

Proof   If X is continuous,

$$E[(aX)^k] = \int_{-\infty}^{\infty} a^k x^k f(x)\, dx$$

$$= a^k \int_{-\infty}^{\infty} x^k f(x)\, dx$$

$$= a^k E(X^k).$$

Definition 5.3.2   *Let X be a random variable with probability density $f(x)$. The kth moment of $f(x)$, with respect to any point b, is given by*

$$E[(X - b)^k] = \sum_{i=1}^{\infty} (x_i - b)^k f(x_i) \tag{5.3.3}$$

if X is discrete, and by

$$E[(X - b)^k] = \int_{-\infty}^{\infty} (x - b)^k f(x)\, dx \tag{5.3.4}$$

if X is continuous.

Example 5.3.2   Let X be uniformly distributed over the interval (α, β). Compute the rth moment of this uniform distribution with respect to any point b.

Solution: Applying Equation (5.3.4), we have

$$E[(X - b)^r] = \int_{-\infty}^{\infty} (x - b)^r f(x)\, dx$$

$$= \frac{1}{\beta - \alpha} \int_{\alpha}^{\beta} (x - b)^r\, dx$$

$$= \frac{1}{\beta - \alpha} \left[\frac{(\beta - b)^{r+1} - (\alpha - b)^{r+1}}{r + 1} \right]$$

$$= \frac{1}{r + 1} \sum_{i=0}^{r} (\alpha - b)^i (\beta - b)^{r-i}.$$

Note that, if $b = 0$ and $r = 1$, we have

$$E(X) = \frac{\beta + \alpha}{2},$$

which is the mean of the uniform distribution over the interval (α, β), as was obtained in Example 5.1.4.

Definition 5.3.3   *Let X be a random variable, with probability density function $f(x)$. The kth moment of $f(x)$, with respect to $E(X) = \mu$, η_k is called the kth central moment of X:*

$$\eta_k = E[X - E(X)]^k = \sum_{i=1}^{\infty} (x_i - \mu)^k f(x_i) \qquad (5.3.5)$$

if X is discrete, and

$$\eta_k = E[X - E(X)]^k = \int_{-\infty}^{\infty} (x - \mu)^k f(x)\, dx \qquad (5.3.6)$$

if X is continuous.

Observe that, if $k = 1$, then $\eta_1 = E[X - \mu] = 0$; that is,

$$\eta_1 = E[X - \mu] = \int_{-\infty}^{\infty} (x - \mu)f(x)\, dx = \int_{-\infty}^{\infty} xf(x)\, dx - \mu \int_{-\infty}^{\infty} f(x)\, dx$$

$$= \mu - \mu = 0.$$

Example 5.3.3   Compute the second central moment of the Poisson distribution, with parameter λ.

Solution: Since $E(X) = \lambda$,

$$E(X - E(X))^2 = \sum_{x=0}^{\infty} (x - \lambda)^2 \frac{e^{-\lambda}\lambda^x}{x!}$$

$$= \sum_{x=0}^{\infty} \frac{x^2 e^{-\lambda}\lambda^x}{x!} - \sum_{x=0}^{\infty} \frac{2\lambda x e^{-\lambda}\lambda^x}{x!} + \sum_{x=0}^{\infty} \frac{\lambda^2 e^{-\lambda}\lambda^x}{x!}$$

$$= \sum_{x=0}^{\infty} \frac{[x(x-1) + x]}{x(x-1)!} e^{-\lambda}\lambda^x - 2\lambda \sum_{x=0}^{\infty} \frac{xe^{-\lambda}\lambda^x}{x(x-1)!} + \lambda^2 \sum_{x=0}^{\infty} \frac{e^{-\lambda}\lambda^x}{x!}$$

$$= \lambda^2 \sum_{x=2}^{\infty} \frac{e^{-\lambda}\lambda^{x-2}}{(x-2)!} + \lambda \sum_{x=1}^{\infty} \frac{e^{-\lambda}\lambda^{x-1}}{(x-1)!} - 2\lambda^2 \sum_{x=1}^{\infty} \frac{e^{-\lambda}\lambda^{x-1}}{(x-1)!} + \lambda^2$$

$$= \lambda^2 + \lambda - 2\lambda^2 + \lambda^2 = \lambda.$$

Thus, the second central moment of the Poisson distribution is equal to its mean.

Example 5.3.4   Express the second and third central moments of the distribution of a random variable X in terms of ordinary moments.

Solution: For the second central moment, we have

$$\eta_2 = E[X - E(X)]^2 = E[X - \mu]^2$$
$$= E[X^2] - 2\mu E[X] + \mu^2$$
$$= \mu_2 - \mu^2.$$

Also,

$$\eta_3 = E[X - E(X)]^3 + E[X - \mu]^3$$
$$= E[X^3] - 3\mu E[X^2] + 3\mu^2 E[X] - \mu^3$$
$$= \mu_3 - 3\mu\mu_2 + 2\mu^3.$$

Thus, from the above example, we can conclude that central moments of a random variable can be expressed in terms of ordinary moments.

Definition 5.3.4   *The second central moment, η_2, of a random variable X is called the* variance *of X, and is denoted by σ^2.*

Thus, if X has a discrete distribution,

$$\text{Var}(X) = \sigma^2 = E[(X - \mu)^2] = \sum_{i=1}^{\infty} (x_i - \mu)^2 f(x_i), \qquad (5.3.7)$$

and if X is a continuous random variable,

$$\sigma^2 = E[(x - \mu)^2] = \int_{-\infty}^{\infty} (x - \mu)^2 f(x) \, dx. \qquad (5.3.8)$$

The variance, σ^2, is a measure of the dispersion of the random variable around its expected value. The smaller the value of σ^2, the more concentrated is the distribution around the mean.

Definition 5.3.5   *The square root of the variance of the distribution of a random variable is called the* standard deviation.

To compute the variance, Theorem 5.3.2 is useful.

Theorem 5.3.2   If X is a random variable with probability density $f(x)$, then

$$\sigma^2 = E[X - E(X)]^2 = E[X^2] - [E(X)]^2. \qquad (5.3.9)$$

Proof   If X is continuous,

$$\sigma^2 = \int_{-\infty}^{\infty} (x - \mu)^2 f(x)\, dx$$

$$= \int_{-\infty}^{\infty} x^2 f(x) - 2\mu \int_{-\infty}^{\infty} xf(x)\, dx + \mu^2$$

$$= E[X^2] - \mu^2.$$

Example 5.3.5   Compute the variance of the binomial distribution with parameters n and p.

We have seen that $E[X] = np$. Next, we compute

$$E(X^2) = \sum_{x=0}^{\infty} x^2 \binom{n}{x} p^x (1-p)^{n-x}$$

$$= \sum_{x=0}^{\infty} [x(x-1) + x] \frac{n(n-1)!}{(n-x)!\,x(x-1)!} p^x (1-p)^{n-x}$$

$$= n(n-1)p^2 \sum_{x=2}^{n} \binom{n-2}{x-2} p^{x-2}(1-p)^{n-x}$$

$$+ np \sum_{x=1}^{n} \binom{n-1}{x-1} p^{x-1}(1-p)^{n-x}$$

$$= n(n-1)p^2 + np.$$

Thus, applying Equation (5.3.9), we obtain

$$\sigma^2 = E[X^2] - [E(X)]^2$$

$$= n(n-1)p^2 + np - n^2 p^2 = np(1-p).$$

Theorem 5.3.3   If a functional form of a random variable X is given by $Y = \alpha X + \beta$, then

$$\mathrm{Var}(Y) = \alpha^2\, \mathrm{Var}(X).$$

Proof   Applying Definition (5.3.5), we have

$$\mathrm{Var}(Y) = \mathrm{Var}(\alpha X + \beta) = E[(\alpha X + \beta) - E(\alpha X + \beta)]^2$$

$$= E[\alpha X + \beta - \alpha E(X) - \beta]^2$$

$$= E[\alpha X - \alpha E(X)]^2$$

$$= E\{\alpha[X - E(X)]\}^2 = E\{\alpha^2[X - E(X)]^2\}$$

$$= \alpha^2 E[X - E(X)]^2$$

$$= \alpha^2\, \mathrm{Var}(X).$$

Theorem 5.3.4   For every constant $c \neq \mu$, the variance of a random variable X satisfies the following inequality,

$$\text{Var}(X) \leq E[(X - c)^2]. \tag{5.3.10}$$

Proof   The quantity $E[(X - c)^2]$ can be written as follows:

$$\begin{aligned}
E[(X - c)^2] &= E\{[(X - \mu) + (\mu - c)]^2\} \\
&= E[(X - \mu)^2] + 2(\mu - c)E(X - \mu) + (\mu - c)^2 \\
&= \text{Var}(X) + (\mu - c)^2.
\end{aligned}$$

Since $(\mu - c)^2 > 0$, from the hypothesis of the theorem, we obtain inequality (5.3.10).

Definition 5.3.6   *A random variable X is called a* standardized random variable *if*

$$E(X) = 0 \quad and \quad \text{Var}(X) = 1.$$

Thus, if the expected value of a random variable X is μ and its standard deviation is σ, then the random variable defined by

$$Z = \frac{X - \mu}{\sigma}$$

is a standardized random variable. That is,

$$E(Z) = E\left(\frac{X - \mu}{\sigma}\right) = \frac{1}{\sigma}[E(X) - \mu] = 0;$$

and, applying Theorem 5.3.3 to the variate Z, we have

$$\text{Var}(Z) = \frac{1}{\sigma^2}\text{Var}(X) = 1.$$

Definition 5.3.7   *The ratio of the standard deviation of a random variable X to its expected value,*

$$V = \frac{\sqrt{E[X - \mu]^2}}{E[X]} = \frac{\sigma}{\mu},$$

is called the coefficient of variation.

The coefficient of variation, V, expresses the magnitude of variation of a random variable relative to its expected value. Thus, if the mean of the variate is one, then V equals the standard deviation, which is a measure of the dispersion of the variate around one.

Example 5.3.6   Compute the coefficient of variation of the random variable X, which is binomially distributed with parameters n and p.

Solution: We have seen in Example 5.1.2 that $E(X) = np$ and in Example 5.3.5 that $\text{Var}(X) = np(1 - p)$. Therefore,

$$V = \frac{\sqrt{np(1 - p)}}{np} = \sqrt{\frac{1 - p}{np}}.$$

We know that, if the probability density function of a random variable is symmetric, then its expected value, if it exists, equals the center of symmetry. Furthermore, the odd central moments of a symmetric distribution, if they exist, are equal to zero. In certain cases, we are interested in establishing the extent to which such a distribution departs from symmetry. Such a measure of asymmetry is given by the following definition.

Definition 5.3.8   *The ratio of the third central moment of the distribution of a random variable X to the cube of its standard deviation,*

$$\gamma = \frac{E[(X - E(X))^3]}{(\sqrt{E[(X - E(X))^2]})^3} = \frac{\eta_3}{\sigma^3},$$

is called the coefficient of skewness.

Thus, if $\gamma = 0$, the distribution is symmetric; if $\gamma > 0$, we speak of positive (skewness) asymmetry; and, if $\gamma < 0$, we refer to negative asymmetry.

Example 5.3.7   Compute the coefficient of skewness for the distribution of the random variable X if it is Poisson distributed.

Solution: We have seen that, if X is Poisson distributed, then $E[X] = \text{Var}(X) = \lambda$. Thus,

$$\gamma = \frac{E[(X - E(X))^3]}{[\sqrt{E[(X - E(X))^2]}]^3} = \frac{E[(X - \lambda)^3]}{(\sqrt{\lambda})^3}$$

and

$$E[(X - \lambda)^3] = E[X^3 - 3X^2\lambda + 3\lambda^2 X - \lambda^3]$$
$$= E[X^3] - 3\lambda E[X^2] + 3\lambda^2 E[X] - \lambda^3.$$

Here

$$E[X^3] = \lambda^3 + 3\lambda^2 + \lambda, \quad E[X^2] = \lambda(\lambda + 1) \quad \text{and} \quad E[X] = \lambda.$$

Thus,

$$E[(X - \lambda)^3] = \lambda^3 + 3\lambda^2 + \lambda - 3\lambda^3 - 3\lambda^2 + 3\lambda^3 - \lambda^3$$

$$= \lambda.$$

Therefore,

$$\gamma = \frac{\lambda}{\lambda^{3/2}} = \frac{1}{\sqrt{\lambda}}.$$

We shall conclude this section by briefly introducing several additional terms which describe the peakedness of a distribution. The degree of peakedness of a distribution is referred to as the *kurtosis* of the distribution. A distribution having a relatively high peak is called *leptokurtic*; a flat-topped distribution is called *platykurtic*; a distribution which is not very peaked or very flat-topped is called *mesokurtic*. Figure 5.3.1 illustrates these types of kurtosis.

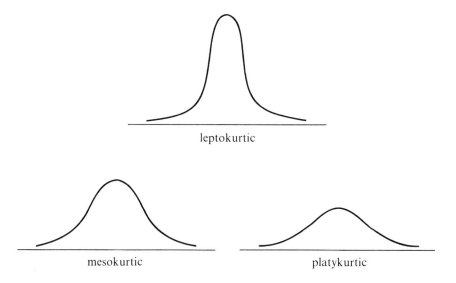

leptokurtic

mesokurtic

platykurtic

Figure 5.3.1

A usual measure of kurtosis is expressed by a dimensionless quantity, given by the ratio of the fourth central moment to the second central moment squared, minus three:

$$\xi = \frac{\eta_4}{\eta_2^2} - 3 .$$

Distributions for which $\xi = 0$ are mesokurtic. Those for which $\xi > 0$ and $\xi < 0$ are leptokurtic and platykurtic, respectively. For the normal distribution with μ and σ^2, ξ is zero.

Example 5.3.8   The kurtosis of the binomial distribution is

$$\xi = \frac{1 - 6pq}{npq} .$$

Note that, as $n \to \infty$, $\xi \to 0$, which is in agreement with the fact that as $n \to \infty$, the binomial distribution tends to the normal distribution. This result will be shown in a later chapter.

5.4 Moment Generating Function

In the theory and application of probability, moments of probability density functions play a very important role. In the preceding section, we saw by working various examples that the manner of computing the moments of various probability distributions can be extremely tedious; it would be useful to obtain an expression that would generate for us all the moments, if they exist, of a density function. Such an expression is called a *moment generating function*, and we define it as follows:

Definition 5.4.1   *Let X be a random variable with probability density $f(x)$. The* moment generating function *(m.g.f.) of $f(x)$ is the expected value of e^{tX}, if it exists, for every value of t in some interval $|t| \leq T$, $T > 0$. We denote the m.g.f. by*

$$m_X(t) = E(e^{tX}) = \sum_{i=1}^{\infty} e^{tx_i} f(x_i) \tag{5.4.1}$$

if the random variable is discrete, and

$$m_X(t) = E(e^{tX}) = \int_{-\infty}^{\infty} e^{tx} f(x) \, dx \tag{5.4.2}$$

if the random variable is continuous. Thus, if the random variable X is discrete, its m.g.f. is defined as the infinite series (5.4.1), and, if it is continuous, its m.g.f. is defined as the improper integral (5.4.2). Such a series or integral may not always converge to a finite value for all values of t. Hence, the m.g.f. may not be defined for all values of t. However, we say that a probability distribution possesses an m.g.f. if there exists a positive number T such that $m_X(t)$ is finite in the interval $-T \le t \le T$. For illustrations of the manner in which an m.g.f. is evaluated, see Examples 5.4.1 through 5.4.5.

Example 5.4.1   Let X be binomially distributed with parameters p and n. Applying Equation (5.4.1), we have

$$m_X(t) = E(e^{tX}) = \sum_{x=0}^{n} e^{tx} \binom{n}{x} p^x (1-p)^{n-x}$$

$$= \sum_{x=0}^{n} \binom{n}{x} (pe^t)^x (1-p)^{n-x}$$

$$= [pe^t + (1-p)]^n.$$

Example 5.4.2   Let X be Poisson distributed, with parameter λ. The m.g.f. is

$$m_X(r) = E[e^{tX}] = \sum_{x=0}^{\infty} e^{tx} \frac{e^{-\lambda} \lambda^x}{x!}$$

$$= e^{-\lambda} \sum_{x=0}^{\infty} \frac{(\lambda e^t)^x}{x!} .$$

Recall that

$$e^{\lambda e^t} = 1 + \lambda e^t + \frac{\lambda^2 e^{2t}}{2!} + \cdots + \frac{\lambda^n e^{nt}}{n!} + \cdots$$

$$= \sum_{x=0}^{\infty} \frac{(\lambda e^t)^x}{x!} .$$

Thus,

$$m_X(t) = e^{-\lambda} e^{\lambda e^t} = e^{\lambda(e^t - 1)}.$$

Example 5.4.3   Suppose that the random variable X is uniformly distributed over the interval (α, β). Then, applying Equation (5.4.2), we obtain the following m.g.f.:

$$m_X(t) = E(e^{tX}) = \frac{1}{\beta - \alpha} \int_{\alpha}^{\beta} e^{tx} \, dx$$

$$= \frac{1}{t(\beta - \alpha)} [e^{\beta t} - e^{\alpha t}].$$

Example 5.4.4   Find the m.g.f. of the random variable X, which is gamma distributed with parameters α and β.

Solution: Here

$$m_X(t) = E(e^{tX}) = \int_{-\infty}^{\infty} e^{tx} f(x) \, dx$$

$$= \frac{1}{\Gamma(\alpha)\beta^{\alpha}} \int_{0}^{\infty} e^{tx} x^{\alpha-1} e^{-x/\beta} \, dx$$

$$= \frac{1}{\Gamma(\alpha)\beta^{\alpha}} \int_{0}^{\infty} x^{\alpha-1} e^{-x/\beta+tx} \, dx$$

$$= \frac{\Gamma(\alpha)\left(\dfrac{\beta}{1-t\beta}\right)^{\alpha}}{\Gamma(\alpha)\beta^{\alpha}}$$

$$= \left(\frac{1}{1-t\beta}\right)^{\alpha} = (1 - t\beta)^{-\alpha},$$

provided that $t < 1/\beta$, since the expression in the brackets represents the area under a gamma density function, with parameters α and $\beta/(1 - t\beta)$, and is by definition equal to one if $t = 0$.

Example 5.4.5   Let the random variable X be normally distributed with parameters μ and σ. The m.g.f. of $f(x)$ is obtained as follows:

$$m_X(t) = E(e^{tX}) = \frac{1}{\sqrt{2\pi}\,\sigma} \int_{-\infty}^{\infty} e^{tx} \exp\left\{ -\frac{1}{2} \left(\frac{x-\mu}{\sigma}\right)^2 \right\} dx$$

$$= \frac{e^{t\mu}}{\sqrt{2\pi}\,\sigma} \int_{-\infty}^{\infty} e^{t(x-\mu)} e^{-(1/2\sigma^2)(x-\mu)^2} \, dx$$

$$= \frac{e^{t\mu}}{\sqrt{2\pi}\,\sigma} \int_{-\infty}^{\infty} e^{-(1/2\sigma^2)[(x-\mu)^2 - 2\sigma^2 t(x-\mu)]} \, dx.$$

Completing the square inside the bracket of the exponent, we have

$$[(x - \mu)^2 - 2\sigma^2 t(x - \mu)] = (x - \mu)^2 - 2\sigma^2 t(x - \mu) + \sigma^4 t^2 - \sigma^4 t^2$$

$$= (x - \mu - \sigma^2 t)^2 - \sigma^4 t^2.$$

Thus,

$$m_X(t) = e^{t\mu + (\sigma^2 t^2/2)} \frac{1}{\sqrt{2\pi}\,\sigma} \int_{-\infty}^{\infty} \exp\left\{ -\frac{1}{2} \left(\frac{x-\mu-\sigma^2 t}{\sigma}\right)^2 \right\} dx.$$

Let

$$y = \frac{x - \mu - \sigma^2 t}{\sigma}, \qquad \sigma \, dy = dx$$

and

$$m_X(t) = e^{t\mu + (\sigma^2 t^2/2)} \left[\frac{1}{\sqrt{2\pi}} \int_{-\infty}^{\infty} e^{-(1/2)y^2} \, dy \right].$$

Therefore, since the integral in the bracket equals one, we have

$$m_X(t) = e^{t\mu + (\sigma^2 t^2/2)}.$$

If the variate X is distributed as a standard normal, that is, $\mu = 0$ and $\sigma^2 = 1$, then its m.g.f. is simply

$$m_X(t) = e^{t^2/2}.$$

5.4.1 *Properties of the Moment Generating Function*   Recall that the Maclaurin series expansion of e^x is

$$e^x = 1 + x + \frac{x^2}{2!} + \frac{x^3}{3!} + \cdots + \frac{x^n}{n!} + \cdots,$$

which converges for all values of x. If the m.g.f. $m_X(t)$ is finite for $|t| \leq T$, $T > 0$, it possesses a power-series expansion, which is valid for $-T \leq t \leq T$. Thus,

$$m_X(t) = E(e^{tX})$$

$$= E\left(1 + tX + \frac{t^2 X^2}{2!} + \frac{t^3 X^3}{3!} + \cdots + \frac{t^n X^n}{n!} + \cdots\right).$$

Taking the expected value of the series by treating t as a constant, we have

$$m_X(t) = 1 + tE(X) + \frac{t^2}{2!} E(X^2) + \frac{t^3}{3!} E(X^3) + \cdots + \frac{t^n}{n!} E(X^n) + \cdots$$

$$= 1 + t\mu + \frac{t^2}{2!} \mu_2 + \frac{t^3}{3!} \mu_3 + \cdots + \frac{t^n}{n!} \mu_n' + \cdots.$$

Differentiating the m.g.f. with respect to t and letting $t = 0$, we obtain the first moment. That is,

$$\frac{dm_X(t)}{dt}\bigg|_{t=0} = \mu + \frac{2t}{2!} \mu_2 + \frac{3t^2}{3!} \mu_3 + \cdots + \frac{nt^{n-1}}{n!} \mu_n + \cdots \bigg|_{t=0}$$

$$= \mu = E(X).$$

Similarly,

$$\frac{d^2 m_X(t)}{dt^2}\bigg|_{t=0} = \mu_2 + t\mu_3 + \cdots + \frac{n(n-1)t^{n-2}}{n!}\mu_n + \cdots \bigg|_{t=0}$$

$$= \mu_2 = E(X^2),$$

$$\frac{d^n m_X(t)}{dt^n} = \mu_n + t\mu_{n+1} + \cdots \bigg|_{t=0} = \mu_n = E(X^n).$$

Thus, we have obtained Theorem 5.4.1.

Theorem 5.4.1   If the moment generating function of a random variable exists for $|t| \le T$, $T > 0$, then

$$\frac{d^n m_X(t)}{dt^n}\bigg|_{t=0} = E(X^n) = \mu_n.$$

We can also develop the theorem as follows: Let X be a continuous variate, with probability density function $f(x)$. Then, differentiating its m.g.f. with respect to t, we have

$$\frac{dm_X(t)}{dt} = \int_{-\infty}^{\infty} \frac{d}{dt}\{e^{tx}\}f(x)\,dx,$$

$$= \int_{-\infty}^{\infty} xe^{tx}f(x)\,dx = E(Xe^{tX}),$$

and

$$\frac{dm_X(t)}{dt}\bigg|_{t=0} = E(X) = \mu.$$

Similarly,

$$\frac{d^n m_X(t)}{dt^n} = \int_{-\infty}^{\infty} \frac{d^n}{dt^n}(e^{tx})f(x)\,dx$$

$$= \int_{-\infty}^{\infty} x^n e^{tx}f(x)\,dx = E(X^n e^{tX}),$$

and

$$\frac{d^n m_X(t)}{dt^n}\bigg|_{t=0} = E(X^n) = \mu_n.$$

Thus, we see that the above function, $m_X(t)$, if it exists, generates all the ordinary moments of a given probability distribution.

Example 5.4.6 We have seen (Example 5.4.1) that the m.g.f. of a binomial distribution, with parameters n and p, is given by

$$m_X(t) = [pe^t + (1 - p)]^n.$$

Applying Theorem 5.3.1, we can obtain the mean and variance of X as follows:

$$E(X) = \frac{dm_X(t)}{dt}\bigg|_{t=0} = n[pe^t + (1 - p)]^{n-1}(pe^t)\bigg|_{t=0} = np,$$

$$E[X^2] = \frac{d^2m_X(t)}{dt^2}\bigg|_{t=0} = n(n - 1)[pe^t + (1 - p)]^{n-2}p^2e^{2t}$$

$$+ n[pe^t + (1 - p)]^{n-1}pe^t\bigg|_{t=0} = n(n - 1)p^2 + np.$$

Thus,

$$\text{Var}(X) = E(X^2) - [E(X)]^2$$
$$= n(n - 1)p^2 + np - n^2p^2 = np(1 - p).$$

Example 5.4.7 Using Theorem 5.3.1, show that the mean and variance of the Poisson distribution, with parameter λ, is equal to λ. In Example 5.4.2, we saw that

$$m_X(t) = e^{\lambda(e^t - 1)}.$$

The mean is obtained by

$$E(X) = \frac{dm_X(t)}{dt}\bigg|_{t=0} = e^{\lambda(e^t - 1)}\lambda e^t\bigg|_{t=0} = \lambda.$$

Also,

$$E(X^2) = \frac{d^2m_X(t)}{dt^2}\bigg|_{t=0} = e^{\lambda(e^t - 1)}\lambda^2e^{2t} + e^{\lambda(e^t - 1)}\lambda e^t\bigg|_{t=0} = \lambda^2 + \lambda,$$

and

$$\text{Var}(X) = E(X^2) - [E(X)]^2 = \lambda^2 + \lambda - \lambda^2 = \lambda.$$

Example 5.4.8 Suppose that the variate X is normally distributed with parameters μ and σ. Find the mean and variance of X.

Solution: The m.g.f. (Example 5.4.5) of X is

$$m_X(t) = e^{t\mu + (\sigma^2 t^2/2)}.$$

Thus,

$$E(X) = \frac{dm_X(t)}{dt}\bigg|_{t=0} = e^{t\mu + (\sigma^2 t^2/2)}(\mu + \sigma^2 t)\bigg|_{t=0} = \mu,$$

$$E(X^2) = \frac{d^2 m_X(t)}{dt^2}\bigg|_{t=0} = e^{t\mu + (\sigma^2 t^2/2)}(\mu + \sigma^2 t)^2 + e^{t\mu + (\sigma^2 t^2/2)}\sigma^2\bigg|_{t=0},$$

$$= \mu^2 + \sigma^2$$

and

$$\text{Var}(X) = E(X^2) - [E(X)]^2 = \mu^2 + \sigma^2 - \mu^2 = \sigma^2.$$

Theorem 5.4.2   Let the random variable X have the m.g.f. $m_X(t)$. If $Y = \alpha X + \beta$, then the m.g.f. of the variate Y is given by

$$m_Y(t) = e^{\beta t} m_X(\alpha t).$$

Proof

$$m_Y(t) = E(e^{Yt}) = E(e^{t(\alpha X + \beta)})$$

$$= E(e^{\alpha t X + \beta t}) = e^{\beta t} E(e^{\alpha t X})$$

$$= e^{\beta t} m_X(\alpha t).$$

We have seen that $m(t)$, if it exists, generates the moments of a probability distribution. In addition, the m.g.f. answers the important question: If we are given a set of moments, what is the probability density function from which these moments came? In relation to this question, we state Theorem 5.4.3.

Theorem 5.4.3   Let X and Y be two random variables with probability densities $f(x)$ and $g(y)$, respectively. If $m_X(t)$ and $m_Y(t)$ exist and are equal for all t in the interval $|t| \le T$, $T > 0$, then X and Y have the same probability distributions, $f(x) = g(y)$.

The proof of this theorem is beyond the scope of this book, but we can illustrate the meaning of the theorem with Example 5.4.9.

Example 5.4.9   Suppose that the random variable X has the m.g.f.

$$m_X(t) = \frac{\alpha}{\alpha - t}, \quad t < \frac{1}{\alpha}.$$

Let the random variable Y have the following function for its probability density:

$$g(y) = \begin{cases} \alpha e^{-\alpha y}, & y > 0, \alpha > 0, \\ 0, & \text{elsewhere.} \end{cases}$$

Can we obtain the probability density of the variate x with the above information?

Here, the m.g.f. of Y is

$$m_Y(t) = E(e^{tY}) = \int_0^\infty \alpha e^{ty} e^{-\alpha y}\, dy$$

$$= \alpha \int_0^\infty e^{-y(\alpha - t)}\, dy$$

$$= \frac{-\alpha}{\alpha - t} e^{-y(\alpha - t)} \Big|_0^\infty$$

$$= \frac{\alpha}{\alpha - t}, \quad t < \frac{1}{\alpha}.$$

Thus, applying Theorem 5.3.3, we have

$$m_X(t) = \frac{\alpha}{\alpha - t} = m_Y(t), \quad t < \frac{1}{a}$$

and, therefore,

$$f(x) \equiv g(y) = \begin{cases} \alpha e^{-\alpha x}, & \alpha > 0, x > 0, \\ 0, & \text{elsewhere.} \end{cases}$$

The theorem says that, if two random variables have the same m.g.f., they have the same probability density function. In fact, the m.g.f. uniquely determines the probability distribution of the random variable.

A moment generating function that sometimes simplifies the problem of finding the moments of discrete probability distributions is the *factorial moment-generating function*, given by

$$g_X(t) = E[(1 + t)^X] = E[e^{X \log(1 + t)}], \quad |t| < 1.$$

The nth derivative, evaluated at $t = 0$, is

$$\frac{d^n g_X(t)}{dt^n} \Big|_{t=0} = E[X(X - 1)(X - 2) \cdots (X - n + 1)].$$

This is the nth factorial moment of the probability distribution of X. Knowing the first n factorial moments of a probability distribution, one can obtain the first n moments of the distribution. For example,

$$\frac{dg_x(t)}{dt}\bigg|_{t=0} = E[X(1+t)^{X-1}]\bigg|_{t=0} = E[X],$$

$$\frac{d^2g_x(t)}{dt^2}\bigg|_{t=0} = E[X(X-1)(1+t)^{X-1}]\bigg|_{t=0} = E[X(X-1)],$$

and

$$E[X(X-1)] = E(X^2) - E(X),$$

or

$$E[X^2] = E[X(X-1)] + E[X].$$

Observe also that we can obtain the factorial moments if we know the moments of a probability distribution.

Example 5.4.10   Find the first three moments of the Poisson distribution using factorial moments.

Solution:

$$g_X(t) = E[(1+t)^X] = \sum_{x=0}^{\infty} \frac{(1+t)^x e^{-\lambda}\lambda^x}{x!}$$

$$= e^{-\lambda}\sum_{x=0}^{\infty}\frac{[\lambda(1+t)]^x}{x!}$$

$$= e^{-\lambda}e^{\lambda(1+t)} = e^{\lambda t}.$$

$$\frac{dg_X(t)}{dt}\bigg|_{t=0} = E[X] = \lambda e^{\lambda t}\bigg|_{t=0} = \lambda,$$

$$\frac{d^2g_X(t)}{dt^2}\bigg|_{t=0} = E[X(X-1)] = \lambda^2 e^{\lambda t}\bigg|_{t=0} = \lambda^2,$$

$$\frac{d^3g_X(t)}{dt^3}\bigg|_{t=0} = E[X(X-1)(X-2)] = \lambda^3 e^{\lambda t}\bigg|_{t=0} = \lambda^3.$$

Therefore,

$$E[X] = \lambda,$$

$$E[X^2] = E[X] + E[X(X - 1)]$$
$$= \lambda + \lambda^2,$$

$$E[X^3] = \lambda^3 + 3E[X^2] - 2E[X]$$
$$= \lambda^3 + 3\lambda^2 + \lambda.$$

5.5 Characteristic Function

We mentioned above that there are probability density functions without finite moments; and, thus, densities exist that do not possess moment generating functions. Here we shall introduce an important function that always exists, which can be used to generate those moments which do exist, and, furthermore, can have its own probability distribution function uniquely determined through an *inversion formula*.

Definition 5.5.1   *The* characteristic function *of a random variable X is given by*

$$\phi_X(t) = E[e^{itX}],$$

where t is a real number and $i = \sqrt{-1}$ *is the imaginary unit.*

Note: In this book, the introduction of $i = \sqrt{-1}$ in no way requires complex integration; i is to be treated as a constant and a constant only.

If X is of the discrete type with density $f(x)$, then

$$\phi_X(t) = E[e^{itX}] = \sum_{i=1}^{\infty} e^{itx_i} f(x_i); \tag{5.5.1}$$

and, if X is continuous, we have

$$\phi_X(t) = E[e^{itX}] = \int_{-\infty}^{\infty} e^{itx} f(x) \, dx. \tag{5.5.2}$$

The moments of the density of a random variable X can be determined from the characteristic function as follows:

$$E(X^n) = \frac{d^n \phi_X(t)}{i^n \, dt^n} \bigg|_{t=0} = \mu_n.$$

To show this, we make use of the Taylor series expansion,

$$\phi_X(t) = E(e^{itX}) = E\left[\sum_{j=0}^{\infty} \frac{(itx)^j}{j!}\right].$$

Next,

$$\frac{d\phi_X(t)}{i\,dt}\bigg|_{t=0} = E\left[\sum_{j=1}^{\infty} \frac{ix(itx)^{j-1}}{i(j-1)!}\right]_{t=0} = E\left[x + \sum_{j=2}^{\infty} \frac{ix(itx)^{j-1}}{i(j-1)!}\right]_{t=0}$$

$$= E[X] = \mu,$$

$$\frac{d^2\phi_X(t)}{i^2\,dt^2}\bigg|_{t=0} = E\left[\sum_{j=2}^{\infty} \frac{i^2x^2(itx)^{j-2}}{i^2(j-2)!}\right]_{t=0} = E\left[x^2 + \sum_{j=3}^{\infty} \frac{i^2x^2(itx)^{j-2}}{i^2(j-2)!}\right]_{t=0}$$

$$= E[X^2] = \mu_2,$$

$$\cdots$$
$$\cdots$$
$$\cdots$$

$$\frac{d^n\phi_X(t)}{i^n\,dt^n}\bigg|_{t=0} = E\left[\sum_{j=n}^{\infty} \frac{i^nx^n(itx)^{j-n}}{i^n(j-n)!}\right]_{t=0} = E\left[x^n + \sum_{j=n+1}^{\infty} \frac{i^nx^n(itx)^{j-n}}{i^n(j-n)!}\right]_{t=0}$$

$$= E(X^n) = \mu_n.$$

Example 5.5.1   Determine the characteristic function of the *geometric distribution* and from it evaluate its mean and variance.

Solution: Applying Equation (5.5.1), we have

$$\phi_X(t) = E[e^{itX}] = \sum_{x=1}^{\infty} e^{itx}f(x)$$

$$= \sum_{x=1}^{\infty} e^{itx}pq^{x-1} = \frac{p}{q}\sum_{x=1}^{\infty}(e^{it}q)^x$$

$$= \frac{pe^{it}}{1 - qe^{it}}.$$

$$E(X) = \frac{d\phi_X(t)}{i\,dt}\bigg|_{t=0} = \frac{pe^{it}}{(1 - qe^{it})^2}\bigg|_{t=0}$$

$$= \frac{p}{(1-q)^2} = \frac{p}{p^2} = \frac{1}{p}.$$

$$(EX^2) = \frac{d^2\phi_X(t)}{i^2\,dt^2}\bigg|_{t=0} = \frac{pe^{it}(1 + qe^{it})}{(1 - qe^{it})^3}\bigg|_{t=0}$$

$$= \frac{p(1+q)}{(1-q)^3} = \frac{1+q}{(1-q)^2} = \frac{1+(1-p)}{p^2} = \frac{2-p}{p^2};$$

thus,

$$\text{Var}(X) = E(X^2) - E(X)^2 = \frac{2-p}{p^2} - \frac{1}{p^2} = \frac{1-p}{p^2} = \frac{q}{p^2}.$$

Example 5.5.2 Let the random variable X be *exponentially distributed*, with parameter β,

$$f(x, \beta) = \begin{cases} \dfrac{1}{\beta} e^{-x/\beta}, & x \geq 0, \beta > 0, \\ 0, & \text{elsewhere.} \end{cases}$$

Evaluate the characteristic function of $f(x, \beta)$ and then obtain its mean and variance. Here,

$$\phi_X(t) = E(e^{itX}) = \int_{-\infty}^{\infty} e^{itx} f(x)\, dx$$

$$= \int_0^{\infty} e^{itx} \frac{1}{\beta} e^{-x/\beta}\, dx$$

$$= \frac{1}{\beta} \int_0^{\infty} e^{-x\{(1-it\beta)/\beta\}}\, dx$$

$$= -\frac{1}{\beta} \frac{\beta}{1-it\beta} e^{-x\{(1-it\beta)/\beta\}} \bigg|_0^{\infty} = \frac{1}{1-it\beta}.$$

Therefore,

$$\phi_X(t) = (1 - it\beta)^{-1},$$

$$E(X) = \frac{d\phi_X(t)}{i\, dt} \bigg|_{t=0} = \beta,$$

$$E(X^2) = \frac{d^2\phi_X(t)}{i^2\, dt^2} \bigg|_{t=0} = 2\beta^2,$$

and

$$\text{Var}(X) = 2\beta^2 - \beta^2 = \beta^2.$$

Example 5.5.3 The characteristic function of the Laplace distribution is obtained as follows:

$$\phi_X(t) = E[e^{itX}] = \int_{-\infty}^{\infty} e^{itx} f(x)\, dx$$

$$= \frac{1}{2\sigma} \int_{-\infty}^{\infty} e^{itx} e^{-(|x-\mu|/\sigma)}\, dx.$$

Let $y = x - \mu$, $dy = dx$, and

$$\phi_X(t) = \frac{1}{2\sigma} \int_{-\infty}^{\infty} e^{it(y+\mu)} e^{-(|y|/\sigma)} \, dy$$

$$= \frac{e^{it\mu}}{2\sigma} \int_{-\infty}^{0} e^{y(it + 1/\sigma)} \, dy + \frac{e^{it\mu}}{2\sigma} \int_{0}^{\infty} e^{y(it - 1/\sigma)} \, dy$$

$$= \frac{e^{it\mu}}{2\sigma} \left\{ \int_{-\infty}^{0} e^{y\{(it\sigma + 1)/\sigma\}} \, dy + \int_{0}^{\infty} e^{y\{(it\sigma - 1)/\sigma\}} \, dy \right\}$$

$$= \frac{e^{it\mu}}{2} \left[\frac{1}{1 + \sigma it} + \frac{1}{1 - \sigma it} \right]$$

$$= \frac{e^{it\mu}}{1 + \sigma^2 t^2} \, .$$

The expected value of X is given by

$$E(X) = \frac{d\phi_X(t)}{i \, dt} \bigg|_{t=0} = \frac{(1 + \sigma^2 t^2) i\mu e^{it\mu} - e^{it\mu} 2\sigma^2 t}{i(1 + \sigma^2 t^2)^2} \bigg|_{t=0} = \mu.$$

$$E(X^2) = \frac{d^2\phi_X(t)}{i^2 \, dt^2} \bigg|_{t=0} = \frac{d}{i^2 \, dt} \left\{ \frac{(1 + \sigma^2 t^2) i\mu e^{it\mu} - 2\sigma^2 t e^{it\mu}}{(1 + \sigma^2 t^2)^2} \right\}_{t=0} = 2\sigma^2 + \mu^2;$$

thus,

$$\text{Var}(X) = E(X^2) - [E(X)]^2$$

$$= 2\sigma^2 + \mu^2 - \mu^2 = 2\sigma^2.$$

Example 5.5.4   The characteristic function of the Cauchy distribution is

$$\phi_X(t) = E[e^{itX}] = \frac{1}{\pi} \int_{-\infty}^{\infty} \frac{e^{itx} \alpha}{\alpha^2 + (x - \mu)^2} \, dx$$

$$= \frac{1}{\pi} \int_{-\infty}^{\infty} \frac{e^{itx} \, dx}{\alpha \left[1 + \left(\dfrac{x - \mu}{\alpha} \right)^2 \right]} \, .$$

Let $u = (x - \mu)/\alpha$, $\alpha \, du = dx$, and

$$\phi_X(t) = \frac{1}{\pi} \int_{-\infty}^{\infty} e^{it(\alpha u + \mu)} \frac{1}{[1 + u^2]} \, du.$$

Recall that

$$e^{itau} = \cos t\alpha u + i \sin t\alpha u$$

and

$$\phi_X(t) = \frac{e^{it\mu}}{\pi} \left[\int_{-\infty}^{\infty} \frac{\cos t\alpha u}{1 + u^2} + i \int_{-\infty}^{\infty} \frac{\sin t\alpha u}{1 + u^2} \, du \right].$$

Since $\sin t\alpha u/(1 + u^2)$ is an odd function of x, that is, $f(x) = -f(-x)$, the second integral vanishes, giving

$$\phi_X(t) = \frac{e^{it\mu}}{\pi} \int_{-\infty}^{\infty} \frac{\cos t\alpha u}{1 + u^2} \, du = \frac{2}{\pi} e^{it\mu} \int_{0}^{\infty} \frac{\cos t\alpha u}{1 + u^2} \, du,$$

because $\cos t\alpha u/(1 + u^2)$ is an even function. It can be shown that

$$\int_{0}^{\infty} \frac{\cos t\alpha u}{1 + u^2} \, du = \frac{\pi}{2} e^{-\alpha|t|},$$

and thus

$$\phi_X(t) = e^{it\mu - \alpha|t|}.$$

It can be shown that $E(X)$ does not exist. That is,

$$\frac{1}{i} \phi_X'(t) \Big|_{t=0} = \frac{1}{i} e^{it\mu - \alpha|t|} \left(i\mu - \alpha \frac{t}{|t|} \right) \Big|_{t=0} = \frac{1}{i} \left[i\mu - \alpha \begin{array}{c} 0 \\ 0 \end{array} \right],$$

which is undefined.

A precise study of the properties of the characteristic function is beyond the scope of this book. However, we shall present some of its basic properties to point out the importance of such a function.

(1) $\phi(t)$ is the expected value of a complex function of a random variable X,

$$e^{itX} = \cos tX + i \sin tX.$$

Because

$$|e^{itX}| = |\cos tX + i \sin tX| = 1,$$

we have

$$\int_{-\infty}^{\infty} |e^{itx}| f(x)\, dx = \int_{-\infty}^{\infty} f(x)\, dx = 1.$$

Thus, if X is a continuous random variable with probability density function $f(x)$, $\phi(t)$ is *absolutely and uniformly convergent*; and, hence, $\phi(t)$ exists and is a continuous function for every value of t. (This, of course, is not true for a moment generating function.)

(2) $\phi(0) = E(e^0) = 1$.

(3) $|\phi(t)| = |E[e^{itX}]| \le E[|e^{itX}|] = 1$

or

$$|\phi(t)| \le \phi(0) = 1.$$

(4) $\phi(-t) = E[e^{-itX}]$

$$= E[\cos tX - i \sin tX]$$

$$= E(\cos tX) - iE(\sin tX)$$

$$= \overline{\phi(t)},$$

where $\overline{\phi(t)}$ is the complex conjugate of the characteristic function.

(5) If $\phi_X(t)$ is the characteristic function of the variate X, then the characteristic function of the random variable $Y = \alpha X + \beta$ is given by

$$\phi_Y(t) = E[e^{itY}] = E[e^{it\alpha X + it\beta}]$$

$$= e^{it\beta} E[e^{it\alpha X}]$$

$$= e^{it\beta} \phi_X(\alpha t).$$

(6) An extremely important feature of this function is that, once we know $\phi(t)$, we can *uniquely determine its distribution function*. This determination is achieved by using the following (*inversion formula*) theorem.

Theorem 5.5.1   Suppose that $F(x)$ and $\phi_X(t)$ denote respectively the distribution and characteristic functions of a random variable. If x, $x + h$, and $x - h$, h representing some positive number, are any continuity points of $F(x)$, then

$$\frac{F(x+h) - F(x-h)}{2h} = \lim_{T \to \infty} \frac{1}{\pi} \int_{-T}^{T} \frac{\sin ht}{t} e^{-ith} \phi_X(t)\, dt.$$

(For the proof of this theorem, refer to the suggested supplementary readings.)
Note that the above inversion formula can be written in a more useful form:

$$f(x) = \lim_{h \to 0} it \; \frac{F(x+h) - F(x-h)}{2h} = \frac{1}{2\pi} \int_{-\infty}^{\infty} e^{itx} \phi_X(t) \, dt.$$

Example 5.5.5   Find the probability density function of the random
variable X, whose characteristic function is given by

$$\phi_X(t) = e^{-|t|}.$$

Solution: Here

$$f(x) = \frac{1}{2\pi} \int_{-\infty}^{\infty} e^{-itx} e^{-|t|} \, dt$$

$$= \frac{1}{2\pi} \left\{ \int_{-\infty}^{0} e^{-itx+t} \, dt + \int_{0}^{\infty} e^{-itx-t} \, dt \right\}$$

$$= \frac{1}{2\pi} \int_{0}^{\infty} e^{-t} (e^{itx} + e^{-itx}) \, dt.$$

Recall that

$$\cos tx = e^{itx} + e^{-itx};$$

and, thus,

$$f(x) = \frac{1}{\pi} \int_{0}^{\infty} e^{-t} \cos tx \, dt.$$

Integrating by parts twice, we have

$$f(x) = \frac{1}{\pi} [-e^{-t} \cos tx]_{0}^{\infty} - \frac{x}{\pi} \int_{0}^{\infty} e^{-t} \sin tx \, dt$$

$$= \frac{1}{\pi} + \frac{x}{\pi} [e^{-t} \sin tx]_{0}^{\infty} - \frac{x^2}{\pi} \int_{0}^{\infty} e^{-t} \cos tx \, dt$$

$$= \frac{1}{\pi} + 0 - \frac{x^2}{\pi} \left[\frac{e^{-t}}{1+x^2} (x \sin xt - \cos xt) \right]_{0}^{\infty}$$

$$= \frac{1}{\pi} - x^2 \left(\frac{1}{\pi} \frac{1}{1+x^2} \right)$$

$$= \frac{1}{\pi} \frac{1}{1+x^2}.$$

Thus, the probability density function of the random variable X is

$$f(x) = \begin{cases} \dfrac{1}{\pi} \dfrac{1}{1+x^2}, & -\infty < x < \infty, \\ 0, & \text{elsewhere.} \end{cases}$$

Example 5.5.6   The characteristic function of the random variable X is

$$\phi_X(t) = e^{\mu i t - (1/2)t^2\sigma^2}.$$

Find the probability density function of X.

Solution: Applying the above inversion formula, we have

$$f(x) = \frac{1}{2\pi} \int_{-\infty}^{\infty} e^{-itx} e^{\mu i t - (1/2)t^2\sigma^2} \, dt$$

$$= \frac{1}{2\pi} \int_{-\infty}^{\infty} e^{-(t^2\sigma^2/2) - (2t\sigma^2/2\sigma^2)(ix - i\mu)} \, dt$$

$$= \frac{1}{2\pi} \int_{-\infty}^{\infty} \exp\left\{ -\frac{\sigma^2}{2}\left[t^2 + 2t\left(\frac{ix - i\mu}{\sigma^2}\right) + \left(\frac{ix - i\mu}{\sigma^2}\right)^2 \right] + \frac{\sigma^2}{2}\left(\frac{ix - i\mu}{\sigma^2}\right)^2 \right\} \, dt$$

$$= \frac{1}{\sqrt{2\pi}} \exp\left\{ \frac{\sigma^2}{2}\left(\frac{ix - i\mu}{\sigma^2}\right)^2 \right\} \cdot \frac{1}{\sqrt{2\pi}} \int_{-\infty}^{\infty} \exp\left\{ -\frac{\sigma^2}{2}\left[t + \left(\frac{ix - i\mu}{\sigma^2}\right) \right] \right\} \, dt.$$

Let

$$u = \sigma\left(t + \frac{ix - i\mu}{\sigma^2} \right), \qquad dt = \frac{du}{\sigma}$$

and

$$f(x) = \frac{1}{\sqrt{2\pi}\,\sigma} e^{-(1/2\sigma^2)(x-\mu)^2} \cdot \frac{1}{\sqrt{2\pi}} \int_{-\infty}^{\infty} e^{-(u^2/2)} \, du.$$

Thus,

$$f(x; \mu, \sigma)$$

$$= \frac{1}{\sqrt{2\pi}\,\sigma} \exp\left\{ -\frac{1}{2}\left(\frac{x-\mu}{\sigma}\right)^2 \right\}, \quad -\infty < x < \infty,\ -\infty < \mu < \infty,\ \sigma > 0.$$

Up to this point, we have been concerned with one-dimensional random variables and their probability distributions. However, in many actual physical situations, we have to deal with two or more random variables. It will be the aim of the next chapter to extend the concepts of one random variable and its probability distribution function to the case of two random variables.

5.6 Summary

Let X be a random variable with probability density function $f(x)$. The series

$$E(X) = \sum_i x_i f(x_i),$$

is the *expected value* of the discrete variate X if

$$\sum_i f(x_i)|x_i| < \infty$$

is satisfied. The integral

$$E(X) = \int_{-\infty}^{\infty} xf(x)\, dx$$

is the *expected value* of the continuous variate X if

$$\int_{-\infty}^{\infty} f(x)|x|\, dx < \infty$$

is satisfied.

The following properties of expectation were discussed: Let X be a random variable with probability density $f(x)$.

(1) If c is a constant, then $E(c) = c$.
(2) If $g(X)$ is a functional form of the variate X, then

$$E[g(X)] = \sum_{i=1}^{\infty} g(x_i) f(x_i)$$

if X is discrete, and

$$E[g(X)] = \int_{-\infty}^{\infty} g(x)f(x)\, dx,$$

if X is continuous, provided

$$\sum_{i=1}^{\infty} |g(x_i)| f(x_i) < \infty \quad \text{and} \quad \int_{-\infty}^{\infty} |g(x)| f(x)\, dx < \infty.$$

(1) If $g(X) = \alpha X + \beta$, then $E[g(X)] = \alpha E(X) + \beta$.

(2) If $f(x)$ is symmetric about the point $x = a$ for all x, then $E(X) = a$.

(3) If $g(X) = g_1(X) + g_2(X)$, then

$$E[g(X)] = E[g_1(X)] + E[g_2(X)].$$

(4) If $g_1(X) \le g_2(X)$ for all possible values that the random variable X can assume, then

$$E[g_1(X)] \le E[g_2(X)]$$

and

$$|E[g_1(X)]| \le E[|g_1(X)|].$$

The *kth ordinary moment* of the distribution of the variate X is

$$\mu_k = E(X^k) = \sum_{i=1}^{\infty} x_i^k f(x_i)$$

if X is discrete, and

$$\mu_k = E(X^k) = \int_{-\infty}^{\infty} x^k f(x)\, dx$$

if X is continuous, provided the series and the integral are absolutely convergent.

The *kth moment of $f(x)$, with respect to a point b*, is given by

$$E[(X - b)^k] = \sum_{i=1}^{\infty} (x_i - b)^k f(x_i)$$

if X is discrete, and

$$E[(X - b)^k] = \int_{-\infty}^{\infty} (x - b)^k f(x)\, dx$$

if X is continuous.

If b is replaced with $E(X) = \mu$, then the $E[(X - \mu)^k]$ is called the *kth central moment* of X. The second central moment of X is the *variance* of the variate X, which is a measure of the dispersion of the random variable around its expected value. The square root of the variance is called the *standard deviation*.

Let X be a random variable with probability density $f(x)$. Then

(1) $\text{Var}(X) = E(X^2) - [E(X)]^2$;

(2) $\text{Var}(Y) = \alpha^2 \text{Var}(X)$,   where $Y = \alpha X + \beta$;

(3) $\text{Var}(X) \leq E[(X - c)^2]$, $c \neq \mu$.

The ratio σ/μ, which expresses the magnitude of variation of a variate relative to its expectation, is called the *coefficient of variation*. The *coefficient of skewness* is the ratio of the third central moment of the distribution of a variate to the cube of its standard deviation.

The *moment generating function* of a probability density, $f(x)$, $m_X(t)$, is the expected value of e^{tX}, if it exists, for every value of t in some interval $|t| \leq T$, $T > 0$. It possesses the properties that:

(1) $\left. \dfrac{d^n m_X(t)}{dt^n} \right|_{t=0} = E(X^n) = \mu_n$;

(2) $M_Y(t) = e^{\beta t} M_X(\alpha t)$,   where $Y = \alpha X + \beta$.

The *factorial moment-generating function*, $g_X(t)$, is given by

$$g_X(t) = E[(1 + t)^X] = E[e^{x \log (1 + t)}], \quad |t| < 1.$$

The *characteristic function* of a random variable is given by

$$\phi_X(t) = E[e^{itX}],$$

where $i = \sqrt{-1}$ is the imaginary unit. It possesses the following properties:

(1) $\phi_X(0) = 1$;
(2) $|\phi_X(t)| \leq 1$;
(3) $\phi_X(-t) = \overline{\phi_X(t)}$;
(4) $\phi_Y(t) = e^{it\beta} \phi_X(\alpha t)$,   where $Y = \alpha X + \beta$;
(5)   if $\phi_X(t)$ is known, we can *uniquely* determine its distribution function.

We conclude this chapter by listing in tabular form the *expected values, variances, coefficient of skewness, coefficient of variation, moment generating and characteristic functions* of most of the discrete and continuous distributions.

Table 5.6.1   Discrete Distributions

Name	Probability Density Function	Conditions on Parameters
	$\sum_{i=1}^{\infty} f(x_i) = 1$ $f(x_i) \geq 0, \quad$ for all x_i	
Point Binomial	$f(x; p) = \begin{cases} p^x(1-p)^{1-x}, & x = 0, 1, \\ 0, & \text{elsewhere.} \end{cases}$	$0 \leq p \leq 1$
Binomial	$f(x; n, p) = \begin{cases} \binom{n}{x} p^x q^{n-x}, & x = 0, 1, \ldots, n, \\ 0, & \text{elsewhere.} \end{cases}$	$0 \leq p \leq 1$ $q = 1 - p$
Poisson	$f(x; \lambda) = \begin{cases} \dfrac{e^{-\lambda}\lambda^x}{x!}, & x = 0, 1, 2, \ldots, \\ 0, & \text{elsewhere.} \end{cases}$	$\lambda = np > 0$
Geometric	$f(x; p) = \begin{cases} p(1-p)^{x-1}, & x = 1, 2, 3, \ldots, \\ 0, & \text{elsewhere.} \end{cases}$	$0 \leq p \leq 1$
Hypergeometric	$f(x; r, n_1, n_2) = \begin{cases} \dfrac{\binom{n_1}{x}\binom{n_2}{r-x}}{\binom{n_1+n_2}{r}}, & \begin{array}{l} x = 1, 2, \ldots, r \leq n_1, \\ \text{or} \\ x = 1, 2, \ldots, n_1 \leq r \end{array} \\ 0, & \text{elsewhere.} \end{cases}$	$r \leq n_1 + n_2$
Negative Binomial	$f(x; p, r) = \begin{cases} \binom{x-1}{r-1} p^r(1-p)^{x-r}, & x = r, \ r+1, \ldots, \\ 0, & \text{elsewhere.} \end{cases}$	$0 \leq p \leq 1$ $r > 0$

Table 5.6.1 *(Continued)*

Expected Value	Variance	Coefficient of Variation
$\mu = E(X)$	$\text{Var}(X) = E(X - \mu)^2$	$V = \dfrac{\sigma}{\mu}$
$E(X) = p$	$\text{Var}(X) = p(1 - p)$	$V = \dfrac{\sqrt{p(1 - p)}}{p}$
$E(X) = np$	$\text{Var}(X) = npq$	$V = \dfrac{\sqrt{npq}}{np}$
$E(X) = \lambda$	$\text{Var}(X) = \lambda$	$V = \dfrac{\sqrt{\lambda}}{\lambda}$
$E(X) = \dfrac{1}{p}$	$\text{Var}(X) = \dfrac{q}{p^2}$	$V = \sqrt{1 - p}$
$E(X) = \dfrac{rn_1}{n_1 + n_2}$	$\text{Var}(X) = \dfrac{n_1 n_2}{(n_1 + n_2)^2}\left(\dfrac{n_1 + n_2 - r}{n_1 + n_2 - 1}\right)$	$V = \dfrac{\sqrt{n_1 n_2}}{rn_1}\sqrt{\dfrac{n_1 + n_2 - 2}{n_1 - n_2 - 1}}$
$E(X) = \dfrac{r}{p}$	$\text{Var}(X) = \dfrac{r(1 - p)}{p^2}$	$V = \sqrt{\dfrac{1 - p}{r}}$

Table 5.6.1   (Continued)

Name	Probability Density Function	Conditions on Parameters
	$\sum_{i=1}^{\infty} f(x_i) = 1$ $f(x_i) \geq 0, \quad$ for all x_i	
Point Binomial	$f(x; p) = \begin{cases} p^x(1-p)^{1-x}, & x = 0, 1, \\ 0, & \text{elsewhere.} \end{cases}$	$0 \leq p \leq 1$
Binomial	$f(x; n, p) = \begin{cases} \binom{n}{x} p^x(1-p)^{n-x}, & x = 0, 1, 2, \ldots, n, \\ 0, & \text{elsewhere.} \end{cases}$	$0 \leq p \leq 1$
Poisson	$f(x; \lambda) = \begin{cases} \dfrac{e^{-\lambda}\lambda^x}{x!}, & x = 0, 1, 2, \ldots, \\ 0, & \text{elsewhere.} \end{cases}$	$\lambda = np > 0$
Geometric	$f(x; p) = \begin{cases} p(1-p)^{x-1}, & x = 1, 2, 3, \ldots, \\ 0, & \text{elsewhere.} \end{cases}$	$0 \leq p \leq 1$
Hypergeometric	$f(x; r, n_1, n_2) = \begin{cases} \dfrac{\binom{n_1}{x}\binom{n_2}{r-x}}{\binom{n_1+n_2}{r}}, & \begin{matrix} x = 1, 2, \ldots, r \leq n_1 \\ \text{or} \\ x = 0, 1, 2, \ldots, n_1 \leq r, \end{matrix} \\ 0, & \text{elsewhere.} \end{cases}$	$r \leq n_1 + n_2$
Negative Binomial	$f(x; p, r) = \begin{cases} \binom{x-1}{r-1} p^r(1-p)^{x-r}, & x = r, r+1, \ldots, \\ 0, & \text{elsewhere.} \end{cases}$	$0 \leq p \leq 1$ $r > 0$

Table 5.6.1   (*Continued*)

Moment Generating Function	Characteristic Function	Coefficient of Skewness
$m(t) = E[e^{tX}]$	$\phi(t) = E[e^{itX}]$	$\gamma = \dfrac{E[(X-\mu)^3]}{\sigma^3}$
$m(t) = pe^t + q$ $q = 1 - p$	$\phi(t) = pe^{it} + q$	$\gamma = \dfrac{q-p}{\sqrt{pq}}$
$m(t) = (pe^t + q)^n$ $q = 1 - p$	$\phi(t) = (pe^{it} + q)^n$	$\gamma = \dfrac{q-p}{\sqrt{npq}}$
$m(t) = e^{\lambda(e^t-1)}$	$\phi(t) = e^{\lambda(e^{it}-1)}$	$\gamma = \dfrac{\lambda}{\lambda^{2/3}}$
$m(t) = \dfrac{pe^t}{1 - qe^t}$ $q = 1 - p$	$\phi(t) = \dfrac{pe^{it}}{1 - qe^{it}}$	$\gamma = \dfrac{2-p}{(1-p)^{1/2}}$
$m(t) = \dfrac{(n_2)^{[r]}}{(n_1 + n_2)^{[r]}} \cdot$ $\displaystyle\sum_{j=0}^{r} \dfrac{(n_1)^{[j]}r^{[j]}e^t}{(n_2 - r + j)^{[j]}j!}$ [r] denotes the largest integer not exceeding r	$\phi(t) = \dfrac{(n_2)^{[r]}}{(n_1 + n_2)^{[r]}} \cdot$ $\displaystyle\sum_{j=0}^{r} \dfrac{(n_1)^{[j]}r^{[j]}e^{it}}{(n_2 - r + j)^{[j]}j!}$	
$m(t) = \dfrac{(pe^t)^r}{(1 - qe^t)^r}$ $q = 1 - p$	$\phi(t) = \dfrac{(pe^{it})^r}{(1 - qe^{it})^r}$	$\gamma = 0$

Table 5.6.2   Continuous Distributions

Name	Probability Density Function	Conditions on Parameters
	$\int_{-\infty}^{\infty} f(x)\, dx = 1$ $f(x) \geq 0, \quad$ for all x	
Uniform	$f(x) = \begin{cases} \dfrac{1}{\beta - \alpha}, & \alpha < x < \beta, \\ 0, & \text{elsewhere.} \end{cases}$	$-\infty < \alpha < \beta < \infty$
Normal or Gauss	$f(x; \mu, \sigma) = \dfrac{1}{\sqrt{2\pi}\,\sigma} \exp\left\{ -\dfrac{1}{2}\left(\dfrac{x - \mu}{\sigma}\right)^2 \right\}, \quad -\infty < x < \infty.$	$-\infty < \mu < \infty$ $\sigma > 0$
Gamma	$f(x; \alpha, \beta) = \begin{cases} \dfrac{1}{\Gamma(\alpha)\beta^\alpha} x^{\alpha - 1} e^{-x/\beta}, & x > 0, \\ 0, & \text{elsewhere.} \end{cases}$	$\alpha > 0$ $\beta > 0$
Exponential	$f(x; \beta) = \begin{cases} \dfrac{1}{\beta} e^{-x/\beta}, & x > 0, \\ 0, & \text{elsewhere.} \end{cases}$	$\beta > 0$
Beta	$f(x; \alpha, \beta) = \begin{cases} \dfrac{\Gamma(\alpha + \beta)}{\Gamma(\alpha)\Gamma(\beta)} x^{\alpha - 1} (1 - x)^{\beta - 1}, & 0 < x \leq 1, \\ 0, & \text{elsewhere.} \end{cases}$	$\alpha > 0$ $\beta > 0$
Triangular	$f(x) = \begin{cases} 2(1 - x), & 0 \leq x \leq 1, \\ 0, & \text{elsewhere.} \end{cases}$ ------------------------------- $f(x) = \begin{cases} 2x, & 0 \leq x \leq 1, \\ 0, & \text{elsewhere.} \end{cases}$	
Cauchy	$f(x; \alpha, \mu) = \begin{cases} \dfrac{1}{\pi} \dfrac{\alpha}{\alpha^2 + (x - \mu)^2}, & -\infty < x < \infty, \\ 0, & \text{elsewhere.} \end{cases}$	$\alpha > 0$ $-\infty < \mu < \infty$

Table 5.6.2 (*Continued*)

Expected Value	Variance	Coefficient of Variation
$\mu = E(X)$	$\text{Var}(X) = E(X - \mu)^2$	$V = \dfrac{\sigma}{\mu}$
$E(X) = \dfrac{\alpha + \beta}{2}$	$\text{Var}(X) = \dfrac{(\beta - \alpha)^2}{12}$	$V = \dfrac{\beta - \alpha}{\sqrt{3}(\alpha + \beta)}$
$E(X) = \mu$	$\text{Var}(X) = \sigma^2$	$V = \dfrac{\sigma}{\mu}$
$E(X) = \alpha\beta$	$\text{Var}(X) = \alpha\beta^2$	$V = \dfrac{\sqrt{\alpha}}{\alpha}$
$E(X) = \beta$	$\text{Var}(X) = \beta^2$	$V = 1$
$E(X) = \dfrac{\alpha}{\alpha + \beta}$	$\text{Var}(X) = \dfrac{\alpha\beta}{(\alpha + \beta + 1)(\alpha + \beta)^2}$	$V = \dfrac{\sqrt{\alpha\beta}}{\alpha\sqrt{\alpha + \beta + 1}}$
$E(X) = \dfrac{1}{3}$	$\text{Var}(X) = \dfrac{1}{18}$	$V = \dfrac{1}{\sqrt{2}}$
$E(X) = \dfrac{2}{3}$	$\text{Var}(X) = \dfrac{1}{18}$	$V = \dfrac{1}{2\sqrt{2}}$
Does not exist.	Does not exist.	Does not exist.

Table 5.6.2   (*Continued*)

Name	Probability Density Function	Conditions on Parameters
	$\int_{-\infty}^{\infty} f(x)\,dx = 1$ $f(x) \geq 0, \quad$ for all x	
Laplace	$f(x; \mu, \sigma) = \begin{cases} \dfrac{1}{2\sigma} e^{-(|x-\mu|/\sigma)}, & -\infty < x < \infty \\ 0, & \text{elsewhere.} \end{cases}$	$\sigma > 0$ $-\infty < \mu < \infty$
Log-Normal	$f(x) = \begin{cases} \dfrac{1}{x\sigma_y \sqrt{2\pi}} \exp\left\{ -\dfrac{1}{2\sigma_y{}^2} (\ln x - \mu_y)^2 \right\}, & x > 0, \\ 0, & \text{elsewhere.} \end{cases}$	$\sigma_x > 0$ $-\infty < \mu_y < \infty$ $\sigma_y = \ln\sqrt{\dfrac{\mu_x{}^2 + \sigma_x{}^2}{\mu_x{}^2}}$ $\mu_y = \ln\sqrt{\dfrac{\mu_x{}^4}{\mu_x{}^2 + \sigma_x{}^2}}$
Weibull	$f(x; \alpha, \beta, \gamma) = \begin{cases} \dfrac{\beta}{\alpha} (x - \gamma)^{\beta-1} e^{-\{(x-\gamma)^\beta/\alpha\}}, & x \geq \gamma, \\ 0, & \text{elsewhere.} \end{cases}$	$\alpha > 0$ $\beta > 0$ $\gamma \geq 0$
Maxwell's	$f(x; \sigma) = \begin{cases} \dfrac{2\sigma^3}{\sqrt{2\pi}} x^2 e^{-(x^2\sigma^2/2)}, & x \geq 0, \\ 0, & \text{elsewhere.} \end{cases}$	$\sigma > 0$
Rayleigh	$f(x; \alpha) = \begin{cases} \dfrac{2}{\alpha} x e^{-(x^2/\alpha)}, & x \geq 0, \\ 0, & \text{elsewhere.} \end{cases}$	$\alpha > 0$
Pareto's	$f(x; r) = \begin{cases} rA^r(x^{r+1})^{-1}, & 0 < A \leq x, \\ 0, & \text{elsewhere.} \end{cases}$	$A > 0$ $r \geq 0$
Extreme Value	$f(x) = e^{-x-e^{-x}}, \quad -\infty < x < \infty.$	

Table 5.6.2 (*Continued*)

Expected Value	Variance	Coefficient of Variation
$\mu = E(X)$	$\text{Var}(X) = E(X - \mu)^2$	$V = \dfrac{\sigma}{\mu}$
$E(X) = \mu$	$\text{Var}(X) = 2\sigma^2$	$V = \dfrac{\sigma\sqrt{2}}{\mu}$
$E(X) = e^{\mu_y + \sigma_y}$	$\text{Var}(X) = e^{2(\mu_y + \sigma_y)}(e^{2\sigma_y} - 1)$	$V = \sqrt{e^{2\sigma_y} - 1}$
$E(X) = \alpha^{1/\beta}\Gamma\left(1 + \dfrac{1}{\beta}\right) + \gamma$	$\text{Var}(X) = \alpha^{2/\beta}\left\{\Gamma\left(1 + \dfrac{2}{\beta}\right) - \left[\Gamma\left(1 + \dfrac{1}{\beta}\right)\right]^2\right\}$	$V = \dfrac{\sqrt{\Gamma\left(1 + \dfrac{2}{\beta}\right) - \left[\Gamma\left(1 + \dfrac{1}{\beta}\right)\right]}}{\Gamma\left(1 + \dfrac{1}{\beta}\right) + \gamma\alpha^{-1/\beta}}$
$E(X) = \dfrac{4}{\sigma\sqrt{2\pi}}$	$\text{Var}(X) = \dfrac{1}{\sigma^2}\left(3 - \dfrac{8}{\pi}\right)$	$V = \sqrt{\dfrac{3}{8}\pi - 1}$
$E(X) = \alpha\dfrac{\sqrt{\pi}}{2}$	$\text{Var}(X) = \alpha^2\left(1 - \dfrac{\pi}{2}\right)$	$V = \sqrt{\alpha}\left(\dfrac{1 - \pi}{\pi}\right)^{1/2}$
$E(X) = A\left(\dfrac{r}{r - 1}\right)$ > 1	$\text{Var}(X) = \dfrac{r^3 - 3r^2 + r}{(r - 2)(r - 1)^2} A^2$ $r > 2$	$V = \dfrac{\sqrt{r^3 - 3r^2 + r}}{r\sqrt{r - 1}}$
$E(X) = 0$	$\text{Var}(X) = 1$	infinite

Table 5.6.2   (Continued)

Name	Probability Density Function	Conditions on Parameters
	$\displaystyle\int_{-\infty}^{\infty} f(x)\, dx = 1$ $f(x) \geq 0, \quad \text{for all } x.$	
Uniform	$f(x) = \begin{cases} \dfrac{1}{\beta - \alpha}, & \alpha < x < \beta, \\ 0, & \text{elsewhere.} \end{cases}$	$-\infty < \alpha < \beta < \infty$
Normal or Gauss	$f(x; \mu, \sigma) = \dfrac{1}{\sqrt{2\pi}\,\sigma} \exp\left\{ -\dfrac{1}{2}\left(\dfrac{x-\mu}{\sigma}\right)^2 \right\}, \quad -\infty < x < \infty$	$\sigma > 0$ $-\infty < \mu < \infty$
Gamma	$f(x; \alpha, \beta) = \begin{cases} \dfrac{1}{\Gamma(\alpha)\beta^{\alpha}}\, x^{\alpha-1} e^{-(x/\beta)}, & x > 0, \\ 0, & \text{elsewhere.} \end{cases}$	$\alpha > 0$ $\beta > 0$
Exponential	$f(x; \beta) = \begin{cases} \dfrac{1}{\beta}\, e^{-(x/\beta)}, & x \geq 0, \\ 0, & \text{elsewhere.} \end{cases}$	$\beta > 0$
Beta	$f(x; \alpha, \beta) = \begin{cases} \dfrac{\Gamma(\alpha + \beta)}{\Gamma(\alpha)\Gamma(\beta)}\, x^{\alpha-1}(1-x)^{\beta-1}, & 0 < x \leq 1, \\ 0, & \text{elsewhere.} \end{cases}$	$\alpha > 0$ $\beta > 0$
Triangular	$f(x) = \begin{cases} 2(1-x), & 0 \leq x \leq 1, \\ 0, & \text{elsewhere.} \end{cases}$ $\rule{0pt}{0pt}$ $f(x) = \begin{cases} 2x, & 0 < x \leq 1, \\ 0, & \text{elsewhere.} \end{cases}$	
Cauchy	$f(x; \alpha, \mu) = \begin{cases} \dfrac{1}{\pi}\, \dfrac{\alpha}{\alpha^2 + (x-\mu)^2}, & -\infty < x < \infty, \\ 0, & \text{elsewhere.} \end{cases}$	$\alpha > 0$ $-\infty < \mu < \infty$

Table 5.6.2   (*Continued*)

Moment Generating Function	Characteristic Function	Coefficient of Skewness
$m(t) = E(e^{tX})$	$\phi(t) = E(e^{itX})$	$\gamma = \dfrac{E[(x - \mu)^3]}{\sigma^3}$
$m(t) = \dfrac{e^{t\beta} - e^{t\alpha}}{t(\beta - \alpha)}$	$\phi(t) = \dfrac{e^{it\beta} - e^{it\alpha}}{it(\beta - \alpha)}$	$\gamma = 0$
$m(t) = e^{t\mu + (1/2)t^2\sigma^2}$	$\phi(t) = e^{it\mu - (t^2\sigma^2/2)}$	$\gamma = 0$
$m(t) = (1 - t\beta)^{-\alpha}$ $t < \dfrac{1}{\beta}$	$\phi(t) = (1 - it\beta)^{-\alpha}$	$\gamma = \dfrac{2\sqrt{\alpha}}{\alpha}$
$m(t) = (1 - t\beta)^{-1}$ $t < \dfrac{1}{\beta}$	$\phi(t) = (1 - it\beta)^{-1}$	$\gamma = 2$
$m(t) = \dfrac{\Gamma(\alpha + \beta)}{\Gamma(\alpha)} \cdot$ $\sum_{j=0}^{\infty} \dfrac{\Gamma(\alpha + j)(t)^j}{\Gamma(\alpha + \beta + j)\Gamma(j + 1)}$	$\phi(t) = \dfrac{\Gamma(\alpha + \beta)}{\Gamma(\alpha)} \cdot$ $\sum_{j=0}^{\infty} \dfrac{\Gamma(\alpha + j)(it)^j}{\Gamma(\alpha + \beta + j)\Gamma(j + 1)}$	$\gamma = \dfrac{2(\beta - \alpha)\sqrt{\alpha + \beta + 1}}{(\alpha + \beta + 2)\sqrt{\alpha\beta}}$
$m(t) = \dfrac{2}{t^2}(e^t - t - 1)$	$\phi(t) = \dfrac{2}{t^2}(it + 1 - e^{it})$	$\gamma = \dfrac{2\sqrt{2}}{5}$
$m(t) = \dfrac{2}{t^2}(te^t - e^t + 1)$	$\phi(t) = \dfrac{2}{t^2}(e^{it} - 1 - ite^{it})$	$\gamma = -\dfrac{2\sqrt{2}}{5}$
Exists only for $t = 0$	$\phi(t) = e^{it\mu - \alpha|t|}$	

Table 5.6.2   *(Continued)*

Name	Probability Density Function	Conditions on Parameters
	$\int_{-\infty}^{\infty} f(x)\, dx = 1,$ $f(x) \geq 0, \quad$ for all $x.$	
Laplace	$f(x; \mu, \sigma) = \begin{cases} \dfrac{1}{2\sigma} e^{-(|x - \mu|/\sigma)}, & -\infty < x < \infty, \\ 0, & \text{elsewhere.} \end{cases}$	$\sigma > 0$ $-\infty < \mu < \infty$
Log-Normal	$f(x) = \begin{cases} \dfrac{1}{x\sigma_y \sqrt{2\pi}} \exp\left\{ -\dfrac{1}{2\sigma_y^2}(\ln x - \mu_y)^2 \right\}, & x > 0, \\ 0, & \text{elsewhere.} \end{cases}$	$-\infty < \mu_y < \infty$ $\mu_y = \ln\left(\dfrac{\mu_x^4}{\mu_x^2 + \sigma_x^2}\right)^{1/2}$ $\sigma_y = \ln\left(\dfrac{\mu_x^2 + \sigma_x^2}{\mu_x^2}\right)^{1/2}$
Weibull	$f(x; \alpha, \beta, \gamma) = \begin{cases} \dfrac{\beta}{\alpha}(x - \gamma)^{\beta - 1} e^{-\{(x - \gamma)^\beta / \alpha\}} & x \geq \gamma, \\ 0, & \text{elsewhere.} \end{cases}$	$\alpha > 0$ $\beta > 0$ $\gamma \geq 0$
Maxwell's	$f(x; \sigma) = \begin{cases} \dfrac{2\sigma^3}{\sqrt{2\pi}} x^2 e^{-(x^2 \sigma^2/2)}, & x \geq 0, \\ 0, & \text{elsewhere.} \end{cases}$	$\sigma > 0$
Rayleigh	$f(x; \alpha) = \begin{cases} \dfrac{2}{\alpha} x e^{-(x^2/\alpha)}, & x \geq 0, \\ 0, & \text{elsewhere.} \end{cases}$	$\alpha > 0$
Pareto's	$f(x; r) = \begin{cases} r A^r (x^{r-1})^{-1}, & 0 < A \leq x, \\ 0, & \text{elsewhere.} \end{cases}$	$r \geq 0$ $A > 0$
Extreme Value	$f(x) = e^{-x - e^{-x}},$ $-\infty < x < \infty$	

Table 5.6.2 (*Continued*)

Moment Generating Function	Characteristic Function	Coefficient of Skewness
$m(t) = E(e^{tX})$	$\phi(t) = E(e^{itX})$	$\gamma = \dfrac{E[(X-\mu)^3]}{\sigma^3}$
$m(t) = \dfrac{e^{t\mu}}{1 - \sigma^2 t^2}$	$\phi(t) = \dfrac{e^{it\mu}}{1 + \sigma^2 t^2}$	
$m(t) = e^{ty} \cdot$ $\displaystyle\int_0^\infty e^{-y + t(\sigma y)^{1/\beta}}\, dy$	$\phi(t) = e^{ity}\displaystyle\int_0^\infty e^{-y + it(\sigma y)^{1/\beta}}\, dy$	$\gamma = \dfrac{\left\{\Gamma\!\left(1+\frac{3}{\beta}\right) - 3\Gamma\!\left(1+\frac{1}{\beta}\right)\cdot\; \Gamma\!\left(1+\frac{2}{\beta}\right) + 2\left[\Gamma\!\left(1+\frac{1}{\beta}\right)\right]^3\right\}}{\left\{\Gamma\!\left(1+\frac{2}{\beta}\right) - \left[\Gamma\!\left(1+\frac{1}{\beta}\right)\right]^2\right\}^{3/2}}$
$m(t) = \dfrac{e^{t^2/2\sigma^2}}{\sqrt{2\pi}\,\sigma^2}\cdot$ $[\sqrt{2\pi}(\sigma^2 + t^2) + 4t\sigma]$	$\phi(t) = \dfrac{e^{-t^2/2\sigma^2}}{\sqrt{2\pi}\,\sigma^2}\cdot$ $[\sqrt{2\pi}(\sigma^2 - t^2) + 4it\sigma]$	$\gamma = \dfrac{2\sqrt{2}(16 - 5\pi)}{(3\pi - 8)^{3/2}}$
$m(t) = e^{\alpha t^2/4}\cdot$ $\left[1 + t\,\dfrac{\sqrt{\alpha\pi}}{2}\right]$	$\phi(t) = e^{-(\alpha t^2/4)}\left[1 + it\,\dfrac{\sqrt{\alpha\pi}}{2}\right]$	
$m(t) =$ $e^{tA}\displaystyle\sum_{j=1}^{r-1} \dfrac{(r-j-1)!\,A^j t^j}{(r-1)!}$	$\phi(t) = e^{itA}\displaystyle\sum_{j=1}^{r-1} \dfrac{(r-j-1)!\,A^j(it)^j}{(r-1)!}$	
$m(t) = \Gamma(1-t)$ $t < 1$	$\phi(t) = \Gamma(1-it)$	

Exercises

5.1. In an experiment the probability of success is equal to p. Find the expected number of trials required for k successes.

5.2. Find the expected value and variance of the random variable X for the following two probability density functions:

(a) $f(x) = \begin{cases} \dfrac{(x-3)^2}{5}, & x = 3, 4, 5, \\ 0, & \text{elsewhere}; \end{cases}$

(b) $f(x) = \begin{cases} \dfrac{14 - 3x}{15}, & x = 2, 3, 4, \\ 0, & \text{elsewhere}. \end{cases}$

5.3. Let the probability density function of the random variable X be

$$f(x) = \begin{cases} \dfrac{3}{16}(x^2 + 5), & 0 \le x \le 1, \\ 0, & \text{elsewhere}. \end{cases}$$

Find (1) the expected value of X,   (2) the variance of X.

5.4. The probability density function of the random variable X is given by

$$f(x) = \begin{cases} 0, & x < -a, \\ \dfrac{a + x}{a^2}, & -a \le x \le 0, \\ \dfrac{a - x}{a^2}, & 0 < x \le a, \\ 0, & a > x. \end{cases}$$

Compute

(a) $E(X)$,   (b) $\text{Var}(X)$.

5.5. If

$$f(x) = \begin{cases} \dfrac{cx}{2}, & 0 \le x \le 1, \\ c - \dfrac{cx}{2}, & 1 < x \le 2, \\ 0, & \text{elsewhere.} \end{cases}$$

Find c so that $f(x)$ is a probability density function. Also find $E(X)$ and Var(X).

5.6. If

$$f(x) = \begin{cases} c \sin xe^{-x}, & 0 \le x \le \pi, \\ 0, & \text{elsewhere,} \end{cases}$$

find c so that $f(x)$ is a probability density function. Compute $E(X)$ and Var(X).

5.7. The probability of a success in an experiment is p. Show that the expected number of trials for two successes in a row is $(p + 1)/p^2$.

5.8. The probability density of the random variable X is given by

$$f(x) = \begin{cases} \dfrac{x^2}{2}, & 0 < x \le 1, \\ \dfrac{6x - 2x^2 - 3}{2}, & 1 < x \le 2, \\ \dfrac{(x-3)^2}{2}, & 2 < x \le 3, \\ 0, & \text{elsewhere.} \end{cases}$$

Find the expected value of the random variable X.

5.9. If

$$f(x) = ce^{-|x|}, \quad -\infty < x < \infty,$$

find c so that $f(x)$ will be the probability density function of the random variable X. Evaluate $E(X)$ and Var(X).

5.10. In Exercise 5.1 find the mean value of the square of the number of trials required for k successes and the variance of the number of trials required for k successes.

5.11. If

$$f(x) = \begin{cases} cx(2x - 1), & x = 1, 2, 3, 4, 5, \\ 0, & \text{elsewhere,} \end{cases}$$

Find

(a) c so that $f(x)$ will be the probability density function of the random variable X,

(b) $E(X)$,   (c) $E(X^2)$,   (d) $E(1/2X^2 - 3)$,

(e) $E\{X - E(X)\}^2$,

(f) $E(X^2) - \mu^2$, and show that the result is the same as the result in (e).

5.12. Show that the expected value of the random variable X whose probability density is given by

$$f(x) = \frac{1}{\pi(x^2 + 1)}, \quad -\infty < x < \infty$$

does not exist.

5.13. Let

$$f(x) = \frac{c}{x^2}, \quad x = \pm 1, \pm 2, \pm 3, \dots.$$

(a) Find that c which will make $f(x)$ a probability density.

(b) Show that the expected value of the random variable X does not exist, that is, that

$$E(X) = 0, \quad \text{but} \quad E(|X|) = \infty.$$

5.14. Show that

$$\{E(X - c)\}^2 \le E(X - c)^2,$$

where c is an arbitrary constant.

5.15. The probability density function of the discrete random variable X is given by

$$f(x) = \begin{cases} \frac{1}{6}(3x^2 - 5x + 2), & 0, 1, 2, \\ 0, & \text{elsewhere.} \end{cases}$$

Find (a) $\phi_X(t)$, (b) μ, (c) η_2, (d) γ, (e) V, and (f) ξ.

5.16. The probability density function of the random variable X is given by

$$f(x) = \begin{cases} \dfrac{1}{2\sqrt{x}}, & 0 < x < 1, \\ 0, & \text{elsewhere.} \end{cases}$$

Find (a) $\phi_X(t)$, (b) μ, (c) σ^2, (d) V, (e) γ.

5.17. The probability density function of the random variable X is given by

$$f(x) = \begin{cases} \dfrac{1}{\beta - \alpha}, & \alpha \leq x \leq \beta, \\ 0, & \text{elsewhere.} \end{cases}$$

Find (a) $\phi_X(t)$, (b) μ, (c) η_2, (d) σ^2, (e) γ, (f) ξ.

5.18. In Exercise 5.3, find (a) μ_2, (b) σ^2, (c) η, (d) γ, (e) ξ.

5.19. Show that

(a) $m_{X+a}(t) = e^{at} m_X(t)$, (b) $m_{bX}(t) = m_X(bt)$

(c) $\phi_{bX+a}(t) = e^{at} \phi_X(bt)$, (d) $\phi_{(X-\mu)/\sigma}(t) = e^{-(\mu/\sigma)t} \phi_X\left(\dfrac{t}{\sigma}\right)$.

5.20. The characteristic function of the probability density function $f(x)$ is given by

$$\phi_X(t) = e^{-(t^2/2)}.$$

Derive $f(x)$ directly from $\phi_X(t)$.

5.21. Obtain the kth ordinary moment for the probability distribution function whose characteristic function is given by

$$\phi_X(t) = \frac{\sin t}{t}.$$

5.22. If the probability density function of the random variable X is given by

$$f(x) = \begin{cases} \dfrac{\Gamma[(n_1 + n_2)/2](n_1/n_2)^{n_1/2}}{\Gamma(n_1/2)\,\Gamma(n_2/2)} x^{n_1/2 - 1}(1 + (n_1/n_2)x)^{-(n_1 + n_2)/2}, & x > 0, \\ 0, & \text{elsewhere,} \end{cases}$$

show that $E(X) = n_2/(n_2 - 2)$, for $n_2 > 2$, and

$$\text{Var}(X) = \frac{2n_2(n_1 + n_2 - 2)}{n_1(n_2 - 2)^2(n_2 - 4)}.$$

Hint: Use the transformation

$$y = \frac{(n_1/n_2)x}{1 + (n_1/n_2)x}.$$

5.23. If the probability density function of the random variable X is given by

$$f(x) = \frac{\Gamma[(n + 1)/2]}{\sqrt{n\pi}\Gamma(n/2)}\left(1 + \frac{x^2}{n}\right)^{-(n+1)/2}, \quad -\infty < x < \infty,$$

show that $E(X) = 0$, and $\text{Var}(X) = n/(n - 2)$, for $n > 2$.

Hint: To integrate

$$K\int_{-\infty}^{\infty} x^2\left(1 + \frac{x}{n}\right)^{-(n+1)/2} dx,$$

use integration by parts, where $u = (n/2)Kx$ and

$$dv = \left(\frac{2x}{n}\right)\left(1 + \frac{x^2}{n}\right)^{-(n+1)/2}.$$

5.24. Show that the kth central moment can be expressed as

$$\eta_k = \sum_{i=0}^{k}(-1)^i\binom{k}{i}\mu^i\mu_{k-i}.$$

5.25. Derive an expression similar to that in Exercise 5.24, that expresses ordinary moments in terms of moments about the mean.

Problems

5.1. Find the average number of spots showing on a throw of k balanced dice, where $k = 1, 2, 3$.

5.2. Suppose that five cards are dealt from a deck containing only the aces, kings, and queens. Find the expected number of aces dealt.

5.3. Let the random variable X assume the number of spots which come up on a single roll of a die. Find the expected value and variance of

(a) X,   (b) $Y = 2X - 6$,

(c) $Z = 6 - X$,   (d) $W = X + Z$.

5.4. Let the random variable X be normally distributed with parameters 0 and σ^2. Show that $E(X^{2k+1}) = 0$, where $k = 0, 1, 2, \ldots$.

5.5. Show that, in the game of craps, the expected number of throws required for the thrower to win is 13144/9075, which is approximately equal to 1.448 throws.

5.6. In Problem 5.1, find the average value of the square of the sum of the spots showing. Also, compute the variance of the number of spots showing.

5.7. In Problem 5.2, find (a) the expected value of the square of the number of aces dealt, (b) the variance of the number of aces dealt.

5.8. Let X be normally distributed with parameters 0 and σ^2. Find

(a) $E(X^2)$,   (b) $E(\alpha X^2 + \beta)$,   (c) $\text{Var}(\alpha X - \beta)$.

5.9. Calculate the mean and variance of (a) the geometric distribution, (b) the negative binomial distribution.

5.10. Find the average value of the difference of the number of spots showing on a pair of balanced dice if they are tossed repeatedly.

5.11. In Exercises 5.2, 5.6 and Problem 5.4, find

(a) $E(3X^2 + 2X + 1)$,   (b) $\text{Var}(X - 2)$.

5.12. Find the expected value of $g(X) = 3X^2 + 2X + 1$, if X is characterized by the

(a) binomial distribution,   (b) Poisson distribution,

(c) negative binomial distribution,   (d) geometric distribution,

(e) hypergeometric distribution,   (f) gamma distribution with parameters α and β,

(g) normal distribution with parameters μ and σ^2.

5.13. Find the expected value of $g(X) = X^k$ for (a) the gamma distribution, (b) the beta distribution, and (c) the log-normal distribution.

5.14. Use the results of Problem 5.13 to find the mean and variance of these probability density functions.

5.15. In Exercise 5.7, find the kth moment of the random variable X about (a) zero, (b) the mean, (c) three; (d) use the results of part (a) to find the mean and variance of X.

5.16. In Exercise 5.1 and Problem 5.6, determine the mean and variance of (a) the geometric distribution, (b) the negative binomial distribution.

5.17. Determine (a) through (d) of Problem 5.15 for the probability density functions given in Problem 5.4 and Exercises 5.2 and 5.6.

5.18. Find the moment generating function of the geometric and negative binomial probability density functions.

5.19. Using the result of Problem 5.18, find the mean and variance of (a) the geometric distribution, and (b) the negative binomial distribution.

5.20. Find the characteristic function of (a) the probability density of Exercise 5.2, and (b) the probability density of Problem 5.4, and (c) the probability density of Problem 5.5 (d) the probability density function of Exercise 5.6.

5.21. Using the results of parts (a) and (b) of Problem 5.20, determine the expected value and variance of the five probability density functions.

5.22. Find the characteristic function of the probability density function given in Exercise 5.10. Using $\phi_X(t)$, obtain $E(X^3)$, $E(2X^2 - X)$.

5.23. Find the expected value of $g(X) = 3X^2 + 2X + 1$ for the probability density functions given in Exercise 3.9.

5.24. Find the characteristic function for the probability density functions given in Exercise 3.9.

5.25. Using the results of Problem 5.24, obtain the mean and variance of the respective probability density functions.

5.26. Find the factorial moment-generating function of (a) the binomial distribution, (b) the geometric distribution, (c) the negative binomial distribution.

5.27. Use the results of Problem 5.26 to find the mean and variance of the three named distributions.

5.28. Compute (a) γ, (b) V, and (c) ξ, for the following distributions: point binomial, binomial, Poisson, hypergeometric, geometric, negative binomial, gamma, beta; check your answers with the accompanying tables.

5.29. Calculate the mean and variance of the log-normal probability distribution (see Equation 3.3.24).

Suggested Supplementary Reading

Cramer, H. *The Elements of Probability Theory and Some of Its Applications.* New York: John Wiley and Sons, Inc., 1955. Stockholm: Almqvist and Wiksell, 1954.

Drake, A. W. *Fundamentals of Applied Probability Theory.* New York: McGraw-Hill Book Company, Inc., 1967.

Feller, W. *An Introduction to Probability Theory and Its Applications.* Vol. 1. 2nd ed. New York: John Wiley and Sons, Inc., 1960.

Fisz, M. *Probability Theory and Mathematical Statistics.* 3rd ed. New York: John Wiley and Sons, Inc., 1962.

Goldberg, S. *Probability: An Introduction.* Englewood Cliffs, New Jersey: Prentice-Hall, Inc., 1960.

Harris, B. *Theory of Probability.* Reading, Massachusetts: Addison-Wesley, Publishing Company, Inc., 1966.

Lindgren, B. W. and G. W. McElrath. *Introduction to Probability and Statistics.* 2nd ed. New York: The Macmillan Company, 1966.

Mendenhall, W. *Introduction to Probability and Statistics.* 3rd ed. Belmont, California: Wadsworth Publishing Company, Inc., 1971.

Meyer, P. L. *Introduction to Probability and Statistical Applications.* Reading, Massachusetts: Addison-Wesley Publishing Company, Inc., 1965.

Monroe, M. E. *Theory of Probability.* New York: McGraw-Hill Book Company, Inc., 1951.

Papoulis, A. *Probability Random Variables and Stochastic Processes.* New York: McGraw-Hill Book Company, Inc., 1965.

Parzen, E. *Modern Probability Theory and Its Applications.* New York: John Wiley and Sons, Inc., 1960.

Two Random Variables

6.0 Introduction

We have until now been concerned with studying the situation of one-dimensional random variables and their distributions. In many physical phenomena, however, we must deal with random variables of more than one dimension. For example, we might be interested in an experiment involving the weight W and height H of a certain group of persons, in which case the sample space will consist of two-tuples. In this situation, we need the two-dimensional random variable (W, H) to describe the numerical characteristics of the experiment. There are many other situations that require the use of the two-dimensional random variable. However, as in the univariate case, it is necessary to develop the joint probability density function of the two-dimensional variate; and, once we know the distribution of the variate, we know the laws that govern it.

In this chapter, we shall extend the concept of a random variable and its probability distribution function to the concept of two random variables. Once the conceptual extension from the univariate to the bivariate case has been accomplished, you will note that the further generalization to the n-dimensional case follows essentially the same idea. The n-dimensional random variable will be the subject of Chapter 7.

6.1 Joint Probability Density Function

We shall define a two-dimensional discrete random variable in Definition 6.1.0.

Definition 6.1.0   *Let S be a sample space and X(s), Y(s) two real valued functions (defined on S) that assign a real number to each element of the sample* space. The pair $(X(s), Y(s))$ is then referred to as a two-dimensional random variable. For convenience, we shall denote $X(s) = X$ and $Y(s) = Y$. Hence, the range space, $R_{X, Y}$, of the two-dimensional discrete variate (X, Y) is a subset of the Euclidean plane (xy-plane).

Definition 6.1.1   Let (X, Y) be a two-dimensional random variable. If the number of possible values of (X, Y) is finite or countably infinite, then (X, Y) is called a two-dimensional discrete random variable.

We shall denote the possible values that (X, Y) may assume by

$$(x_i, y_j), \ i = 1, 2, \ldots, n, \ldots \quad \text{and} \quad j = 1, 2, \ldots, k, \ldots.$$

As it was in the one-dimensional case, our aim now is to calculate the probability that the two-dimensional random variable will assume certain values. Some of these probabilities are $Pr(X = x_1, Y = y_1)$, the probability that the values that X and Y assume simultaneously are x_1 and y_1, respectively; and $Pr(x_1 < X < x_2, y_1 < Y < y_2)$, the probability that the values that X and Y assume fall in the intervals (x_1, x_2) and (y_1, y_2), respectively. More precisely, if $E_1 = \{(x, y) : x_1 < x < x_2, \ y_1 < y < y_2\}$, then

$$Pr(x_1 < X < x_2, y_1 < Y < y_2) = Pr[(X, Y) \text{ in } E_1],$$

the probability that the values that the two-dimensional variate assumes lie in a certain set $E_1 \subset R_{X, Y}$, where $R_{X, Y}$ is the range space.

A mathematical function that will be used to calculate the above probabilities is the *joint probability density function* of the random variable (X, Y).

Definition 6.1.2   Let (X, Y) be a two-dimensional discrete random variable. A function $f(x_i, y_j)$ is called the joint probability density function *of the random variable* (X, Y) *if the following conditions are satisfied:*

(1) $f(x_i, y_j) \geq 0, \quad \text{for all} \quad (x_i, y_j) \in R_{X, Y}$;

(2) $\displaystyle\sum\sum_{(x_i, y_j) \in R_{x,y}} f(x_i, y_j) = 1,$

where the summation is over all possible values (x_i, y_j), $i = 1, 2, \ldots, n, \ldots$, $j = 1, 2, \ldots, k, \ldots$. Furthermore, for any real valued pair (x_i, y_j) we have $f(x_i, y_j) = Pr(X = x_i, Y = y_j)$.

Example 6.1.1   An experiment consists of drawing four objects from a container, which holds eight operable, six defective, and ten semi-operable objects. Let X be the number of operable objects drawn and Y the number of defective objects drawn. The probability density function of the two-dimensional random variable (X, Y) is

$$f(x, y) = \begin{cases} \dfrac{\binom{8}{x}\binom{6}{y}\binom{10}{4-(x+y)}}{\binom{24}{4}}, & x, y = 0, 1, 2, \dots, 4 \\ & \text{such that} \quad 0 \le x + y \le 4, \\ 0, & \text{elsewhere.} \end{cases}$$

It can be shown that $f(x, y) \ge 0$ for $0 \le x + y \le 4$ and that

$$\sum_{x=0}^{4-y} \sum_{y=0}^{4} \frac{\binom{8}{x}\binom{6}{y}\binom{10}{4-x-y}}{\binom{24}{4}} = 1.$$

Now we can use $f(x, y)$ to calculate various probabilities. For example,

$$Pr(X = 3, Y = 0) = f(3, 0) = \frac{\binom{8}{3}\binom{6}{0}\binom{10}{1}}{\binom{24}{4}} = .0527$$

is the probability that the sample will consist of three operable components and one semi-operable component;

$$Pr(X < 3, Y = 1) = \sum_{x=0}^{2} f(x, 1) = \sum_{x=0}^{2} \frac{\binom{8}{x}\binom{6}{1}\binom{10}{3-x}}{\binom{24}{4}} = .4291$$

is the probability that the random sample will consist of two or less operable components and one defective component.

Figure 6.1.1 shows the graph of $f(x, y)$; the length of the vertical lines indicates the probabilities for all possible values that the random variable (X, Y) can assume.

Example 6.1.2   Let X denote the number of aces and Y the number of kings occurring in a bridge hand of 13 cards. Here the values that the random variable (X, Y) can assume are $(0, 0)$, $(0, 1)$, $(0, 2)$, ..., $(4, 4)$. Thus, if we assume that the $\binom{52}{13}$ possible bridge hands are equally likely to occur, the joint probability density function is given by

$$f(x, y) = \begin{cases} \dfrac{\dbinom{4}{x}\dbinom{4}{y}\dbinom{44}{13 - x - y}}{\dbinom{52}{13}}, & x, y = 0, 1, 2, 3, 4, \\[2ex] 0, & \text{elsewhere.} \end{cases}$$

It can be shown that $f(x, y) \geq 0$ for all x and y and that

$$\sum_{y=0}^{4} \sum_{x=0}^{4} \frac{\dbinom{4}{x}\dbinom{4}{y}\dbinom{44}{13 - x - y}}{\dbinom{52}{13}} = 1.$$

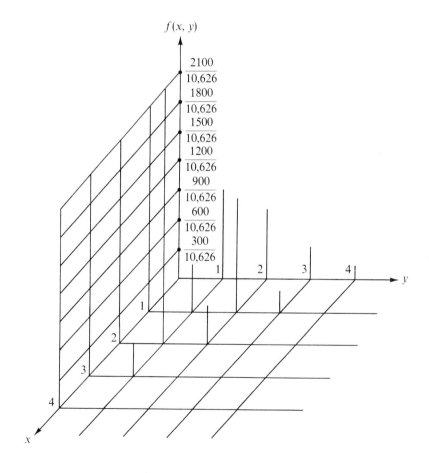

Figure 6.1.1

Now we can use $f(x, y)$ to calculate various probabilities. For example, the probability of having neither an ace nor a king in a bridge hand is

$$Pr(X = 0, \ Y = 0) = f(0, 0) = \frac{\binom{4}{0}\binom{4}{0}\binom{44}{13}}{\binom{52}{13}} = \frac{51{,}915{,}526{,}432}{635{,}013{,}559{,}600} = 0.0818.$$

Also, the probability of having no ace or one ace and exactly four kings in such a hand is

$$Pr(X < 2, \ Y = 4) = \sum_{x=0}^{1} f(x, 4) = \sum_{x=0}^{1} \frac{\binom{4}{x}\binom{4}{4}\binom{44}{9-x}}{\binom{52}{13}} = 0.0022.$$

Definition 6.1.3   *Let $(X, \ Y)$ be a two-dimensional random variable. If $(X, \ Y)$ can assume all values in some uncountable (nondenumerable) subset of the Euclidean plane, then $(X, \ Y)$ is called a* two-dimensional continuous random variable.

Here the range space of the two-dimensional variate $(X, \ Y)$ is the set of all possible values of $(X, \ Y)$, which is an uncountable subset of the Euclidean plane. For example, if $(X, \ Y)$ assumes its values from the set $S_1 = \{(x, y) : x_1 \leq x \leq x_2, \ y_1 \leq y \leq y_2\}$, we would say that $(X, \ Y)$ is a two-dimensional continuous random variable, the range space of which is a rectangular subset of the xy-plane. Furthermore, for any two real valued pairs (a, b), (c, d) such that $a < b$ and $c < d$, we have

$$Pr(a \leq X \leq b, c \leq Y \leq d) = \int_a^b \int_c^d f(x, y) \, dy \, dx.$$

Definition 6.1.4   *Let $(X, \ Y)$ be a two-dimensional continuous random variable. A function $f(x, y)$ is called the* joint probability density function *of the variate $(X, \ Y)$ if the following conditions are satisfied:*

(1) $f(x, y) \geq 0 \quad \text{for all} \quad (x, y) \in R_{X, Y}$;

(2) $\iint\limits_{R_{X, Y}} f(x, y) \, dx \, dy = 1,$

where the integration is over $R_{X, Y}$, the range space in which $(X, \ Y)$ assumes all values.

In order for the double integral to exist in a given plane, the joint function $f(x, y)$ must be continuous almost everywhere on the plane. (We shall assume that this condition exists throughout this book.) Notice that condition (2) states that the total volume under the surface given by $f(x, y)$ is one, which is analogous to the total area under $f(x)$.

Given the joint probability density $f(x, y)$ of the continuous variate (X, Y) and letting $E_1 = \{(x, y) : a \le x \le b, c \le y \le d)\}$, we can define

$$Pr(E_1) = Pr(a \le X \le b, c \le Y \le d) = \iint\limits_{E_1} f(x, y)\, dx\, dy$$

$$= \int_c^d \int_a^b f(x, y)\, dx\, dy.$$

The probability is represented as the volume above the shaded rectangle, shown in Figure 6.1.2.

Example 6.1.3   Use the function $g(x, y) = 4x + 2y + 1$, defined over the rectangle $0 \le x \le 2$, $0 \le y \le 2$, to define a joint probability density function over that region.

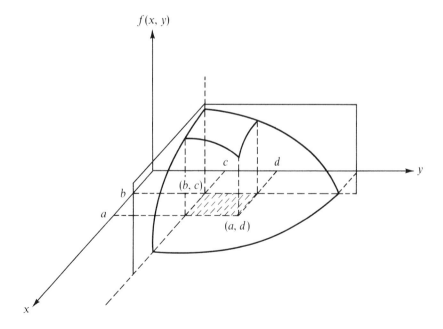

Figure 6.1.2

Solution: Here

$$\int_0^2 \int_0^2 (4x + 2y + 1) \, dx \, dy = 28;$$

thus,

$$f(x, y) = \begin{cases} \dfrac{1}{28}(4x + 2y + 1), & 0 \le x \le 2, 0 \le y \le 2, \\ 0, & \text{elsewhere,} \end{cases}$$

is the joint probability density function of the random variable (X, Y). The probability that the variate (X, Y) will assume a value in the region $x \le 1$, $y < 1/2$ is

$$Pr\left(X \le 1, Y < \frac{1}{2}\right) = \int_{-\infty}^{1/2} \int_{-\infty}^1 f(x, y) \, dx \, dy$$

$$= \int_0^{1/2} \int_0^1 \frac{1}{28}(4x + 2y + 1) \, dy \, dx$$

$$= \frac{1}{16}.$$

Furthermore, the probability that $x + y$ will be less than one is

$$Pr(X + Y < 1) = \int_0^1 \int_0^{1-x} \frac{1}{28}(4x + 2y + 1) \, dx \, dy$$

$$= \frac{3}{56}.$$

The graph of the joint probability density $f(x, y)$ is shown in Figure 6.1.3. In addition, the $Pr(X \le 1, Y < 1/2)$ is shown as the volume above the area of the rectangle in the xy-plane, shaded ▨▨▨▨; the volume above the area of the triangle in the xy-plane, shaded ⧄⧄⧄⧄, represents $Pr(X + Y < 1)$.

Example 6.1.4   Find k so that $f(x, y) = kxy$, $1 \le x \le y \le 2$ will be a probability density function.

Solution: Here

$$\frac{1}{k} = \int_1^2 \int_x^2 xy \, dy \, dx = \frac{9}{8}.$$

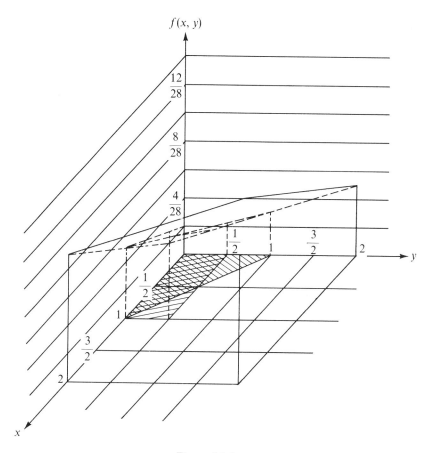

Figure 6.1.3

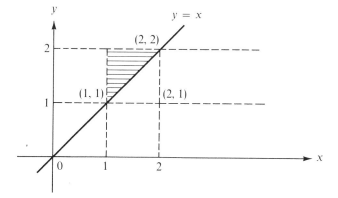

Figure 6.1.4

Thus $k = 8/9$; and

$$f(x, y) = \begin{cases} \dfrac{8}{9}\, xy, & 1 \le x \le y \le 2, \\ \\ 0, & \text{elsewhere} \end{cases}$$

is a probability density function. Figure 6.1.4 clearly shows the region in which $f(x, y)$ is defined.

Thus,

$$Pr\left(X \le \frac{3}{2},\ Y \le \frac{3}{2}\right) = \frac{8}{9} \int_1^{3/2} \int_x^{3/2} xy\, dy\, dx = \frac{25}{144}$$

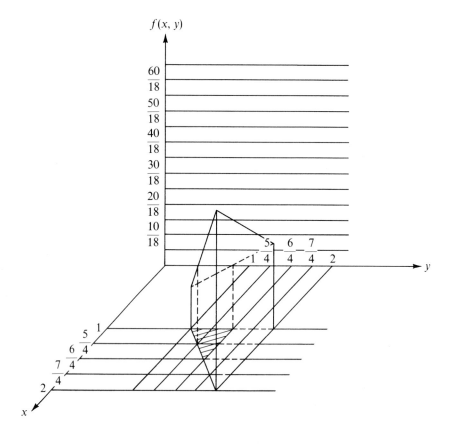

Figure 6.1.5

and

$$Pr\left(X + Y \le \frac{3}{2}\right) = 0,$$

because both X and Y are greater than or equal to one.

Figure 6.1.5 shows the graph of $f(x, y)$ and the $Pr(X \le 3/2,\ Y \le 3/2)$, which is the volume above the shaded area in the xy-plane.

6.2   Bivariate Cumulative Distribution Function

The cumulative distribution function played an important role in our study of the one-dimensional random variable. In this section, we shall extend the discussion of the cumulative distribution function to the two-dimensional random variable.

Definition 6.2.1   *Let (X, Y) be a two-dimensional random variable. The bivariate function, defined by*

$$F(x, y) = Pr(X \le x, Y \le y),$$

is called the cumulative distribution function *of the variate (X, Y).*

If (X, Y) is of the discrete type, then

$$F(x, y) = Pr(X \le x, Y \le y) = \sum_{y_j \le y} \sum_{x_j \le x} f(x_i, y_j);$$

and, if (X, Y) is of the continuous type, then

$$F(x, y) = Pr(X \le x, Y \le y) = \int_{-\infty}^{y} \left\{ \int_{-\infty}^{x} f(t, s)\, dt \right\} ds,$$

where $f(x, y)$ is the joint probability density function of the random variable (X, Y). (*Note:* The comma in the probability parentheses means "and also.")

The two-dimensional cumulative distribution has a number of properties that are analogous to those of the one-dimensional case. We shall state these properties, omitting the proofs of the first four properties because these properties are completely analogous to those of the univariate cumulative distribution function.

Theorem 6.2.1   If $F(x, y)$ is the bivariate cumulative distribution function of the random variable (X, Y), then $F(x, y)$ has the following properties:

(1) $F(\infty, \infty) = 1$;
(2) $F(-\infty, y) = F(x, -\infty) = 0$;
(3) $F(x, y)$ is a monotone nondecreasing function in each variable separately;
(4) $F(x, y)$ is continuous, at least from the right, in each variable;
(5)   for all values x_1, x_2 $(x_2 > x_1)$ and y_1, y_2 $(y_2 > y_1)$, the relation

$$F(x_2, y_2) - F(x_1, y_2) - F(x_2, y_1) + F(x_1, y_1) \geq 0$$

is satisfied.

We shall verify condition (5) by showing that it is equal to $Pr(x_1 < X \leq x_2, y_1 < Y \leq y_2)$, which is certainly nonnegative. As you can observe from Figure 6.2.1, it is possible to write

$$\{X \leq x_2, Y \leq y_2\} = \{X \leq x_1, Y \leq y_1\}$$
$$\cup \{X \leq x_1, y_1 < Y \leq y_2\}$$
$$\cup \{x_1 < X \leq x_2, Y \leq y_1\}$$
$$\cup \{x_1 < X \leq x_2, y_1 < Y \leq y_2\}.$$

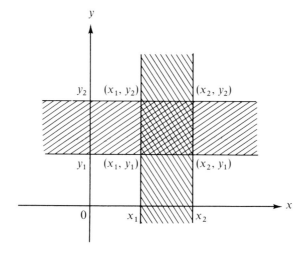

Figure 6.2.1

Thus, the event $\{X \le x_2, \ Y \le y_2\}$ is expressed in terms of mutually exclusive events, and, upon taking the probability of both sides, we have

$$Pr(x_1 < X \le x_2, \ y_1 < Y \le y_2) = Pr(X \le x_2, \ Y \le y_2) - Pr(X \le x_1, \ Y \le y_1)$$
$$- Pr(X \le x_1, \ y_1 < Y \le y_2)$$
$$- Pr(x_1 < X \le x_2, \ Y \le y_1). \quad (6.2.1)$$

But

$$\{X \le x_1, \ Y \le y_2\} = \{X \le x_1, \ Y \le y_1\} \cup \{X \le x_1, \ y_1 < Y \le y_2\} \quad (6.2.2)$$

and

$$\{X \le x_2, \ Y \le y_1\} = \{X \le x_1, \ Y \le y_1\} \cup \{x_1 < X \le x_2, \ Y \le y_1\}. \quad (6.2.3)$$

Taking the probabilities of both sides of Equations (6.2.2) and (6.2.3), we have

$$Pr(X \le x_1, \ y_1 < Y \le y_2) = Pr(X \le x_1, \ Y \le y_2) - Pr(X \le x_1, \ Y \le y_1)$$
$$(6.2.4)$$

and

$$Pr(x_1 < X \le x_2, \ Y \le y_1) = Pr(X \le x_2, \ Y \le y_1) - Pr(X \le x_1, \ Y \le y_1). \quad (6.2.5)$$

Substituting Equations (6.2.4) and (6.2.5) into Equation (6.2.1) results in

$$Pr(x_1 < X \le x_2, \ y_1 < Y \le y_2)$$
$$= Pr(X \le x_2, \ Y \le y_2) - Pr(X \le x_1, \ Y \le y_1)$$
$$- Pr(X \le x_1, \ Y \le y_2) + Pr(X \le x_1, \ Y \le y_1)$$
$$- Pr(X \le x_2, \ Y \le y_1) + Pr(X \le x_1, \ Y \le y_1). \quad (6.2.6)$$

Applying the definition of the function $F(x, y)$ to Equation (6.2.6), we obtain the desired result:

$$Pr(x_1 < X \le x_2, \ y_1 < Y \le y_2)$$
$$= F(x_2, y_2) - F(x_1, y_2) - F(x_2, y_1) + F(x_1, y_1) \ge 0. \quad (6.2.7)$$

Furthermore, if $F(x, y)$ is the bivariate cumulative distribution function of the two-dimensional continuous random variable, (X, Y), whose first and second partial derivatives exist, then

$$\frac{\partial^2 F(x, y)}{\partial x \, \partial y} = f(x, y),$$

where $f(x, y)$ is the joint probability density function of the variate (X, Y). This statement is true because

$$\frac{\partial^2 F(x, y)}{\partial x\, \partial y} = \frac{\partial}{\partial x} \left\{ \lim_{\Delta y \to 0} \frac{F(x, y + \Delta y) - F(x, y)}{\Delta y} \right\}$$

$$= \lim_{\Delta x \to 0} \lim_{\Delta y \to 0} \left\{ \frac{F(x + \Delta x, y + \Delta y) - F(x, y + \Delta y) - F(x + \Delta x, y) + F(x, y)}{\Delta x\, \Delta y} \right\},$$

which from inequality (6.2.7), we can write as

$$\lim_{\Delta x \to 0} \lim_{\Delta y \to 0} \left\{ \frac{Pr(x < X \le x + \Delta x, y < Y \le y + \Delta y)}{\Delta x\, \Delta y} \right\} = f(x, y).$$

Hence,

$$Pr(x < X \le x + dx, y < Y \le y + dy) = f(x, y)\, dx\, dy,$$

and, since the left-hand side is nonnegative, we have

$$f(x, y) \ge 0.$$

Example 6.2.1   The joint probability mass of the discrete random variable (X, Y) is given in Table 6.2.1.

The cumulative distribution function of the discrete variate (X, Y) is

$$F(x, y) = \begin{cases} 0, & x < 0 \ \ \text{or} \ \ y < 0, \\[4pt] 0, & x < 1, \ \ \text{or} \ \ y < 1, \\[4pt] \dfrac{1}{4}, & x < 1, \ \ \text{or} \ \ y < 2, \\[4pt] \dfrac{1}{4}, & x < 1, \ \ \text{or} \ \ 1 \le y < \infty, \\[4pt] \dfrac{1}{4}, & x < 2, \ \ \text{or} \ \ y < 1, \\[4pt] \dfrac{1}{4}, & 1 \le x < \infty, \ \ \text{or} \ \ y < 1, \\[4pt] \dfrac{7}{8}, & x < 2, \ \ \text{or} \ \ 1 \le y < \infty, \\[4pt] \dfrac{7}{8}, & 1 \le x < \infty, \ \ \text{or} \ \ y < 2, \\[4pt] 1, & 2 \le x < \infty, \ \ \text{or} \ \ 2 \le y < \infty. \end{cases}$$

Table 6.2.1

x \ y	0	1	2	
0	0	$\frac{1}{4}$	0	$\frac{1}{4}$
1	$\frac{1}{4}$	$\frac{3}{8}$	0	$\frac{5}{8}$
2	0	0	$\frac{1}{8}$	$\frac{1}{8}$
	$\frac{1}{4}$	$\frac{5}{8}$	$\frac{1}{8}$	1.0

Example 6.2.2 The cumulative distribution of the probability density function given in Example 6.1.3 is obtained in the following manner. For $0 \le x \le 2$ and $0 \le y \le 2$,

$$F(x, y) = Pr(X \le x, Y < y) = \int_0^y \left\{ \int_0^x \frac{1}{28} (4t + 2s + 1) \, dt \right\} ds$$

$$= \int_0^y \frac{1}{28} (2x^2 + 2sx + x) \, ds$$

$$= \frac{1}{28} (2x^2 y + y^2 x + xy)$$

$$= \frac{xy}{28} (2x + y + 1).$$

Thus,

$$F(x, y) = \begin{cases} 0, & x \le 0 \quad \text{or} \quad y \le 0, \\[2mm] \dfrac{y}{28}(2x + y + 1), & 0 < x \le 2, 0 < y \le 2, \\[2mm] \dfrac{x}{14}(2x + 3), & 0 < x \le 2, y > 2 \\[2mm] \dfrac{y}{14}(y + 5), & x > 2, 0 < y \le 2, \\[2mm] 1, & x, y > 2. \end{cases}$$

The graph of $F(x, y)$ is shown in Figure 6.2.2.

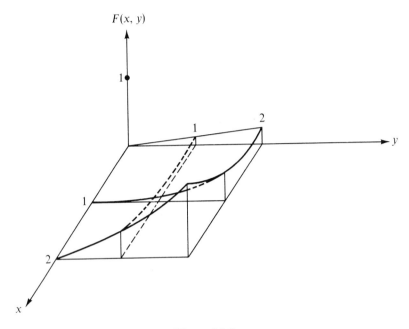

Figure 6.2.2

Example 6.2.3   Determine the cumulative distribution function of the bivariate density function,

$$(x, y) = \begin{cases} \dfrac{8}{9} xy, & 1 \le x \le y \le 2, \\ 0, & \text{elsewhere,} \end{cases}$$

given in Example 6.1.4.

Solution: Here, to find $F(x, y)$, we must integrate $f(x, y)$ first with respect to y and then with respect to x. We use this technique because we are trying to find various volumes under $f(x, y)$, the graph of which is shown in Figure 6.2.3. The density $f(x, y)$ is simply a surface in three-dimensional space and may be thought of as a family of hyperbolas. Satisfaction of the restriction $1 \le x \le y \le 2$ means that we are interested only in the volume under $f(x, y)$ and over the shaded area between the lines $x = y$, $x = 1$, and $y = 2$. Thus, finding $F(x, y)$ may be thought of as finding various volumes under the surface $f(x, y)$, subject to the restrictions $1 \leq x \leq y \leq 2$. To find any volume under a surface, we take the double integral of the equation of the surface between appropriate limits of integration for the variables involved. The shaded area of Figure 6.2.3(a), above which we wish to find various volumes, is shown more clearly in Figures 6.2.3(b) and 6.2.3(c).

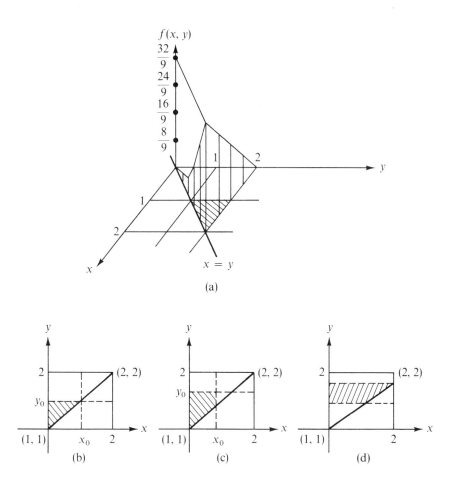

Figure 6.2.3

In calculating $F(x, y)$, we must find volumes over the shaded areas, as shown in Figures 6.2.3(b) and 6.2.3(c); however, we will never have a shaded area similar to that in Figure 6.2.3(d). Thus, in order to insure that we involve the correct area, we must always integrate first with respect to y. For the shaded area in Figure 6.2.3(b), it would not matter with which variable we integrated first; but, for the area shown in Figure 6.2.3(c), we must integrate first with respect to y. Proceeding in this manner, we shall derive $F(x, y)$ for the various intervals:

(a)   *For $x < 1$ or $y < 1$:* $F(x, y) = 0$.

(b)   *For $1 \le x \le y \le 2$:* $F(x, y) = Pr(X \le x, Y \le y)$

$$= \int_1^x \left\{ \int_t^y \frac{8}{9} ts \, ds \right\} dt = \frac{4}{9} \int_1^x t(y^2 - t^2) \, dt$$

$$= \frac{1}{9}(x^2 - 1)(2y^2 - x^2 - 1).$$

(c)   *For $x > y$, $1 \le y \le 2$:* $F(x, y) = Pr(X \le x, Y \le y)$

$$= \int_1^y \left\{ \int_t^y \frac{8}{9} ts \, ds \right\} dt = \frac{4}{9} \int_1^y t(y^2 - t^2) \, dt$$

$$= \frac{1}{9}(y^2 - 1)^2.$$

Note that part (c) could have been obtained simply by replacing x with y (the upper limit of x) in part (b).

(d)   *For $1 \le x \le 2$, $y > 2$:* $F(x, y) = Pr(X \le x, Y \le y)$

$$= \int_1^x \left\{ \int_t^2 \frac{8}{9} st \, ds \right\} dt = \frac{4}{9} \int_1^x t(4 - t^2) \, dt$$

$$= \frac{1}{9}(x^2 - 1)(7 - x^2).$$

Note that part (d) could have been obtained by letting $y = 2$ (the upper limit of y) in part (b).

(e)   *For $x > 2$ and $y > 2$:* $F(x, y) = Pr(X \le x, Y \le y)$

$$= \int_1^2 \left\{ \int_x^2 \frac{8}{9} ts \, ds \right\} dt = \frac{4}{9} \int_1^2 t(4 - t^2) \, dt$$

$$= \frac{4}{9} \left[2x^2 - \frac{x^4}{4} \right]_1^2 = \frac{1}{9}[32 - 16 - 8 + 1]$$

$$= \frac{1}{9}(9) = 1.$$

However, part (e) could have been obtained in any of the following ways:

(1) let $x = y$ (x's upper limit) and $y = 2$ (y's upper limit) in part (b), or let $y = 2$ (the upper limit of y) and $x = 2$ (x's upper limit), also in part (b);
(2) let $y = 2$ (y's upper limit) in part (c);
(3) let $x = 2$ (the upper limit of x) in part (d).

Thus,

$$F(x, y) = \begin{cases} 0, & x < 1 \quad \text{or} \quad y < 1, \\[2mm] \dfrac{1}{9}(x^2 - 1)(2y^2 - x^2 - 1), & 1 \le x \le y \le 2, \\[2mm] \dfrac{1}{9}(y^2 - 1)^2, & x > y, 1 \le y \le 2, \\[2mm] \dfrac{1}{9}(x^2 - 1)(7 - x^2), & 1 \le x \le 2, y > 2, \\[2mm] 1, & x > 2 \quad \text{and} \quad y > 2. \end{cases}$$

Example 6.2.4   If the bivariate cumulative distribution function of the random variable (X, Y) is

$$F(x, y) = \begin{cases} 0, & x \le 0 \quad \text{or} \quad y \le 0, \\[2mm] \dfrac{xy}{(1 + x)(1 + y)}, & x, y > 0, \end{cases}$$

then the joint probability density function is obtained by

$$\frac{\partial F(x, y)}{\partial x} = \frac{y}{(1 + x)^2(1 + y)}, \quad x, y > 0;$$

$$\frac{\partial^2 F(x, y)}{\partial x \, \partial y} = \frac{1}{(1 + x)^2(1 + y)^2}, \quad x, y > 0.$$

Thus,

$$f(x, y) = \begin{cases} \dfrac{1}{(1 + x)^2(1 + y)^2}, & x, y > 0. \\[2mm] 0, & \text{elsewhere.} \end{cases}$$

6.3   *Marginal Probability Distributions*

Let $f(x, y)$ be the joint probability density function of the random variable (X, Y). In problems that involve more than one random variable, we are occasionally interested in obtaining the probability density of the variate X alone, say $f_1(x)$, or that of Y, $f_2(y)$, the *marginal probability density functions* of the random variables X and Y, respectively.

First consider the discrete case. Suppose that the joint probability density function of the discrete random variable (X, Y) is given by Table 6.3.1.

Table 6.3.1

			y			
x	y_1	y_2	y_3	$\cdots$	y_m	Sum
x_1	$f(x_1, y_1)$	$f(x_1, y_2)$	$f(x_1, y_3)$	$\cdots$	$f(x_1, y_m)$	$\sum_{j=1}^{m} f(x_1, y_j)$
x_2	$f(x_2, y_1)$	$f(x_2, y_2)$	$f(x_2, y_3)$	$\cdots$	$f(x_2, y_m)$	$\sum_{j=1}^{m} f(x_2, y_j)$
$\vdots$	$\vdots$	$\vdots$	$\vdots$	$\cdots$	$\vdots$	$\vdots$
x_n	$f(x_n, y_1)$	$f(x_n, y_2)$	$f(x_n, y_3)$	$\cdots$	$f(x_n, y_m)$	$\sum_{j=1}^{m} f(x_n, y_j)$
sum	$\sum_{i=1}^{n} f(x_i, y_1)$	$\sum_{i=1}^{n} f(x_i, y_2)$	$\sum_{i=1}^{n} f(x_i, y_3)$	$\cdots$	$\sum_{i=1}^{n} f(x_i, y_m)$	1.00

Thus, Table 6.3.1 represents

$$Pr(X = x_i, \; Y = y_j) = f(x_i, y_j)$$

such that

$$\sum_{i=1}^{n} \sum_{j=1}^{m} f(x_i, y_j) = 1.$$

Suppose that we are interested in finding the probability that $X = x_k$, $k = 0$, $1, 2, \ldots, n$. Since $X = x_k$ must occur with $Y = y_j$ for some $j = 0, 1, 2, \ldots, m$, and can occur with $Y = y_j$ for only one j, we can write this probability as follows:

$$f_1(x_k) = Pr[X = x_k] = Pr[X = x_k, \; Y = y_1 \quad \text{or} \quad X = x_k, \; Y = y_2 \quad \text{or} \quad \cdots$$

$$\text{or} \quad X = x_k, \; Y = y_m]$$

$$= \sum_{j=1}^{m} Pr(X = x_k, \; Y = y_j)$$

$$= \sum_{j=1}^{m} f(x_k, y_j).$$

The function $f_1(x_k)$, $k = 1, 2, \ldots, n$ is called the *marginal probability density function* of the random variable X. Similarly,

$$f_2(y_j) = Pr(Y = y_j) = \sum_{i=1}^{n} Pr(X = x_i, \, Y = y_j)$$

$$= \sum_{i=1}^{n} f(x_i, y_j)$$

is the *marginal density function* of the variate Y. Therefore, the last column and last row of Table 6.3.1 give the marginal probability density functions of the variates X and Y, respectively.

Example 6.3.1   Find the marginal probability density function of the random variables X and Y, if their joint probability density function is given by Table 6.3.2.

Table 6.3.2

		y			
x	−2	0	1	4	Sum
−1	.3	.1	0	.2	.6
3	0	.2	.1	0	.3
5	.1	0	0	0	.1
Sum	.4	.3	.1	.2	

Solution: Table 6.3.3 is based upon the information in Table 6.3.2 and gives the marginal densities of the variates X and Y.

Table 6.3.3

x_i	−1	3	5	Other-wise
$f_1(x_i)$	.6	.3	.1	0

and

y_j	−2	0	1	4	Other-wise
$f_2(y_j)$	.4	.3	.1	.2	0

Note that $f_1(x_i)$ and $f_2(y_j)$ satisfy the conditions of a probability density function.

Definition 6.3.1   *Let $f(x_i, y_j)$ be the discrete probability density function of the random variable (X, Y). The marginal probability density functions of the random variables X and Y are given by*

$$f_1(x_i) = \sum_{j=1}^{\infty} f(x_i, y_j) \quad and \quad f_2(y_j) = \sum_{i=1}^{\infty} f(x_i, y_j),$$

respectively. Furthermore, their marginal cumulative distribution functions are given by

$$F_1(x) = F(x, \infty) = Pr(X \le x, Y \le \infty) = \sum_{x_i \le x} \sum_{j=1}^{\infty} f(x_i, y_j)$$

$$= \sum_{x_i \le x} f_1(x_i)$$

and

$$F_2(y) = F(\infty, y) = Pr(X \le \infty, Y \le y) = \sum_{y_j \le y} \sum_{i=1}^{\infty} f(x_i, y_j)$$

$$= \sum_{y_j \le y} f_2(y_j).$$

Note that $f_1(x_i)$ and $f_2(y_j)$ are actually probability density functions. However, because they are derived from $f(x_i, y_j)$, they are, in this case, called marginal probability density functions.

Definition 6.3.2   *Let $f(x, y)$ be the joint probability density function of the continuous random variable (X, Y). The marginal probability density functions of the continuous variates X and Y are given by*

$$f_1(x) = \int_{-\infty}^{\infty} f(x, y)\, dy \quad and \quad f_2(y) = \int_{-\infty}^{\infty} f(x, y)\, dx,$$

respectively.

Example 6.3.2   The joint probability density function of the two dimensional random variable (X, Y) is given by

$$(x, y) = \begin{cases} \dfrac{x^3 y^3}{16}, & 0 \le x \le 2, 0 \le y \le 2, \\ 0, & \text{elsewhere.} \end{cases}$$

The marginal densities of X and Y are

$$f_1(x) = \int_{-\infty}^{\infty} f(x, y)\, dy = \int_0^2 \frac{x^3 y^3}{16}\, dy = \begin{cases} \dfrac{x^3}{4} & 0 \le x \le 2, \\[2mm] 0, & \text{elsewhere} \end{cases}$$

and

$$f_2(y) = \int_{-\infty}^{\infty} (x, y)\, dx = \int_0^2 \frac{x^3 y^3}{16}\, dx = \begin{cases} \dfrac{y^3}{4}, & 0 \le y \le 2, \\[2mm] 0, & \text{elsewhere.} \end{cases}$$

The cumulative distribution of X is obtained as follows: For $0 \le x \le 2$,

$$F_1(x) = Pr(X \le x) = Pr(X \le x, Y \le \infty) = \int_{-\infty}^{x} \left\{ \int_{-\infty}^{\infty} f(t, y)\, dy \right\} dt$$

$$= \int_{-\infty}^{x} f_1(t) = \int_0^x \frac{t^3}{4}\, dt = \frac{x^4}{16}.$$

Therefore,

$$F_1(x) = \begin{cases} 0, & x < 0, \\[2mm] \dfrac{x^4}{16}, & 0 \le x \le 2, \\[2mm] 1, & x > 2. \end{cases}$$

For $0 \le y \le 2$,

$$F_2(y) = Pr(Y \le y) = \int_{-\infty}^{y} f_2(s)\, ds = \int_0^y \frac{s^3}{4}\, ds = \frac{y^4}{16}.$$

Therefore,

$$F_2(y) = \begin{cases} 0, & y < 0, \\[2mm] \dfrac{y^4}{16}, & 0 \le y \le 2, \\[2mm] 1, & y > 2. \end{cases}$$

Figure 6.3.1 gives a graphical presentation of $f_1(x)$, $f_2(y)$, $F_1(x)$, and $F_2(y)$.

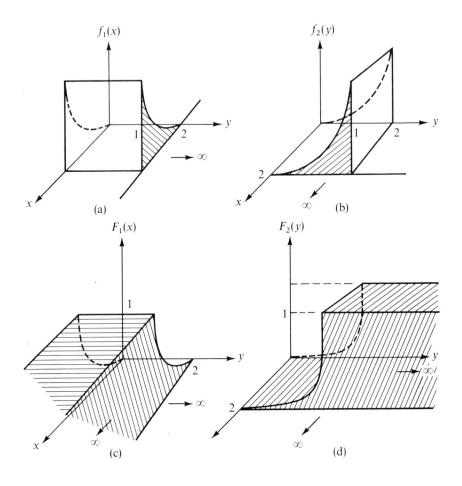

Figure 6.3.1

Example 6.3.3   Obtain the marginal densities of the variates X and Y from the bivariate density function of the two-dimensional random variable (X, Y), as given in Example 6.1.4.

Solution: Here

$$f(x, y) = \begin{cases} \dfrac{8}{9} xy, & 1 \le x \le y \le 2, \\ 0, & \text{elsewhere}, \end{cases}$$

for $1 \leq x \leq 2$,

$$f_1(x) = \int_{-\infty}^{\infty} f(x, y) \, dy = \int_x^2 \frac{8}{9} xy \, dy = \frac{4}{9} x (4 - x^2);$$

and, for $1 \leq y \leq 2$,

$$f_2(y) = \int_{-\infty}^{\infty} f(x, y) \, dx = \int_1^y \frac{8}{9} xy \, dx = \frac{4}{9} y(y^2 - 1).$$

Thus,

$$f_1(x) = \begin{cases} \frac{4}{9} x(4 - x^2), & 1 \leq x \leq 2, \\ 0, & \text{elsewhere,} \end{cases} \quad \text{and} \quad f_2(y) = \begin{cases} \frac{4}{9} y(y^2 - 1), & 1 \leq y \leq 2, \\ 0, & \text{elsewhere.} \end{cases}$$

Furthermore, for $1 \leq x \leq 2$,

$$F_1(x) = Pr(X \leq x) = \int_1^x \left\{ \int_t^2 \frac{8}{9} ty \, dy \right\} dt;$$

or, for $1 \leq x \leq 2$,

$$F_1(x) = \int_1^x f_1(t) \, dt = \int_1^x \frac{4}{9} t(4 - t^2) \, dt$$

$$= \frac{4}{9} \left[2t^2 \frac{t^4}{4} \right]_1^x = \frac{1}{9} (x^2 - 1)(7 - x^2).$$

Thus,

$$F_1(x) = \begin{cases} 0, & x < 1, \\ \frac{1}{9} (x^2 - 1)(7 - x^2), & 1 \leq x \leq 2, \\ 1, & x > 2. \end{cases}$$

Also, for $1 \leq y \leq 2$,

$$F_2(y) = Pr(Y \leq y) = \int_1^y \left\{ \int_1^s \frac{8}{9} xs \, dx \right\} ds;$$

for $1 \leq y \leq 2$,

$$F_2(y) = \int_1^y \left\{ \int_x^y \frac{8}{9} xs \, ds \right\} dx;$$

or, for $1 \leq y \leq 2$,

$$F_2(y) = \int_1^y f_2(s)\, ds = \int_1^y \frac{4}{9} s(s^2 - 1)\, ds$$

$$= \frac{4}{9} \left[\frac{s^4}{4} - \frac{s^2}{2} \right]_1^y = \frac{1}{9}(y^2 - 1)^2.$$

Hence,

$$F_2(y) = \begin{cases} 0, & y < 1, \\ \dfrac{1}{9}(y^2 - 1)^2, & 1 \leq y \leq 2, \\ 1, & y > 2. \end{cases}$$

6.4 Conditional Probability Density and Cumulative Distribution Functions

In Chapter 1, we discussed the conditional probability of events. That is, if S_1 and S_2 are events or subsets of the sample space S, the *conditional probability* of the event S_1, given that event S_2 has occurred, was defined as the probability of $S_1 \cap S_2$ divided by the probability of S_2:

$$Pr(S_1 | S_2) = \frac{Pr(S_1 \cap S_2)}{Pr(S_2)}, \quad Pr(S_2) > 0.$$

In this section, we shall investigate *conditional distributions*.

Let $f(x_i, y_j)$, $i = 1, 2, 3, \ldots, j = 1, 2, 3, \ldots$ be the bivariate probability density function of the discrete random variable (X, Y). Thus,

$$f(x_i, y_j) = Pr(X = x_i, Y = y_j);$$

and we can obtain the marginal densities by

$$f_1(x_i) = Pr(X = x_i) = \sum_{j=1}^{\infty} f(x_i y_j)$$

and

$$f_2(y_j) = Pr(Y = y_j) = \sum_{i=1}^{\infty} f(x_i, y_j).$$

Definition 6.4.1   *For every i and j, we define the probabilities*

$$h_1(x_i|y_j) = Pr(X = x_i | Y = y_j) = \frac{Pr(X = x_i, Y = y_j)}{Pr(Y = y_j)} = \frac{f(x_i, y_j)}{f_2(y_j)}$$

$$(6.4.1)$$

and

$$h_2(y_j|x_i) = Pr(Y = y_j | X = x_i) = \frac{Pr(X = x_i, Y = y_j)}{Pr(X = x_i)} = \frac{f(x_i, y_j)}{f_1(x_i)}.$$

$$(6.4.2)$$

If y_j is fixed and x_i varies over all possible values, then expression (6.4.1) is the conditional probability density function *of the random variable X of the discrete type, under the condition $Y = y_j$.*

Similarly, if x_i is fixed and y_j varies over all possible values, then expression (6.4.2) is the *conditional probability density function* of the discrete variate Y, given that $X = x_i$. Moreover, it is clear that $f_1(x_i)$ and $f_2(y_j)$ must be greater than zero. The conditional densities (6.4.1) and (6.4.2) are nonnegative;

$$\sum_{i=1}^{\infty} h(x_i|y_j) = \frac{\sum_{i=1}^{\infty} f(x_i, y_j)}{f_2(y_j)} = \frac{f_2(y_j)}{f_2(y_j)} = 1$$

and

$$\sum_{j=1}^{\infty} h(y_j|x_i) = \frac{\sum_{j=1}^{\infty} f(x_i, y_j)}{f_1(x_i)} = \frac{f_1(x_i)}{f_1(x_i)} = 1.$$

Thus, the conditions of a probability density are satisfied.

Example 6.4.1   Consider Example 6.3.1; we want to determine the conditional probability $Pr(X = -1 | Y = 0)$.

Solution: Applying Equation (6.4.1), we obtain

$$h_1(-1|0) = Pr(X = -1 | Y = 0) = \frac{Pr(X = -1, Y = 0)}{Pr(Y = 0)}$$

$$= \frac{0.1}{0.1 + 0.2 + 0} = \frac{0.1}{0.3} = \frac{1}{3}.$$

Similarly,

$$h_2(4|-1) = Pr(Y = 4 | X = -1) = \frac{Pr(X = -1, Y = 4)}{Pr(X = -1)}$$

$$= \frac{0.2}{0.3 + 0.1 + 0 + 0.2} = \frac{0.2}{0.6} = \frac{1}{3}.$$

Definition 6.4.2   *Let $f(x, y)$ be the joint probability density function of the continuous random variable (X, Y). The conditional density function of the random variable X for a given value $Y = y$ is defined by*

$$h_1(x|y) = \frac{f(x, y)}{f_2(y)}, \quad f_2(y) > 0, \tag{6.4.3}$$

and the conditional probability density function *of the variate Y for a given value $X = x$ is defined by*

$$h_2(y|x) = \frac{f(x, y)}{f_1(x)}, \quad f_1(x) > 0. \tag{6.4.4}$$

Note that $f_1(x)$ and $f_2(y)$ are the marginal probability density functions of the variates X and Y:

$$f_1(x) = \int_{-\infty}^{\infty} f(x, y) \, dy \quad \text{and} \quad f_2(y) = \int_{-\infty}^{\infty} f(x, y) \, dx.$$

As in the discrete case, expressions (6.4.3) and (6.4.4) satisfy all the requirements of a one-dimensional probability density function. For a fixed y, $h_1(x|y) \geq 0$, and

$$\int_{-\infty}^{\infty} h_1(x|y) \, dx = \int_{-\infty}^{\infty} \frac{f(x, y)}{f_2(y)} \, dx = \frac{1}{f_2(y)} \int_{-\infty}^{\infty} f(x, y) \, dx = \frac{f_2(y)}{f_2(y)} = 1.$$

The situation is similar for the conditional density $h_2(y|x)$. Thus, if we want to obtain the probability that the value of X is in $S_1 = \{x : a \leq x \leq b\}$, given that Y is known, we have

$$Pr(a \leq X \leq b | y) = \int_a^b h_1(x|y) \, dx.$$

The conditional cumulative distribution functions of the continuous random variables X, given Y, and Y, given X, are

$$F_X(x|y) = Pr(X \le x|\, Y \le y) = \frac{Pr(X \le x,\, Y \le y)}{Pr(Y \le y)}$$

$$= \frac{\int_{-\infty}^{x} \{ \int_{-\infty}^{y} f(t, s)\, ds \}\, dt}{\int_{-\infty}^{y} \{ \int_{-\infty}^{\infty} f(x, s)\, dx \}\, ds} = \frac{\int_{-\infty}^{x} \{ \int_{-\infty}^{y} f(t, s)\, ds \}\, dt}{\int_{-\infty}^{y} f_2(s)\, ds} \quad (6.4.5)$$

and

$$F_Y(y|x) = Pr(Y \le y|\, X \le x) = \frac{Pr(X \le x,\, Y \le y)}{Pr(X \le x)}$$

$$= \frac{\int_{-\infty}^{x} \{ \int_{-\infty}^{y} f(t, s)\, ds \}\, dt}{\int_{-\infty}^{x} f_1(t)\, dt}. \quad (6.4.6)$$

However, a more common way of introducing the concept of cumulative distribution functions is

$$F_X(x|y) = \int_{-\infty}^{x} h(t|y)\, dt = \int_{-\infty}^{x} \frac{f(t, y)}{f_2(y)}\, dt, \quad (6.4.7)$$

and we shall discuss the development of Equation (6.4.7) in view of what has come before it. From Equation (6.4.5), we have

$$F_X(x|y) = \frac{F(x, y)}{F_2(y)}. \quad (6.4.8)$$

Suppose that $f_2(y) \ne 0$. We can then define $F_X(x|\, Y = y)$ as the limit

$$F_X(x|\, Y = y) = \lim_{\Delta y \to 0} F_X(x|y < Y \le y + \Delta y).$$

Equation (6.4.8) can also be written as

$$F_X(x|\, Y = y) = \frac{\displaystyle \lim_{\Delta y \to 0} \frac{F(x, y + \Delta y) - F(x, y)}{\Delta y}}{\displaystyle \lim_{\Delta y \to 0} \frac{F(y + \Delta y) - F(y)}{\Delta y}}$$

$$= \frac{\dfrac{\partial}{\partial y} F(x, y)}{\dfrac{d}{dy} F_2(y)}.$$

Assuming that the partial derivative of $F(x, y)$ with respect to y and the derivative of $F_2(y)$ exist, then

$$F_X(x \mid Y = y) = \frac{\int_{-\infty}^{x} f(t, y) \, dt}{f_2(y)}, \quad f_2(y) > 0. \tag{6.4.9}$$

Similarly,

$$F_Y(y \mid X = x) = \frac{\int_{-\infty}^{y} f(x, s) \, ds}{f_1(x)}, \quad f_1(x) > 0.$$

We shall now illustrate that we can express marginal cumulative distributions as functions of conditional cumulative distributions. In view of Equation (6.4.9), we have

$$\int_{-\infty}^{x} f(t, y) \, dt = f_2(y) F_X(x \mid y).$$

It follows that

$$\int_{-\infty}^{x} \left\{ \int_{-\infty}^{\infty} f(t, y) \, dy \right\} dt = \int_{-\infty}^{\infty} f_2(y) F_X(x \mid y) \, dy,$$

$$\int_{-\infty}^{x} f_1(t) \, dt = \int_{-\infty}^{\infty} f_2(y) F_X(x \mid y) \, dy,$$

or

$$F_1(x) = \int_{-\infty}^{\infty} f_2(y) F_X(x \mid y) \, dy.$$

Similarly,

$$F_2(y) = \int_{-\infty}^{\infty} f_1(x) F_Y(y \mid x) \, dx.$$

The conditional distribution function satisfies the properties of ordinary distributions:

(1) $F_X(\infty \mid y) = \dfrac{\int_{-\infty}^{\infty} f(x, y) \, dx}{f_2(y)} = \dfrac{f_2(y)}{f_2(y)} = 1;$

(2) $F_X(-\infty \mid y) = \displaystyle\int_{-\infty}^{-\infty} \dfrac{f(x, y) \, dx}{f_2(y)} = 0;$

(3) $F_X(x_2 \mid y) - F_X(x_1 \mid y) = Pr(x_1 < X \leq x_2 \mid y)$

$$= \frac{Pr(x_1 < X \leq x_2, Y = y)}{f_2(y)} \geq 0 \quad \text{for} \quad f_2(y) > 0.$$

(4)   If the random variable X is of the continuous type, then

$$h(x \mid y) = \frac{d}{dx} F_X(x \mid y) = \lim_{h \to 0} \frac{Pr\{x \le X \le x + h \mid Y = y\}}{h}.$$

Example 6.4.2   The joint probability density function of the continuous random variable (X, Y) is

$$f(x, y) = \begin{cases} \dfrac{1}{28}(4x + 2y + 1), & 0 \le x \le 2, 0 \le y \le 2, \\ \\ 0, & \text{elsewhere.} \end{cases}$$

The marginal densities of X and Y are as follows: for $0 \le x \le 2$,

$$f_1(x) = \frac{1}{28} \int_0^2 (4x + 2y + 1)\, dy = \frac{1}{14}(4x + 3);$$

therefore,

$$f_1(x) = \begin{cases} \dfrac{1}{14}(4x + 3), & 0 \le x \le 2, \\ \\ 0, & \text{elsewhere.} \end{cases}$$

For $0 \le y \le 2$,

$$f_2(y) = \frac{1}{28} \int_0^2 (4x + 2y + 1)\, dx = \frac{1}{14}(2y + 5);$$

therefore,

$$f_2(y) = \begin{cases} \dfrac{1}{14}(2y + 5), & 0 \le y \le 2, \\ \\ 0, & \text{elsewhere.} \end{cases}$$

From Equation (6.4.3), the conditional density of X for a given value of Y is as follows: for $0 \le x \le 2$ and $0 \le y \le 2$,

$$h_1(x \mid y) = \frac{\dfrac{1}{28}(4x + 2y + 1)}{\dfrac{1}{14}(2y + 5)} = \frac{1}{2}\frac{(4x + 2y + 1)}{(2y + 5)};$$

therefore,

$$h_1(x|y) = \begin{cases} \dfrac{1}{2} \dfrac{(4x + 2y + 1)}{(2y + 5)}, & 0 \le x \le 2 \quad \text{and} \quad 0 \le y \le 2, \\ 0, & \text{elsewhere.} \end{cases}$$

Also, for $0 \le y \le 2$ and $0 \le x \le 2$,

$$h_2(y|x) = \frac{\dfrac{1}{28}(4x + 2y + 1)}{\dfrac{1}{14}(4x + 3)} = \frac{1}{2} \frac{(4x + 2y + 1)}{(4x + 3)};$$

therefore,

$$h_2(y|x) = \begin{cases} \dfrac{1}{2} \dfrac{(4x + 2y + 1)}{(4x + 3)}, & 0 \le y \le 2 \quad \text{and} \quad 0 \le x \le 2, \\ 0, & \text{elsewhere.} \end{cases}$$

Example 6.4.3   We have seen that the marginal densities of the bi-variate density function given in Example 6.3.3 are

$$f_1(x) = \begin{cases} \dfrac{4}{9} x(4 - x)^2, & 1 \le x \le 2, \\ 0, & \text{elsewhere,} \end{cases} \quad \text{and} \quad f_2(y) = \begin{cases} \dfrac{4}{9} y(y^2 - 1), & 1 \le y \le 2, \\ 0, & \text{elsewhere.} \end{cases}$$

The conditional probability density function of X for a fixed $Y = y_0$ is, for $1 \le x \le y_0$ and $1 \le y_0 \le 2$,

$$h_1(x|y_0) = \frac{f(x, y_0)}{f_2(y_0)} = \frac{\dfrac{8}{9} x y_0}{\dfrac{4}{9} y_0(y_0^2 - 1)} = \frac{2x}{y_0^2 - 1}.$$

Therefore,

$$h_1(x|y) = \begin{cases} \dfrac{2x}{y_0^2 - 1}, & 1 \le x \le y_0 \quad \text{and} \quad 1 \le y_0 \le 2, \\ 0, & \text{elsewhere.} \end{cases}$$

Similarly, for $x_0 \leq y \leq 2$ and $1 \leq x_0 \leq 2$,

$$h_2(y|x_0) = \frac{f(x_0, y)}{f_1(x_0)} = \frac{\dfrac{8}{9} x_0 y}{\dfrac{4}{9} x_0 (4 - x_0^2)} = \frac{2y}{4 - x_1^2} \, ;$$

therefore,

$$h_2(y|x_0) = \begin{cases} \dfrac{2y}{4 - x_0^2}, & x_0 \leq y \leq 2, \; 1 \leq x_0 \leq 2, \\ 0, & \text{elsewhere.} \end{cases}$$

Furthermore, for $1 \leq x \leq y_0$ and $1 \leq y_0 \leq 2$,

$$F_X(x|y_0) = Pr(X \leq x | Y = y_0) = \frac{Pr(X \leq x, \; Y = y_0)}{Pr(Y = y_0)}$$

$$= \frac{\displaystyle\int_1^x \frac{8}{9} t y_0 \, dt}{\displaystyle\int_1^{y_0} \frac{8}{9} x y_0 \, dx} = \frac{x^2 - 1}{y_0^2 - 1} \, ;$$

thus,

$$F_X(x|y_0) = \begin{cases} 0, & x < 1, \\ \dfrac{x^2 - 1}{y_0^2 - 1}, & 1 \leq x \leq y_0 \quad \text{and} \quad 1 \leq y_0 \leq 2, \\ 1, & x > y_0. \end{cases}$$

Note that the same result can be obtained for $1 \leq x \leq y_0$ and $1 \leq y_0 \leq 2$ by

$$F_X(x|y_0) = \int_1^x h_1(t|y_0) \, dt = \int_1^x \frac{2t}{y_0^2 - 1} \, dt = \frac{x^2 - 1}{y_0^2 - 1}.$$

Also, for $x_0 \leq y \leq 2$ and $1 \leq x_0 \leq 2$,

$$F_Y(y|x_0) = \frac{\displaystyle\int_{x_0}^y \frac{8}{9} x_0 s \, ds}{\displaystyle\int_{x_0}^2 \frac{8}{9} x_0 y \, dy} \, ;$$

or, for $x_0 \leq y \leq 2$ and $1 \leq x_0 \leq 2$,

$$F_Y(y\,|\,x_0) = \int_{x_0}^{y} h_2(s\,|\,x_0)\,ds = \int_{x_0}^{y} \frac{2s}{4 - x_0^2}\,ds = \frac{y^2 - x_0^2}{4 - x_0^2}.$$

Thus,

$$F_Y(y\,|\,x_0) = \begin{cases} 0, & y < x_0, \\[2mm] \dfrac{y^2 - x_0^2}{4 - x_0^2}, & x_0 \leq y \leq 2 \quad \text{and} \quad 1 \leq x_0 \leq 2, \\[2mm] 1, & y > 2. \end{cases}$$

6.5   Independent Random Variables

In Section 2.6, we studied the notion of independent events. That is, two random events S_1 and S_2 are *independent* of one another if

$$Pr(S_1 \cap S_2) = Pr(S_1)Pr(S_2).$$

In this section, we shall introduce the notion of independent random variables. Throughout the section, we shall let $F(x, y)$, $F_1(x)$, and $F_2(y)$ represent the cumulative distribution function of the two-dimensional random variable (X, Y) and the marginal cumulative distribution functions of the variates X and Y, respectively.

Definition 6.5.1   *Two random variables X and Y are said to be independent (mutually independent) if*

$$F(x, y) = F_1(x)F_2(y) \tag{6.5.1}$$

is satisfied for every real pair of numbers (x, y).

Thus, the random variables X and Y are independent if the events $\{X \leq x\}$ and $\{Y \leq y\}$ are independent for every real x and y. That is,

$$Pr(X \leq x, Y \leq y) = Pr(X \leq x)Pr(Y \leq y).$$

Furthermore, for all values x_1, x_2 $(x_2 > x_1)$ and y_1, y_2 $(y_2 > y_1)$, we show that, if X and Y are independent,

$$Pr(x_1 < X \le x_2, y_1 < Y \le y_2) = Pr(x_1 < X \le x_2)Pr(y_1 < Y \le y_2):$$

$$
\begin{aligned}
Pr(x_1 < X \le x_2, y_1 < Y \le y_2) &= F(x_1, y_1) - F(x_1, y_2) \\
&\quad - F(x_2, y_1) + F(x_2, y_2) \\
&= F_1(x_1)F_2(y_1) - F_1(x_1)F_2(y_2) \\
&\quad - F_1(x_2)F_2(y_1) + F_1(x_2)F_2(y_2) \\
&= \{F_1(x_2) - F_1(x_1)\}\{F_2(y_2) - F_2(y_1)\} \\
&= Pr(x_1 < X \le x_2)Pr(y_1 < Y \le y_2).
\end{aligned}
$$

Thus, if X and Y are independent, the probability that the random variable (X, Y) assumes values in the rectangle, shown in Figure 6.2.1, is equal to the product of the probabilities that X assumes its values in the vertical strip and that Y assumes its values in the horizontal strip, both shown in the figure.

Theorem 6.5.1   Let $f(x, y)$ be the joint probability density function of the random variable (X, Y).

(1) If (X, Y) is of the discrete type, then X and Y are independent random variables if and only if

$$f(x_i, y_j) = f_1(x_i)f_2(y_j) \tag{6.5.2}$$

for all i and j.

(2) If (X, Y) is of the continuous type, then X and Y are independent random variables if and only if

$$f(x, y) = f_1(x)f_2(y) \tag{6.5.3}$$

for all real (x, y).

Proof   We shall prove part (2) of the theorem. Applying the relation between probability density and cumulative distribution functions, we have

$$f(x, y) = \frac{\partial^2 F(x, y)}{\partial x\, \partial y} = \frac{dF_1(x)}{dx}\frac{dF_2(y)}{dy} = f_1(x)f_2(y).$$

Conversely,

$$F(x, y) = \int_{-\infty}^{x} \left\{ \int_{-\infty}^{y} f(t, s)\, ds \right\} dt$$

$$= \int_{-\infty}^{x} \left\{ \int_{-\infty}^{y} f_1(t) f_2(t)\, ds \right\} dt$$

$$= \int_{-\infty}^{x} f_1(t)\, dt \int_{-\infty}^{y} f_2(s)\, ds$$

$$= Pr(X \le x) Pr(Y \le y)$$

$$= F_1(x) F_2(y).$$

Independence of random variables can be equivalently defined by using the notion of conditional probability density functions, as shown by Theorem 6.5.2.

Theorem 6.5.2   Let $f(x, y)$, $f_1(x)$, and $f_2(y)$ be the joint probability density function of the random variable (X, Y) and the marginal densities of X and Y, respectively.

(1) If (X, Y) is of the discrete type, then X and Y are independent if and only if

$$h(x_i | y_j) = f_1(x_i) \quad \text{or} \quad h_2(y_j | x_i) = f_2(y_j) \tag{6.5.4}$$

for all i and j.

(2) If (X, Y) is of the continuous type, then X and Y are independent if and only if

$$h_1(x | y) = f_1(x) \quad \text{or} \quad h_2(y | x) = f_2(y) \tag{6.5.5}$$

for all real parts (x, y), such that $f_1(x)$ and $f_2(x)$ are positive.

The proof is straightforward, applying the definition of conditional probability density function and Theorem 6.5.1.

Example 6.5.1   Suppose that a fair coin is tossed twice. Let the random variable X assume the value 0 or 1, depending upon whether a head or a tail appears on the first toss. The random variable Y assumes the value 0 or 1, depending upon whether a head or a tail appears on the second toss. Table 6.5.1 gives the joint probability density of (X, Y).

Thus, because

$$f(x_i, y_j) = f_1(x_i) f_2(y_j),$$

X and Y are independent random variables.

Table 6.5.1

x	y 0	1	$f_1(x_i)$
0	$\dfrac{1}{4}$	$\dfrac{1}{4}$	$\dfrac{1}{2}$
1	$\dfrac{1}{4}$	$\dfrac{1}{4}$	$\dfrac{1}{2}$
$f_2(y_j)$	$\dfrac{1}{2}$	$\dfrac{1}{2}$	1.0

Example 6.5.2   The cumulative distribution function of the continuous random variable (X, Y) is given by

$$F(x, y) = \begin{cases} 1 - e^{-x} - e^{-y} + e^{-(x+y)}, & x, y \geq 0, \\ 0, & \text{elsewhere.} \end{cases}$$

The joint probability density function is

$$\frac{\partial^2 F(x, y)}{\partial x \, \partial y} = f(x, y) = \begin{cases} e^{-(x+y)}, & x, y \geq 0, \\ 0, & \text{elsewhere.} \end{cases}$$

The marginal probability density and marginal cumulative functions of X and Y are

$$f_1(x) = \begin{cases} e^{-x}, & x \geq 0, \\ 0, & \text{elsewhere,} \end{cases} \qquad f_2(y) = \begin{cases} e^{-y}, & y \geq 0, \\ 0, & \text{elsewhere,} \end{cases}$$

$$F_1(x) = \begin{cases} 0, & y < 0, \\ 1 - e^{-x}, & x \geq 0, \end{cases} \quad \text{and} \quad F_2(y) = \begin{cases} 0, & x < 0, \\ 1 - e^{-y}, & y \geq 0. \end{cases}$$

In view of Equation (6.5.1), we have

$$F_1(x)F_2(y) = (1 - e^{-x})(1 - e^{-y}) = 1 - e^{-x} - e^{-y} + e^{-(x+y)} = F(x, y).$$

Hence, X and Y are independent. Their independence is also clear from Equations (6.5.3) and (6.5.5).

Example 6.5.3   Referring to Example 6.1.4,

$$f(x, y) = \begin{cases} \dfrac{8}{9} xy, & 1 \le x \le y \le 2, \\ 0, & \text{elsewhere,} \end{cases}$$

$$f_1(x) = \begin{cases} \dfrac{4}{9} x(4 - x^2), & 1 \le x \le 2, \\ 0, & \text{elsewhere,} \end{cases} \quad \text{and} \quad f_2(y) = \begin{cases} \dfrac{4}{9} y(y^2 - 1), & 1 \le y \le 2, \\ 0, & \text{elsewhere.} \end{cases}$$

Thus,

$$f_1(x)f_2(y) = \frac{16}{81} xy(4 - x^2)(y^2 - 1) \ne f(x, y),$$

and the random variables X and Y are not independent.

Theorem 6.5.3   If X and Y are independent random variables, then the one-to-one functional forms of X and Y, $W_1 = g_1(X)$ and $W_2 = g_2(Y)$, are also independent.

Proof   Since W_1 amd W_2 are single-valued functions, their inverses exist. Thus,

$$\begin{aligned} F(w_1, w_2) = Pr(W_1 \le w_1, W_2 \le w_2) &= Pr(g_1(X) \le w_1, g_2(Y) \le w_2) \\ &= Pr(X \le g_1^{-1}(w_1), Y \le g_2^{-1}(w_2)) \\ &= Pr(X \le g_1^{-1}(w_1))Pr(Y \le g_2^{-1}(w_2)) \\ &= Pr(g_1(X) \le w_1)Pr(g_2(X) \le w_2) \\ &= Pr(W_1 \le w_1)Pr(W_2 \le w_2) \\ &= F_1(w_1)F_2(w_2). \end{aligned}$$

The usefulness of this theorem will be shown in later sections.

6.6   Function of Two Random Variables

We have seen in Chapter 4 that a functional form of a random variable is also a random variable, and we have discussed the manner in which we can derive such distribution functions. In this section, we shall study some functional forms of two random variables.

6.6.1 One Function of Two Discrete Random Variables   We begin by investigating one function of two discrete random variables. Let (X, Y) be a discrete two-dimensional random variable whose distribution is known;

we wish to obtain the distribution of $H = g(X, Y)$. To obtain the probability mass function of H is quite easy, and we illustrate the function by considering Example 6.6.1.

Example 6.6.1   Consider an experiment in which there are two consecutive throws of a die. Let X and Y denote the results of the first and second throw, respectively. Thus, both X and Y take on the values 1, 2, ..., 6, each with probability 1/6, because they are independent, as shown in Table 6.6.1.

Table 6.6.1

x	1	2	3	4	5	6	$f_1(x_i)$
				y			
1	$\frac{1}{36}$	$\frac{1}{36}$	$\frac{1}{36}$	$\frac{1}{36}$	$\frac{1}{36}$	$\frac{1}{36}$	$\frac{1}{6}$
2	$\frac{1}{36}$	$\frac{1}{36}$	$\frac{1}{36}$	$\frac{1}{36}$	$\frac{1}{36}$	$\frac{1}{36}$	$\frac{1}{6}$
3	$\frac{1}{36}$	$\frac{1}{36}$	$\frac{1}{36}$	$\frac{1}{36}$	$\frac{1}{36}$	$\frac{1}{36}$	$\frac{1}{6}$
4	$\frac{1}{36}$	$\frac{1}{36}$	$\frac{1}{36}$	$\frac{1}{36}$	$\frac{1}{36}$	$\frac{1}{36}$	$\frac{1}{6}$
5	$\frac{1}{36}$	$\frac{1}{36}$	$\frac{1}{36}$	$\frac{1}{36}$	$\frac{1}{36}$	$\frac{1}{36}$	$\frac{1}{6}$
6	$\frac{1}{36}$	$\frac{1}{36}$	$\frac{1}{36}$	$\frac{1}{36}$	$\frac{1}{36}$	$\frac{1}{36}$	$\frac{1}{6}$
$f_2(y_i)$	$\frac{1}{6}$	$\frac{1}{6}$	$\frac{1}{6}$	$\frac{1}{6}$	$\frac{1}{6}$	$\frac{1}{6}$	1.0

Solution: (a) We want to obtain the probability density of the one-dimensional random variable H, where $H = g(X, Y) = X + Y$. Here the variate H can assume the values 2, 3, 4, ..., 12; and, using the fact that X and Y are independent, we can compute the probability function of H. That is,

$$Pr(H = 2) = Pr(X = 1)Pr(Y = 1) = \frac{1}{36}$$

$$Pr(H = 3) = Pr(X = 1)Pr(Y = 2) + Pr(X = 2)Pr(Y = 1) = \frac{1}{36} + \frac{1}{36} = \frac{1}{18}$$

$$Pr(H = 4) = Pr(X = 1)Pr(Y = 3) + Pr(X = 3)Pr(Y = 1)$$

$$+ Pr(X = 2)Pr(Y = 2) = \frac{1}{36} + \frac{1}{36} + \frac{1}{36} = \frac{1}{12},$$

and so on. Table 6.6.2 shows the probability mass function of the variate H.

Table 6.6.2

h_i	2	3	4	5	6	7	8	9	10	11	12
$f(h_i)$	$\dfrac{1}{36}$	$\dfrac{2}{36}$	$\dfrac{3}{36}$	$\dfrac{4}{36}$	$\dfrac{5}{36}$	$\dfrac{6}{36}$	$\dfrac{5}{36}$	$\dfrac{4}{36}$	$\dfrac{3}{36}$	$\dfrac{2}{36}$	$\dfrac{1}{36}$

(b) Similarly, we can obtain the probability density function of W, where $W = g(X, Y) = X - Y$. The variate W can assume the values $-5, -4, -3, \ldots, 0, \ldots, 4, 5$, and its distribution is shown in Table 6.6.3.

Table 6.6.3

w_i	-5	-4	-3	-2	-1	0	1	2	3	4	5
$f(w_i)$	$\dfrac{1}{36}$	$\dfrac{2}{36}$	$\dfrac{3}{36}$	$\dfrac{4}{36}$	$\dfrac{5}{36}$	$\dfrac{6}{36}$	$\dfrac{5}{36}$	$\dfrac{4}{36}$	$\dfrac{3}{36}$	$\dfrac{2}{36}$	$\dfrac{1}{36}$

Therefore, to obtain the probability mass function of H, we have

$$f(h_k) = Pr(H = h_k) = \sum_{x_i + y_j = h_k} Pr(X = x_i, Y = y_j)$$

$$= \sum_{x_i + y_j = h_k} f(x_i, y_j);$$

and, for the variate W,

$$f(w_r) = Pr(W = w_r) = \sum_{x_i - y_j = w_r} Pr(X = x_i, Y = y_j)$$

$$= \sum_{x_i - y_j = w_r} f(x_i, y_j).$$

The cumulative distribution function of H is simply

$$F(h) = Pr(H \leq h) = \sum_{x_i + y_j \leq h} f(x_i, y_j).$$

6.6.2   Two Functions of Two Continuous Random Variables   Before we study the manner in which we can obtain the distribution of a function of two continuous random variables, we shall consider the joint distribution of two functional forms of such a variate. Suppose that we are given $f(x, y)$, the joint probability density function of the continuous random variable (X, Y), and we are interested in obtaining a new probability density function $z(u, v)$ of the random variable (U, V), where the relation between the new and old variates is given by

$$U = g_1(X, Y) \quad \text{and} \quad V = g_2(X, Y). \tag{6.6.1}$$

To obtain this new density function, we must assume that the functions g_1 and g_2 define a one-to-one transformation that maps a two-dimensional set, S, of the xy-plane onto a two-dimensional set, E^*, in the uv-plane and has continuous first partial derivatives with respect to x and y. (See Figure 6.6.1.) These conditions imply that we can uniquely solve for the inverse of the transformation:

$$x = z_1^{-1}(u, v) \quad \text{and} \quad y = z_2^{-1}(u, v). \tag{6.6.2}$$

Furthermore, we shall assume that the inverse of the transformation has continuous first partial derivatives with respect to u and v.

Under the above assumptions, the joint probability density function of the new random variable (U, V) is given by

$$z(u, v) = f[z_1^{-1}(u, v), z_2^{-1}(u, v)] |J|, \tag{6.6.3}$$

where $|J|$ is the absolute value of the Jacobian of the transformation, defined by the determinant

$$J = \frac{\partial(x, y)}{\partial(u, v)} = \begin{vmatrix} \dfrac{\partial x}{\partial u} & \dfrac{\partial x}{\partial v} \\[2mm] \dfrac{\partial y}{\partial u} & \dfrac{\partial y}{\partial v} \end{vmatrix},$$

which cannot be equal to zero. For the complete justification of the development of $z(u, v)$, we need certain concepts of advanced calculus, which are beyond the scope of this book; however, one can see how this function is obtained by considering the following formulation: Let $E_1 \subset E$ be a two-dimensional subset (an event of E) in the xy-plane, and let $E_2 \subset E^*$ be a two-dimensional subset (an event of E^*) in the uv-plane, denote the image of E_1 under a one-to-one transformation, as shown in Figure 6.6.1. Thus, the events E_1 and E_2, as shown in Figure 6.6.1, where $(X, Y) \in E_1$ and $(U, V) \in E_2$, are equivalent, and

$$Pr[(X, Y) \in E_1] = \iint_{E_1} f(x, y) \, dx \, dy = Pr[(U, V) \in S_2]$$

$$= \iint_{E_2} f[z_1^{-1}(u, v), z_2^{-1}(u, v)] |J| \, du \, dv,$$

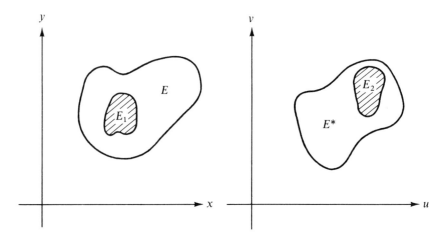

Figure 6.6.1

where

$$x = z_1^{-1}(u, v) \quad \text{and} \quad y = z_2^{-1}(u, v).$$

This situation implies that the joint probability density function of the random variable (U, V) is

$$z(u, v) = f[z_1^{-1}(u, v), z_2^{-1}(u, v)]|J|.$$

Hence, from the knowledge of $z(u, v)$, one can obtain the marginal distributions of U and V, say $f_1(u)$ and $f_2(v)$, by integrating $z(u, v)$ with respect to v and u, respectively:

$$f_1(u) = \int_{-\infty}^{\infty} z(u, v) \, dv \quad \text{and} \quad f_2(v) = \int_{-\infty}^{\infty} z(u, v) \, du.$$

We shall summarize the above discussion in Theorem 6.6.1.

Theorem 6.6.1   Let $f(x, y)$ be the joint probability density function of the continuous random variable (X, Y). Suppose that

$$U = g_1(X, Y) \quad \text{and} \quad V = g_2(X, Y),$$

such that g_1 and g_2 define a one-to-one transformation of the random variable (X, Y) and that this random variable has continuous first partial derivatives, with respect to x and y. Then the joint probability density function of the random variable (U, V) is given by

$$z(u, v) = f[z_1^{-1}(u, v), z_2^{-1}(u, v)]|J|,$$

where

$$x = z_1^{-1}(u, v), \qquad y = z_2^{-1}(u, v)$$

and the Jacobian $|J| \neq 0$.

Example 6.6.2   Let

$$f(x, y; \sigma) = \frac{1}{2\pi\sigma^2} e^{-(1/2\sigma^2)(x^2 + y^2)}, \quad -\infty < x, y < \infty$$

be the joint probability density function of the variate (X, Y), let

$$U = \sqrt{X^2 + Y^2} \quad \text{and} \quad V = \tan^{-1}\left(\frac{Y}{X}\right), \quad 0 \leq V \leq 2\pi.$$

We wish to determine the probability density function of the random variables U and V.

Solution: In order that the transformation be one-to-one, we write

$$f(x, y; \sigma) = \begin{cases} \dfrac{1}{2\pi\sigma^2} e^{-(1/2\sigma^2)(x^2 + y^2)}, & x < 0, \ -\infty < y < \infty, \\[2ex] \dfrac{1}{2\pi\sigma^2} e^{-(1/2\sigma^2)(x^2 + y^2)}, & x \geq 0, \ -\infty < y < \infty, \end{cases}$$

then

$$\left. \begin{array}{l} X = U \cos V \\[1ex] Y = U \sin V \end{array} \right\} \begin{array}{l} U > 0 \\[1ex] \dfrac{\pi}{2} < V < \dfrac{3\pi}{2} \end{array}$$

for the first part of $f(x, y; \sigma)$, and

$$\left. \begin{array}{l} X = U \cos V \\[1ex] Y = U \sin V \end{array} \right\} \begin{array}{l} U > 0 \\[1ex] -\dfrac{\pi}{2} < V \leq \dfrac{\pi}{2} \end{array}$$

for the second part of the joint probability density function, $f(x, y; \sigma)$. (See Figure 6.6.2.)

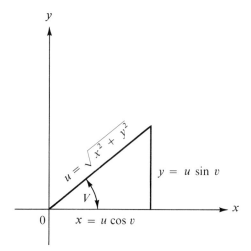

Figure 6.6.2

The Jacobian of the transformation is

$$J = \begin{vmatrix} \dfrac{\partial x}{\partial u} & \dfrac{\partial x}{\partial v} \\[2ex] \dfrac{\partial y}{\partial u} & \dfrac{\partial y}{\partial v} \end{vmatrix} = \begin{vmatrix} \cos v & -u \sin v \\[1ex] \sin v & u \cos v \end{vmatrix}$$

$$= u \cos^2 v + u \sin^2 v = u.$$

Thus, applying Equation (6.6.3), we have

$$z(u, v) = \begin{cases} \dfrac{u}{2\pi\sigma^2} e^{-(u^2/2\sigma^2)}, & u > 0, \dfrac{\pi}{2} < v < \dfrac{3\pi}{2} \\[3ex] \dfrac{u}{2\pi\sigma^2} e^{-(u^2/2\sigma^2)}, & u > 0, -\dfrac{\pi}{2} < v < \dfrac{\pi}{2}, \\[3ex] 0, & \text{elsewhere.} \end{cases}$$

The marginal probability density of the random variable U is obtained as follows:

$$z_1(u) = \frac{1}{2\pi\sigma^2} \int_{\frac{\pi}{2}}^{\frac{3\pi}{2}} u e^{-(u^2/2\sigma^2)} \, dv + \frac{1}{2\pi\sigma^2} \int_{-\frac{\pi}{2}}^{\frac{\pi}{2}} u e^{-(u^2/2\sigma^2)} \, dv$$

$$= \frac{1}{2\pi\sigma^2} u e^{-(u^2/2\sigma^2)} \int_0^{2\pi} dv = \frac{1}{\sigma^2} u e^{-(u^2/2\sigma^2)}.$$

Therefore,

$$
z_1(u) = \begin{cases} \dfrac{1}{\sigma^2}\, u e^{-(u^2/2\sigma^2)}, & u > 0, \\[2mm] 0, & \text{elsewhere.} \end{cases}
$$

The marginal probability density of the variate V is derived as follows. For $\pi/2 < v < 3\pi/2$, we obtain $\int_0^\infty z(u, v)\, du = 1/2\pi$; and, for $-(\pi/2) < v < \pi/2$, we obtain also the value $1/2\pi$. Combining these two results gives

$$
z_2(v) = \begin{cases} \dfrac{1}{2\pi}, & 0 < v < 2\pi, \\[2mm] 0, & \text{elsewhere.} \end{cases}
$$

Hence, the variate V is uniformly distributed over the interval from 0 to 2π. When we replace σ^2 by $\alpha/2$ in $z_1(u)$, we obtain the Rayleigh distribution, as defined in Section 3.3.

Example 6.6.3   Let the probability density function of the random variable (X, Y) be

$$
f(x, y) = \begin{cases} \beta^{-(1/2)} e^{-\{(x+y)/\beta\}}, & x, y > 0,\ \beta > 0, \\[2mm] 0, & \text{elsewhere.} \end{cases}
$$

Let

$$
U = \frac{X - Y}{2} \quad \text{and} \quad V = Y.
$$

We wish to determine the probability density function of (U, V).

Solution: Here $x = 2u + v$ and $y = v$ define a one-to-one transformation from the event $E_1 = \{(x, y): x,\ y > 0\}$ onto the event $E_2 = \{(u, v): -2u < v$ and $0 < v,\ -\infty < u < \infty\}$. The Jacobian of the transformation is

$$
J = \begin{vmatrix} \dfrac{\partial x}{\partial u} & \dfrac{\partial x}{\partial v} \\[3mm] \dfrac{\partial y}{\partial u} & \dfrac{\partial y}{\partial v} \end{vmatrix} = \begin{vmatrix} 2 & 1 \\ 0 & 1 \end{vmatrix} = 2.
$$

Thus, in view of Equation (6.6.3), the joint probability density function of the random variable (U, V) is

$$z(u, v) = \begin{cases} \dfrac{|2|}{\beta^2} e^{-(2/\beta)(u+v)}, & -\infty < u < \infty, \; v > -2u \quad \text{if} \quad u < 0, \\ & \hspace{5.5em} v > 0 \hspace{3em} \text{if} \quad u \geq 0 \\ 0, & \text{elsewhere.} \hspace{8em} \beta > 0 \end{cases}$$

The marginal probability density function of U is

$$z_1(u) = \begin{cases} \displaystyle\int_{-2u}^{\infty} \dfrac{2}{\beta^2} e^{-(2/\beta)(u+v)} \, dv, & u < 0, \\[2ex] \displaystyle\int_{0}^{\infty} \dfrac{2}{\beta^2} e^{-(2/\beta)(u+v)} \, dv, & u \geq 0, \end{cases}$$

or

$$z_1(u) = \begin{cases} \dfrac{1}{\beta} e^{2u/\beta}, & u < 0, \\[2ex] \dfrac{1}{\beta} e^{-(2u/\beta)}, & u \geq 0. \end{cases}$$

Thus,

$$z_1(u) = \frac{1}{\beta} e^{-(2/\beta)|u|}, \quad -\infty < u < \infty.$$

It can easily be shown that

$$\int_{-\infty}^{0} \frac{1}{\beta} e^{2u/\beta} \, du + \int_{0}^{\infty} \frac{1}{\beta} e^{-(2u/\beta)} \, du = 1.$$

Example 6.6.4   Let X and Y be two independent chi-square-distributed variates with n_1 and n_2 degrees of freedom, respectively. We wish to obtain the distribution of (U, V), where

$$U = X + Y \quad \text{and} \quad V = \frac{X}{Y}.$$

Solution: The joint probability density function of X and Y can be written as

$$f(x, y) = f_1(x) f_2(y) = \frac{1}{\Gamma(n_1/2)} \frac{1}{2^{n_1/2}} x^{(n_1/2)-1} e^{-(1/2)x} \cdot$$

$$\cdot \frac{1}{\Gamma(n_2/2)} \frac{1}{2^{n_2/2}} y^{(n_2/2)-1} e^{-(1/2)y}, \quad x, y > 0$$

$$= \begin{cases} \dfrac{1}{\Gamma(n_1/2)\Gamma(n_2/2)2^{(n_1+n_2)/2}} x^{(n_1/2)-1} y^{(n_2/2)-1} e^{-(1/2)(x+y)}, \\ \hspace{18em} x, y > 0, \\ 0, \quad \text{elsewhere.} \end{cases}$$

Here the functions z_1^{-1} and z_2^{-2} are given by $x = uv/(v+1)$ and $y = u/(v+1)$. The Jacobian is

$$J = \begin{vmatrix} \dfrac{\partial x}{\partial u} & \dfrac{\partial x}{\partial v} \\[2mm] \dfrac{\partial y}{\partial u} & \dfrac{\partial y}{\partial v} \end{vmatrix} = \begin{vmatrix} \dfrac{v}{v+1} & \dfrac{u}{(v+1)^2} \\[2mm] \dfrac{1}{v+1} & \dfrac{-u}{(v+1)^2} \end{vmatrix} = \dfrac{-u}{(v+1)^2}.$$

Thus,

$$z(u, v) = f\left(\frac{uv}{v+1}, \frac{u}{v+1}\right)\left|\frac{-u}{(v+1)^2}\right|, \quad u, v > 0, \text{ and zero elsewhere}$$

or

$$z(u, v) = \begin{cases} \dfrac{u^{(n_1+n_2-2)/2} v^{(n_1-2)/2} e^{-u/2}}{\Gamma(n_1/2)\Gamma(n_2/2)[2(v+1)]^{(n_1+n_2)/2}}, & u, v \ge 0, \\[4mm] 0, & \text{elsewhere.} \end{cases}$$

6.6.3 Transformations of Variables of the Discrete Type We shall now illustrate that there are essentially no difficulties involved in transformations of variables of the discrete type. Let $f(x, y)$ be the joint probability density function of the discrete random variable (X, Y), defined on a two-dimensional set of points, S. If the new random variable (U, V), given by

$$U = g_1(X, Y) \quad \text{and} \quad V = g_2(X, Y),$$

defines a one-to-one transformation that maps the set E_1 of the xy-plane onto E^*, the two-dimensional set of the uv-plane, then the joint probability density function of the new random variable is given by

$$z(u, v) = \begin{cases} f(z_1^{-1}(u, v), z_2^{-1}(u, v)), & (u, v) \in E^*, \\ 0, & \text{elsewhere,} \end{cases}$$

where $x = z_1^{-1}(u, v)$ and $y = z_2^{-1}(u, v)$ are the single-valued inverses of g_1 and g_2, respectively. With the knowledge of $z(u, v)$, we can obtain the marginal probability mass functions of the discrete random variables U and V by summing on v and u, respectively.

Example 6.6.5   If X and Y are independent and Poisson distributed, with parameters λ_1 and λ_2, respectively, their joint probability density function is given by

$$f(x, y) = \begin{cases} \dfrac{e^{-(\lambda_1+\lambda_2)}\lambda_1{}^x\lambda_2{}^y}{x!\,y!}, & x = 0, 1, 2, \ldots, y = 0, 1, 2, \ldots, \\ 0, & \text{elsewhere.} \end{cases}$$

We wish to find the probability mass function of a new random variable (U, V), defined by

$$U = X + Y \quad \text{and} \quad V = Y.$$

Solution: Here $f(x, y)$ is defined on the two-dimensional set $E = \{(x, y) : x = 0, 1, 2, \ldots \text{ and } y = 0, 1, \ldots\}$, and the new random variable (U, V) represents a one-to-one transformation that maps the set S onto the set $E^* = \{(u, v) : u = 0, 1, 2, \ldots \text{ and } v = 0, 1, 2, \ldots\}$. The inverse functions are

$$x = u - v \quad \text{and} \quad y = v.$$

Thus, the joint probability mass function of the variate (U, V) is

$$z(u, v) = \begin{cases} \dfrac{e^{-(\lambda_1+\lambda_2)}\lambda_1{}^{u-v}\lambda_2{}^v}{(u-v)!\,v!}, & \begin{array}{l} u, v = 0, 1, 2, \ldots \\ \text{such that } 0 \le v \le u, \end{array} \\ 0, & \text{elsewhere.} \end{cases}$$

The marginal density of U is obtained by

$$z_1(u) = \sum_{v=0}^{u} \frac{e^{-(\lambda_1+\lambda_2)}\lambda_1{}^{u-v}\lambda_2{}^v}{(u-v)!\,v!}$$

$$= \frac{e^{-(\lambda_1+\lambda_2)}}{u!} \sum_{v=0}^{u} \frac{u!}{(u-v)!\,v!}\lambda_1{}^{u-v}\lambda_2{}^v$$

$$= \frac{e^{-(\lambda_1+\lambda_2)}}{u!} \sum_{v=0}^{u} \binom{u}{v}\lambda_2{}^v\lambda_1{}^{u-v}$$

or

$$z_1(u) = \begin{cases} \dfrac{e^{-(\lambda_1+\lambda_2)}(\lambda_1+\lambda_2)^u}{u!}, & u = 0, 1, 2, \ldots, \\ 0, & \text{elsewhere.} \end{cases}$$

Similarly,

$$z_2(v) = \begin{cases} \dfrac{e^{-\lambda_2}\lambda_2^{v}}{v!}, & v = 0, 1, 2, \ldots, \\ 0, & \text{elsewhere.} \end{cases}$$

Thus, we conclude that the new random variable $U = X + Y$ is Poisson distributed, with parameter $\lambda_1 + \lambda_2$; and $V = Y$ is, of course, Poisson distributed, with parameter λ_2.

6.6.4 One Function of Two Continuous Random Variables: Auxiliary Variable In many problems, we are interested in determining the probability density function of a single functional form of the two-dimensional random variable (X, Y). That is, if the probability distribution of the variate (X, Y) is known, we wish to find the distribution of a new random variable, U, given by

$$U = g_1(X, Y).$$

To obtain the probability density of U, we introduce an *auxiliary variable*, either

$$V = g_2(X, Y) = X \quad \text{or} \quad V = g_2(X, Y) = Y;$$

and, under the assumptions given in Theorem 6.6.1, we can obtain the joint density of the random variable (U, V). Thus, the probability density function of U is found by integrating out all V. We shall use the above technique to obtain the distribution of some of the most important functions of the random variable (X, Y): namely, the sum, product, and quotient of the variates X and Y.

Theorem 6.6.2 Let $f(x, y)$ be the probability density function of the continuous random variable (X, Y). If

$$U = X + Y,$$

then the probability density function of the variate U is given by

$$h(u) = \int_{-\infty}^{\infty} f(u - v, v)\, dv.$$

Proof Here we introduce the auxiliary variable $V = Y$, so that the new random variable (U, V), defined by

$$U = X + Y \quad \text{and} \quad V = Y,$$

is a one-to-one mapping of the random variable (X, Y). Thus, $x = u - v$ and $y = v$. The Jacobian of the transformation is

$$J = \begin{vmatrix} 1 & -1 \\ 0 & 1 \end{vmatrix} = 1.$$

Hence, the joint probability density function of (U, V) is

$$z(u, v) = f(u - v, v)|J| \, ;$$

and the marginal density of U is

$$h(u) = \int_{-\infty}^{\infty} f(u - v, v) \, dv.$$

   Example 6.6.6   Let the probability density function of the random variable (X, θ) be

$$f(x, \theta) = \begin{cases} \dfrac{1}{\sigma \pi \sqrt{2\pi}} e^{-(1/2\sigma^2)x^2}, & -\infty < x < \infty, 0 < \theta < \pi, \sigma < 0, \\ 0, & \text{elsewhere.} \end{cases}$$

If

$$U = X + a \cos \theta,$$

where a is an arbitrary constant, find the probability distribution of the variate U.

   Solution: Here, in view of Theorem 6.6.2, we have

$$h(u) = \frac{1}{\sigma \pi \sqrt{2\pi}} \int_{0}^{\pi} e^{-(1/2\sigma^2)(u - a \cos \phi)^2} \, d\phi, \quad -\infty < u < \infty.$$

Note that $h(u)$ can be obtained by introducing the auxiliary variable $\Phi = \theta$; and, together with $U = X + a \cos \theta$, we have the single-valued inverses

$$x = u - a \cos \phi \quad \text{and} \quad \theta = \phi.$$

The Jacobian of the transformation is

$$J = \begin{vmatrix} 1 & -a \sin \phi \\ 0 & 1 \end{vmatrix} = 1.$$

Thus,

$$z(u, \phi) = \begin{cases} \dfrac{1}{\sigma\pi\sqrt{2\pi}}\, e^{-(1/2\sigma^2)(u - a\cos\phi)^2}, & -\infty < u < \infty,\ 0 < \phi < \pi,\ \sigma > 0, \\ 0, & \text{elsewhere.} \end{cases}$$

Hence, integrating out ϕ, we obtain $h(u)$.

Theorem 6.6.3   Let $f(x, y)$ be the probability density function of the continuous random variable (X, Y). If

$$U = XY,$$

then the probability density function of the variate U is given by

$$h(u) = \int_{-\infty}^{\infty} f\left(\frac{u}{v}, v\right) \left|\frac{1}{v}\right| dv.$$

Proof   Let

$$U = XY \quad \text{and} \quad V = Y.$$

Thus, the single-valued inverses are $x = u/v$ and $y = v$. The Jacobian is

$$J = \begin{vmatrix} \dfrac{1}{v} & -\dfrac{u}{v^2} \\ 0 & 1 \end{vmatrix} = \frac{1}{v}.$$

Therefore,

$$z(u, v) = f\left(\frac{u}{v}, v\right) \left|\frac{1}{v}\right|,$$

and the marginal density of U is

$$h(u) = \int_{-\infty}^{\infty} f\left(\frac{u}{v}, v\right) \left|\frac{1}{v}\right| dv.$$

Example 6.6.7   The joint density of the random variable (X, Y) is

$$f(x, y) = \begin{cases} \theta e^{-(x + \theta y)}, & x, y > 0,\ \theta > 0, \\ 0, & \text{elsewhere.} \end{cases}$$

We wish to obtain the probability density function of the variate U, given by $U = XY$.

Solution: Applying Theorem 6.6.3, we have

$$h(u) = \int_{-\infty}^{\infty} f\left(\frac{u}{v}, v\right) \left|\frac{1}{v}\right| dv$$

$$= \int_{0}^{\infty} \theta e^{-(u/v + \theta v)} \left|\frac{1}{v}\right| dv.$$

Since $v = y > 0$, we have $1/v > 0$; thus,

$$h(u) = \int_{0}^{\infty} \frac{1}{v} \theta e^{-(u/v + \theta v)} dv.$$

Theorem 6.6.4   Let $f(x, y)$ be the probability density function of the continuous random variable (X, Y). If

$$U = \frac{X}{Y},$$

then the probability density function of the variate U is given by

$$h(u) = \int_{-\infty}^{\infty} f(uv, v) |v| \, dv.$$

Proof   Let

$$U = \frac{X}{Y} \quad \text{and} \quad V = Y.$$

Thus, the single-valued inverses are $x = uv$ and $y = v$. The Jacobian of the transformation is

$$J = \begin{vmatrix} v & u \\ 0 & 1 \end{vmatrix} = v.$$

Therefore,

$$z(u, v) = f(uv, v) |v|$$

and

$$h(u) = \int_{-\infty}^{\infty} f(uv, v) |v| \, dv.$$

Example 6.6.8   The joint probability density of the random variable (X, Y) is given by

$$f(x, y) = \frac{1}{2\pi\sigma_x\sigma_y} \exp\left\{-\frac{1}{2}\left(\frac{x^2}{\sigma_x^2} + \frac{y^2}{\sigma_y^2}\right)\right\}, \quad -\infty < x, y < \infty, \sigma_x, \sigma_y > 0.$$

Determine the probability density function of the variate U, defined by

$$U = \frac{X}{Y}.$$

Solution: In view of Theorem 6.6.4, the probability density of U is given by

$$h(u) = \frac{1}{2\pi\sigma_x\sigma_y} \int_{-\infty}^{\infty} |v| \exp\left\{-\frac{1}{2}\left(\frac{u^2v^2}{\sigma_x^2} + \frac{v^2}{\sigma_y^2}\right)\right\} dv$$

$$= \frac{1}{2\pi\sigma_x\sigma_y} \int_0^{\infty} v \exp\left\{-\frac{1}{2}\left(\frac{u^2v^2}{\sigma_x^2} + \frac{v^2}{\sigma_y^2}\right)\right\} dv$$

$$- \int_{-\infty}^0 v \exp\left\{-\frac{1}{2}\left(\frac{u^2 + v^2}{\sigma_x^2} + \frac{v^2}{\sigma_y^2}\right)\right\} dv$$

$$= \frac{1}{2\pi\sigma_x\sigma_y} \int_0^{\infty} v \exp\left\{\frac{-\frac{1}{2}v^2}{\frac{\sigma_x^2\sigma_y^2}{\sigma_x^2 + u^2\sigma_y^2}}\right\} dv - \int_{\infty}^0 v \exp\left\{\frac{-\frac{1}{2}v^2}{\frac{\sigma_x^2\sigma_y^2}{\sigma_x^2 + u^2\sigma_y^2}}\right\} dv.$$

Let

$$t = \frac{v}{\dfrac{\sigma_x\sigma_y}{(\sigma_x^2 + u^2\sigma_y^2)^{1/2}}}, \qquad \frac{\sigma_x\sigma_y}{(\sigma_x^2 + u^2\sigma_y^2)^{1/2}} dt = dv,$$

and

$$v = \sigma_x\sigma_y/(\sigma_x^2 + u^2\sigma_y^2)^{1/2}t.$$

Thus,

$$h(u) = \frac{\sigma_x\sigma_y}{2\pi(\sigma_x^2 + u^2\sigma_y^2)} \int_0^{\infty} t e^{-(1/2)t^2} dt - \frac{\sigma_x\sigma_y}{2\pi(\sigma_x^2 + u^2\sigma_y^2)} \int_{-\infty}^0 t e^{-(t^2/2)} dt$$

$$= \frac{\sigma_x\sigma_y}{2\pi(\sigma_x^2 + u^2\sigma_y^2)} + \frac{\sigma_x\sigma_y}{2\pi(\sigma_x^2 + u^2\sigma_y^2)} = \frac{\sigma_x\sigma_y}{\pi(\sigma_x^2 + u^2\sigma_y^2)}, \quad -\infty < u < \infty,$$

or

$$h(u) = \frac{1}{\pi\{\sigma_x/\sigma_y + [(\sigma_y/\sigma_x)u^2]\}}, \quad -\infty < u < \infty.$$

Hence, $h(u)$ has the form of the *Cauchy distribution*.

6.7 *Expected Value, Moments, and Characteristic Functions*

In this section, we shall extend the basic concepts of expectation, moments, and characteristic functions, all of which were introduced in Chapter 5, to two random variables and functions of those random variables.

6.7.1 *Expected Value*

Definition 6.7.1   *Let (X, Y) be a two-dimensional random variable of the discrete type, with probability mass function $p(x, y)$. The series*

$$E(XY) = \sum_i \sum_j x_i y_j p(x_i, y_j) \tag{6.7.1}$$

is called the expected value of the product of X and Y, if the inequality

$$\sum_i \sum_j |x_i y_j| p(x_i, y_j) < \infty \tag{6.7.2}$$

is satisfied.

Example 6.7.1   The joint probability density function of the discrete random variable (X, Y) is given in Table 6.7.1.

Table 6.7.1

x	y			
	1	2	3	$p_1(x)$
1	$\frac{1}{6}$	$\frac{1}{6}$	$\frac{1}{6}$	$\frac{1}{2}$
2	$\frac{1}{6}$	$\frac{1}{12}$	$\frac{1}{12}$	$\frac{1}{3}$
3	$\frac{1}{12}$	$\frac{1}{12}$	0	$\frac{1}{6}$
$p_2(y)$	$\frac{5}{12}$	$\frac{1}{3}$	$\frac{1}{4}$	1

The expected value of the product of the random variables X and Y is

$$E(XY) = \sum_{x=1}^{3} \sum_{y=1}^{3} (xy)p(x, y)$$

$$= \sum_{x=1}^{3} \{(x)(1)p(x, 1) + (x)(2)p(x, 2) + (x)(3)p(x, 3)\}$$

$$= (1)(1)p(1, 1) + (1)(2)p(1, 2) + (1)(3)p(1, 3)$$
$$+ (2)(1)p(2, 1) + (2)(2)p(2, 2) + (2)(3)p(2, 3)$$
$$+ (3)(1)p(3, 1) + (3)(2)p(3, 2) + (3)(3)p(3, 3)$$

$$= \frac{1}{6} + (2)\frac{1}{6} + (3)\frac{1}{6} + (2)\frac{1}{6} + (4)\frac{1}{12}$$

$$+ (6)\frac{1}{12} + (3)\frac{1}{12} + (6)\frac{1}{12} + (9)0$$

$$= \frac{35}{12}.$$

Example 6.7.2   The expected value of the product of the two discrete random variables X and Y, whose joint probability mass function is given in Example 6.1.1, is

$$E(XY) = \sum_{y=0}^{4-x} \sum_{x=0}^{4} xy f(x, y)$$

$$= \sum_{y=1}^{4-x} \sum_{x=1}^{4} \frac{xy \binom{8}{x}\binom{6}{y}\binom{10}{4 - x - y}}{\binom{24}{4}}$$

$$= (1)f(1, 1) + (2)f(1, 2) + (3)f(1, 3) + (2)f(2, 1) + (4)f(2, 2)$$
$$+ (3)f(3, 1)$$

$$= \frac{2160}{10,626} + \frac{2400}{10,626} + \frac{480}{10,626} + \frac{3360}{10,626} + \frac{1680}{10,626} + \frac{1008}{10,626}$$

$$= \frac{24}{23}.$$

Definition 6.7.2   *Let (X, Y) be a two-dimensional continuous random variable, with joint probability density function $f(x, y)$. The double integral*

$$E(XY) = \int_{-\infty}^{\infty} \int_{-\infty}^{\infty} xy f(x, y)\, dx\, dy \qquad (6.7.3)$$

is called the expected value of the product of the variates *X and Y, if the inequality*

$$\int_{-\infty}^{\infty} \int_{-\infty}^{\infty} |xy| f(x, y) \, dx \, dy < \infty. \qquad (6.7.4)$$

is satisfied.

Example 6.7.3   The joint probability density function of the continuous random variable, (X, Y), given in Example 6.1.3, is

$$f(x, y) = \begin{cases} \dfrac{1}{28}(4x + 2y + 1), & 0 \le x < 2, 0 \le y < 2, \\ 0, & \text{elsewhere.} \end{cases}$$

The expected value of the product of the variates X and Y is

$$E(XY) = \int_0^2 \left\{ \int_0^2 xy \frac{1}{28}(4x + 2y + 1) \, dx \right\} dy$$

$$= \int_0^2 \left(\frac{8}{21} y + \frac{y^2}{7} + \frac{y}{14} \right) dy$$

$$= \frac{8y^2}{42} + \frac{y^3}{21} + \frac{y^2}{28} \bigg|_0^2$$

$$= \frac{9}{7}.$$

Example 6.7.4   The expected value of the product of the random variables X and Y, the joint density of which is given in Example 6.1.4, is

$$E(XY) = \int_{-\infty}^{\infty} \int_{-\infty}^{\infty} xy f(x, y) \, dx \, dy$$

$$= \int_1^2 \left\{ \int_1^y \frac{8}{9} x^2 y^2 \, dx \right\} dy$$

$$= \int_1^2 \frac{8}{27} (y^5 - y^2) \, dy$$

$$= \frac{196}{81}.$$

The expected value of a random variable, as we mentioned in Chapter 5, does not always exist. That is, if the right side of Equation (6.7.1) or (6.7.3) exists but the inequality (6.7.2) or (6.7.4) is not satisfied, then the expected value of the product of two random variables does not exist.

6.7.2 Properties of Expectation The properties of expectation that we discussed in Section 5.2 for a one-dimensional random variable are also present in a two-dimensional random variable. We shall present here some additional properties of the two-dimensional variate.

Theorem 6.7.1 Let (X, Y) be a two-dimensional random variable, with joint probability density function $f(x, y)$. If $U = g(X, Y)$ is a functional form of the variate (X, Y), then the expected value of U is

$$E(U) = E[g(X, Y)] = \sum_i \sum_j g(x_i, y_j) f(x_i, y_j) \qquad (6.7.5)$$

if (X, Y) is discrete, and

$$E(U) = E[g(X, Y)] = \int_{-\infty}^{\infty} \int_{-\infty}^{\infty} g(x, y) f(x, y) \, dx \, dy \qquad (6.7.6)$$

if (X, Y) is continuous.

The proof of this theorem is similar to that of Theorem 5.2.2; however, we must note that the expected value of $g(X, Y)$ exists only if the right-hand sides of Equations (6.7.5) and (6.7.6) are *absolutely convergent*.

Example 6.7.5 If $U = g(X, Y) = X + Y$, then $E(U) = E(X) + E(Y)$. Let (X, Y) be a continuous two-dimensional random variable, with joint probability density function $f(x, y)$. Then the expected value of U is

$$E(U) = E(X + Y) = \int_{-\infty}^{\infty} \int_{-\infty}^{\infty} (x + y) f(x, y) \, dx \, dy$$

$$= \int_{-\infty}^{\infty} x \int_{-\infty}^{\infty} f(x, y) \, dy \, dx + \int_{-\infty}^{\infty} y \int_{-\infty}^{\infty} f(x, y) \, dx \, dy$$

$$= \int_{-\infty}^{\infty} x f_1(x) \, dx + \int_{-\infty}^{\infty} y f_2(y) \, dy$$

$$= E(X) + E(Y);$$

the situation is similar in the discrete case. Thus, the expected value of the sum of any two random variables is equal to the sum of their expected values. The variance of U is

$$\text{Var}(U) = \text{Var}(X + Y) = E[(X + Y)^2] - [E(X + Y)]^2$$

$$= E(X^2) - [E(X)]^2 + E(Y^2) - [E(Y)]^2 + 2E(XY)$$

$$- 2E(X)E(Y).$$

Then

$$\text{Var}(X + Y) = \text{Var}(X) + \text{Var}(Y) + 2E(XY) - 2E(X)E(Y).$$

Similarly,

$$\text{Var}(X - Y) = \text{Var}(X) + \text{Var}(Y) - 2E(XY) + 2E(X)E(Y).$$

Example 6.7.6   The expected value of $U = X^2 + Y^2$, where the joint density of the two-dimensional random variable (X, Y) is given in Example 6.7.4, is

$$E(U) = E(X^2 + Y^2) = \int_{-\infty}^{\infty} \int_{-\infty}^{\infty} (x^2 + y^2) f(x, y) \, dx \, dy$$

$$= \int_{1}^{2} \left\{ \int_{1}^{y} \frac{8}{9} (x^2 + y^2) \, xy \, dx \right\} dy$$

$$= \int_{1}^{2} \frac{8}{9} \left(\frac{3y^5}{4} - \frac{y^3}{2} - \frac{y}{4} \right) dy$$

$$= \frac{45}{9}$$

$$= 5.$$

It can be shown that

$$\int_{1}^{2} \left\{ \int_{1}^{y} |x^2 + y^2| \frac{8}{9} xy \, dx \right\} dy < \infty.$$

Thus, we are assured of the existence of the $E(U)$.

Theorem 6.7.2   Let (X, Y) be a two-dimensional random variable, with joint probability density function $f(x, y)$. If

$$U = g_1(X, Y) \quad \text{and} \quad V = g_2(X, Y),$$

then

$$E(UV) = E[g_1(X, Y)g_2(X, Y)].$$

Thus, if (X, Y) is of the discrete type, we have

$$E(UV) = \sum_{i} \sum_{j} g_1(x_i, y_j) g_2(x_i, y_j) f(x_i, y_j);$$

and we have

$$E(UV) = \int_{-\infty}^{\infty} \int_{-\infty}^{\infty} g_1(x, y)g_2(x, y)f(x, y)\, dx\, dy$$

if the variate is of the continuous type. Of course, in order for the $E(UV)$ to exist, the above expressions must be absolutely convergent.

We remark here that one can also obtain the $E(UV)$ by first finding the joint probability density function of (U, V), $z(u, v)$ (as illustrated in Section 6.6), if possible, and then applying either Equation (6.7.1) or Equation (6.7.3). That is,

$$E(UV) = \int_{-\infty}^{\infty} \int_{-\infty}^{\infty} uv z(u, v)\, du\, dv$$

or

$$E(UV) = \sum_i \sum_j u_i v_j z(u_i, v_j).$$

We illustrate the above remarks with Example 6.7.7.

Example 6.7.7   In Example 6.6.3, we saw that, if the joint probability density function of the variate (X, Y) is given by

$$f(x, y) = \begin{cases} \dfrac{1}{\beta^2}\, e^{-[(x+y)/\beta]}, & x, y > 0, \beta > 0, \\[2mm] 0, & \text{elsewhere}, \end{cases}$$

the joint density of the random variable (U, V), where

$$U = \frac{X - Y}{2} \quad \text{and} \quad V = Y,$$

is

$$z(u, v) = \begin{cases} \dfrac{2}{\beta^2}\, e^{-(2/\beta)(u+v)}, & \begin{array}{ll} -\infty < u < \infty, v > -2u & \text{if} \quad u < 0 \\ v > 0 & \text{if} \quad u \geq 0 \end{array} \\[4mm] 0, \quad \text{elsewhere}. & \qquad\qquad\qquad\qquad \beta > 0, \end{cases}$$

We shall show that $E(UV) = E[g_1(X, Y)g_2 X, Y]$:

$$E(UV) = \int_{-\infty}^{\infty} \int_{-\infty}^{\infty} uvz(u, v) \, du \, dv$$

$$= \int_{-\infty}^{0} \left\{ \int_{-2u}^{\infty} uv\left(\frac{2}{\beta^2}\right) e^{-(2/\beta)(u+v)} \, dv \right\} du$$

$$+ \int_{0}^{\infty} \left\{ \int_{0}^{\infty} uv\left(\frac{2}{\beta^2}\right) e^{-(2/\beta)(u+v)} \, dv \right\} du$$

$$= \frac{2}{\beta^2} \int_{-\infty}^{0} ue^{-(2u/\beta)} \left\{ -\frac{\beta^2}{4} e^{(4u/\beta)} \left(\frac{4u}{\beta} - 1\right) \right\} du$$

$$+ \frac{2}{\beta^2} \int_{0}^{\infty} ue^{-(2u/\beta)} \left\{ -\frac{\beta^2}{4}(-1) \right\} du$$

$$= -\frac{1}{\beta} \int_{-\infty}^{0} u^2 e^{(2u/\beta)} \, du + \frac{1}{2} \int_{-\infty}^{0} ue^{(2u/\beta)} \, du + \frac{1}{2} \int_{0}^{\infty} ue^{-(2u/\beta)} \, du$$

$$= 2\left[\frac{\beta}{4}(-1)\right] + \frac{1}{2}\left(\frac{\beta^2}{4}\right) + \frac{1}{2}\frac{\beta^2}{4}$$

$$= -\frac{\beta^2}{2}.$$

$$E[g_1(X, Y)g_2(X, Y)] = E\left[\left(\frac{X - Y}{2}\right)(Y)\right]$$

$$= \int_{0}^{\infty} \int_{0}^{\infty} \left(\frac{x - y}{2}\right) y \frac{1}{\beta^2} e^{-[(x+y)/\beta]} \, dx \, dy$$

$$= \frac{1}{2} \left\{ \int_{0}^{\infty} x \frac{1}{\beta} e^{-(x/\beta)} \left[\int_{0}^{\infty} y \frac{1}{\beta} e^{-(y/\beta)} \, dy \right] dx \right.$$

$$\left. - \int_{0}^{\infty} y^2 \frac{1}{\beta} e^{-(y/\beta)} \left[\int_{0}^{\infty} \frac{1}{\beta} e^{-(x/\beta)} \, dx \right] dy \right\}$$

$$= \frac{1}{2} \left\{ \beta^2 - 2\beta \int_{0}^{\infty} \frac{1}{\beta} ye^{-(y/\beta)} \, dy \right\}$$

$$= -\frac{\beta^2}{2}.$$

Here it is also clear that the double integral

$$\int_{0}^{\infty} \int_{0}^{\infty} \left|\frac{x - y}{2}\right| |y| \frac{1}{\beta^2} e^{-[(x+y)/\beta]} \, dx \, dy$$

converges to $(5/8)\beta^2$, which assures the existence of the expected value of the product of the two random variables U and V.

Theorem 6.7.3   Let (X, Y) be a two-dimensional random variable, with joint probability density function $f(x, y)$. If X and Y are independent variates, then

$$E(XY) = E(X)E(Y).$$

Proof   If (X, Y) is discrete, then

$$
\begin{aligned}
E(XY) &= \sum_i \sum_j x_i y_j f(x_i, y_j) \\
&= \sum_i \sum_j x_i y_j f_1(x_i) f_2(y_j) \\
&= \sum_i x_i f_1(x_i) \sum_j y_j f_2(y_j) \\
&= E(X)E(Y),
\end{aligned}
$$

where

$$f_1(x_i) = \sum_j f(x_i, y_j) \quad \text{and} \quad f_2(y_j) = \sum_i f(x_i, y_j).$$

The situation is similar in regard to the continuous case.

Example 6.7.8   If, in Example 6.7.5, the random variables X and Y are independent, then

$$
\begin{aligned}
\text{Var}(X + Y) &= \text{Var}(X) + \text{Var}(Y) + 2E(XY) - 2E(X)E(Y) \\
&= \text{Var}(X) + \text{Var}(Y).
\end{aligned}
$$

Similarly,

$$\text{Var}(X - Y) = \text{Var}(X) + \text{Var}(Y).$$

Example 6.7.9   Let (X, Y) be a discrete random variable whose joint probability mass function is given by

$$
f(x, y; \lambda_1, \lambda_2) = \begin{cases} \dfrac{e^{-(\lambda_1 + \lambda_2)} \lambda_1{}^x \lambda_2{}^y}{x! \, y!}, & \begin{aligned} x &= 0, 1, 2, 3, \ldots, \\ y &= 0, 1, 2, 3, \ldots, \end{aligned} \\[2ex] 0, & \text{elsewhere.} \end{cases}
$$

Since

$$
f_1(x; \lambda_1) = \begin{cases} \dfrac{e^{-\lambda_1} \lambda_1{}^x}{x!}, & x = 0, 1, 2, \ldots, \\[2ex] 0, & \text{elsewhere,} \end{cases}
$$

and

$$
f_2(y; \lambda_2) = \begin{cases} \dfrac{e^{-\lambda_2}\lambda_2^{\,y}}{y!}, & y = 0, 1, 2, \ldots, \\[2mm] 0, & \text{elsewhere,} \end{cases}
$$

X and Y are independently distributed; and, in view of Theorem 6.7.3, we have

$$
\begin{aligned}
E(XY) &= \sum_{x=0}^{\infty} \sum_{y=0}^{\infty} xy \, \frac{e^{-(\lambda_1+\lambda_2)}\lambda_1^{\,x}\lambda_2^{\,y}}{x!\,y!} \\[2mm]
&= \sum_{x=0}^{\infty} \frac{xe^{-\lambda_1}\lambda_1^{\,x}}{x!} \sum_{y=0}^{\infty} \frac{ye^{-\lambda_2}\lambda_2^{\,y}}{y!} \\[2mm]
&= \lambda_1\lambda_2 .
\end{aligned}
$$

Example 6.7.10   Note that, in Example 6.7.3, the marginal densities of the random variables X and Y are

$$
f_1(x) = \begin{cases} \dfrac{2}{7}x + \dfrac{3}{14}, & 0 \le x < 2, \\[2mm] 0, & \text{elsewhere,} \end{cases}
$$

and

$$
f_2(y) = \begin{cases} \dfrac{1}{7}y + \dfrac{5}{14}, & 0 \le y < 2, \\[2mm] 0, & \text{elsewhere,} \end{cases}
$$

respectively. Thus,

$$
E(X) = \int_0^2 \left(\frac{2}{7}x^2 + \frac{3}{14}x \right) dx = \frac{25}{21},
$$

and

$$
E(Y) = \int_0^2 \left(\frac{1}{7}y^2 + \frac{5}{14}y \right) dy = \frac{23}{21}.
$$

As expected, $E(XY) \ne E(X)E(Y)$ because X and Y are dependent variables.

6.7.3 Moments We proceed by defining various moments of bivariate probability distributions.

Definition 6.7.3 *Let (X, Y) be a two-dimensional random variable, with joint density function $f(x, y)$. The moment of order $k + m$ of the distribution of the variate (X, Y) is defined by*

$$E(X^k Y^m) = \sum_i \sum_j x_i^k y_j^m f(x_i, y_j) \tag{6.7.7}$$

if (X, Y) is discrete, and by

$$E(X^k Y^m) = \int_{-\infty}^{\infty} \int_{-\infty}^{\infty} x^k y^m f(x, y)\, dx\, dy \tag{6.7.8}$$

if (X, Y) is continuous.

Again, the *moment of order $k + m$* of the distribution of (X, Y) will exist only if Equations (6.7.7) and (6.7.8) are absolutely convergent.

We shall denote the moment of order $k + m$ of a bivariate distribution by

$$\mu_{km} = E(X^k Y^m).$$

Thus, if $k = 1$, $m = 0$ and $k = 0$, $m = 1$, we have

$$\mu_{10} = E(X^1 Y^0) = E(X) \quad \text{and} \quad \mu_{01} = E(X^0 Y^1) = E(Y),$$

the expected value of the marginal distributions of X and Y, respectively.

Example 6.7.11 With reference to Example 6.7.1, we can calculate the following moments:

(a) $\mu_{10} = \sum_{x=1}^{3} x p_1(x) = (1)\dfrac{1}{2} + (2)\dfrac{1}{3} + (3)\dfrac{1}{6} = \dfrac{5}{3}$;

(b) $\mu_{01} = \sum_{y=1}^{3} y p_2(y) = (1)\dfrac{5}{12} + (2)\dfrac{1}{3} + (3)\dfrac{1}{4} = \dfrac{11}{6}$;

(c) $\mu_{20} = \sum_{x=1}^{3} x^2 p_1(x) = (1)^2\dfrac{1}{2} + (2)^2\dfrac{1}{3} + (3)^2\dfrac{1}{6} = \dfrac{10}{3}$;

(d) $\mu_{02} = \sum_{y=1}^{3} y^2 p_2(y) = (1)^2\dfrac{5}{12} + (2)^2\dfrac{1}{3} + (3)^2\dfrac{1}{4} = 4$.

Example 6.7.12   In Example 6.7.4, we can calculate the moment of order $k + m$ as follows:

$$\mu_{km} = E(X^k Y^m) = \int_{-\infty}^{\infty} \int_{-\infty}^{\infty} x^k y^m f(x, y) \, dx \, dy$$

$$= \int_{1}^{2} \left\{ \int_{1}^{y} \frac{8}{9} x^{k+1} y^{m+1} \, dx \right\} dy$$

$$= \int_{1}^{2} \frac{8}{9} \left(\frac{y^{k+m+3} - y^{m+1}}{k+2} \right) dy$$

$$= \frac{8}{9(k+2)} \left[\frac{y^{k+m+4}}{k+m+4} - \frac{y^{m+2}}{m+2} \right]_{1}^{2}$$

$$= \frac{8}{9(k+2)} \left[\frac{2^{k+m+4} - 1}{k+m+4} - \frac{2^{m+2} - 1}{m+2} \right].$$

Thus, if we let $k = m = 1$, we obtain $E(XY) = 196/81$, as expected.

Definition 6.7.4   *Let (X, Y) be a two-dimensional random variable, with joint probability density function $f(x, y)$. The central moment of order $k + m$ of the distribution of the variate (X, Y) is given by*

$$\eta_{km} = E[(X - \mu_{10})^k (Y - \mu_{01})^m]$$
$$= \sum_i \sum_j (x_i - \mu_{10})^k (y_j - \mu_{01})^m f(x_i, y_j)$$

if (X, Y) is discrete, and by

$$\eta_{km} = E[(X - \mu_{10})^k (Y - \mu_{01})^m]$$
$$= \int_{-\infty}^{\infty} \int_{-\infty}^{\infty} (x - \mu_{10})^k (y - \mu_{01})^m f(x, y) \, dx \, dy$$

if (X, Y) is continuous.

Thus, if $k = 1$, $m = 0$ and $k = 0$, $m = 1$, we have

$$\eta_{10} = E[(X - \mu_{10})] = E(X) - \mu_{10} = 0$$

and

$$\eta_{01} = E[(Y - \mu_{01})] = E(Y) - \mu_{01} = 0.$$

Also, if $k = 2$, $m = 0$ and $k = 0$, $m = 2$, we have the variance of the marginal distributions of the random variables X and Y:

$$\eta_{20} = E[(X - \mu_{10})^2] = \sigma_x^2$$

and

$$\eta_{02} = E[(Y - \mu_{01})^2] = \sigma_y^2.$$

Example 6.7.13   We can express central moments of a bivariate distribution in terms of ordinary moments:

$$\eta_{20} = E[(X - \mu_{10})^2] = E(X^2) - \mu_{10}^2$$

or

$$\eta_{20} = \mu_{20} - \mu_{10}^2$$

and

$$\eta_{02} = E[(Y - \mu_{01})^2] = E(Y^2) - \mu_{01}^2$$

or

$$\eta_{02} = \mu_{02} - \mu_{01}^2.$$

Thus, in reference to Example 6.7.11, we have

$$\eta_{20} = \mu_{20} - \mu_{10}^2 = \frac{10}{3} - \left(\frac{5}{3}\right)^2 = \frac{5}{9}$$

and

$$\eta_{02} = \mu_{02} - \mu_{01}^2 = 4 - \left(\frac{11}{6}\right)^2 = \frac{23}{36}.$$

Definition 6.7.5   *The second $(k = 1$, $m = 1)$ central moment of the distribution of the two-dimensional random variable (X, Y),*

$$\eta_{11} = E[(X - \mu_{10})(Y - \mu_{01})],$$

is called the covariance *of X and Y.*

Hence, η_{11} can be expressed as follows:

$$\begin{aligned}
\eta_{11} &= E[(X - \mu_{10})(Y - \mu_{01})] \\
&= E(XY) - \mu_{10}E(Y) - \mu_{01}E(X) + \mu_{10}\mu_{01} \\
&= \mu_{11} - \mu_{10}\mu_{01} - \mu_{01}\mu_{10} + \mu_{10}\mu_{01} \\
&= \mu_{11} - \mu_{10}\mu_{01}.
\end{aligned}$$

The covariance of the random variables X and Y is usually denoted by $\text{Cov}(X, Y)$.

Example 6.7.14   The covariance of the variates X and Y in Example 6.7.1 is

$$\eta_{11} = \text{Cov}(X, Y) = \mu_{11} - \mu_{10}\mu_{01}$$

$$= \frac{35}{12} - \left(\frac{5}{3}\right)\left(\frac{11}{6}\right)$$

$$= -\frac{5}{36}.$$

Example 6.7.15   In reference to Example 6.7.10, we have

$$\mu_{10} = E(X) = \frac{25}{21}, \mu_{01} = E(Y) = \frac{23}{21} \quad \text{and} \quad \mu_{11} = E(XY) = \frac{9}{7}.$$

Thus, the covariance of the continuous random variables X and Y is

$$\eta_{11} = \text{Cov}(X, Y) = \mu_{11} - \mu_{10}\mu_{01}$$

$$= \frac{9}{7} - \left(\frac{25}{21}\right)\left(\frac{23}{21}\right)$$

$$= -\frac{8}{441}.$$

Theorem 6.7.4   If X and Y are independent random variables, then the $\text{Cov}(X, Y) = 0$.

Proof

$$\text{Cov}(X, Y) = E[(X - \mu_{10})(Y - \mu_{01})]$$
$$= E[XY - \mu_{10}Y - \mu_{01}X + \mu_{10}\mu_{01}]$$
$$= E(X)E(Y) - \mu_{10}E(Y) - \mu_{01}E(X) + \mu_{10}\mu_{01}$$
$$= \mu_{10}\mu_{01} - \mu_{10}\mu_{01} - \mu_{01}\mu_{10} + \mu_{10}\mu_{01}$$
$$= 0.$$

The converse of this theorem is not true; that is, if $\text{Cov}(X, Y) = 0$, it does *not* follow that X and Y are independent.

Example 6.7.16   The joint mass function of the discrete random variable (X, Y) is given by Table 6.7.2.

Table 6.7.2

		y			
x	-1	0	1	2	$p_1(x)$
-2	0	$\dfrac{1}{6}$	0	0	$\dfrac{1}{6}$
-1	$\dfrac{1}{3}$	0	0	$\dfrac{1}{6}$	$\dfrac{1}{2}$
0	$\dfrac{1}{6}$	0	$\dfrac{1}{6}$	0	$\dfrac{1}{3}$
$p_2(y)$	$\dfrac{1}{2}$	$\dfrac{1}{6}$	$\dfrac{1}{6}$	$\dfrac{1}{6}$	1.0

Here

$$\mu_{10} = \sum_{x=-2}^{0} x p_1(x) = (-2)\frac{1}{6} + (-1)\frac{1}{2} = -\frac{5}{6}$$

$$\mu_{01} = \sum_{y=-1}^{2} y p_2(y) = (-1)\frac{1}{2} + (1)\frac{1}{6} + (2)\frac{1}{6} = 0$$

$$\mu_{11} = \sum_{x=-1}^{0} x \sum_{y=-1}^{2} y p(x, y)$$

$$= (-2)[(-1)0 + 0 + (1)0 + (2)0]$$

$$+ (-1)\left[(-1)\frac{1}{3} + 0 + (1)0 + (2)\frac{1}{6}\right]$$

$$= 0.$$

Thus,

$$\text{Cov}(X, Y) = \mu_{11} - \mu_{10}\mu_{01} = 0,$$

but

$$p_1(-2) \cdot p_2(-1) = \left(\frac{1}{6}\right)\left(\frac{1}{2}\right) = \frac{1}{12} \neq p(-2, -1) = 0,$$

$$p_1(-1) \cdot p_2(-1) = \left(\frac{1}{2}\right)\left(\frac{1}{2}\right) = \frac{1}{4} \neq p(-1, -1) = \frac{1}{3},$$

and so on. Hence, $\text{Cov}(X, Y) = 0$ does not imply independence.

Theorem 6.7.5   If X and Y are any random variables and

$$U = \alpha_1 X + \beta_1, \qquad V = \alpha_2 Y + \beta_2,$$

then

$$\text{Cov}(U, V) = \alpha_1 \alpha_2 \, \text{Cov}(X, Y).$$

Proof

$$
\begin{aligned}
\text{Cov}(U, V) &= E(UV) - E(U)E(V) \\
&= E[(\alpha_1 X + \beta_1)(\alpha_2 Y + \beta_2)] - E(\alpha_1 X + \beta_1)E(\alpha_2 Y + \beta_2) \\
&= \alpha_1 \alpha_2 E(XY) + \alpha_2 \beta_1 \mu_{01} + \alpha_1 \beta_2 \mu_{10} + \beta_1 \beta_2 \\
&\quad - \alpha_1 \alpha_2 \mu_{10} \mu_{01} - \alpha_2 \beta_1 \mu_{01} - \alpha_1 \beta_2 \mu_{10} - \beta_1 \beta_2 \\
&= \alpha_1 \alpha_2 E(XY) - \alpha_1 \alpha_2 \mu_{10} \mu_{01} \\
&= \alpha_1 \alpha_2 \{E(XY) - \mu_{10} \mu_{01}\} \\
&= \alpha_1 \alpha_2 \, \text{Cov}(X, Y).
\end{aligned}
$$

Thus, if the variates are equal, $X = Y$, then

$$\text{Cov}(U, V) = \alpha_1 \alpha_2 \, \text{Var}(X).$$

The *covariance* of two random variables is the expected value of the product of the deviations of the two random variables from their respective means. It is also referred to as the *first product-moment*.

One important parameter that characterizes the distribution of a two-dimensional random variable, (X, Y), is the *coefficient of correlation*.

Definition 6.7.6   *The coefficient of correlation, ρ_{XY}, between X and Y is defined by*

$$\rho_{XY} = \frac{E[(X - \mu_{10})(Y - \mu_{01})]}{\sqrt{\text{Var}(X)}\sqrt{\text{Var}(Y)}} = \frac{\eta_{11}}{\sigma_X \sigma_Y}.$$

Thus, when we define the coefficient of correlation between two random variables, we assume that their expected values and variances exist and that their standard deviations are different from zero. The correlation coefficient is a dimensionless quantity that measures the linear relationship between two (quantitative) variables. It is also known as the *Pearson product-moment coefficient of correlation*. Its value ranges from -1 to $+1$, where zero indicates the absence of any linear relationship and where -1 and $+1$ indicate a perfect *negative* (*inverse*) and a perfect *positive* (*direct*) relationship, respectively. In order to better understand the meaning and interpretation of the correlation coefficient, we shall exhibit its properties in Theorems 6.7.6 through 6.7.10.

Theorem 6.7.6 If the random variables X and Y are independent, then $\rho_{XY} = 0$.

Proof The proof follows immediately from Theorem 6.7.4. The converse of this theorem is, in general, not true. That is, if $\rho_{XY} = 0$, the random variables X and Y need not be independent.

Theorem 6.7.7 For every pair of random variables, (X, Y), the coefficient of correlation, if it exists, assumes a value between -1 and $+1$:

$$-1 \le \rho_{XY} \le +1.$$

Proof Let

$$U = X - \mu_{10} \quad \text{amd} \quad V = Y - \mu_{01}. \qquad (6.7.9)$$

Consider the following quadratic function of the arbitrary real number c:

$$h(c) = E(U + cV)^2 \ge 0. \qquad (6.7.10)$$

Expanding Equation (6.7.10), we have

$$h(c) = E(c^2 V^2 + 2cVU + U^2)$$
$$= E(V^2)c^2 + 2E(UV)c + E(U^2). \qquad (6.7.11)$$

Equation (6.7.11) is a quadratic function in c and, according to Equation (6.7.10), is greater than or equal to zero for all c. If the discriminant of Equation (6.7.11) were positive, there would exist some values that could be selected for c so that this equation would be negative. Therefore, the discriminant must be less than or equal to zero, insuring that Equation (6.7.11) always remains nonnegative:

$$4[E(UV)]^2 - 4E(U^2)E(V^2) \le 0$$

or

$$[E(UV)]^2 \le E(U^2)E(V^2). \qquad (6.7.12)$$

Dividing both sides of inequality (6.7.12) by $E(U^2)E(V^2)$, we obtain

$$\frac{[E(UV)]^2}{E(U^2)E(V^2)} \le 1. \qquad (6.7.13)$$

Substituting Equation (6.7.9) into inequality (6.7.13), we have

$$\frac{\{E[(X - \mu_{10})(Y - \mu_{01})]\}^2}{E[(X - \mu_{10})^2]E[(Y - \mu_{01})^2]} \leq 1$$

or

$$\rho_{XY}^2 \leq 1.$$

Hence,

$$-1 \leq \rho_{XY} \leq 1.$$

Theorem 6.7.8 shows that the correlation coefficient does not change with respect to a location change and a scale change.

Theorem 6.7.8   If X and Y are random variables and

$$U = \alpha_1 X + \beta_1, \qquad V = \alpha_2 Y + \beta_2,$$

where α_i, β_i, $i = 1, 2$ are arbitrary real numbers, then

$$\rho_{UV} = \rho_{XY}.$$

Proof

$$\rho_{UV} = \frac{\text{Cov}(U, V)}{\sqrt{\text{Var}(U)}\sqrt{\text{Var}(V)}} \qquad (6.7.14)$$

In view of Theorem 6.7.5 and the fact that

$$\text{Var}(U) = \text{Var}(\alpha_1 X + \beta_1) = \alpha_1^2 \, \text{Var}(X)$$

and

$$\text{Var}(V) = \text{Var}(\alpha_2 Y + \beta_2) = \alpha_2^2 \, \text{Var}(Y),$$

Equation (6.7.14) becomes

$$\rho_{UV} = \frac{\alpha_1 \alpha_2 \, \text{Cov}(X, Y)}{\alpha_1 \sqrt{\text{Var}(X)} \, \alpha_2 \sqrt{\text{Var}(Y)}}$$

$$= \frac{\text{Cov}(X, Y)}{\sqrt{\text{Var}(X)}\sqrt{\text{Var}(Y)}}.$$

Thus,

$$\rho_{UV} = \rho_{XY}.$$

Theorem 6.7.9   If X and Y are two random variables for which $Y = \alpha X + \beta$, where α and β are constants and $(\alpha \neq 0)$, then

(1) $\rho_{XY} = 1$ if $\alpha > 0$,   and

(2) $\rho_{XY} = -1$ if $\alpha < 0$.

Proof   From Theorem 6.7.5, we have

$$\text{Cov}(X, Y) = \text{Cov}(X, \alpha X + \beta) = \alpha \, \text{Var}(X).$$

Also,

$$\text{Var}(Y) = \text{Var}(\alpha X + \beta) = \alpha^2 \, \text{Var}(X).$$

Thus,

$$\rho_{XY} = \frac{\text{Cov}(X, Y)}{\sqrt{\text{Var}(X)}\sqrt{\text{Var}(Y)}} = \frac{\alpha \, \text{Var}(X)}{\sqrt{\sigma_x^2}\sqrt{\alpha^2 \sigma_x^2}}$$

or

$$\rho_{XY} = \frac{\alpha}{|\alpha|}.$$

Therefore,

$$\rho_{XY} = +1 \quad \text{if} \quad \alpha > 0;$$

and

$$\rho_{XY} = -1 \quad \text{if} \quad \alpha < 0.$$

Theorem 6.7.10 shows that, if $|\rho_{XY}| = 1$, then, with probability one, Y is a linear function of X.

Theorem 6.7.10   If $|\rho_{XY}| = 1$,   then $Pr(Y = \alpha X + \beta) = 1$.

Proof   Let

$$Z = \frac{X - \mu_{10}}{\sigma_X} \quad \text{and} \quad W = \frac{Y - \mu_{01}}{\sigma_Y}.$$

Then

$$E(Z) = \frac{1}{\sigma_X}\,[E(X) - \mu_{10}] = 0, \qquad E(W) = 0,$$

and

$$\text{Var}(Z) = \frac{1}{\sigma_X^2} \text{Var}(X) = 1, \qquad \text{Var}(W) = 1.$$

Thus,

$$\rho_{ZW} = \frac{\text{Cov}(Z, W)}{\sigma_Z \sigma_W} = \frac{E(ZW) - E(Z)E(W)}{\sigma_Z \sigma_W}$$

or

$$\rho_{ZW} = E(ZW).$$

Let

$$G_1 = Z + W \quad \text{and} \quad G_2 = Z - W.$$

From Example 6.7.5, we have

$$\text{Var}(G_1) = \sigma_{Z+W}^2 = \sigma_Z^2 + \sigma_W^2 + 2E(ZW)$$

and

$$\text{Var}(G_2) = \sigma_{Z-W}^2 = \sigma_Z^2 + \sigma_W^2 - 2E(ZW).$$

Hence,

$$0 \leq \sigma_Z^2 + \sigma_W^2 + 2\rho_{ZW} \quad \text{and} \quad 0 \leq \sigma_Z^2 + \sigma_W^2 - 2\rho_{ZW} \, ;$$

and, since $\sigma_Z^2 = \sigma_W^2 = 1$, we have

$$0 \leq 2 + 2\rho_{ZW} \quad \text{and} \quad 0 \leq 2 - 2\rho_{ZW}.$$

Assume that $|\rho_{XY}| = 1$. Then from Theorem 6.7.8, we have

$$\rho_{XY} = \rho_{ZW} \, ;$$

and, thus, $|\rho_{ZW}| = 1$. If $\rho_{ZW} = -1$, then $\sigma_{G_1}^2 = \sigma_{Z+W}^2 = 2 + 2\rho_{ZW} = 0$; and, thus, $Z + W$ equals zero, with probability one. We conclude that, with probability one, $Z = -W$. This condition exists because the distribution of G_1 has variance zero, which implies that its distribution is discrete; in fact, the total probability of the distribution is massed at its mean, which, in this case, is zero. Such a distribution is called a *degenerate distribution*. We say that $G_1 = 0$, with probability one. Therefore, we can write

$$\frac{X - \mu_{10}}{\sigma_X} = -\frac{Y - \mu_{01}}{\sigma_Y}$$

with probability one, or

$$Y = \alpha X + \beta,$$

with probability one, where

$$\alpha = -\frac{\sigma_Y}{\sigma_X} \quad \text{and} \quad \beta = \mu_{01} + \frac{\sigma_Y}{\sigma_X}\mu_{10}.$$

Note that α is simply the slope of the line and β its y-intercept. If $\rho_{ZW} = 1$, then $\sigma_{G_2}^2 = \sigma_{Z-W}^2 = 2 - 2\rho_{ZW} = 0$. Similarly, we conclude that

$$Y = \alpha X + \beta,$$

with probability one, where

$$\alpha = \frac{\sigma_Y}{\sigma_X} \quad \text{and} \quad \beta = \mu_{01} - \frac{\sigma_Y}{\sigma_X}\mu_{10}.$$

(See Figure 6.7.1.)

We conclude by giving an analogous interpretation of the correlation coefficient. If $\rho_{XY} = 0$, we say that the variates X and Y are *uncorrelated*; and, if $\rho_{XY} = \pm1$, then X and Y are *perfectly correlated*. Thus, in a linear relation, we can predict Y if X has been observed, with ρ_{XY} indicating the accuracy of the predicted value.

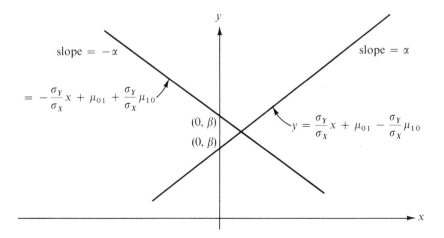

Figure 6.7.1

Example 6.7.17   For the discrete bivariate density given in Example 6.7.1, we have seen that

$$\mu_{10} = \frac{5}{3}, \quad \mu_{01} = \frac{11}{6}, \quad \mu_{11} = \frac{35}{12}, \quad \mu_{20} = \frac{10}{3},$$

and

$$\mu_{02} = 4.$$

Thus, the correlation coefficient of X and Y is

$$\rho_{XY} = \frac{\text{Cov}(X, Y)}{\sigma_X \, \sigma_Y} = \frac{\eta_{11}}{\sqrt{\mu_{20} - \mu_{10}^2} \, \sqrt{\mu_{02} - \mu_{01}^2}}$$

$$= \frac{\mu_{11} - \mu_{10}\mu_{01}}{\sqrt{\eta_{20}} \, \sqrt{\eta_{02}}} = \frac{\left(\dfrac{35}{12}\right) - \left(\dfrac{5}{3}\right)\left(\dfrac{11}{6}\right)}{\sqrt{\dfrac{5}{9}} \sqrt{\dfrac{23}{36}}}$$

$$= \frac{-\dfrac{5}{36}}{\dfrac{1}{3}\sqrt{5}\,\dfrac{1}{6}\sqrt{23}} = \frac{-5}{2\sqrt{115}}.$$

6.7.4 Characteristic Function   The notion of the characteristic function can be extended to a random variable with a finite number of dimensions. However, in this section, we shall restrict ourselves to the two-dimensional random variable.

Definition 6.7.7   *The* characteristic function *of a two-dimensional random variable, (X, Y), is given by*

$$\phi_{XY}(t_1, t_2) = E[e^{i(t_1 X + t_2 Y)}], \tag{6.7.15}$$

where t_1, t_2 are real numbers and $i = \sqrt{-1}$ is the imaginary unit. If (X, Y) is of the discrete type, with joint density $f(x, y)$, then

$$\phi_{XY}(t_1, t_2) = \sum_{j=1}^{\infty} \sum_{k=1}^{\infty} e^{i(t_1 x_k + t_2 y_j)} f(x_k, y_j);$$

and, if (X, Y) is continuous, we have

$$\phi_{XY}(t_1, t_2) \quad \int_{-\infty}^{\infty} \int_{-\infty}^{\infty} e^{i(t_1 x + t_2 y)} f(x, y) \, dx \, dy.$$

Thus, by putting $t_2 = 0$ or $t_1 = 0$ in Equation (6.7.15), we obtain the characteristic functions of the marginal distributions of the random variables X and Y, respectively.

Example 6.7.18 The characteristic function of the discrete two-dimensional random variable (X, Y), the joint density of which is given in Example 6.7.16, is

$$\phi_{XY}(t_1, t_2) = E[e^{i(t_1 X + t_2 Y)}]$$

$$= \sum_{y=-1}^{2} \sum_{x=-2}^{0} e^{i(t_1 x + t_2 y)} f(x, y)$$

$$= \frac{1}{6} e^{-2it} 1 + \frac{1}{3} e^{-i(t_1 + t_2)} + \frac{1}{6} e^{-i(t_1 - 2t_2)} + \frac{1}{6} e^{-it_2} + \frac{1}{6} e^{it_2}$$

$$= \frac{1}{6} [e^{-it_2} + e^{it_2} + e^{-2it_1} + 2e^{-i(t_1 + t_2)} + e^{-i(t_1 - 2t_2)}].$$

As in the one-dimensional case, we can obtain the moments of order $k_1 + k_2$ of a two-dimensional variate, if they exist.

Solution: Assume that

$$\frac{\partial^{k_1 + k_2} \phi_{XY}(t_1, t_2)}{\partial t_1^{k_1} \partial t_2^{k_2}} = \frac{\partial^{k_1 + k_2}}{\partial t_1^{k_1} \partial t_2^{k_2}} E[e^{i(t_1 X + t_2 Y)}]$$

$$= E \frac{\partial^{k_1 + k_2}}{\partial t_1^{k_1} \partial t_2^{k_2}} [e^{i(t_1 X + t_2 Y)}];$$

that is, the operations of differentiation and integration can be interchanged. Then

$$\frac{\partial^{k_1 + k_2} \phi_{XY}(t_1, t_2)}{\partial t_1^{k_1} \partial t_2^{k_2}} = E[i^{k_1 + k_2} X^{k_1} Y^{k_2} e^{i(t_1 X + t_2 Y)}]$$

$$= i^{k_1} + E^{k_2} [X^{k_1} Y^{k_2} e^{i(t_1 X + t_2 Y)}].$$

Thus, we can obtain the ordinary moment of order, $k_1 + k_2$, by

$$\frac{\partial^{k_1 + k_2} \phi_{XY}(t_1, t_2)}{i^{k_1 + k_2} \partial t_1^{k_1} \partial t_2^{k_2}} \Bigg|_{\substack{t_1 = 0 \\ t_2 = 0}} = E(X^{k_1} Y^{k_2}) = \mu_{k_1 k_2},$$

provided that the operations may be interchanged and the required partial derivatives exist. Hence, the first and second order ordinary moments can be obtained by the following expressions:

$$\mu_{10} = \frac{\partial \phi_{XY}(t_1, t_2)}{i \, \partial t_1} \bigg|_{\substack{t_1 = 0 \\ t_2 = 0}} = E(X),$$

$$\mu_{01} = \frac{\partial \phi_{XY}(t_1, t_2)}{i \, \partial t_2} \bigg|_{\substack{t_1 = 0 \\ t_2 = 0}} = E(Y),$$

$$\mu_{11} = \frac{\partial^2 \phi_{XY}(t_1, t_2)}{i^2 \, \partial t_1 \, \partial t_2} \bigg|_{\substack{t_1 = 0 \\ t_2 = 0}} = E(XY),$$

$$\mu_{20} = \frac{\partial^2 \phi_{XY}(t_1, t_2)}{i^2 \, \partial t_1{}^2} \bigg|_{\substack{t_1 = 0 \\ t_2 = 0}} = E(X^2),$$

and

$$\mu_{02} = \frac{\partial^2 \phi_{XY}(t_1, t_2)}{i^2 \, \partial t_2{}^2} \bigg|_{\substack{t_1 = 0 \\ t_2 = 0}} = E(Y^2).$$

Example 6.7.19   Using the characteristic function obtained in Example 6.7.18, we can compute the following moments:

$$\mu_{10} = \frac{\partial \phi_{XY}(t_1, t_2)}{i \, \partial t_1} \bigg|_{\substack{t_1 = 0 \\ t_2 = 0}}$$

$$= \frac{1}{6i} \left[-2ie^{-2it_1} - 2ie^{-i(t_1 + t_2)} - ie^{-i(t_1 - 2t_2)} \right]_{\substack{t_1 = 0 \\ t_2 = 0}}$$

$$= -\frac{5}{6},$$

$$\mu_{01} = \frac{\partial \phi_{XY}(t_1, t_2)}{i \, \partial t_2} \bigg|_{\substack{t_1 = 0 \\ t_2 = 0}}$$

$$= \frac{1}{6i} \left[-ie^{-it_2} + ie^{it_2} - 2ie^{-i(t_1 + t_2)} + 2ie^{-i(t_1 - 2t_2)} \right]_{\substack{t_1 = 0 \\ t_2 = 0}}$$

$$= 0,$$

and

$$\mu_{11} = \frac{\partial^2 \phi_{XY}(t_1, t_2)}{i^2 \, \partial t_1 \, \partial t_2} \bigg|_{\substack{t_1 = 0 \\ t_2 = 0}}$$

$$= \frac{1}{6i^2} \left[-ie^{-it_1}(2ie^{2it_2} - 2ie^{-it_2}) \right]_{\substack{t_1 = 0 \\ t_2 = 0}}$$

$$= 0.$$

The characteristic function of the random variable (X, Y) can also be expanded in a series.

$$\phi_{XY}(t_1, t_2) = E[e^{i(t_1X + t_2Y)}]$$

$$= E[1 + i(t_1X + t_2Y) + \frac{i^2(t_1X + t_2Y)^2}{2!} = \frac{i^3(t_1X + t_2Y)^3}{3!} + \cdots$$

$$+ \frac{i^{k_1+k_2}(t_1X + t_2Y)^{k_1+k_2} + \cdots]}{(k_1 + k_2)!}$$

$$= 1 + it_1E(X) + it_2E(Y) + \frac{i^2}{2!}t_1{}^2E(X)^2$$

$$+ i^2t_1t_2E(XY) + \frac{i^2}{2!}t_2{}^2E(Y^2) + \cdots.$$

Thus,

$$\mu_{k_1k_2} = E(X^{k_1}Y^{k_2}) = \frac{\partial^{k_1+k_2}\phi_{XY}(t_1, t_2)}{i^{k_1+k_2}\partial t_1{}^{k_1}\partial t_2{}^{k_2}}\bigg|_{\substack{t_1=0 \\ t_2=0}}.$$

In Section 5.5, we discussed some of the basic properties of the characteristic function of a one-dimensional variate. Here we give the analogous properties for the two-dimensional case:

Property (a) $\phi_{XY}(0, 0) = E[e^{i(0X + 0Y)}] = 1.$

Property (b) $|\phi_{XY}(t_1, t_2)| = |E[e^{i(t_1X + t_2Y)}]|$

$$\leq E[|e^{i(t_1X + t_2Y)}|]$$

$$= 1$$

because

$$|e^{i(t_1X + t_2Y)}| = |\cos(t_1X + t_2Y) + i\sin(t_1X + t_2Y)|$$

$$= 1.$$

Thus,

$$|\phi_{XY}(t_1, t_2)| \leq 1.$$

Property (c) $\phi_{XY}(-t_1, -t_2) = E[e^{-i(t_1X + t_2Y)}]$

$$= E[\cos(t_1X + t_2Y) - i\sin(t_1X + t_2Y)]$$

$$= \overline{\phi_{XY}(t_1, t_2)},$$

where $\overline{\phi_{XY}(t_1, t_2)}$ is the complex conjugate of the characteristic function of the variate (X, Y).

Property (d)   If X and Y are independent random variables, then

$$\phi_{XY}(t_1, t_2) = E[e^{i(t_1 X + t_2 Y)}]$$

$$= \int_{\infty}^{\infty} \int_{\infty}^{\infty} e^{i(t_1 x + t_2 y)} f(x, y) \, dx \, dy$$

$$= \int_{-\infty}^{\infty} e^{it_1 x} f_1(x) \, dx \int_{-\infty}^{\infty} e^{it_2 y} f_2(y) \, dy$$

$$= E(e^{it_1 X}) E(e^{it_2 y})$$

$$= \phi_X(t_1) \, \phi_Y(t_2).$$

Property (e)   If $U = \alpha_1 X + \beta_1 Y$ and $V = \alpha_2 X + \beta_2 Y$, where $\alpha_1, \alpha_2, \beta_1$ and β_2 are real constants, then

$$\phi_{UV}(t_1, t_2) = \phi_{XY}[(\alpha_1 t_1 + \alpha_2 t_2), (\beta_1 t_1 + \beta_2 t_2)].$$

This situation may be shown as follows:

$$\phi_{UV}(t_1, t_2) = E[e^{i(t_1 U + t_2 V)}]$$

$$= E\{e^{i[t_1(\alpha_1 X + \beta_1 Y) + t_2(\alpha_2 X + \beta_2 Y)]}\}$$

$$= E\{e^{i[(t_1 \alpha_1 + t_2 \alpha_2)X + (t_1 \beta_1 + t_2 \beta_2)Y]}\}$$

$$= \phi_{XY}[(t_1 \alpha_1 + t_2 \alpha_2), (t_1 \beta_1 + t_2 \beta_2)].$$

Property (f)   As we mentioned previously, an important feature of the characteristic function is that, once we know $\phi_{XY}(t_1, t_2)$, we can *uniquely determine the joint distribution function of* (X, Y).

Theorem 6.7.11   Suppose that $\phi_{XY}(t_1, t_2)$ is the characteristic function of the random variable (X, Y). If the inequalities

$$x - \Delta x \le X \le x + \Delta x \quad \text{and} \quad y - \Delta y \le Y \le y + \Delta y$$

form a region of continuity (see Theorem 6.2.1(d)), then

$$Pr(x - \Delta x \le X \le x + \Delta x, y - \Delta y \le Y \le y + \Delta y)$$

$$= \lim_{T \to \infty} \frac{1}{\pi^2} \int_{-T}^{T} \int_{-T}^{T} \frac{\sin \Delta x t_1}{t_1} \frac{\sin \Delta y t_2}{t_2} e^{-i(xt_1 + yt_2)} \phi_{XY}(t_1, t_2) \, dt_1 \, dt_2.$$

The above inversion formula, as in the one-dimensional case, can be written in the more useful form

$$f(x, y) = \frac{1}{4\pi^2} \int_{-\infty}^{\infty} \int_{-\infty}^{\infty} e^{-i(t_1 x + t_2 y)} \phi_{XY}(t_1, t_2) \, dt_1 \, dt_2. \tag{6.7.16}$$

Theorem 6.7.12 shows that the converse of *property* (d) is also true.

Theorem 6.7.12   Suppose that $\phi_{XY}(t_1, t_2)$, $\phi_X(t_1)$, $\phi_Y(t_2)$, $F(x, y)$, $F_1(x)$, and $F_2(y)$ denote the characteristic functions, joint cumulative distribution functions, and marginal distribution functions of (X, Y), X, and Y, respectively. Then the random variables X and Y are independent if and only if

$$\phi_{XY}(t_1, t_2) = \phi_X(t_1)\phi_Y(t_2). \tag{6.7.17}$$

Proof   From *property* (*d*), if X and Y are independent, then

$$\phi_{XY}(t_1, t_2) = \phi_X(t_1)\phi_Y(t_2).$$

If expression (6.7.17) is true, then, using Equation (6.7.16), we have

$$f(x, y) = \frac{1}{4\pi^2} \int_{-\infty}^{\infty} \int_{-\infty}^{\infty} e^{-it_1 x} e^{-it_2 y} \phi_X(t_1)\phi_Y(t_2)\, dt_1\, dt_2$$

$$= \frac{1}{2\pi} \int_{-\infty}^{\infty} e^{-it_1 x}\phi_X(t_1)\, dt_1 \frac{1}{2\pi} \int_{-\infty}^{\infty} e^{-it_2 y}\phi_Y(t_2)\, dt_2 .$$

In view of Theorem 5.5.1,

$$f(x, y) = f_1(x)f_2(y).$$

Therefore, X and Y are independent.

Example 6.7.20   In reference to Example 6.7.8, if X and Y are independent variates and each is Poisson distributed with parameters λ_1 and λ_2, respectively, then, in view of property (4), we have

$$\phi_{XY}(t_1, t_2) = \sum_{x=0}^{\infty} \sum_{y=0}^{\infty} e^{i(t_1 x + t_2 y)} f(x, y)$$

$$= \sum_{x=0}^{\infty} \sum_{y=0}^{\infty} \frac{e^{i(t_1 x + t_2 y)} e^{-(\lambda_1 + \lambda_2)}\lambda_1^{\,x}\lambda_2^{\,y}}{x!\, y!}$$

$$= \sum_{x=0}^{\infty} \sum_{y=0}^{\infty} \frac{(\lambda_1 e^{it_1})^x}{x!} e^{-\lambda_1} \frac{(\lambda_2 e^{it_2})^y}{y!} e^{-\lambda_2}$$

$$= \left[e^{-\lambda_1} \sum_{x=0}^{\infty} \frac{(\lambda_1 e^{it_1})^x}{x!} \right]\left[e^{-\lambda_2} \sum_{y=0}^{\infty} \frac{(\lambda_2 e^{it_2})^y}{y!} \right]$$

$$= [e^{\lambda_1}(e^{it_1} - 1)][e^{\lambda_2}(e^{t_2 i} - 1)]$$

$$= \phi_X(t_1)\phi_Y(t_2).$$

Using Theorem 6.7.12, it is clear that the converse of the above statement is true.

6.8   Conditional Expectation

In this section, we shall discuss conditional expectations, which are expected values computed with respect to conditional distributions.

Definition 6.8.1   *Let* (X, Y) *be a two-dimensional random variable. The* conditional expected value *of the variate X for a given $Y = y$ is*

$$E(X \mid Y = y_j) = \sum_i x_i h_1(x_i \mid y_j) \qquad (6.8.1)$$

if (X, Y) *is discrete, and*

$$E(X \mid Y = y) = \int_{-\infty}^{\infty} x h_1(x \mid y) \, dx \qquad (6.8.2)$$

if (X, Y) *is of the continuous type.*

Similarly, we can define the *conditional expected value* of Y for a given $X = x$. We may write Equations (6.8.1) and (6.8.2) as

$$E(X \mid Y = y_j) = \sum_i x_i \frac{f(x_i, y_j)}{f_2(y_j)}, \quad f_2(y_j) > 0$$

and

$$E(X \mid Y = y) = \int_{-\infty}^{\infty} x \frac{f(x, y)}{f_2(y)} \, dx, \quad f_2(y) > 0,$$

where

$$p_2(y_j) = \sum_i f(x_i, y_j) \quad \text{and} \quad f_2(y) = \int_{-\infty}^{\infty} f(x, y) \, dx.$$

Of course, in order for the conditional expected value to exist, the right-hand sides of Equations (6.8.1) or (6.8.2) must be absolutely convergent. Furthermore, if X and Y are independent random variables, then

$$E(X \mid Y = y) = E(X) \quad \text{and} \quad E(Y \mid X = x) = E(Y).$$

Example 6.8.1 The conditional expectation of X, given $Y = -2$ in Example 6.3.1, is

$$E(X \mid Y = -2) = \sum_{x=-1}^{5} x \frac{f(x, -2)}{f_2(-2)}$$

$$= \frac{1}{p_2(-2)} \{(-1)p(-1, -2) + (3)p(3, -2) + (5)p(5, -2)\}$$

$$= \frac{5}{2} \{(-1)(.3) + (3)(0) + (5)(.1)\}$$

$$= \frac{1}{2}.$$

Also,

$$E(Y \mid X = -1) = \sum_{y=-2}^{4} y \frac{p(-1, y)}{p_1(-1)}$$

$$= \frac{1}{p_1(-1)} \{(-2)p(-1, -2) + (1)p(-1, 1) + (4)p(-1, 4)\}$$

$$= \frac{5}{2} \{(-2)(.3) + (1)(0) + (4)(.2)\}$$

$$= \frac{1}{3}.$$

Example 6.8.2 The conditional expected value of the random variable X, given $Y = y_0$, whose conditional distribution is given in Example 6.4.3, is

$$E(X \mid Y = y_0) = \int_{-\infty}^{\infty} x h_1(x \mid y_0) \, dx$$

$$= \int_{1}^{y_0} x \frac{2x}{y_0^2 - 1} \, dx$$

$$= \frac{2}{3} \left(\frac{y_0^2 + y_0 + 1}{y_0 + 1} \right).$$

Also,

$$E(Y \mid X = x_0) = \int_{-\infty}^{\infty} y h_2(y \mid x_0) \, dy$$

$$= \int_{x_0}^{2} y \frac{2y}{4 - x_0^2} \, dy$$

$$= \frac{2}{3} \left(\frac{x_0^2 + 2x_0 + 4}{x_0 + 2} \right).$$

We emphasize again that, in order for the conditional expectation of a random variable to exist, Equations (6.8.1) and (6.8.2) must be absolutely convergent. Also, the conditional expected value of one random variable is a constant for a fixed value of the second variate. But $E(X \mid Y = y)$ is a function of y, where y represents a value of the random variable Y; and, thus, it is not a random variable. Similarly, $E(Y \mid X = x)$ is not a random variable because the conditional expectation is a function of x, where x represents a value that the variate X may assume. However, in general, $E[X \mid Y]$ is a function of the random variable Y and $E[Y \mid X]$ is a function of the random variable X.

Theorem 6.8.1   Let (X, Y) be a two-dimensional random variable. If the conditional expected values $E(X \mid Y = y)$ and $E(Y \mid X = x)$ exist, then

(1) $E[E(X \mid Y = y)] = E(X)$;

(2) $E[E(Y \mid X = x)] = E(Y)$.

Proof   (1)   For the discrete case, we have

$$
\begin{aligned}
E[E(X \mid Y = y_j)] &= \sum_{j=1}^{\infty} E(X \mid Y = y_j) f_2(y_j) \\
&= \sum_{j=1}^{\infty} \sum_{i=1}^{\infty} x_i h(x_i \mid y_j) f_2(y_j) \\
&= \sum_{j=1}^{\infty} \sum_{i=1}^{\infty} x_i \frac{f(x_i, y_j)}{f_2(y_j)} f_2(y_j) \\
&= \sum_{i=1}^{\infty} x_i \sum_{j=1}^{\infty} f(x_i, y_j) \\
&= \sum_{i=1}^{\infty} x_i f_1(x_i) \\
&= E(X).
\end{aligned}
$$

(2)   For the continuous case, we have

$$
\begin{aligned}
E[E(Y \mid X = x)] &= \int_{-\infty}^{\infty} E(Y \mid X = x) f_1(x) \, dx \\
&= \int_{-\infty}^{\infty} \left\{ \int_{-\infty}^{\infty} y h_2(y \mid x) \, dy \right\} f_1(x) \, dx \\
&= \int_{-\infty}^{\infty} \left\{ \int_{-\infty}^{\infty} y \frac{f(x, y)}{f_1(x)} \, dy \right\} f_1(x) \, dx.
\end{aligned}
$$

Because the expected values exist, we may change the order of integration in the above integral. Hence,

$$E[E(Y \mid X = x)] = \int_{-\infty}^{\infty} y \left\{ \int_{-\infty}^{\infty} \frac{f(x, y)}{f_1(x)} f_1(x) \, dx \right\} dy$$

$$= \int_{-\infty}^{\infty} y \left\{ \int_{-\infty}^{\infty} f(x, y) \, dx \right\} dy$$

$$= E(Y).$$

If $g(X, Y)$ is a functional form of the random variable (X, Y), which has a probability density of $f(x, y)$, then

$$E[g(X, Y) \mid x_1 \le X \le x_2] = \int_{-\infty}^{\infty} \int_{x_1}^{x_2} \frac{g(x, y) f(x, y)}{Pr(x_1 \le X \le x_2)} \, dx \, dy$$

$$\int_{-\infty}^{\infty} \int_{x_1}^{x_2} \frac{g(x, y) f(x, y)}{F(x_2) - F(x_1)} \, dx \, dy.$$

Of course, this conditional expected value exists only if the above integral is absolutely convergent and $Pr(x_1 \le X \le x_2) \ne 0$.

$$E[g(X, Y) \mid Y = y] = \lim_{\Delta y \to 0} \{ E[g(X, Y) \mid y \le Y \le y + \Delta y] \}$$

$$= \int_{-\infty}^{\infty} \left\{ \lim_{\Delta y \to 0} \int_{y}^{y + \Delta y} \frac{g(x, s) f(x, s)}{F(y + \Delta y) - F(y)} \, ds \right\} dx$$

$$= \int_{-\infty}^{\infty} \frac{g(x, y) f(x, y)}{f_2(y)} \, dx.$$

Applying an argument similar to that used in Theorem 6.8.1, we can show that

$$E\{E[g(X, Y) \mid X = x]\} = E\{E[g(X, Y) \mid Y = y]\} = E[g(X, Y)].$$

Example 6.8.3 If the probability density function of the random variable (X, Y) is given by

$$f(x, y) = \begin{cases} \dfrac{8}{9} xy, & 1 \le x \le y \le 2, \\ 0, & \text{elsewhere}, \end{cases}$$

and

$$f_1(x) = \begin{cases} \dfrac{4}{9} x(4 - x^2), & 1 \le x \le 2, \\ 0, & \text{elsewhere}, \end{cases}$$

compute $E[g(X, Y)|X = x]$, where

$$g(X, Y) = X^2 + Y^2.$$

Solution: We write

$$E[X^2 + Y^2 | X = x] = \int_x^2 (x^2 + y^2) \frac{f(x, y)}{f_1(x)} \, dy$$

$$= \int_x^2 2(x^2 + y^2) \frac{y}{(4 - x^2)} \, dy$$

$$= \frac{3x^2 + 4}{2}, \quad 1 \le x \le 2.$$

Thus, $E[g(X, Y)|X = x]$ is a random variable. Furthermore,

$$E\{E[X^2 + Y^2 | X = x]\} = E[X^2 + Y^2]$$

$$= \int_1^2 \left\{ \int_1^y \frac{8}{9} (x^2 + y^2) xy \, dx \right\} dy$$

$$= \frac{8}{9} \int_1^2 \left(\frac{3}{4} y^5 - \frac{1}{2} y^3 - \frac{1}{4} y \right) dy$$

$$= 5.$$

6.8.1 Regression Curve
An important geometrical interpretation of conditional expectation is that of a *regression curve*. Let (X, Y) be a two-dimensional random variable, with joint probability density function $f(x, y)$. If (X, Y) is of the discrete type, we shall denote the conditional expected values of the variate X, given $Y = y_j$, and Y, given $X = x_i$, by $\xi_1(y_j)$ and $\xi_2(x_i)$, respectively. Thus,

$$\xi_1(y_j) = E(X | Y = y_j) = \sum_i x_i \frac{f(x_i, y_j)}{f_2(y_j)} \tag{6.8.3}$$

and

$$\xi_2(x_i) = E(Y | X = x_i) = \sum_j y_j \frac{f(x_i, y_j)}{f_1(x_i)}. \tag{6.8.4}$$

Similarly, for the continuous case,

$$\xi_1(y) = E(X \mid Y = y) = \int_{-\infty}^{\infty} x \, \frac{f(x, y)}{f_2(y)} \, dx \qquad (6.8.5)$$

and

$$\xi_2(x) = E(Y \mid X = x) = \int_{-\infty}^{\infty} y \, \frac{f(x, y)}{f_1(x)} \, dy. \qquad (6.8.6)$$

The graph of the collection of points $(x = \xi_1(y_j), \ y = y_j)$ from Equation (6.8.3) is known as the *regression curve* of X on Y. Analogously, the graph of the set of points $(x = x_i, \ y = \xi_2(x_i))$ is called the *regression curve* of the random variable Y on X. Similar interpretations may be made for Equations (6.8.5) and (6.8.6). (See Figure 6.8.1.)

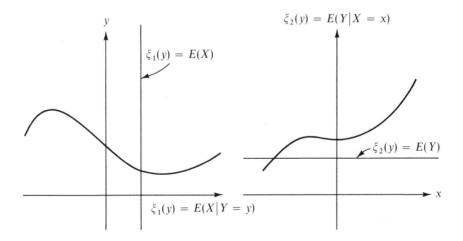

Figure 6.8.1

We formulate the above discussion in Definition 6.8.2.

Definition 6.8.2   *The graph of the collection of points $(\xi_1(y_j), \ y_j)$ or $(\xi_1(y), \ y)$ from Equations (6.8.3) and (6.8.5) is called* the regresssion curve *of the random variable X on the random variable Y. Similarly, the graph of the set of points $(x_i, \ \xi_2(x_i))$ or $(x, \ \xi_2(x))$ from Equations (6.8.4) or (6.8.6) is called the regression curve of the random variable Y on the random variable X.*

Thus, as we stated previously, the conditional expectation of X, given Y, is a function of y; that is, it runs over all possible values that the random variable Y can assume, and the values of $E(X|Y=y)$ are located on the regression curve of X on Y. The situation is similar for the regression curve of Y on X.

If the random variables X and Y are independent, then

$$\xi_1(y) = E(X|Y=y) = E(X)$$

and

$$\xi_2(x) = E(Y|X=x) = E(Y).$$

Thus, the conditional expectation $\xi_1(y)$ does not depend on Y, and the regression curve is a line with infinite slope. Similarly, the conditional expectation of $\xi_2(x)$ does not depend on X, and the regression curve is a line parallel to the x-axis, as shown in Figure 6.8.1.

Example 6.8.4   The regression curves for the discrete bivariate distribution, given in Example 6.3.1, are computed as follows:

$$\xi_1(y_j) = E(X|Y=y_j) = \sum_i x_i \frac{f(x_i, y_j)}{f_2(y_j)}$$

$$\xi_1(-2) = \frac{1}{f_2(-2)} [(-1)f(-1, -2) + (3)f(3, -2) + (5)f(5, -2)]$$

$$= \frac{1}{.4} [(-1)(.3) + (3)(0) + (5)(.1)]$$

$$= \frac{1}{2};$$

$$\xi_1(0) = \frac{1}{f_2(0)} [(-1)f(-1, 0) + (3)f(3, 0) + (5)f(5, 0)]$$

$$= \frac{1}{.3} [(-1)(.1) + (3)(.2) + (5)(0)]$$

$$= \frac{5}{3};$$

$$\xi_1(1) = \frac{1}{f_2(1)} [(-1)f(-1, 1) + (3)f(3, 1) + (5)f(5, 1)]$$

$$= \frac{1}{.1} [(-1)(0) + (3)(.1) + (5)(0)]$$

$$= 3;$$

$$\xi_1(4) = \frac{1}{f_2(4)} [(-1)f(-1, 4) + (3)f(3, 4) + (5)f(5, 4)]$$

$$= \frac{1}{.2} [(-1)(.2) + (3)(0) + (5)(0)]$$

$$= -1;$$

$$\xi_2(x_i) = E[Y \mid X = x_i] = \sum_i y_j \frac{f(x_i, y_j)}{f_1(x_i)}$$

$$\xi_2(-1) = \frac{1}{f_1(-1)} [(-2)f(-1, -2) + (0)f(-1, 0) + (1)f(-1, 1)$$

$$+ (4)f(-1, 4)]$$

$$= \frac{1}{.6} [(-2)(.3) + (4)(.2)]$$

$$= \frac{1}{3};$$

$$\xi_2(3) = \frac{1}{f_1(3)} [(-2)f(3, -2) + (0)f(3, 0) + (1)f(3, 1) + (4)f(3, 4)]$$

$$= \frac{1}{.3} [(1)(.1)]$$

$$= \frac{1}{3};$$

$$\xi_2(5) = \frac{1}{f_1(5)} [(-2)f(5, -2) + (0)f(5, 0) + (1)f(5, 1) + (4)f(5, 4)]$$

$$= \frac{1}{.1} [(-2)(.1)]$$

$$= -2.$$

Thus, the regression curves of X on Y and Y on X consist of the following points:

$$\underline{X \text{ on } Y:} \quad \left(\frac{1}{2}, -2\right), \quad \left(\frac{5}{3}, 0\right), \quad (3, 1), \quad \text{and} \quad (-1, 4).$$

$$\underline{Y \text{ on } X:} \quad \left(-1, \frac{1}{3}\right), \quad \left(3, \frac{1}{3}\right), \quad \text{and} \quad (5, -2).$$

Example 6.8.5   The regression curves for the continuous bivariate distribution, given in Example 6.4.2, are as follows:

X on Y:

$$\xi_1(y) = E(X \mid Y = y) = \int_{-\infty}^{\infty} x h_1(x \mid y) \, dx$$

$$= \frac{1}{2(2y + 5)} \int_0^2 x(4x + 2y + 1) \, dx$$

$$= \frac{1}{(2y + 5)} \left(2y + \frac{19}{3} \right) = \frac{1}{3} \frac{6y + 19}{2y + 5}.$$

Y on X:

$$\xi_2(x) = E(Y \mid X = x) = \int_{-\infty}^{\infty} y h_2(y \mid x) \, dy$$

$$= \frac{1}{2(4x + 3)} \int_0^2 y(4x + 2y + 1) \, dy$$

$$= \frac{1}{(4x + 3)} \left(4x + \frac{11}{3} \right) = \frac{1}{3} \frac{12x + 11}{4x + 3}.$$

Thus, the regression curve of X on Y is simply the location of the mean of X for various values of Y in the conditional of X, given Y; the situation is similar for the regression curve Y on X. (See Figure 6.8.2.)

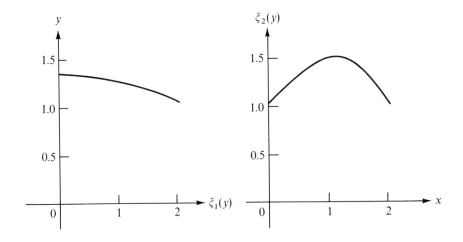

Figure 6.8.2

6.9   The Bivariate Normal Distribution

We conclude our discussion of two random variables by illustrating with a very important bivariate distribution most of the important probabilistic concepts we have studied.

Definition 6.9.1   *A two-dimensional random variable* (X, Y) *is said to be distributed as a* bivariate normal *if its joint probability density function is*

$$f(x, y; \mu_X, \mu_Y, \sigma_X, \sigma_Y) = K \exp\left\{ - \frac{1}{2(1 - \rho^2)} \left[\left(\frac{x - \mu_X}{\sigma_X} \right)^2 - 2\rho \left(\frac{x - \mu_X}{\sigma_X} \right) \right.\right.$$

$$\left.\left. \times \left(\frac{y - \mu_Y}{\sigma_Y} \right) + \left(\frac{y - \mu_Y}{\sigma_Y} \right)^2 \right] \right\}, \quad -\infty < x, y < \infty,$$

where

$$K = \frac{1}{2\pi\sigma_X\sigma_Y\sqrt{1 - \rho^2}}, \quad -\infty < \mu_X < \infty, \ -\infty < \mu_Y < \infty,$$

$$\sigma_X > 0, \ \sigma_Y > 0, \ -1 < \rho < 1.$$

(1)   We shall show that the conditions of a joint probability density function are satisfied. It is clear that $f(x, y; \mu_X, \mu_Y, \sigma_X, \sigma_Y) > 0$ for all (x, y). Thus, we must show that

$$\int_{-\infty}^{\infty} \int_{-\infty}^{\infty} f(x, y; \mu_X, \mu_Y, \sigma_X, \sigma_Y) \, dx \, dy = 1.$$

Consider

$$A = \int_{-\infty}^{\infty} \int_{-\infty}^{\infty} \frac{1}{2\pi\sigma_X\sigma_Y\sqrt{1 - \rho^2}}$$

$$\cdot \exp\left\{ - \frac{1}{2(1 - \rho^2)} \left[\left(\frac{x - \mu_X}{\sigma_X} \right)^2 - 2\rho \left(\frac{x - \mu_X}{\sigma_X} \right) \left(\frac{y - \mu_Y}{\sigma_Y} \right) \right.\right.$$

$$\left.\left. + \left(\frac{y - \mu_Y}{\sigma_Y} \right)^2 \right] \right\} dx \, dy.$$

Let

$$u = \frac{x - \mu_X}{\sigma_X}, \qquad v = \frac{y - u_Y}{\sigma_Y}$$

or

$$x = \sigma_X u + \mu_X, \qquad y = \sigma_Y v + \mu_Y.$$

The Jacobian of the transformation is

$$J = \begin{vmatrix} \dfrac{\partial x}{\partial u} & \dfrac{\partial x}{\partial v} \\[2mm] \dfrac{\partial y}{\partial u} & \dfrac{\partial y}{\partial v} \end{vmatrix} = \begin{vmatrix} \sigma_X & 0 \\ 0 & \sigma_Y \end{vmatrix} = \sigma_X \sigma_Y.$$

We then have

$$A = \int_{-\infty}^{\infty} \int_{-\infty}^{\infty} \frac{1}{2\pi\sqrt{1-\rho^2}} \exp\left\{ -\frac{1}{2(1-\rho^2)} (u^2 - 2\rho uv + v^2) \right\} du\, dv;$$

however, we can write

$$(u^2 - 2\rho uv + v^2) \quad \text{as} \quad u^2 - 2\rho uv + \rho^2 v^2 - \rho^2 v^2 + v^2,$$

which equals

$$(u - \rho v)^2 - \rho^2 v^2 + v^2,$$

or

$$(u - \rho v)^2 + v^2(1 - \rho^2).$$

Thus,

$$A = \int_{-\infty}^{\infty} \int_{-\infty}^{\infty} \frac{1}{2\pi\sqrt{1-\rho^2}} \exp\left\{ -\frac{1}{2(1-\rho^2)} (u - \rho v)^2 - \frac{v^2}{2} \right\} du\, dv$$

$$= \int_{-\infty}^{\infty} \int_{-\infty}^{\infty} \frac{1}{2\pi\sqrt{1-\rho^2}} \exp\left\{ -\frac{1}{2} \left(\frac{u - \rho v}{\sqrt{1-\rho^2}} \right)^2 \right\} e^{-(1/2)v^2} du\, dv.$$

Now let

$$t_1 = \frac{u - \rho v}{\sqrt{1-\rho^2}}, \qquad t_2 = v$$

or

$$u = \sqrt{1-\rho^2}\, t_1 + \rho t_2, \qquad v = t_2$$

and

$$J = \begin{vmatrix} \sqrt{1 - \rho^2} & \rho \\ 0 & 1 \end{vmatrix} = \sqrt{1 - \rho^2}.$$

Hence,

$$A = \int_{-\infty}^{\infty} \left\{ \int_{-\infty}^{\infty} \frac{1}{\sqrt{2\pi}} e^{-(1/2)t_1^2} dt_1 \right\} \frac{1}{\sqrt{2\pi}} e^{-(1/2)t_2^2} dt_2 = 1.$$

(2)   We shall now compute the marginal probability densities of the random variables X and Y.

$$f_1(x; \mu_X, \sigma_X) = \int_{-\infty}^{\infty} f(x, y, \mu_X, \mu_Y, \sigma_X, \sigma_Y) \, dy, \quad -\infty < x < \infty$$

$$= \int_{-\infty}^{\infty} \frac{1}{2\pi\sigma_X \sigma_Y \sqrt{1 - \rho^2}}$$

$$\cdot \exp\left\{ -\frac{1}{2(1 - \rho^2)} \left[\left(\frac{x - \mu_X}{\sigma_X}\right)^2 - 2\rho\left(\frac{x - \mu_X}{\sigma_X}\right)\left(\frac{y - \mu_Y}{\sigma_Y}\right) \right.\right.$$

$$\left.\left. + \left(\frac{y - \mu_Y}{\sigma_Y}\right)^2 \right] \right\} dy, \quad -\infty < x < \infty.$$

Let

$$v = \frac{y - \mu_Y}{\sigma_Y} \quad \text{and} \quad dy = \sigma_Y \, dv.$$

Then

$$f_1(x; \mu_X, \sigma_Y) = \int_{-\infty}^{\infty} \frac{1}{2\pi\sigma_X \sqrt{1 - \rho^2}}$$

$$\cdot \exp\left\{ -\frac{1}{2(1 - \rho^2)} \left[\left(\frac{x - \mu_X}{\sigma_X}\right)^2 - 2\rho\left(\frac{x - \mu_X}{\sigma_X}\right)v + v^2 \right] \right\} dv,$$

$$-\infty < x < \infty.$$

We may write

$$\left(\frac{x - \mu_X}{\sigma_X}\right)^2 - 2\rho\left(\frac{x - \mu_X}{\sigma_X}\right)v + v^2 \quad \text{as} \quad \left(\frac{x - \mu_X}{\sigma_X}\right)^2 - 2\rho\left(\frac{x - \mu_X}{\sigma_X}\right) \cdot$$

$$v + \rho^2\left(\frac{x - \mu_X}{\sigma_X}\right)^2 - \rho^2\left(\frac{x - \mu_X}{\sigma_X}\right)^2 + v^2,$$

which equals

$$\left[v - \rho\left(\frac{x - \mu_X}{\sigma_X}\right)\right]^2 + (1 - \rho^2)\left(\frac{x - \mu_X}{\sigma_X}\right)^2 .$$

Thus,

$$f_1(x; \mu_X, \sigma_X) = \int_{-\infty}^{\infty} \frac{1}{2\pi\sigma_X \sqrt{1 - \rho^2}}$$

$$\cdot \exp\left\{ -\frac{1}{2(1 - \rho^2)}\left[v - \rho\left(\frac{x - \mu_X}{\sigma_X}\right)\right]^2\right\}$$

$$\cdot \exp\left\{ -\frac{1}{2}\left(\frac{x - \mu_X}{\sigma_X}\right)^2\right\} dv, \quad -\infty < x < \infty$$

$$= \frac{1}{\sqrt{2\pi}\,\sigma_X} \exp\left\{ -\frac{1}{2}\left[\frac{x - \mu_X}{\sigma_X}\right]^2\right\} \int_{-\infty}^{\infty} \frac{1}{\sqrt{2\pi}\sqrt{1 - \rho^2}}$$

$$\cdot \exp\left\{ -\frac{1}{2}\left[\frac{v - \rho\left(\frac{x - \mu_X}{\sigma_X}\right)}{\sqrt{1 - \rho^2}}\right]^2\right\} dv, \quad -\infty < x < \infty.$$

Now let

$$t = \frac{v - \rho[(x - \mu_X)/\sigma_X]}{\sqrt{1 - \rho^2}}; \quad \text{then} \quad \sqrt{1 - \rho^2}\, dt = dv.$$

Hence,

$$f_1(x; \mu_X, \sigma_X) = \frac{1}{\sqrt{2\pi}\,\sigma_X} \exp\left\{ -\frac{1}{2}\left(\frac{x - \mu_X}{\sigma_X}\right)^2\right\} \int_{-\infty}^{\infty} \frac{1}{\sqrt{2\pi}} e^{-(1/2)t^2}\, dt,$$

$$-\infty < x < \infty.$$

Therefore, the marginal probability density of the random variable X is

$$f_1(x; \mu_X, \sigma_X) = \frac{1}{\sqrt{2\pi}\,\sigma_X} \exp\left\{ -\frac{1}{2}\left[\frac{x - \mu_X}{\sigma_X}\right]^2\right\}, \quad -\infty < x < \infty, \quad \sigma_X > 0.$$

Similarly, the marginal probability density function of the variate Y is

$$f_2(y; \mu_Y, \sigma_Y) = \frac{1}{\sqrt{2\pi}\,\sigma_Y} \exp\left\{ -\frac{1}{2}\left[\frac{y - \mu_Y}{\sigma_Y}\right]^2\right\}, \quad -\infty < y < \infty, \quad \sigma_Y > 0.$$

(3) The conditional probability density function of the random variable X, given that $Y = y$, is

$$h_1(x \mid y) = h_1(x; \mu_X, \sigma_X \mid y; \mu_Y, \sigma_Y), \quad -\infty < x < \infty$$

$$= \frac{f(x, y; \mu_X, \mu_Y, \sigma_X, \sigma_Y)}{f_2(y; \mu_Y, \sigma_Y)}$$

$$= \frac{\dfrac{1}{2\pi\sigma_X\sigma_Y\sqrt{1-\rho^2}} \exp\left\{ -\dfrac{1}{2(1-\rho^2)} \left[\left(\dfrac{x-\mu_X}{\sigma_X}\right)^2 - 2\rho\left(\dfrac{x-\mu_X}{\sigma_X}\right) \cdot \left(\dfrac{y-\mu_Y}{\sigma_Y}\right) + \left(\dfrac{y-\mu_Y}{\sigma_Y}\right)^2 \right] \right\}}{\dfrac{1}{\sqrt{2\pi}\,\sigma_Y} \exp\left\{ -\dfrac{1}{2}\left[\dfrac{y-\mu_Y}{\sigma_Y}\right]^2 \right\}}, \quad -\infty < x < \infty, -\infty < y < \infty$$

$$= \frac{1}{\sqrt{2\pi}\,\sigma_X\sqrt{1-\rho^2}} \exp\left\{ -\frac{1}{2(1-\rho^2)} \left[\left(\frac{x-\mu_X}{\sigma_X}\right)^2 - 2\rho\left(\frac{x-\mu_X}{\sigma_X}\right) \cdot \left(\frac{y-\mu_Y}{\sigma_Y}\right) + \rho^2\left(\frac{y-\mu_Y}{\sigma_Y}\right)^2 \right] \right\}, \quad \begin{array}{l} -\infty < x < \infty \\ -\infty < y < \infty. \end{array}$$

$$= \frac{1}{\sqrt{2\pi}\,\sigma_X\sqrt{1-\rho^2}}$$

$$\cdot \exp\left\{ -\frac{1}{2\sigma_X{}^2(1-\rho^2)} \left[(x-\mu_X)^2 - 2\rho\sigma_X(x-\mu_X) \right. \right.$$

$$\left. \left. \cdot \left(\frac{y-\mu_Y}{\sigma_Y}\right) + \rho^2\sigma_X{}^2\left(\frac{y-\mu_Y}{\sigma_Y}\right)^2 \right] \right\},$$

$$-\infty < x < \infty, \; -\infty < y < \infty.$$

Therefore,

$$h_1(x \mid y) = \frac{1}{\sqrt{2\pi}\,\sigma_X\sqrt{1-\rho^2}}$$

$$\cdot \exp\left\{ -\frac{1}{2\sigma_X{}^2(1-\rho^2)} \left[(x-\mu_X) - \rho\sigma_X\left(\frac{y-\mu_Y}{\sigma_Y}\right) \right]^2 \right\}, \quad \begin{array}{l} -\infty < x < \infty \\ -\infty < y < \infty. \end{array}$$

Similarly, we can compute the conditional probability density of Y, given that $X = x$:

$$h_2(y \mid x) = \frac{1}{\sqrt{2\pi}\,\sigma_Y\sqrt{1-\rho^2}}$$

$$\cdot \exp\left\{ -\frac{1}{2\sigma_Y{}^2(1-\rho^2)} \left[(y-\mu_Y) - \rho\sigma_Y\left(\frac{x-\mu_X}{\sigma_X}\right) \right]^2 \right\}.$$

$$-\infty < x < \infty, \; -\infty < y < \infty.$$

Thus, the conditional density $h_1(x|y)$ is a univariate normal probability density function, with mean $\mu_X + \rho\sigma_Y(y - \mu_X)/\sigma_X$ and variance $\sigma_X^2(1 - \rho^2)$. That is,

$$h_1(x|y) = \frac{1}{\sqrt{2\pi}\sqrt{\sigma_X^2(1 - \rho^2)}}$$

$$\cdot \exp\left(-\frac{1}{2}\left\{\frac{x - \left[\mu_X + \rho\sigma_X\left(\frac{y - \mu_Y}{\sigma_Y}\right)\right]}{\sqrt{\sigma_X^2(1 - \rho^2)}}\right\}^2\right),$$

$$-\infty < x < \infty, \quad -\infty < y < \infty.$$

An analogous interpretation can be given to the conditional probability density $h_2(y|x)$.

(4) Special cases:
  (a) If the coefficient of correlation is zero, $\rho_{XY} = 0$, then X and Y are independently distributed. That is,

$$f(x, y; \mu_X, \mu_Y, \sigma_X, \sigma_Y) = \frac{1}{2\pi\sigma_X\sigma_Y} \exp\left\{-\frac{1}{2}\left[\frac{x - \mu_X}{\sigma_X}\right]^2 + \left[\frac{y - \mu_Y}{\sigma_Y}\right]^2\right\}$$

$$= \frac{1}{\sqrt{2\pi}\,\sigma_X}\exp\left\{-\frac{1}{2}\left[\frac{x - \mu_X}{\sigma_X}\right]^2\right\} \cdot \frac{1}{\sqrt{2\pi}\,\sigma_Y}$$

$$\cdot \exp\left\{-\frac{1}{2}\left[\frac{y - \mu_Y}{\sigma_Y}\right]^2\right\}$$

$$= f_1(x; \mu_X, \sigma_X)f_2(y; \mu_Y, \sigma_Y).$$

  (b) If $\rho_{XY} \neq 0$, it is clear from part (3) that $h_1(x|y)$ and $h_2(y|x)$ depend on y and x, respectively.
Thus, in the bivariate normal distribution, we have independence if and only if the coefficient of correlation is zero.

(5) In this part, we shall show that, if $f(x, y; \mu_X, \mu_Y, \sigma_X, \sigma_Y)$ equals a constant, then the contour lines for this density are ellipses. It has been shown that $f(x, y; \mu_X, \mu_Y, \sigma_X, \sigma_Y)$ can be reduced to

$$z(u, v, \rho) = \frac{1}{2\pi\sqrt{1 - \rho^2}}$$

$$\cdot \exp\left\{-\frac{1}{2(1 - \rho^2)}(u - \rho v)^2 - \frac{v^2}{2}\right\},$$

$$-\infty < v < \infty, \quad -\infty < u < \infty, \quad -1 < \rho < 1.$$

It is clear that the exponent of this density is always negative and that its constant is always positive. In fact, $z(u, v; \rho)$ will attain a maximum when $u = 0 = v$. Thus, if we let

$$\frac{1}{2\pi\sqrt{1-\rho^2}}\exp\left\{-\frac{1}{2(1-\rho^2)}(u-\rho v)^2 - \frac{v^2}{2}\right\} = c$$

or equivalently,

$$\frac{(u-\rho v)^2}{2(1-\rho^2)} + \frac{v^2}{2} = -\ln 2\pi - \frac{1}{2}\ln(1-\rho^2) - \ln c,$$

we have

$$\frac{(u-\rho v)^2}{-(1-\rho^2)2\ln[2\pi c\sqrt{1-\rho^2}]} + \frac{v^2}{-2\ln[2\pi c\sqrt{1-\rho^2}]} = 1.$$

Then

$$\frac{(u-\rho v)^2}{\ln\left[\dfrac{1}{2\pi c\sqrt{1-\rho^2}}\right]^{2(1-\rho^2)}} + \frac{v^2}{\ln\left[\dfrac{1}{2\pi c\sqrt{1-\rho^2}}\right]^2} = 1,$$

which is in the form of the equation of an ellipse. Note that, if $\rho = 0$, the above expression reduces to the circle

$$u^2 + v^2 = \ln\left[\frac{1}{2\pi c}\right]^2,$$

which has its center at the origin and a radius of $\sqrt{2\ln[1/2\pi c]}$. Furthermore, it is clear that, if $\rho = 1$, the bivariate normal density function is indeterminate; however, if ρ approaches ± 1, the ellipses degenerate into a line, as shown below. This is consistent with our earlier remarks regarding the interpretation of the coefficient of correlation: namely, the random variables are linearly related. This relation is illustrated as follows. The expression

$$-\frac{1}{2(1-\rho^2)}(u^2 - 2\rho uv + v^2) - \ln(2\pi\sqrt{1-\rho^2}) - \ln c = 0$$

can be written as

$$(u-\rho v)^2 = (\rho^2 - 1)\{v^2 + \ln[4\pi^2 c^2(1-\rho^2)]\}$$

or

$$u - \rho v = \pm\sqrt{\rho^2 - 1}\{v^2 + \ln[4\pi^2 c^2(1-\rho^2)]\}^{1/2}.$$

Taking the limit of both sides of the above equation as $\rho \to \pm 1$, we have the desired result:

$$u - v = 0 \quad \text{and} \quad u + v = 0.$$

(6) Let X and Y be independent normally distributed random variables with means μ_X and μ_Y and variances σ_X^2 and σ_Y^2, respectively. We shall show that $U = X + Y$ is also normally distributed with mean $\mu_X + \mu_Y$ and variance $\sigma_X^2 + \sigma_Y^2$. Let $U = X + Y$ and $V = Y$. Thus, $x = u - v$, $v = y$, and $|J| = 1$. Because X and Y are independent, we can use part (4) and write

$$z_1(u) = \int_{-\infty}^{\infty} f_1(u-v) f_2(v) |J| \, dv, \quad -\infty < u < \infty$$

$$= \int_{-\infty}^{\infty} \frac{1}{\sigma_X \sqrt{2\pi}} e^{-(1/2\sigma_X^2)[(u-v)-\mu_X]^2} \cdot \frac{1}{\sigma_y \sqrt{2\pi}} e^{-(1/2\sigma_y^2)(v-u_y)^2} \, dv, \quad -\infty < u < \infty$$

$$= \frac{1}{2\pi\sigma_X \sigma_Y} \int_{-\infty}^{\infty} \exp\left\{-\frac{1}{2}\left[\frac{(u-v)-\mu_X}{\sigma_X}\right]^2 - \frac{1}{2}\left(\frac{v-u_y}{\sigma_y}\right)^2\right\} \, dv, \quad -\infty < u < \infty.$$

The exponent can be written as follows:

$$-\frac{1}{2}\left[\frac{(u-v)-\mu_X}{\sigma_X}\right]^2 - \frac{1}{2}\left(\frac{v-\mu_Y}{\sigma_Y}\right)^2$$

$$= -\frac{1}{2}\left[\frac{u^2 - 2uv + v^2 + 2\mu_X v + \mu_X^2}{\sigma_X^2}\right.$$

$$\left. + \frac{v^2 - 2v\mu_Y + \mu_Y^2}{\sigma_Y^2} - \frac{2\mu_X u}{\sigma_X^2}\right]$$

$$= -\frac{1}{2}\left\{\left[v^2\left(\frac{1}{\sigma_X^2} + \frac{1}{\sigma_Y^2}\right) - 2v\left(\frac{u-\mu_X}{\sigma_X^2} + \frac{\mu_Y}{\sigma_Y^2}\right)\right]\right.$$

$$\left. + \left(\frac{u^2 - 2\mu_X u + \mu_X^2}{\sigma_X^2} + \frac{\mu_Y^2}{\sigma_Y^2}\right)\right\}$$

$$= -\frac{1}{2}\left\{v^2\left(\frac{\sigma_Y^2 + \sigma_X^2}{\sigma_X^2 \sigma_Y^2}\right) - 2v\left(\frac{\sigma_Y^2 u - \sigma_Y^2 \mu_X + \sigma_X^2 \mu_Y}{\sigma_X^2 \sigma_Y^2}\right)\right\}$$

$$- \frac{1}{2}\left[\frac{(u-\mu_X)^2}{\sigma_X^2} + \frac{\mu_Y^2}{\sigma_Y^2}\right]$$

$$= -\frac{\sigma_X^2 + \sigma_Y^2}{2\sigma_X^2 \sigma_Y^2}\left\{v^2 - 2\left[\frac{\sigma_Y^2(u-\mu_X) + \sigma_X^2 \mu_Y}{\sigma_X^2 + \sigma_Y^2}\right]v\right\}$$

$$- \frac{1}{2}\left[\frac{(u-\mu_X)^2}{\sigma_X^2} + \frac{\mu_Y^2}{\sigma_Y^2}\right].$$

Completing the square on v, the exponent can be written as

$$-\frac{\sigma_X^2 + \sigma_Y^2}{2\sigma_X^2 \sigma_Y^2}\left\{\left[v - \frac{\sigma_Y^2(u-\mu_X) + \sigma_X^2 \mu_Y}{\sigma_X^2 + \sigma_Y^2}\right]^2 - \left[\frac{\sigma_Y^2(u-\mu_X) + \sigma_X^2 \mu_Y}{\sigma_X^2 + \sigma_Y^2}\right]^2\right\}$$

$$- \frac{1}{2}\left[\frac{(u-\mu_X)^2}{\sigma_X^2} + \frac{\mu_Y^2}{\sigma_Y^2}\right].$$

Thus,

$$z_1(u) = \frac{1}{2\pi\sigma_X\sigma_Y}\exp\left\{-\frac{1}{2}\left[\frac{(u-\mu_X)^2}{\sigma_X^2}+\frac{\mu_Y^2}{\sigma_Y^2}\right]-\left[\frac{\sigma_Y^2(u-\mu_X)+\sigma_X^2\mu_Y}{\sigma_X\sigma_Y\sqrt{\sigma_X^2+\sigma_Y^2}}\right]^2\right\}$$

$$\int_{-\infty}^{\infty}\exp\left\{-\frac{\sigma_X^2+\sigma_Y^2}{2\sigma_X^2\sigma_Y^2}\left[v-\frac{\sigma_Y^2(u-\mu_X)+\sigma_X^2\mu_Y}{\sigma_X^2+\sigma_Y^2}\right]^2\right\}\,dv,\quad -\infty<u<\infty.$$

Let

$$h=\left[v-\frac{\sigma_Y^2(u-\mu_X)+\sigma_X^2\mu_Y}{\sigma_X^2+\sigma_Y^2}\right]\frac{\sqrt{\sigma_X^2+\sigma_Y^2}}{\sigma_X\sigma_Y};$$

then

$$\frac{\sigma_X\sigma_Y}{\sqrt{\sigma_X^2+\sigma_Y^2}}\,dh=dv.$$

Hence,

$$z_1(u)=\frac{1}{\sqrt{2\pi}\sqrt{\sigma_X^2+\sigma_Y^2}}\exp\left\{-\frac{1}{2}\left[\frac{(u-\mu_X)^2}{\sigma_X^2}+\frac{\mu_Y^2}{\sigma_Y^2}\right]\right.$$

$$\left.-\left[\frac{\sigma_Y^2(u-\mu_X)+\sigma_X^2\mu_Y}{\sigma_X\sigma_Y\sqrt{\sigma_X^2+\sigma_Y^2}}\right]^2\right\}$$

$$\cdot\frac{1}{\sqrt{2\pi}}\int_{-\infty}^{\infty}e^{-(1/2)h^2}\,dh,\quad -\infty<u<\infty.$$

The exponent of e can be simplified as follows:

$$-\frac{1}{2}\left[\frac{(u-\mu_X)^2}{\sigma_X^2}+\frac{\mu_Y^2}{\sigma_Y^2}\right]-\left[\frac{\sigma_Y^2(u-\mu_X)+\sigma_X^2\mu_Y}{\sigma_X\sigma_Y\sqrt{\sigma_X^2+\sigma_Y^2}}\right]^2$$

$$=-\frac{1}{2}\left\{\frac{(u-\mu_X)^2}{\sigma_X^2}+\frac{\mu_Y^2}{\sigma_Y^2}-\frac{\sigma_Y^2(u-\mu_X)^2}{\sigma_X^2(\sigma_X^2+\sigma_Y^2)}\right.$$

$$\left.-\frac{\sigma_X^2\mu_Y^2}{\sigma_Y^2(\sigma_X^2+\sigma_Y^2)}-\frac{2(u-\mu_X)\mu_Y}{\sigma_X^2+\sigma_Y^2}\right\}$$

$$=-\frac{1}{2}\left\{(u-\mu_X)^2\left[\frac{1}{\sigma_X^2}-\frac{\sigma_Y^2}{\sigma_X^2(\sigma_X^2+\sigma_Y^2)}\right]\right.$$

$$\left.+\mu_Y^2\left[\frac{1}{\sigma_Y^2}-\frac{\sigma_X^2}{\sigma_Y^2(\sigma_X^2+\sigma_Y^2)}\right]-\frac{2\mu_Y(u-\mu_X)}{\sigma_X^2+\sigma_Y^2}\right\}$$

$$=-\frac{1}{2}\left[\frac{1}{\sigma_X^2+\sigma_Y^2}(u-\mu_X)^2-\frac{2\mu_Y(u-\mu_X)}{\sigma_X^2+\sigma_Y^2}+\frac{\mu_Y^2}{\sigma_X^2+\sigma_Y^2}\right]$$

$$=-\frac{1}{2(\sigma_X^2+\sigma_Y^2)}[(u-\mu_X)^2-2\mu_Y(u-\mu_X)+\mu_Y^2]$$

$$=-\frac{1}{2(\sigma_X^2+\sigma_Y^2)}[(u-\mu_X)-\mu_Y]^2=-\frac{1}{2}\frac{[u-(\mu_X+\mu_Y)]^2}{\sigma_X^2+\sigma_Y^2}.$$

Therefore,

$$z_1(u) = \frac{1}{\sqrt{2\pi}\sqrt{\sigma_X{}^2 + \sigma_Y{}^2}}$$

$$\cdot \exp\left\{-\frac{1}{2}\left[\frac{u - (\mu_X + \mu_Y)}{\sqrt{\sigma_X{}^2 + \sigma_Y{}^2}}\right]^2\right\}, \quad -\infty < u < \infty.$$

Thus, the random variable U is normally distributed with expected value $\mu_X + \mu_Y$ and variance $\sigma_X{}^2 + \sigma_Y{}^2$.

(7) The characteristic function of the bivariate normal distribution is

$$\phi_{YX}(t_1, t_2) = E[e^{i(t_1 X + t_2 Y)}]$$

$$= \int_{-\infty}^{\infty}\int_{-\infty}^{\infty} e^{i(t_1 x + t_2 y)} f(x, y)\, dx\, dy$$

$$= \int_{-\infty}^{\infty}\int_{-\infty}^{\infty} e^{i(t_1 x + t_2 y)} \frac{1}{2\pi\sigma_X\sigma_Y\sqrt{1 - \rho^2}}$$

$$\cdot \exp\left\{-\frac{1}{2(1 - \rho^2)}\left[\left(\frac{x - \mu_X}{\sigma_X}\right)^2 - 2\rho\left(\frac{x - \mu_X}{\sigma_X}\right)\left(\frac{y - \mu_Y}{\sigma_Y}\right)\right.\right.$$

$$\left.\left. + \left(\frac{y - \mu_Y}{\sigma_Y}\right)^2\right]\right\} dx\, dy.$$

Let

$$u = \frac{x - \mu_X}{\sigma_X}, \qquad v = \frac{y - \mu_Y}{\sigma_Y},$$

or

$$x = \sigma_X u + \mu_X, \qquad y = \sigma_Y v + \mu_Y;$$

and, as before, the Jacobian of the transformation is $J = \sigma_X \sigma_Y$. Thus,

$$\phi_{XY}(t_1, t_2) = \int_{-\infty}^{\infty}\int_{-\infty}^{\infty} \frac{e^{i(t_1\sigma_X u + t_2\sigma_Y v + t_1\mu_X + t_2\mu_Y)}}{2\pi\sqrt{1 - \rho^2}}$$

$$\cdot e^{-[1/2(1 - \rho^2)](u^2 - 2\rho uv + v^2)}\, du\, dv$$

$$= e^{i(t_1\mu_X + t_2\mu_Y)} \int_{-\infty}^{\infty}\int_{-\infty}^{\infty} \frac{e^{i(t_1\sigma_X u + t_2\sigma_Y v)}}{2\pi\sqrt{1 - \rho^2}}$$

$$\cdot e^{-[1/2(1 - \rho^2)](u^2 - 2\rho uv + v^2)}\, du\, dv$$

$$= e^{i(t_1\mu_X + t_2\mu_Y)} \int_{-\infty}^{\infty} \int_{-\infty}^{\infty} \frac{1}{2\pi\sqrt{1-\rho^2}}$$

$$\cdot\, e^{-[1/2(1-\rho^2)][u^2 - 2\rho uv + v^2 - 2(1-\rho^2)it_1\sigma_X u - 2(1-\rho^2)it_2\sigma_Y v]}du\; dv.$$

Completing the square on the exponent first on u and then on v gives us

$$-\frac{1}{2(1-\rho^2)}[u^2 - 2\rho uv + v^2 - 2(1-\rho^2)it_1\sigma_X u - 2(1-\rho^2)it_2\sigma_Y v]$$

$$= -\frac{1}{2(1-\rho^2)}\{[u - \rho v - (1-\rho^2)it_1\sigma_X]^2 + (1-\rho^2)(v - \rho it_1\sigma_X - it_2\sigma_Y)^2$$

$$- (1-\rho^2)(i^2 t_1{}^2\sigma_X{}^2 + 2\rho i^2 t_1 t_2 \sigma_X \sigma_Y + i^2 t_2{}^2\sigma_Y{}^2)\}.$$

If, in the above expression, we let

$$w_1 = \frac{u - \rho v - (1-\rho^2)it_1\sigma_X}{\sqrt{1-\rho}} \quad \text{and} \quad w_2 = v - \rho it_1\sigma_X - it_2\sigma_Y,$$

we obtain

$$-\frac{1}{2}w_1{}^2 - \frac{1}{2}w_2{}^2 - \frac{1}{2}(t_1{}^2\sigma_X{}^2 + 2\rho t_1 t_2 \sigma_X \sigma_Y + t_2{}^2\sigma_Y{}^2).$$

Because $|J| = \sqrt{1-\rho^2}$, we can write the characteristic function of the bivariate normal as follows:

$$\phi_{XY}(t_1, t_2) = e^{i(t_1\mu_X + t_2\mu_Y) - (1/2)(t_1{}^2\sigma_X{}^2 + 2\rho t_1 t_2 \sigma_X \sigma_Y + t_2{}^2\sigma_Y{}^2)}$$

$$\cdot \int_{-\infty}^{\infty} \frac{1}{\sqrt{2\pi}} e^{-(1/2)w_1{}^2}\, dw_1 \int_{-\infty}^{\infty} \frac{1}{\sqrt{2\pi}} e^{-(1/2)w_2{}^2}\, dw_2$$

$$= e^{i(t_1\mu_X + t_2\mu_Y) - (1/2)(t_1{}^2\sigma_X{}^2 + 2\rho t_1 t_2 \sigma_X \sigma_Y + t_2{}^2\sigma_Y{}^2)}.$$

Note that the property $\phi_{XY}(0, 0) = 1$ is satisfied.

(8)   We shall now use part (7) to compute the following moments:

$$\mu_{10} = \frac{\partial \phi_{XY}(t_1, t_2)}{i \, \partial t_1} \bigg|_{\substack{t_1=0 \\ t_2=0}} = (i\mu_X - \sigma_X^2 t_1 - \rho\sigma_X\sigma_Y t_2) \frac{\phi_{XY}(t_1, t_2)}{i} \bigg|_{\substack{t_1=0 \\ t_2=0}}$$

$$= \frac{i\mu_X}{i} = \mu_X = E(X);$$

$$\mu_{01} = \frac{\phi_{XY}(t_1, t_2)}{i \, \partial t_2} \bigg|_{\substack{t_1=0 \\ t_2=0}} = (i\mu_Y - \sigma_Y^2 t_2 - \rho\sigma_X\sigma_Y t_1) \frac{\phi_{XY}(t_1, t_2)}{i} \bigg|_{\substack{t_1=0 \\ t_2=0}}$$

$$= \frac{i\mu_Y}{i} = \mu_Y = E(Y);$$

$$\mu_{11} = \frac{\partial^2 \phi_{XY}(t_1, t_2)}{i^2 \, \partial t_1 \, \partial t_2} \bigg|_{\substack{t_1=0 \\ t_2=0}}$$

$$= \{[(i\mu_X - \sigma_X^2 t_1 - \rho\sigma_X\sigma_Y t_2)(i\mu_Y - \sigma_Y^2 t_2 - \rho\sigma_X\sigma_Y t_1)]$$

$$- \rho\sigma_X\sigma_Y\} \frac{\phi_{XY}(t_1, t_2)}{i^2} \bigg|_{\substack{t_1=0 \\ t_2=0}}$$

$$= \frac{1}{i^2}(i^2\mu_X\mu_Y - \rho\sigma_X\sigma_Y) = \mu_X\mu_Y + \rho\sigma_X\sigma_Y$$

$$= E(XY);$$

$$\mu_{20} = \frac{\partial^2 \phi_{XY}(t_1, t_2)}{i^2 \, \partial t_1^2}$$

$$= [(i\mu_X - \sigma_X^2 t_1 - \rho\sigma_X\sigma_Y t_2)^2 + (-\sigma_X^2)] \frac{\phi_{XY}(t_1, t_2)}{i^2} \bigg|_{\substack{t_1=0 \\ t_2=0}}$$

$$= \frac{i^2\mu_X^2 - \sigma_X^2}{i^2} = \mu_X^2 + \sigma_X^2$$

$$= E(X^2);$$

$$\mu_{02} = \frac{\partial^2 \phi_{XY}(t_1, t_2)}{i^2 \, \partial t_2^2} \bigg|_{\substack{t_1=0 \\ t_2=0}}$$

$$= [(i\mu_Y - \sigma_Y^2 t_2 - \rho\sigma_X\sigma_Y t_1)^2 + (-\sigma_Y^2)] \frac{\phi_{XY}(t_1, t_2)}{i^2} \bigg|_{\substack{t_1=0 \\ t_2=0}}$$

$$= \frac{i^2\mu_Y^2 - \sigma_Y^2}{i^2} = \mu_Y^2 + \sigma_Y^2$$

$$= E(Y^2).$$

Also, the covariance of the bivariate normal distribution is given by

$$\text{Cov}(X, Y) = E[(X - \mu_{10})(Y - \mu_{01})]$$

$$= \mu_{11} - \mu_{10}\mu_{01}$$

or

$$\text{Cov}(X, Y) = \mu_X \mu_Y + \rho\sigma_X\sigma_Y - \mu_X\mu_Y$$

$$= \rho\sigma_X\sigma_Y.$$

Therefore,

$$\rho_{X, Y} = \frac{\text{Cov}(X, Y)}{\sigma_X\sigma_Y}.$$

Thus, it is clear that the coefficient of correlation between X and Y is $\rho_{XY} = \rho$.

(9) If either t_1 or t_2 equals zero in the characteristic function of the bivariate normal distribution, then we obtain the characteristic function of the marginal distribution:

$$\phi_{XY}(t_1, 0) = e^{it_1\mu_X - (1/2)t_1^2\sigma_X^2} = \phi_X(t_1)$$

and

$$\phi_{XY}(0, t_2) = e^{it_2\mu_Y - (1/2)t_2^2\sigma_Y^2} = \phi_Y(t_2).$$

This function verifies the fact that the marginal probability densities of X and Y are normal, with parameters μ_X, σ_X and μ_Y, σ_Y, respectively.

(10) The conditional expectation of X, given $Y = y$, is computed as follows:

$$E(X \mid Y = y) = \int_{-\infty}^{\infty} x h_1(x \mid y)\, dx = \int_{-\infty}^{\infty} \frac{x}{\sqrt{2\pi}\,\sigma_X\sqrt{1 - \rho^2}}$$

$$\cdot e^{-(1/2)\{x - [\mu_X + \rho\sigma_X(y - \mu_Y/\sigma_Y)]/\sqrt{\sigma_X^2(1 - \rho^2)}\}^2}\, dx.$$

Let

$$w = \frac{x - \left[\mu_X + \rho\sigma_X\left(\dfrac{y - \mu_Y}{\sigma_Y}\right)\right]}{\sqrt{\sigma_X^2(1 - \rho^2)}},$$

or

$$x = \sqrt{\sigma_X^2(1 - \rho^2)}\, w + \mu_X + \rho\sigma_X\left(\frac{y - \mu_Y}{\sigma_Y}\right),$$

and

$$\sqrt{\sigma_X^2(1 - \rho^2)} \, dw = dx.$$

Thus,

$$E(X \mid Y = y) = \sqrt{\sigma_X^2(1 - \rho^2)} \int_{-\infty}^{\infty} \frac{w}{\sqrt{2\pi}} e^{-(1/2)w^2} \, dw$$

$$+ \mu_X + \rho \sigma_X \left(\frac{y - \mu_Y}{\sigma_Y} \right) \int_{-\infty}^{\infty} \frac{1}{\sqrt{2\pi}} e^{-(1/2)w^2} \, dw$$

$$= \mu_X + \rho \sigma_X \left(\frac{y - \mu_Y}{\sigma_Y} \right).$$

In view of the comments in part (3), this result was expected. Similarly, we can obtain

$$E[Y \mid X = x] = \mu_Y + \rho \sigma_Y \left(\frac{x - \mu_X}{\sigma_X} \right).$$

(11) In view of part (9), the regression curves of X on Y and Y on X for the bivariate normal density function are given by

$$\xi_1(y) = E(X \mid Y = y) = \mu_X + \rho \sigma_X \left(\frac{y - \mu_Y}{\sigma_Y} \right)$$

and

$$\xi_2(x) = E(Y \mid X = x) = \mu_Y + \rho \sigma_Y \left(\frac{x - \mu_X}{\sigma_X} \right)$$

respectively.

Thus, for the bivariate normal distribution, the regression curves are straight lines.

6.10   Summary

Let S be a sample space; let $X(s)$ and $Y(s)$ be two real valued functions (defined on S) that assign a real number to each element of the sample space. Then we call the pair $(X(s) = X, Y(s) = Y)$ a *two-dimensional random variable*.

Let (X, Y) be a two-dimensional random variable. If the number of possible values of (X, Y) is finite or countably infinite, then (X, Y) is called a *two-dimensional discrete random variable*. If (X, Y) can assume all values in some uncountable (nondenumerable) subset of the Euclidean plane, then (X, Y) is called a *two-dimensional continuous random variable*.

Let (X, Y) be a two-dimensional discrete random variable. A function $f(x_i, y_j)$ is called the *joint probability density function* of the random variable (X, Y) if

(1) $f(x_i, y_j) \geq 0$ for all $(x_i, y_j) \in R_{X, Y}$

(2) $\displaystyle\sum\sum_{(x_i, y_j) \in R_{X,Y}} f(x_i, y_j) = 1$

for $i = 1, 2, \ldots, n, \ldots$ and $j = 1, 2, \ldots, k, \ldots$. If (X, Y) is a two-dimensional continuous random variable, then a function $f(x, y)$ is called the *joint probability density function* of the random variable (X, Y) if

(1) $f(x, y) \geq 0$ for all $(x, y) \in R_{X, Y}$

(2) $\displaystyle\iint_{R_{X,Y}} f(x, y)\, dx\, dy = 1.$

The *cumulative distribution function*, $F(x, y)$, of a two-dimensional random variable, (X, Y), is defined by

$$F(x, y) = Pr(X \leq x, Y \leq y).$$

If (X, Y) is of the discrete type, then

$$F(x, y) = Pr(X \leq x, Y \leq y) = \sum_{y_i \leq y} \sum_{x_i \leq x} f(x_i, y_j);$$

and, if (X, Y) is of the continuous type, then

$$F(x, y) = Pr(X \leq x, Y \leq y) = \int_{-\infty}^{y} \left\{ \int_{-\infty}^{x} f(t, s)\, dt \right\} ds.$$

$F(x, y)$ possesses the following properties:

(1) $F(\infty, \infty) = 1$;
(2) $F(-\infty, y) = F(x, -\infty) = 0$;
(3) $F(x, y)$ is a monotone nondecreasing function in each variable;
(4) $F(x, y)$ is continuous, at least from the right, in each variable;
(5) for all real values, x_1, x_2 $(x_1 < x_2)$ and y_1, y_2 $(y_1 < y_2)$, the relation $F(x_2, y_2) - F(x_1, y_2) - F(x_2, y_1) + F(x_1, y_1) \geq 0$ is satisfied;
(6) if the first and second partial derivatives of $F(x, y)$ exist, then

$$\frac{\partial^2 F(x, y)}{\partial x\, \partial y} = f(x, y).$$

Let $f(x_i, y_j)$ be the probability density function of the discrete random variable (X, Y). The *marginal probability density functions* of the variates X and Y are given by

$$f_1(x_i) = \sum_{j=1}^{\infty} f(x_i, y_j) \quad \text{and} \quad f_2(y_j) = \sum_{i=1}^{\infty} f(x_i, y_j),$$

respectively. If $f(x, y)$ is the probability density function of the continuous random variable (X, Y), then the *marginal densities* of the variates X and Y are given by

$$f_1(x) = \int_{-\infty}^{\infty} f(x, y)\, dy \quad \text{and} \quad f_2(y) = \int_{-\infty}^{\infty} f(x, y)\, dx,$$

respectively.

For every i and j, we define the following probabilities,

$$h_1(x_i|y_j) = \frac{f(x_i, y_j)}{f_2(y_j)} \quad \text{and} \quad h_2(y_j|x_i) = \frac{f(x_i, y_j)}{f_1(x_i)},$$

where $f_2(y_j)$ and $f_1(x_i)$ are greater than zero. If y_j is fixed and x_i varies over all possible values, then $h_1(x_i|y_j)$ is called the *conditional probability density function* of the discrete variate, under the condition that $Y = y_j$. Similarly, if x_i is fixed and y_j varies over all possible values, then $h_2(y_j|x_i)$ is called the *conditional probability density function* of the discrete variate Y, given that $X = x_i$. Conditional probability density functions of continuous variates can be defined similarly.

The *conditional cumulative distribution functions* of the continuous random variable X, given Y, and Y, given X, are

$$F_X(x|y) = Pr(X \le x | Y \le y) = \frac{Pr(X \le x, Y \le y)}{Pr(Y \le y)}$$

and

$$F_Y(y|x) = Pr(Y \le y | X \le x) = \frac{Pr(X \le x, Y \le y)}{Pr(X \le x)},$$

respectively, provided $Pr(Y \le y) > 0$ and $Pr(X \le x) > 0$.

Two random variables X and Y are said to be *independent* (*mutually independent*) if

$$F(x, y) = F_1(x)F_2(y)$$

is satisfied for every real pair of numbers (x, y).

Let $f(x, y)$ be the joint probability density function of the random variable (X, Y). If (X, Y) is of the continuous type, then X and Y are independent random variables if and only if

$$f(x, y) = f_1(x)f_2(y)$$

for all real (x, y).

One function of two discrete random variables was studied, as were two functions of two continuous random variables. More precisely, let $f(x, y)$ be the joint probability density function of the continuous random variable (X, Y). Suppose that

$$U = g_1(X, Y) \quad \text{and} \quad V = g_2(X, Y),$$

such that g_1 and g_2 define a one-to-one transformation of the random variable (X, Y) and that the transformation has continuous first partial derivatives, with respect to x and y. Then the joint probability density function of the variate (U, V) is given by

$$z(u, v) = f[z_1^{-1}(u, v), z_2^{-1}(u, v)]|J|,$$

where $x = z_1^{-1}(u, v)$, $y = z_2^{-1}(u, v)$, and the Jacobian $|J| \neq 0$. The joint probability density function of the discrete type was also studied.

Let $f(x, y)$ be the probability density function of the continuous random variable (X, Y). Then the probability densities of $U = X + Y$, $U = XY$, and $U = X/Y$ are

$$g(u) = \int_{-\infty}^{\infty} f(u - v, v) \, dv,$$

$$h(u) = \int_{-\infty}^{\infty} f\left(\frac{u}{v}, v\right) \left|\frac{1}{v}\right| dv,$$

and

$$k(u) = \int_{-\infty}^{\infty} f(uv, v)|v| \, dv,$$

respectively.

Let (X, Y) be a two-dimensional random variable with joint probability density function $f(x, y)$. The *moment of order* $k + m$ of the distribution of the variate (X, Y) is given by

$$\mu_{km} = E(X^k Y^m) = \sum_i \sum_j x_i^k y_j^m f(x_i, y_j)$$

if (X, Y) is discrete and by

$$\mu_{km} = E(X^k Y^m) = \int_{-\infty}^{\infty} \int_{-\infty}^{\infty} x^k y^m f(x, y) \, dx \, dy$$

if (X, Y) is continuous. The *central moment of order $k + m$* of the distribution of the variate (X, Y) is

$$\eta_{km} = E[X - \mu_{10})^k (Y - \mu_{01})^m].$$

The second central moment $(k = 1, m = 1)$ of the probability distribution of the variate (X, Y) is the *covariance of X and Y*; that is,

$$\eta_{11} = E[(X - \mu_{10})(Y - \mu_{01})].$$

The coefficient of correlation, ρ_{XY}, between the variates X and Y is given by

$$\rho_{XY} = \frac{\eta_{11}}{\sigma_X \sigma_Y}.$$

The coefficient of correlation, if it exists, assumes a value between -1 and $+1$. The *characteristic function* of the random variable (X, Y) is

$$\phi_{XY}(t_1, t_2) = E[e^{i(t_1 X + t_2 Y)}],$$

where t_1, t_2 are real numbers and $i = \sqrt{-1}$ is the imaginary unit. The function $\phi_{XY}(t_1, t_2)$ possesses the following properties:

(1) $\phi_{XY}(0, 0) = 1$;
(2) $|\phi_{XY}(t_1, t_2)| = 1$;
(3) $\phi_{XY}(-t_1, -t_2) = \overline{\phi_{XY}(t_1, t_2)}$, where $\overline{\phi_{XY}(t_1, t_2)}$ is the complex conjugate of $\phi_{XY}(t_1, t_2)$;
(4) if X and Y are independent random variables, then

$$\phi_{XY}(t_1, t_2) = \phi_X(t_1)\phi_Y(t_2);$$

(5) if $U = \alpha_1 X + \beta_1 Y$ and $V = \alpha_2 X + \beta_2 Y$, α_1, α_2, β_1, and β_2 are real constants, then

$$\phi_{UV}(t_1, t_2) = \phi_{XY}[t_1\alpha_1 + t_2\alpha_2), (t_1\beta_1 + t_2\beta_2)];$$

(6)   the moment of order $k_1 + k_2$ is given by

$$\frac{\partial^{k_1+k_2}\phi_{XY}(t_1, t_2)}{i^{k_1+k_2} \partial t_1{}^{k_1} \partial t_2{}^{k_2}}\bigg|_{\substack{t_1=0 \\ t_2=0}} = E(X^{k_1} Y^{k_2}) = \mu_{k_1 k_2}.$$

Let (X, Y) be a two-dimensional random variable. The *conditional expected value* of the variate X, given $Y = y_j$, is

$$E(X \mid Y = y_j) = \sum_i x_i h_1(x_i \mid y_j)$$

if (X, Y) is discrete, and

$$E(X \mid Y = y) = \int_{-\infty}^{\infty} x h_1(x \mid y) \, dx$$

if (X, Y) is of the continuous type.
   If the $E(X \mid Y = y)$ and $E(Y \mid X = x)$ exist, then

$$E[E(X \mid Y = y)] = E(X)$$

and

$$E[E(Y \mid X = x)] = E(Y).$$

The geometrical interpretation of conditional expectation is illustrated by a *regression curve*. Let the expected value of the variate X, given $Y = y_j$, and Y, given $X = x_i$, be denoted by

$$\xi_1(y_j) = E(X \mid Y = y_j) \quad \text{and} \quad \xi_2(x_i) = E(Y \mid X = x_i).$$

The graph of the collection of points $(\xi_1(y_j), y_j)$ is called the regression curve of the *random variable X on the random variable Y*. Similarly, the graph of the set of points $(x_i, \xi_2(x_i))$ is called the regression curve of *the random variable Y on the random variable X*. One can obtain similar results if the variate (X, Y) is of the continuous type.
   The bivariate normal distribution has been studied in depth.
   In this chapter, we have been concerned with a precise and comprehensive study of two random variables and their probability distributions. However, in many cases, we have to deal with random variables of more than two dimensions. It is the aim of Chapter 7 to extend the concept of a two dimensional random variable and its probability distribution function to n-dimensional random variables.

Exercises

6.1. Let

$$f(x, y) = \begin{cases} \dfrac{1}{50}(x^2 + 2y), & x = 0, 1, 2, 3 \quad \text{and} \quad y = x + 3, \\ 0, & \text{elsewhere.} \end{cases}$$

(a) Show that $f(x, y)$ satisfies the conditions of a probability density function.

(b) Sketch $f(x, y)$.

6.2. Show that the bivariate function given by

$$f(x, y) = \begin{cases} \left(\dfrac{2}{n(n + 1)}\right)^2 xy, & x, y = 1, 2, \ldots, n, \\ 0, & \text{elsewhere,} \end{cases}$$

is the joint probability density function of the random variable (X, Y). *Hint:* $\sum_{i=1}^{n} i = [n(n + 1)/2]$.

6.3. Let

$$f(x, y) = c(1 - x)(1 - y), \quad -1 \le x \le 1, \; -1 \le y \le 1.$$

Find that c that makes $f(x, y)$ the joint probability density function of the random variable (X, Y).

6.4. Find c so that

$$f(x, y) = cx(y - x), \quad 0 \le x \le 4, \, 4 \le y \le 8$$

will be a bivariate probability density function.

6.5. Let

$$f(x, y) = xe^{-xy}, \quad x \ge 0, \, y \ge 1.$$

Is $f(x, y)$ a probability density function? If not, find the proper constant to multiply with $f(x, y)$ so that it will be a probability density.

6.6. Find c so that

$$f(x, y) = cxe^{-(x^2+y)}, \quad x \geq 0, y \geq 0$$

will be the joint probability density function of the random variable (X, Y).

6.7. Prove Theorem 6.2.1.

6.8. The joint probability density function of the random variable (X, Y) is given by

$$f(x, y) = \begin{cases} \dfrac{1}{5}(3x - y), & 1 \leq x \leq 2, 1 \leq y \leq 3, \\ 0, & \text{elsewhere.} \end{cases}$$

Find the cumulative distribution function of the random variable (X, Y).

6.9. Find $F(x, y)$ of the random variable (X, Y) whose probability density function is given by

$$f(x, y) = \begin{cases} 2, & 0 \leq y \leq x \leq 1, \\ 0, & \text{elsewhere.} \end{cases}$$

6.10. In Exercises 6.1, 6.2, 6.3, and 6.4, find the cumulative distribution function of the random variable (X, Y).

6.11. Find the joint probability density function of the random variable (X, Y) if its cumulative distribution function is given by

$$F(x, y) = \begin{cases} 0, & x \leq 1 \quad \text{or} \quad y \leq 1, \\ (x-1)(2y-x-1), & 1 < x < y < 2, \\ (x-1)(3-x), & 1 < x < 2, y \geq 2, \\ (y-1)^2, & x \geq y, 1 < y < 2, \\ 1, & x \geq 2, y \geq 2. \end{cases}$$

6.12. The cumulative distribution function of the random variable (X, Y) is given by

$$F(x, y) = \begin{cases} 0, & x \leq 1 \quad \text{or} \quad y \leq 2, \\ \dfrac{1}{6}(x-1)(y-2)(3x-y+1), & 1 < x < 2, 2 < y < 4, \\ \dfrac{1}{6}(y-2)(7-y), & x \geq 2, 2 < y < 4, \\ (x-1)^2, & 1 < x < 2, y \geq 4, \\ 1, & x \geq 2, \quad y \geq 4. \end{cases}$$

Find the joint probability density function of the random variable (X, Y).

6.13. Find the marginal probability density function of the random variables X and Y if their joint probability density function is given in Exercise 6.8.

6.14. The joint probability density function of the random variable (X, Y) is given by

$$f(x, y) = \begin{cases} \frac{1}{9}(2x - y), & x, y = 0, 1, 2 \text{ such that } y \le 2x \\ 0, & \text{elsewhere.} \end{cases}$$

Find

(a) $f_1(x)$

(b) $f_2(y)$

(c) $F_1(x)$

(d) $F_2(x)$

(e) Sketch the graphs of parts (a) through (d).

6.15. Let

$$f(x, y) = \begin{cases} \left(\frac{y}{x}\right)p^x(1 - p)^{y-x}\dfrac{e^{-\lambda}\lambda^y}{y!}, & \begin{aligned} &x = 0, 1, 2, \ldots, y, \\ &y = 0, 1, 2, \ldots, \\ &\text{with } y \ge x, \end{aligned} \\ 0, & \text{elsewhere,} \end{cases}$$

where $0 \le p \le 1$. Find (a) $f_1(x)$, (b) $f_2(y)$. What is (c) $Pr(X \le r)$, $r \le y$? (d) $Pr(Y \ge k)$?

6.16. The bivariate probability density function of the random variable (X, Y) is given by

$$f(x, y) = \begin{cases} \frac{2}{19}xy^2, & 1 \le x \le 2, 2 \le y \le 3, \\ 0, & \text{elsewhere.} \end{cases}$$

Find

(a) $F(x, y)$ (b) $f_1(x)$ (c) $f_2(y)$ (d) $F_1(x)$

(e) $F_2(y)$

6.17. The joint probability density function of the random variable (X, Y) is given by

$$f(x, y) = \begin{cases} e^{-(x+y)}, & x, y > 0 \\ 0, & \text{elsewhere.} \end{cases}$$

Find

(a) $F(x, y)$

(b) $f_1(x)$

(c) $f_2(y)$

(d) $F_1(x)$

(e) $F_2(y)$

(f) $h_1(x|y)$

(g) $h_2(y|x)$

(h) $F_X(x|y)$

(i) $F_Y(y|x)$

(j) Are the random variables X and Y independent?

6.18. Prove Theorem 6.5.2.

6.19. In Exercise 6.8, are the random variables X and Y independent?

6.20. In Exercise 6.8, Find

(a) $f_1(x)$

(b) $f_2(y)$

(c) $h_1(x|y = 1)$ $h_1(x|y = 2)$ $h_1(x|y = 3)$ $h_1(x|y = 4)$ $h_1(x|y = 5)$

(d) $h_2(y|x = 1)$ $h_2(y|x = 2)$ $h_2(y|x = 3)$ $h_2(y|x = 4)$ $h_2(y|x = 5)$.

6.21. In Exercise 6.15, find

(a) $h_1(x|y)$

(b) $h_2(y|x)$

(c) Determine whether the random variables X and Y are independent.

6.22. Let the random variable (X, Y) have the following joint probability density functions:

(a) $f(x, y) = \begin{cases} \dfrac{1}{14} xy(x - y), & x = 2, 3, y = 1, 2, \\ 0, & \text{elsewhere;} \end{cases}$

(b) $f(x, y) = \begin{cases} \dfrac{1}{15}(x-3)(x-y), & x = 3, 4, 5, y = 2, 3, 4, \\ 0, & \text{elsewhere}; \end{cases}$

(c) $f(x, y) = \begin{cases} \dfrac{1}{11}x(x-y), & x = 2, 3, y = 1, 2, \\ 0, & \text{elsewhere}; \end{cases}$

(d) $f(x, y) = \begin{cases} \dfrac{y}{21}(2x-y), & x = 1, 2, 3, y = 0, 1, 2, \\ 0, & \text{elsewhere}; \end{cases}$

(e) $f(x, y) = \begin{cases} \dfrac{3}{2ab}\left(\dfrac{x^2}{a^2} + \dfrac{y^2}{b^2}\right), & 0 \le x \le a, 0 \le y \le b, \\ 0, & \text{elsewhere}; \end{cases}$

(f) $f(x, y) = \begin{cases} 3x(1-xy), & 0 \le x \le 1, 0 \le y \le 1, \\ 0, & \text{elsewhere}; \end{cases}$

(g) $f(x, y) = \begin{cases} \dfrac{2}{a^2}, & 0 \le x \le y \le a, \\ 0, & \text{elsewhere}; \end{cases}$

(h) $f(x, y) = \begin{cases} 2xe^{-(x^2+y)}, & x, y \ge 0, \\ 0, & \text{elsewhere}; \end{cases}$

(i) $f(x, y) = \begin{cases} 3, & 0 \le y \le x^2 \le 1, 0 \le x \le 1, \\ 0, & \text{elsewhere}; \end{cases}$

(j) $f(x, y) = \begin{cases} \dfrac{3}{4}, & 0 \le x^2 \le y \le 1, \\ 0, & \text{elsewhere}; \end{cases}$

(k) $f(x, y) = \begin{cases} \dfrac{3}{2}, & 0 \le y \le x^2 \le 1, \\ 0, & \text{elsewhere}; \end{cases}$

(l) $f(x, y) = \begin{cases} y, & 0 \le x, y \le 1, \\ \dfrac{1}{4}(2-y), & 0 \le x \le 1, 0 \le y \le 2, \\ 0, & \text{elsewhere}. \end{cases}$

Find

(a) $f_1(x)$

(b) $f_2(y)$

(c) $F(x, y)$

(d) $F_1(x)$

(e) $F_2(y)$

(f) $h_1(x|y)$ $h_1(x|y_0)$

(g) $h_2(y|x)$ $h_2(y|x_0)$

(h) $F_X(x|y)$

(i) $F_Y(y|x)$

(j) Determine whether the random variables X and Y are independent.

6.23. If the probability density function of the random variable X and $Y|X$ is given by

$$f(x) = \begin{cases} e^{-x}, & x \geq 0, \\ 0, & \text{elsewhere} \end{cases} \quad \text{and} \quad h_2(y|x) = \begin{cases} \dfrac{e^{-x}x^y}{y!}, & y > 0, \\ 0, & \text{elsewhere}, \end{cases}$$

respectively, find the probability density function of the random variable Y.

6.24. Let

$$f(x, y) = \frac{c}{(1 + x^2)\sqrt{1 - y^2}}, \quad -\infty < x < \infty, \; -1 < y < 1.$$

Find that c that makes $f(x, y)$ the probability density function of the random variable (X, Y). Determine if X and Y are independent.

6.25. The joint probability density function of a discrete random variable is given by

$$f(x, y) = \begin{cases} \left[\dfrac{6xy}{n(n + 1)(2n + 1)} \right]^2, & x, y = 1, 2, \ldots, n, \\ 0, & \text{elsewhere}. \end{cases}$$

Find

(a) $h_1(x|y)$ (b) $h_2(y|x)$

Hint: $\sum_{i=1}^{n} i^2 = [n(n + 1)(2n + 1)/6]$.

6.26. Let X and Y be two independent random variables each normally distributed, with parameters μ_1, σ_1^2 and μ_2, σ_2^2, respectively. Show that the probability density function of $Z = X/Y$ is the *Cauchy distribution*; that is show that

$$f(z) = \frac{\sigma_1 \sigma_2}{\pi(\sigma_1^2 + \sigma_2^2 z^2)}, \quad -\infty < z < \infty.$$

6.27. If X_1, X_2 are independent variates with joint probability density function

$$f(x_1, x_2) = \begin{cases} \dfrac{x_1^{\alpha-1} x_2^{\beta-1} e^{-(x_1+x_2)}}{\Gamma(\alpha)\,\Gamma(\beta)}, & \begin{array}{l} 0 < x_1 < \infty, \\ 0 < x_2 < \infty, \\ \alpha, \beta > 0, \end{array} \\ 0, & \text{elsewhere.} \end{cases}$$

(a) Find the joint probability density function of (Z_1, Z_2)

$$Z_1 = \frac{X_1}{X_1 + X_2}, \quad Z_2 = X_1 + X_2;$$

(b) Find the marginal probability density functions of the random variables Z_1 and Z_2.
(c) Determine whether the variates Z_1 and Z_2 are independent.
(d) If $\alpha = \beta = 1$, what is the probability that $Z_2 < Z_1$?

6.28. The bivariate probability density function of the random variable (X, Y) is given by

$$f(x, y) = \begin{cases} \dfrac{1}{9} x(y - x), & 0 \le x \le 3, \, 2 \le y \le 4, \\ 0, & \text{elsewhere.} \end{cases}$$

(a) Find the probability density function of the random variable $Z = X + Y$.
(b) What is the probability that Z will assume a value between 2.5 and 5.5?

6.29. The joint probability density function of the random variable (X, Y) is given by

$$f(x, y) = \begin{cases} \dfrac{2x}{y^2}, & 0 \le x \le 1, \, y \ge 1, \\ 0, & \text{elsewhere.} \end{cases}$$

Find the probability density function of the random variable

(a) $Z_1 = X + Y$ \hspace{2cm} (b) $Z_2 = X - Y$
(c) $Z_3 = X/Y$ \hspace{2cm} (d) $Z_4 = XY$

6.30. Show that, if the random variables X and Y are independent and follow the gamma distribution with parameters α_1 and α_2, respectively, then the functional form of the variates,

$$Z = \frac{X}{X + Y},$$

has a *beta distribution* with parameters α_1 and α_2.

6.31. Let two independent random variables, X_1 and X_2, follow the *Rayleigh distribution*; that is, for $i = 1, 2$, let

$$f(x_i) = \begin{cases} \dfrac{2}{\alpha} x_i e^{-(x_i^2/\alpha)}, & x_i \geq 0,\ \alpha > 0, \\ 0, & \text{elsewhere.} \end{cases}$$

Show that the probability density function of the ratio, V, of these variables is given by

$$f(v) = \begin{cases} \dfrac{2v}{(1 + v^2)^2}, & v \geq 0, \\ 0, & \text{elsewhere.} \end{cases}$$

6.32. Let the variate X have a uniform distribution on $(0, 1)$, and let Y have a symmetrical triangular distribution on $(0, 2)$. That is, let

$$f(y) = \begin{cases} y, & 0 \leq y \leq 1, \\ \dfrac{1}{4}(2 - y), & 1 \leq y \leq 2 \\ 0, & \text{elsewhere.} \end{cases}$$

Assume that X and Y are independent random variables, and find the probability density function of $Z = X + Y$.

6.33. Let the bivariate probability density function of the random variable (X, Y) be

$$f(x, y) = \frac{1}{2\pi} e^{-(1/2)(x^2 + y^2)}, \quad -\infty < x, y < \infty.$$

(a) Are the random variables X and Y independent?

(b) Are X and Y identically distributed?

(c) Find $Pr(X^2 + Y^2 \leq 4)$.

(d) Find the probability density functions of the random variables X^2 and Y^2.

6.34. Prove Theorem 6.7.1.

6.35. Prove Theorem 6.7.6.

Problems

6.1. An experiment consists of drawing six balls from an urn that contains nine red, eight green, and three yellow balls. Let X and Y be, respectively, the number of red and green balls drawn.

(a) Determine the joint probability density function of the random variable (X, Y). What is the

(b) $Pr(X = 3, Y = 3)$?

(c) $Pr(X = 1, Y \leq 4)$?

6.2. Let X and Y be the number of jacks and queens appearing in a bridge hand of 13 cards.

(a) Obtain the joint probability density function of the random variable (X, Y). What is the

(b) $Pr(X = 4, Y \leq 2)$?

(c) $Pr(X = 4, Y = 4)$?

(d) $Pr(X \leq 4, Y \geq 2)$?

6.3. From a standard deck of cards, 20 cards are drawn. Find the joint probability density function of X, the number of hearts drawn and Y, the number of black cards drawn:

(a) with replacement   (b) without replacement.

6.4. In Exercise 6.3, find the following probabilities:

(a) $Pr\left(X > \dfrac{1}{2}, Y \leq \dfrac{3}{4}\right)$

(b) $Pr\left(0 < X < \dfrac{3}{4}, -\dfrac{1}{2} \leq Y \leq \dfrac{1}{2}\right)$

(c) $Pr\left(X \geq \dfrac{1}{2} \middle| Y \leq -\dfrac{1}{2}\right) - Pr\left(Y \geq \dfrac{1}{2} \middle| X \leq -\dfrac{1}{2}\right)$

6.5. In Exercise 6.4, find the following probabilities:

(a) $Pr(X \le 1, Y \ge 1)$

(b) $Pr(2 \le X \le 6, Y \le 6)$

(c) $Pr(X \le 3 | Y \le 3) - Pr(Y \le 3 | X \le 3)$

6.6. In Exercise 6.5, evaluate the following probabilities:

(a) $Pr(X \ge 1, Y \ge 3)$

(b) $Pr(4 \le X \le 6, Y \le 3)$

(c) $Pr(X \le 2, Y \ge 3)$

6.7. In Exercise 6.6, obtain the following probabilities:

(a) $Pr\left(X > \frac{1}{2}, Y \ge 1\right)$

(b) $Pr(X \le 3, Y \ge 3)$

(c) $Pr\left(X < \frac{1}{2} | Y \le 1\right)$

6.8. The joint probability density function of the random variable (X, Y) is given by Table 6.P.1.
Find the cumulative distribution function of the random variable (X, Y).

Table 6.P.1

			x		
y	1	2	3	4	5
1	$\frac{1}{12}$	$\frac{1}{24}$	0	$\frac{1}{24}$	$\frac{1}{30}$
2	$\frac{1}{24}$	$\frac{1}{24}$	$\frac{1}{24}$	$\frac{1}{24}$	$\frac{1}{30}$
3	$\frac{1}{12}$	$\frac{1}{24}$	$\frac{1}{24}$	0	$\frac{1}{30}$
4	$\frac{1}{12}$	0	$\frac{1}{24}$	$\frac{1}{24}$	$\frac{1}{30}$
5	$\frac{1}{24}$	$\frac{1}{24}$	$\frac{1}{24}$	$\frac{1}{24}$	$\frac{1}{30}$

6.9. An urn contains 14 balls: four red, five white, and five blue. Six balls are drawn at random from the urn, without replacement. The joint probability density of X, the number of red balls drawn, and Y, the number of white balls drawn, is given by

$$f(x, y) = \begin{cases} \dfrac{\binom{4}{x}\binom{5}{y}\binom{5}{6-x-y}}{\binom{14}{6}}, & \begin{array}{l} x = 0, 1, 2, 3, 4, \\ y = 0, 1, 2, 3, 4, 5, \\ 1 \le x + y \le 6, \end{array} \\[4mm] 0, & \text{elsewhere.} \end{cases}$$

(a) Find the marginal probability density function of the random variables X and Y. What is the

(b) $Pr(X \le 3)$?

(c) $Pr(1 < Y \le 4)$?

6.10. In Exercise 6.16, find the following probabilities:

(a) $Pr\left(\dfrac{1}{2} \le X \le 1\right)$ (b) $Pr(Y \ge 2.5)$

6.11. A container contains 30 electrical components, 9 of which are operable, 10 of which are defective, and 11 of which are semi-defective. Fifteen components are drawn from the container, without replacement. The joint probability density function of X, the number of operable components drawn, and Y, the number of defective components drawn, is given by

$$f(x, y) = \begin{cases} \dfrac{\binom{9}{x}\binom{10}{y}\binom{11}{15-x-y}}{\binom{30}{15}}, & \begin{array}{l} x = 0, 1, 2, \ldots, 9 \\ y = 0, 1, 2, \ldots, 10 \\ 4 \le x + y \le 15. \end{array} \end{cases}$$

Find

(a) $h_1(x|y_0)$

(b) $h_2(y|x_0)$

(c) $h_1(x|y = 5)$

(d) $h_2(y|x = 5)$

(e) Are the random variables X and Y independent?

6.12. The probability densities of the random variables X and Y are given by

$$f_1(x) = \begin{cases} 2, & -\dfrac{1}{4} \le x \le \dfrac{1}{4}, \\ 0, & \text{elsewhere} \end{cases} \quad \text{and} \quad f_2(y) = \begin{cases} \dfrac{1}{2}, & 0 \le y \le 2, \\ 0, & \text{elsewhere,} \end{cases}$$

respectively.

(a) Find the probability density function of the random variable $Z = X - Y$.

(b) What is the probability that Z will assume a value greater than zero?

6.13. Let the two-dimensional random variable (X, Y) be uniformly distributed over the parallelogram with vertices $(0, 0)$, $(1, 0)$, $(1, 1)$, and $(2, 1)$. What is

(a) $Pr\left(X < \dfrac{1}{2}, \ 0 \le Y \le \dfrac{3}{4}\right)$?

(b) $Pr\left(X \ge 1, \ Y \le \dfrac{1}{2}\right)$?

(c) $Pr\left(Y \le \dfrac{1}{2} \middle| X \le 1\right)$?

(d) What is the marginal probability density function of the random variable X, defined for $0 \le x \le 2$?

6.14. In Problem 6.13, let $Z = X + Y$. Find

(a) the probability density function of Z,

(b) the cumulative distribution function of Z.

(c) Sketch $f(z)$.

(d) What is the probability that Z will assume a value less than or equal to $3/4$?

6.15. In Exercise 6.1, find the expected value of the random variable

(a) X (b) Y (c) (XY)

6.16. In Exercises 6.4, 6.5, and 6.6, find the expected value of the random variable

(a) X (b) Y (c) (XY)

6.17. In Problems and Exercises 6.8 and 6.9, find the expected value of the random variable

(a) X (b) Y (c) (XY)

6.18. The joint probability density of the discrete random variable (X, Y) is given by

Table 6.P.2

		x	
y	1	2	3
2	$\frac{1}{12}$	$\frac{1}{6}$	$\frac{1}{12}$
3	$\frac{1}{6}$	0	$\frac{1}{6}$
4	0	$\frac{1}{3}$	0

(a) Determine the marginal probability density functions of X and Y.

(b) Calculate the expected value of $X + Y$ and $X - Y$.

(c) Calculate the second central moment of (X, Y).

(d) Are X and Y independent?

6.19. In Exercises 6.1, 6.2, 6.6, and 6.8, find

(a) $\text{Var}(X)$ (b) $\text{Var}(Y)$

(c) $\text{Cov}(X, Y)$ (d) coefficient of correlation ρ_{XY}.

6.20. In Exercise 6.22, find the expected value of

(a) X (b) Y (c) (X, Y)

Find the variance of

(d) X (e) Y (f) (X, Y)

(g) Find $\text{Cov}(X, Y)$.

6.21. In Exercise 6.26, find the expected value and variance of the variate Z.

6.22. In Exercise 6.27, find the expected value and variance of

(a) Z_1 (b) Z_2 (c) (Z_1, Z_2) (d) $\mathrm{Cov}(Z_1 Z_2)$.

6.23. In Exercise 6.28, find the mean and variance of the random variable Z.

6.24. Using the bivariate probability density of the discrete random variable (X, Y) given in Problem 6.8, find the expected value and variance of $Z = (1/2)X - 3Y^2$.

6.25. Using the joint probability density functions given in Exercises 6.4, 6.8, 6.14, and 6.16, find the expected value and variance of

(a) $g(X, Y) = X^2 - 3XY + Y^2$
(b) $V = X - XY + Y^2$
(c) $Z = e^{X+Y}$

6.26. In Exercises 6.3 and 6.4, calculate the ordinary moment of order $k + m$.

6.27. If the random variables X and Y are independent and have equal variances, what is the coefficient of correlation between the random variables X and $\alpha X + Y$, where α is some constant?

6.28. In Exercise 6.1, find the characteristic function of the random variable (X, Y). Calculate μ_{10}, μ_{01}, μ_{11}, μ_{20}, and μ_{02}.

6.29. The joint probability density function of the random variable (X, Y) is given by

$$f(x, y) = \begin{cases} \dfrac{1}{25} xy, & 0 \le x \le 2, 0 \le y \le 5, \\ 0, & \text{elsewhere.} \end{cases}$$

Find the characteristic function of the random variable (X, Y). Calculate μ_{10}, μ_{01}, μ_{11}, μ_{20}, μ_{02}, and ρ_{XY}.

6.30. In Problem 6.8, calculate

(a) $E(X \mid Y = 3)$ (b) $E(X \mid Y = 5)$
(c) $E(Y \mid X = 3)$ (d) $E(Y \mid X = 5)$

6.31. In Problem 6.31, calculate

(a) $E(X \mid Y = y_0)$ (b) $E(Y \mid X = x_0)$
(c) $E\{E(X \mid Y = y_0)\}$ (d) $E\{E(Y \mid X = x_0)\}$

6.32. In Exercise 6.22, calculate

    (a) $E(X \mid Y = y_0)$ (b) $E(Y \mid X = x_0)$ (c) $E\{E(X \mid Y = y_0)\}$

6.33. In Problem 6.18, calculate

    (a) the regression curve of the random variable X on the random variable Y

    (b) the regression curve of the random variable Y on the random variable X

    (c) Sketch parts (a) and (b).

6.34. Find and sketch the regression curves of X on Y and Y on X for the continuous bivariate distribution given in Exercises 6.3, 6.4, and 6.22 (k), (l).

6.35. The joint density of the random variable is given by

$$f(x, y) = \begin{cases} 2xe^{-(x^2 + y)}, & x, y \geq 0, \\ 0, & \text{elsewhere.} \end{cases}$$

Find and sketch the regression curves of X on Y and Y on X.

Suggested Supplementary Reading

Drake, A. W. *Fundamentals of Applied Probability Theory.* New York: McGraw-Hill Book Company, Inc., 1967.

Feller, W. *An Introduction to Probability Theory and Its Applications.* Vol. 1, 2nd ed. New York: John Wiley and Sons, Inc., 1960.

Fisz, M. *Probability Theory and Mathematical Statistics.* 3rd ed. New York: John Wiley and Sons, Inc., 1962.

Goldberg, S. *Probability: An Introduction.* Englewood Cliffs, New Jersey: Prentice-Hall, Inc., 1960.

Harris, B. *Theory of Probability.* Reading, Massachusetts: Addison-Wesley Publishing Company, Inc., 1966.

Meyer, P. L. *Introduction to Probability and Statistical Applications.* Reading, Massachusetts: Addison-Wesley Publishing Company, Inc., 1965.

Papoulis, A. *Probability Random Variables and Stochastic Processes.* New York: McGraw-Hill Book Company, Inc., 1965.

Parzen, E. *Modern Probability Theory and Its Applications.* New York: John Wiley and Sons, Inc., 1960.

Sequence of Random Variables

7

7.0. Introduction

In Chapter 6, we extended the study of the one-dimensional random variable to the two-dimensional random variable and the joint probability density function. Many practical problems, involving a natural phenomenon may be characterized by more than two attributes. Thus, it is often necessary to consider n-dimensional random variables, $(X_1, X_2, \ldots, X_n)$, and their multivariate distributions. Once the transition from the univariate to the bivariate case is understood, the similar generalization of the concept to higher dimensions is readily grasped.

In this chapter, we extend the concept of a random variable and its probability density function to the n-dimensional case. To be brief, we restrict our study to the continuous case; however, many of the generalizations are illustrated with a discrete probability density function.

7.1 Multivariate Probability Density Functions

We begin our discussion with the definition of an n-dimensional continuous random variable.

Definition 7.1.0   Let S be a sample space and $X_1(s), X_2(s), \ldots, X_n(s)$ real valued functions (defined on S), each assigning a number to each element of the sample space. Then we call $(X_1(s) = X_1, X_2(s) = X_2, \ldots, X_n(s) = X_n)$ an n-dimensional discrete random variable.

Thus, the range space, $R_{X_1, X_2, \ldots, X_n}$, is the set of all possible values of $(X_1, X_2, \ldots, X_n)$, which is a subset of n-dimensional Euclidean space.

Definition 7.1.1   *Let* $(X_1, X_2, \ldots, X_n)$ *be an n-dimensional random variable. If* $(X_1, X_2, \ldots, X_n)$ *can assume all values in some noncountable (nondenumerable) set of the n-dimensional Euclidean space, then we call* $(X_1, X_2, \ldots, X_n)$ *an* n-dimensional continuous random variable.

The range space of the n-dimensional variate $(X_1, X_2, \ldots, X_n)$ is the set of all possible values of $(X_1, X_2, \ldots, X_n)$, which is a subset of the n-dimensional Euclidean space. For example, if (X, Y, Z) assumes values from the subset $E_1 \subset E$, where $E_1 = \{(x, y, z): x_1 \leq x \leq x_2, y_1 \leq y \leq y_2, z_1 \leq z \leq z_2\}$, we would say that (X, Y, Z) is a three-dimensional continuous random variable, the range space of which is a rectangular parallelepiped, a subset of the three-dimensional Euclidean space. As in the bivariate case, our objective is to obtain probabilities than the n-dimensional random variable will assume certain values. For example, if E_1 is the set above $Pr[(X, Y, Z)$ in $E_1] = Pr[x_1 \leq X \leq x_2, y_1 \leq Y \leq y_2, z_1 \leq Z \leq z_2]$, the probability that the values which X, Y, and Z assume simultaneously lies in the set $E_1 \subset E$. The mathematical function that is needed to calculate such a probability is defined in Definition 7.1.2.

Definition 7.1.2   *Let* $(X_1, X_2, \ldots, X_n)$ *be an n-dimensional continuous random variable. A function* $f(x_1, x_2, \ldots, x_n)$ *is called a* multivariate *or* joint probability density function *of the random variable* $(X_1, X_2, \ldots, X_n)$ *if the following conditions are satisfied:*

(1) $f(x_1, x_2, \ldots, x_n) \geq 0$ for all $(x_1, x_2, \ldots, x_n) \in R_{X_1, X_2, \ldots, X_n}$;

(2) $\iint \ldots \int f(x_1, x_2, \ldots, x_n) dx_1 \, dx_2 \cdots dx_n = 1,$

$R_{X_1, X_2, \ldots, X_n}$

where the integration is performed over $R_{X_1, X_2, \ldots, X_n}$, *in which* $(X_1, X_2, \ldots, X_n)$ *assumes all values.*

Furthermore, for all real valued pairs, $(a_i b_i)$, $i = 1, 2, \ldots n$, such that $a_i < b_i$, we have

$$Pr(a_1 \leq X_1 \leq b_1, a_2 \leq X_2 \leq b_2, \ldots, a_n \leq X_n \leq b_n)$$

$$= \int_{a_n}^{b_n} \cdots \int_{a_2}^{b_2} \int_{a_1}^{b_1} f(x_1, x_2, \ldots, x_n) \, dx_1 \, dx_2 \ldots dx_n.$$

Thus, with the aid of the multivariate density function, we can calculate various probabilities, such as

$$Pr[(X, Y, Z) \in E_1] = \iiint_{E_1} f(x, y, z) \, dz \, dy \, dx$$

$$= \int_{x_1}^{x_2} \int_{y_1}^{y_2} \int_{z_1}^{z_2} f(x, y, z) dz \, dy \, dx$$

$$= Pr[x_1 \le X \le x_2, y_1 \le Y \le y_2, z_1 \le Z \le z_2].$$

Similar definitions can be given for the discrete case.

Example 7.1.1   The function defined by

$$f(x_1, x_2, x_3, \beta) = \begin{cases} \dfrac{1}{\beta^3} e^{-(1/\beta)(x_1 + x_2 + x_3)}, & x_1, x_2, x_3 > 0, \beta > 0, \\ \\ 0, & \text{elsewhere,} \end{cases}$$

is a probability density function of the three-dimensional variate (X_1, X_2, X_3) because it satisfies the above requirements. Thus,

(a) $Pr(X_1 \le 2, X_2 \ge 3, X_3 < 1) = \int_0^2 \int_3^\infty \int_0^1 f(x_1, x_2, x_3) \, dx_3 \, dx_2 \, dx_1$

$$= \int_0^2 \int_3^\infty \int_0^1 \frac{1}{\beta^3} e^{-(1/\beta)(x_1 + x_2 + x_3)} dx_3 \, dx_2 \, dx_1$$

$$= e^{-(6/\beta)} - e^{-(5/\beta)} - e^{-(4/\beta)}$$
$$+ e^{-(3/\beta)}, \quad \beta > 0.$$

(b) $Pr\left(X_1 + X_2 < 3, X_3 \le \dfrac{1}{2}\right)$

$$= \int_0^{1/2} \int_0^3 \int_0^{3-x_2} f(x_1, x_2, x_3) dx_1 \, dx_2 \, dx_3$$

$$= \int_0^{1/2} \int_0^3 \int_0^{3-x_2} \frac{1}{\beta^3} e^{-(1/\beta)(x_1 + x_2 + x_3)} dx_1 \, dx_2 \, dx_3$$

$$= \frac{1}{\beta^2} \left\{ \int_0^{1/2} e^{-(x_3/\beta)} \int_0^3 (e^{-(x_2/\beta)} - e^{-(3/\beta)}) dx_1 \, dx_3 \right\}$$

$$= \frac{1}{\beta^2} \{(\beta - \beta e^{-(3/\beta)} - 3e^{-(3/\beta)}) \int_0^{1/2} e^{-(x_3/\beta)} dx_3\}$$

$$= (1 - e^{-(1/2\beta)}) + \frac{1}{\beta}(3 + \beta)(e^{-(7/2\beta)} - e^{-(3/\beta)})$$

$$= (1 - e^{-(1/2\beta)})\left(1 - \frac{\beta + 3}{\beta} e^{-(3/\beta)}\right), \quad \beta > 0.$$

7.1.1 The Multinomial Distribution   A discrete distribution of importance is a generalization of the Bernoulli distribution, which was discussed in Section 2.3. Consider an experiment consisting of n independent trials, where each trial can have one of several outcomes. Let $x_1, x_2, \ldots, x_k$ denote the possible outcomes of each trial, with $p_1, p_2, \ldots, p_k$ being their corresponding probabilities of occurrence, subject to the conditions

$$\sum_{i=1}^{k} p_i = 1, \quad p_i \geq 0 \quad (i = 1, 2, \ldots, k).$$

As a result of n independent trials of the experiment, what is the total probability of obtaining exactly x_1 results of the first type, x_2 of the second type, $\ldots, x_k$ of the kth type, where $x_1 + x_2 + \cdots + x_k = n$? Because the trials are independent, the probability of obtaining any specific type $x_i, i = 1, 2, \ldots, k$, on a given trial is not affected by the outcome of the other trials. Thus, the probability of any sequence of outcomes is equal to the product of their separate probabilities,

$$p_1^{x_1} p_2^{x_2} \cdots p_k^{x_k}. \tag{7.1.1}$$

The total number of distinct sequences yielding the stated number of outcomes of each kind is given by

$$\binom{n}{x_1, x_2, \ldots, x_k} = \frac{n!}{x_1! \, x_2! \cdots x_k!}. \tag{7.1.2}$$

Therefore, the total probability is the product of expressions (7.1.1) and (7.1.2):

$$\frac{n!}{x_1! \, x_2! \cdots x_k!} \, p_1^{x_1} p_2^{x_2} \cdots p_k^{x_k}.$$

We formally define the multinomial distribution in Definition 7.1.3.

Definition 7.1.3   *The k-dimensional discrete random variable $(X_1, X_2, \ldots, X_k)$ is distributed as a multinomial distribution if its joint probability density function is given by*

$$f(x_1, x_2, \ldots, x_k; p_1, p_2, \ldots p_k, n) = \begin{cases} \dfrac{n!}{x_1! x_2! \cdots x_k!} \ p_1^{x_1} p_2^{x_2} \cdots p_k^{x_k}, \\[2mm] \qquad x_i = 0, 1, 2, \ldots, n, \\ \qquad 0 \leq p_i \leq 1, \\ \qquad i = 1, 2, \ldots, k, \\[2mm] 0, \quad \text{elsewhere}, \end{cases} \tag{7.1.3}$$

where

$$\sum_{i=1}^{k} p_i = 1 \quad \text{and} \quad \sum_{i=1}^{k} x_i = n.$$

It should be pointed out that we can replace x_k with

$$n - \sum_{i=1}^{k-1} x_i$$

and

$$p_k = 1 - \sum_{i=1}^{k-1} p_i.$$

Thus, the multinomial probability density function actually involves $k - 1$ of the x_i's because $k - 1$ of them are independent and x_k is exactly determined.

Clearly, $f(x_1, x_2, \ldots, x_k; p_1, p_2, \ldots, p_k, n) \geq 0$. Applying the multinomial theorem,

$$(y_1 + y_2 + \cdots + y_k)^n = \sum_{r_1, r_2, \ldots, r_k \geq 0} \binom{n}{r_1, r_2, \ldots, r_k} y_1^{r_1} y_2^{r_2} \cdots y_k^{r_k},$$

where the summation is over all nonnegative integral k-tuples such that $r_1 + r_2 + \cdots + r_k = n$, we can show that

$$\sum_{x_1, x_2, \ldots, x_k \geq 0} f(x_1, x_2, \ldots, x_k; p_1, p_2, \ldots, p_k, n) = 1.$$

Thus, if $k = 2$, the multinomial distribution reduces to the binomial distribution with $p_1 = p, p_2 = 1 - p, x_1 = x$, and $x_2 = n - x$.

Example 7.1.2   Consider the experiment of rolling 10 fair dice, in which we desire to obtain the probability of rolling four aces, two deuces, one three, two fours, and one six. Here $p_i = 1/6$, $i = 1, 2, \ldots, 6$; and, in view of the multinomial density function, we have

$$f(4, 2, 1, 2, 0, 1) = \frac{10!}{4!2!1!2!0!1!} \left(\frac{1}{6}\right)^{10}$$

$$= .0075.$$

Example 7.1.3   A type of electrical system that consists of five major components, which we will denote by X_1, X_2, X_3, X_4, and X_5, will fail to operate if any one of the five components fails. If simultaneous defects are negligible and the probabilities of failure of the components are .3, .2, .1, .3, and .1, respectively, what is the probability that a random sample of eight defective systems would consist of three due to failure of component X_1, none due to failure of X_2 and X_3, four due to failure of X_4, and one due to failure of X_5?

Solution: Assuming independent trials, we can obtain the necessary probability by applying the multinomial distribution law. Thus,

$$Pr(X_1 = 3, X_2 = 0, X_3 = 0, X_4 = 4, X_5 = 1) = \frac{8!}{3!0!0!4!1!} (.3)^3(.3)^4(.1)$$

$$= .0061.$$

7.1.2 The Multivariate Normal Distribution   In Chapter 3, we discussed and emphasized the importance of the univariate normal density function. The normal distribution in the multivariate case is of equal importance. A comprehensive presentation of this distribution is beyond the scope of this book; however, we shall define it here and refer the reader to the book of T. W. Anderson, Reference [1], which gives an extensive study of the multivariate normal distribution.

Definition 7.1.4   *The n-dimensional continuous random variable* $(X_1, X_2, \ldots, X_n)$ *is distributed as* multivariate normal *if its joint probability density function is given by*

$$f(X, P, \mu) = \frac{\sqrt{|P|}}{(2\pi)^{n/2}} e^{-(1/2)(X-\mu)^T P(X-\mu)}, \quad -\infty < x_i < \infty,$$

$$i = 1, 2, \ldots, n$$

where

(1) *X is an $n \times 1$ vector, the elements of which are random variables*
    $X = (x_1, x_2, \ldots, x_n)^T, \quad -\infty < x_i < \infty, i = 1, 2, \ldots, n$;
(2) *μ is an $n \times 1$ vector, the elements of which are constants*;
(3) *P is a positive definitive symmetric matrix, whose elements, p_{ij}, are constants;* $|P|$ *denotes the determinant of the matrix P.*

The product $(X - \mu)^T P(X - \mu)$ is called a *quadratic form* in the elements $x_i - \mu_i$, $i = 1, 2, \ldots, n$, and P is called the *matrix of the quadratic form*. If the quadratic form $(X - \mu)^T P(X - \mu)$ is positive for every nonzero vector $X - \mu$, then $(X - \mu)^T P(X - \mu)$ is called a *positive definite form* and P is called a *positive definite symmetric matrix*. The matrix P is the inverse of the covariance matrix, C, of the sequence of random variables $(X_1, X_2, \ldots, X_n)$, given by

$$C = \begin{pmatrix} \sigma_{11} & \sigma_{12} & \cdots & \sigma_{1n} \\ \sigma_{21} & \sigma_{22} & \cdots & \sigma_{2n} \\ \vdots & \vdots & & \vdots \\ \sigma_{n1} & \sigma_{n2} & \cdots & \sigma_{nn} \end{pmatrix},$$

where $\sigma_{ij} = E[(X_i - \mu_i)(X_j - \mu_j)]$ and $E[X_i] = \mu_i$. Of course, if $n = 2$, the multivariate normal density function reduces to the bivariate normal density function, which was defined in Chapter 7.

7.2 Multivariate Cumulative Distribution Functions

In this section, we shall extend the study of cumulative distribution functions to the n-dimensional random variable.

Definition 7.2.1   *The function defined by*

$$F(x_1, x_2, \ldots, x_n) = Pr(X_1 \leq x_1, X_2 \leq x_2, \ldots, X_n \leq x_n)$$

$$= \int_{-\infty}^{x_n} \int_{-\infty}^{x_{n-1}} \cdots \int_{-\infty}^{x_1} f(y_1, y_2, \ldots, y_n) dy_1 \cdots dy_{n-1} \, dy_n$$

is called the multivariate or joint cumulative distribution function *of the continuous n-dimensional random variable* $(X_1, X_2, \ldots, X_n)$, *having joint probability density function* $f(x_1, x_2, \ldots, x_n)$.

Theorem 7.2.1 states the properties of the multivariate cumulative distribution function, which are completely analogous to the univariate and bivariate cases.

Theorem 7.2.1   If $F(x_1, x_2, \ldots, x_n)$ is the joint cumulative distribution function of the random variable $(X_1, X_2, \ldots, X_n)$, then $F(x_1, x_2, \ldots, x_n)$ has the following properties:

(1) $F(\infty, \infty, \ldots, \infty) = 1$;

(2) $F(x_1, x_2, \ldots, x_n) = 0$ if at least one of the x_i's is $-\infty$;

(3) $F(x_1, x_2, \ldots, x_n)$ is monotone nondecreasing in each variate separately;

(4) $F(x_1, x_2, \ldots, x_n)$ is continuous from the right in each variate separately.

It is also possible to obtain the joint probability density function of $F(x_1, x_2, \ldots, x_n)$ of the continuous n-dimensional random variable $(X_1, X_2, \ldots, X_n)$. That is, if $F(x_1, x_2, \ldots, x_n)$ is continuous and if its partial derivatives exist for all x_i's, then

$$\frac{\partial^n}{\partial x_1, \partial x_2, \ldots, \partial x_n} F(x_1, x_2, \ldots, x_n) = f(x_1, x_2, \ldots, x_n)$$

exists and satisfies the conditions of a multivariate probability density function.

In Section 6.2, we showed that, for the two-dimensional random variable (X, Y), we can write

$$Pr(x_1 \le X \le x_2, y_1 \le Y \le y_2)$$
$$= F(x_2, y_2) - F(x_2, y_1) - F(x_1, y_2) + F(x_1, y_1). \quad (7.2.1)$$

A generalization of Equation (7.2.1) to the n-dimensional random variable $(X_1, X_2, \ldots, X_n)$ is given by the following expression:

$$Pr(x_1 \le X_1 \le x_1 + \Delta x_1, x_2 \le X_2 \le x_2 + \Delta x_2, + \cdots + x_n \le X_n \le x_n + \Delta x_n)$$

$$= F(x_1 + \Delta x_1, x_2 + \Delta x_2, \ldots, x_n + \Delta x_n)$$

$$- \sum_{i=1}^{n} F(x_1 + \Delta x_1, \ldots, x_{i-1} + \Delta x_{i-1}, x_i, x_{i+1} + \Delta x_{i+1}, \ldots, x_n + \Delta x_n)$$

$$+ \sum_{\substack{i,j=1 \\ i<j}}^{n} F(x_1 + \Delta x_1, \ldots, x_{i-1} + \Delta x_{i-1}, x_i, x_{i+1} + \Delta x_{i+1}, \ldots,$$

$$+ \cdots + (-1)^n F(x_1, x_2, \ldots, x_n),$$

for $\Delta x_i > 0$, $i = 1, 2, \ldots, n$.

Example 7.2.1   The cumulative distribution function of the three-dimensional random variable (X_1, X_2, X_3), the joint probability density function of which is given in Example 7.1.1, is

$$F(x_1, x_2, x_3)$$
$$= Pr(X_1 \le x_1, X_2 \le x_2, X_3 \le x_3)$$
$$= \int_{-\infty}^{x_3} \int_{-\infty}^{x_2} \int_{-\infty}^{x_1} f(y_1, y_2, y_3) dy_1\, dy_2\, dy_3$$
$$= \int_{0}^{x_3} \int_{0}^{x_2} \left\{ \int_{0}^{x_1} \frac{1}{\beta^3} e^{-(1/\beta)(y_1 + y_2 + y_3)} dy_1 \right\} dy_2\, dy_3$$

$$= e^{-(1/\beta)(x_1 + x_2)} + e^{-(1/\beta)(x_2 + x_3)} + e^{-(1/\beta)(x_1 + x_3)} - e^{-(x_1/\beta)} - e^{-(x_2/\beta)}$$
$$- e^{-(x_3/\beta)} - e^{-(1/\beta)(x_1 + x_2 + x_3)} + 1.$$

Thus,

$F(x_1, x_2, x_3)$

$$= \begin{cases} 1 - e^{-(x_1/\beta)} - e^{-(x_2/\beta)} - e^{-(x_3/\beta)} + e^{-(1/\beta)(x_1+x_2)} + e^{-(1/\beta)(x_1+x_3)} \\ + e^{-(1/\beta)(x_2+x_3)} - e^{-(1/\beta)(x_1+x_2+x_3)}, \quad x_1, x_2, x_3 \geq 0, \beta > 0, \\ 0, \quad \text{elsewhere.} \end{cases}$$

It is clear that we can obtain the joint probability density function from $F(x_1, x_2, x_3)$:

$$\frac{\partial^3}{\partial x_1 \, \partial x_2 \, \partial x_3} F(x_1, x_2, x_3) = f(x_1, x_2, x_3).$$

7.3 Marginal Probability Distributions

Consider a sequence of random variables, $(X_1, X_2, \ldots, X_n)$, with multivariate probability density function $f(x_1, x_2, \ldots, x_n)$. At times, it is required to obtain the probability density function of a selected subset of the given sequence. For example, we might be interested in the trivariate probability distribution of the variate (X_2, X_3, X_5). As in the bivariate case, this probability density function can be obtained simply by integrating over the entire range of the variate $(X_1, X_4, X_6, \ldots, X_n)$ if the n-dimensional random variable is of the continuous type. Similarly, we sum over the entire range of the random variable $(X_1, X_4, X_6, \ldots, X_n)$ if it is of the discrete type. We call the joint probability density function $h_3(x_2, x_3, x_5)$ the marginal probability density function of the random variable (X_2, X_3, X_5).

Definition 7.3.1 *Let $f(x_1, x_2, \ldots, x_n)$ be the multivariate probability density function of the continuous random variable $(X_1, X_2, \ldots, X_n)$. The marginal probability density function of the variate $(X_1, X_2, \ldots, X_r)$, $r < n$ is given by*

$$h_r(x_1, x_2, \ldots, x_r) = \int_{-\infty}^{\infty} \cdots \int_{-\infty}^{\infty} f(x_1, x_2, \ldots, x_n) dx_{r+1}, \ldots, dx_n.$$

The marginal probability density function of any other subset of the sequence $(X_1, X_2, \ldots, X_n)$ is obtained in similar fashion.

Example 7.3.1   Let the k-dimensional discrete random variable $(X_1, X_2, \ldots, X_k)$ be multinomially distributed,

$$f(x_1, x_2, \ldots, x_k; p_1, p_2, \ldots, p_k, n)$$

$$= \begin{cases} \dfrac{n!}{x_1! \, x_2! \cdots x_k!} \, p_1^{x_1} p_2^{x_2} \cdots p_k^{x_k}, \\[2mm] \qquad 0 \le p_i \le 1, \ x_i = 0, 1, 2, \cdots, k, \\[2mm] 0, \quad \text{elsewhere,} \end{cases}$$

where $\sum_{i=1}^{k} p_i = 1$ and $\sum_{i=1}^{k} x_i = n$. The marginal probability mass function of $(X_1, X_2, \ldots, X_r)$, $r < k$ is obtained as follows:

$$h_r(x_1, x_2, \ldots, x_r, p_1, p_2, \ldots, p_r, n)$$

$$= \sum_{x_{r+1}, x_{r+2}, \ldots, x_k} \frac{n!}{x_1! \, x_2! \cdots x_k!} \, p_1^{x_1} p_2^{x_2} \cdots p_k^{x_k}$$

$$= \frac{n!}{x_1! \, x_2! \ldots x_r! (n - \sum_{i=1}^{r} x_i)!} \, p_1^{x_1} p_2^{x_2} \cdots p_r^{x_r} \left(1 - \sum_{i=1}^{r} p_i\right)^{(n - \sum_{i=1}^{r} x_i)}$$

$$\sum_{x_{r+1}, x_{r+2}, \ldots, x_k} \frac{(n - \sum_{i=1}^{r} x_i)!}{x_{r+1}! \, x_{r+2}! \cdots x_k!} \left[\frac{p_{r+1}}{1 - \sum_{i=1}^{r} p_i}\right]^{x_{r+1}}$$

$$\left[\frac{p_{r+2}}{1 - \sum_{i=1}^{r} p_i}\right]^{x_{r+2}} \cdots \left[\frac{p_k}{1 - \sum_{i=1}^{r} p_i}\right]^{x_k}.$$

In the above expression, we have

$$\frac{p_{r+1}}{1 - \sum_{j=1}^{r} p_j} \ge 0, \quad i = 1, 2, 3, \ldots, k - r$$

and

$$\sum_{i=1}^{k-r} \frac{p_{r+i}}{1 - \sum_{j=1}^{r} p_j} = 1,$$

with the assumption that

$$\left(1 - \sum_{j=1}^{r} p_j\right) > 0.$$

Thus, we have adjusted the sum in $h_r(x_1, x_2, \ldots, x_r; p_1, p_2, \ldots, p_r, n)$ to be unity because we are simply summing the multinomial probability density function. Hence, the marginal probability density function of the r-dimensional random variable is

$h_r(x_1, x_2, \ldots, x_r, p_1, p_2, \ldots, p_r, n)$

$$= \begin{cases} \dfrac{n!}{x_1! \, x_2! \cdots x_r!(n - \sum_{i=1}^{r} x_i)!} \, p_1^{x_1} p_2^{x_2} \cdots p_r^{x_r} \left[1 - \displaystyle\sum_{j=1}^{r} p_j\right]^{(n - \sum_{i=1}^{r} x_i)} & x_i = 0, 1, 2, \ldots, r, \\ 0, & \text{elsewhere.} \end{cases}$$

Given the multivariate cumulative distribution function $F(x_1, x_2, \ldots, x_n)$ of the random variable $(X_1, X_2, \ldots, X_n)$, one can obtain various marginal cumulative distribution functions. For example, the marginal cumulative distribution function of $(X_1, X_2, \ldots, X_k)$, $k < n$, is $G_k(x_1, x_2, \ldots, x_k)$. That is,

$$Pr(X_1 \leq x_1, X_2 \leq x_2, \ldots, X_k \leq x_k) = Pr(X_1 \leq x_1, X_2 \leq x_2, \ldots,$$
$$X_k \leq x_k, X_{k+1} \leq \infty, \ldots, X_n \leq \infty)$$

$$= F(x_1, x_2, \ldots, x_k, \infty, \infty \cdots \infty)$$

$$= G_k(x_1, x_2, \ldots, x_k).$$

The marginal cumulative distribution function of any subset of the variates $X_1, X_2, \ldots, X_n$ is obtained in a similar fashion.

Example 7.3.2 Using the cumulative distribution function of the trivariate random variable (X_1, X_2, X_3) given in Example 7.2.1, we obtain the following marginal cumulative distribution functions:

(a) $G_1(x_1) = Pr(X_1 \leq x_1, X_2 \leq \infty, X_3 \leq \infty)$

$\qquad = F(x_1, \infty, \infty)$

$\qquad = 1 - e^{(x_1/\beta)};$

(b) $G_2(x_1, x_3) = Pr(X_1 \leq x_1, X_2 \leq \infty, X_3 \leq x_3)$

$\qquad\qquad = F(x_1, \infty, x_3)$

$\qquad\qquad = 1 - e^{-(x_1/\beta)} - e^{-(x_3/\beta)} + e^{-(1/\beta)(x_1 + x_3)}.$

Thus,

$$G_1(x_1) = \begin{cases} 1 - e^{-(x_1/\beta)}, & x_1 \geq 0, \beta > 0, \\ 0, & \text{elsewhere,} \end{cases}$$

and

$$G_2(x_1, x_3) = \begin{cases} 1 - e^{-(x_1/\beta)} - e^{-(x_3/\beta)} + e^{-(1/\beta)(x_1 + x_3)}, & x_1, x_3 \geq 0, \beta > 0, \\ 0, & \text{elsewhere.} \end{cases}$$

7.4 Conditional Probability Density and Cumulative Distribution Functions

We begin by generalizing the basic definitions introduced in Section 6.4 for the bivariate random variable to the *n*-dimensional case.

Definition 7.4.1   *Let* $f(x_1, x_2, \ldots, x_n)$ *be the multivariate density function of the continuous random variable* $(X_1, X_2, \ldots, X_n)$. *The* conditional probability density function *of the random variable* $(X_1, X_2, \ldots, X_r)$, $r < n$, *given* $(X_{r+1}, X_{r+2}, \ldots, X_n)$, *is defined by*

$$g_r(x_1, x_2, \ldots, x_r \mid x_{r+1}, \ldots, x_n) = \frac{f(x_1, x_2, \ldots, x_n)}{h_{n-r}(x_{r+1}, x_{r+2}, \ldots, x_n)}. \quad (7.4.1)$$

Of course, $h_{n-r}(x_{r+1}, x_{r+2}, \ldots, x_n)$ is the marginal probability density function, which must be greater than zero, that was discussed in the previous section. Also, the conditional density (7.4.1) is nonnegative; and

$$\int_{-\infty}^{\infty} \cdots \int_{-\infty}^{\infty} g_r(x_1, x_2, \ldots, x_r \mid x_{r+1}, \ldots, x_n) dx_1, \ldots, dx_r$$

$$= \int_{-\infty}^{\infty} \cdots \int_{-\infty}^{\infty} \frac{f(x_1, x_2, \ldots, x_r, \ldots, x_n)}{h_{n-r}(x_{r+1}, x_{r+2}, \cdots, x_n)} dx_1, \ldots, dx_r$$

$$= \frac{h_{n-r}(x_{r+1}, x_{r+2}, \ldots, x_n)}{h_{n-r}(x_{r+1}, x_{r+2}, \ldots, x_n)}$$

$$= 1.$$

The conditional probability density function of any other collection of the variates, given the others, is defined similarly.

Example 7.4.1   Using the results of Example 7.3.1, we shall calculate the conditional probability density function, $g_r(x_{r+1}, \ldots, x_k | x_1, x_2, \ldots, x_r)$, of the multinomial distribution law.

$$g_{k-r}(x_{r+1}, \cdots, x_k | x_1, x_2, \cdots, x_r) = \frac{f(x_1, x_2, \ldots, x_k; p_1, p_2, \ldots, p_k, n)}{h_r(x_1, x_2, \ldots, x_r; p_1, p_2, \ldots, p_r, n)}$$

$$= \frac{\dfrac{n!}{x_1! \, x_2! \cdots x_k!} p_1^{x_1} p_2^{x_2} \cdots p_k^{x_k}}{\dfrac{n!}{x_1! \, x_2! \cdots x_r! [n - \sum_{i=1}^{r} x_i]!} p_1^{x_1} p_2^{x_2} \cdots p_r^{x_r} \left[1 - \sum_{i=1}^{r} p_i\right]^{[n - \sum_{i=1}^{r} x_i]}}$$

$$= \frac{[n - \sum_{i=1}^{r} x_i]!}{x_{r+1}! \, x_{r+2}! \cdots x_k!} \left[\frac{p_{r+1}}{1 - \sum_{i=1}^{r} p_i}\right]^{x_{r+1}} \left[\frac{p_{r+2}}{1 - \sum_{i=1}^{r} p_i}\right]^{x_{r+2}} \cdots \left[\frac{p_k}{1 - \sum_{i=1}^{r} p_i}\right]^{x_k},$$

where

$$\sum_{i=1}^{k} x_i = n, \; p_i \geq 0, \quad \text{and} \quad \sum_{i=1}^{k} p_k = 1.$$

The conditional cumulative distribution function of the continuous $(k - r)$-dimensional random variable $(X_{r+1}, X_{r+2}, \ldots, X_k)$, given $(X_1, X_2, \ldots, X_r)$, $r < k$, is given by

$$
\begin{aligned}
F(x_{r+1}, &x_{r+2}, \ldots, x_k | x_1, x_2, \ldots, x_r) \\
&= Pr(X_{r+1} \leq x_{r+1}, X_{r+2} \leq x_{r+2}, \ldots, \\
&\quad \times X_k \leq x_k | X_1 \leq x_1, X_2 \leq x_2, \ldots, X_r \leq x_r) \\
&= \frac{Pr(X_1 \leq x_1, X_2 \leq x_2, \ldots, X_k \leq x_k)}{Pr(X_1 \leq x_1, X_2 \leq x_2, \ldots, X_r \leq x_r)} \\
&= \frac{F(x_1, x_2, \ldots, x_k)}{F_r(x_1, x_2, \ldots, x_r)}.
\end{aligned}
\tag{7.4.2}
$$

Extending the mathematical reasoning used in Section 6.4 for the two-dimensional random variable to show that

$$F(x | y) = \frac{\int_{-\infty}^{x} \int_{-\infty}^{x} f(t, s) \, ds \, dt}{F(y)}, \quad F(y) > 0,$$

we can write expression (7.4.2) as follows:

$$
\begin{aligned}
F(x_{r+1}, &x_{r+2}, \ldots, x_k | x_1, x_2, \ldots, x_r) \\
&= \frac{\int_{-\infty}^{x_1} \int_{-\infty}^{x_2} \cdots \int_{-\infty}^{x_k} f(s_1, s_2, \ldots, s_k) \, ds_1 \, ds_2 \cdots ds_k}{F_r(x_1, x_2, \ldots, x_r)}
\end{aligned}
\tag{7.4.3}
$$

where $f(x_1, x_2, \ldots, x_k)$ is the multivariate probability density function of the k-dimensional continuous random variable $(X_1, X_2, \ldots, X_k)$, and $F_r(x_1, x_2, \ldots, x_r)$, $r < k$, is the marginal cumulative distribution function of the random variable $(X_1, X_2, \ldots, X_r)$. It is assumed, of course, that the denominator of Equation (7.4.3) is positive.

We have seen in Section 6.4 that we can express marginal cumulative distribution functions in terms of their conditional cumulative distributions. This result can be generalized to apply to more than two random variables. For simplicity in notation, we shall illustrate this extension using a four-dimensional random variable. Let the joint probability density function of the continuous random variable (X_1, X_2, X_3, X_4) be $f(x_1, x_2, x_3, x_4)$. The conditional distribution of the random variable (X_3, X_4), given (X_1, X_2), is

$$F(x_3, x_4 | x_1, x_2) = \int_{-\infty}^{x_3} \int_{-\infty}^{x_4} h(s_3, s_4 | x_1, x_2) ds_4 \, ds_3$$

$$= \int_{-\infty}^{x_3} \int_{-\infty}^{x_4} \frac{f(x_1, x_2, s_3, s_4)}{h_2(x_1, x_2)} ds_4 \, ds_3$$

or

$$\int_{-\infty}^{x_3} \int_{-\infty}^{x_4} f(x_1, x_2, s_3, s_4) ds_4 \, ds_3 = h_2(x_1, x_2) F(x_3, x_4 | x_1, x_2).$$

It follows that

$$\int_{-\infty}^{x_3} \int_{-\infty}^{x_4} \left\{ \int_{-\infty}^{\infty} \int_{-\infty}^{\infty} f(x_1, x_2, s_3, s_4) dx_1 \, dx_2 \right\} ds_3 \, ds_4$$

$$= \int_{-\infty}^{\infty} \int_{-\infty}^{\infty} h_2(x_1, x_2) F(x_3, x_4 | x_1, x_2) dx_1 \, dx_2$$

or

$$\int_{-\infty}^{x_3} \int_{-\infty}^{x_4} f_2(s_3, s_4) ds_3 \, ds_4 = \int_{-\infty}^{\infty} \int_{-\infty}^{\infty} h_2(x_1, x_2) F(x_3, x_4 | x_1, x_2) dx_1 \, dx_2.$$

Thus, we can express the marginal cumulative distribution function of the random variable (X_3, X_4) as a function of the conditional cumulative distribution function $F(x_3, x_4 | x_1, x_2)$,

$$F_2(x_3, x_4) = \int_{-\infty}^{\infty} \int_{-\infty}^{\infty} h_2(x_1, x_2) F(x_3, x_4 | x_1, x_2) dx_1 \, dx_2.$$

Similarly,

$$F_1(x_4) = \int_{-\infty}^{\infty} \int_{-\infty}^{\infty} \int_{-\infty}^{\infty} h_1(x_1, x_2, x_3) F(x_4 | x_1, x_2, x_3) dx_1 dx_2 \, dx_3$$

and

$$F_3(x_2, x_3, x_4) = \int_{-\infty}^{\infty} h_1(x_1)F(x_2, x_3, x_4|x_1)dx_1.$$

The conditional distribution function in the multivariate case satisfies the properties of the ordinary cumulative distribution function, as has been shown in Section 6.4 for the two-dimensional random variable.

7.5 Sequence of Independent Random Variables

Let $F(x_1, x_2, \ldots, x_n)$, $F_1(x_1), F_2(x_2), \ldots, F_n(x_n)$ represent the cumulative distribution function of the n-dimensional random variable $(X_1, X_2, \ldots, X_n)$ and the marginal cumulative distribution functions of the random variables $X_1, X_2, \ldots$, and X_n, respectively.

Definition 7.5.1   *The random variables in the sequence $(X_1, X_2, \ldots, X_n)$ are said to be* independent (mutually independent) *if*

$$F(x_1, x_2, \ldots, x_n) = F_1(x_1)F_2(x_2) \cdots F_n(x_n) \tag{7.5.1}$$

for all real n-tuples, $(x_1, x_2, \ldots, x_n)$.

Thus, the random variables in the sequence $(X_1, X_2, \ldots, X_n)$ are *independent* if the events of the sequence $\{X_1 \leq x_1\}$, $\{X_2 \leq x_2\}, \ldots, \{X_n \leq x_n\}$ are independent for every real number $x_1, x_2, \ldots$, and x_n, or

$$Pr(X_1 \leq x_1, X_2 \leq x_2, \ldots, X_n \leq x_n)$$
$$= Pr(X_1 \leq x_1)Pr(X_2 \leq x_2) \cdots Pr(X_n \leq x_n).$$

Theorem 7.5.1   Let $f(x_1, x_2, \ldots, x_n)$ be the multivariate probability density function of the n-dimensional random variable $(X_1, X_2, \ldots, X_n)$ of the continuous type. The random variables $X_1, X_2, \ldots, X_n$ are mutually independent if and only if

$$f(x_1, x_2, \ldots, x_n) = f_1(x_1)f_2(x_2) \cdots f_n(x_n),$$

where $f_1(x_1), f_2(x_2), \ldots$, and $f_n(x_n)$ are the marginal probability density functions of the variates $X_1, X_2, \ldots$, and X_n, respectively.

Proof   Applying the relation between probability density and cumulative distribution functions, as stated in Section 7.2, we have

$$\frac{\partial^n F(x_1, x_2, \ldots, x_n)}{\partial x_1 \partial x_2 \cdots \partial x_n} = f(x_1, x_2, \ldots, x_n)$$

$$= \frac{dF_1(x_1)}{dx_1} \cdot \frac{\partial F_2(x_2)}{dx_2} \cdots \frac{dF_n(x_n)}{dx_n}$$

$$= f_1(x_1)f_2(x_2) \cdots f_n(x_n).$$

Conversely,

$$F(x_1, x_2, \ldots, x_n) = \int_{-\infty}^{x_n} \int_{-\infty}^{x_{n-1}} \cdots \int_{-\infty}^{x_1} f(s_1, s_2, \ldots, s_n)ds_1\, ds_2 \cdots ds_n$$

$$= \int_{-\infty}^{x_n} \int_{-\infty}^{x_{n-1}} \cdots \int_{-\infty}^{x_1} f_1(s_1)f_2(s_2) \cdots f_n(s_n)ds_1 \cdots ds_n$$

$$= \int_{-\infty}^{x_1} f_1(s_1)ds_1 \cdots \int_{-\infty}^{x_{n-1}} f_{n-1}(s_{n-1})ds_{n-1}$$

$$\int_{-\infty}^{x_n} f_n(s_n)ds_n$$

$$= F_1(x_1) \cdots F_{n-1}(x_{n-1})F_n(x_n).$$

Of course, a similar theorem can be stated for a sequence of discrete random variables.

Example 7.5.1   Using the cumulative distribution function of the three-dimensional random variable (X_1, X_2, X_3) of the continuous type, as given in Example 7.2.1, we can obtain the marginal cumulative distributions of the variates X_1, X_2, and X_3:

$$F_1(x_1) = \begin{cases} 1 - e^{-(x_1/\beta)}, & x_1 > 0, \beta > 0, \\ 0, & \text{elsewhere,} \end{cases}$$

$$F_2(x_2) = \begin{cases} 1 - e^{-(x_2/\beta)}, & x_2 > 0, \beta > 0, \\ 0, & \text{elsewhere,} \end{cases}$$

and

$$F_3(x_3) = \begin{cases} 1 - e^{-(x_3/\beta)}, & x_3 > 0, \beta > 0, \\ 0, & \text{elsewhere.} \end{cases}$$

In view of Equation (7.5.1), we have

$$F_1(x_1)F_2(x_2)F_3(x_3) = \{1 - e^{-(x_1/\beta)}\}\{1 - e^{-(x_2/\beta)}\}\{1 - e^{-(x_3/\beta)}\}$$

$$= 1 - e^{-(x_1/\beta)} - e^{-(x_2/\beta)} - e^{-(x_3/\beta)} + e^{-(1/\beta)(x_1 + x_2)}$$

$$+ e^{-(1/\beta)(x_1 + x_3)} + e^{-(1/\beta)(x_2 + x_3)} - e^{-(1/\beta)(x_1 + x_2 + x_3)}$$

$$= F(x_1, x_2, x_3).$$

Hence, the random variables X_1, X_2, and X_3 are independent. This independence can also be shown by using Theorem 7.5.1.

Mutual independence of a sequence of random variables can equivalently be defined using the notion of the conditional probability density function, as has been illustrated for the two-dimensional case in Section 6.5. We shall show that any subsequence of random variables of a sequence of independent random variables is also independent. Let $(X_1, X_2, \ldots, X_n)$ be a sequence of n independent variates. Then, for every $r \leq n$, the random variables $X_{i_1}, X_{i_2}, \ldots, X_{i_r}, 1 \leq i_1 < i_2 < \cdots < i_r \leq n$ are also independent. For simplicity, we shall show this independence for $i_1 = 1, i_2 = 2, \ldots, i_r = r$. It follows from Equation 7.5.1 that

$$F_r(x_1, x_2, \ldots, x_r) = F(x_1, x_2, \ldots, x_r, \infty, \infty, \ldots, \infty)$$

$$= \lim_{x_{r+1} \to \infty} \cdots \lim_{x_n \to \infty} [F(x_1, x_2, \ldots, x_r, x_{r+1}, \ldots, x_n)]$$

$$= \lim_{x_{r+1} \to \infty} \cdots \lim_{x_n \to \infty} [F_1(x_1)F_2(x_2) \cdots F_r(x_r)F(x_{r+1}) \cdots F(x_n)]$$

$$= F_1(x_1)F_2(x_2) \cdots F_r(x_r) \lim_{x_{r+1} \to \infty} F_{r+1}(x_{r+1}) \cdots \lim_{x_n \to \infty} F(x_n)$$

$$= F_1(x_1)F_2(x_2) \cdots F_r(X_r)F_{r+1}(\infty) \cdots F_n(\infty)$$

$$= F_1(x_1)F_2(x_2) \cdots F_r(x_r).$$

Thus, if the random variables $X_1, X_2, \ldots, X_n$ are mutually independent, then the random variables $X_1, X_2, \ldots, X_r, r \leq n$ are also independent.

7.6 Functions of Random Variables

In Section 6.6, we discussed in detail various aspects of deriving distributions of functions of two-dimensional random variables. In this section, we will extend the discussion to the more complicated derivation of distributions of a sequence of functions of the n-dimensional random variable.

Suppose that $f(x_1, x_2, \ldots, x_n)$ is the multivariate probability density function of the n-dimensional random variable $(X_1, X_2, \ldots, X_n)$ of the continuous type; we are interested in obtaining the joint probability density function of the random variable $(Y_1, Y_2, \ldots, Y_n)$, where

$$
\begin{aligned}
Y_1 &= g_1(X_1, X_2, \ldots, X_n) \\
Y_2 &= g_2(X_1, X_2, \ldots, X_n) \\
&\;\;\vdots \qquad \vdots \\
Y_n &= g_n(X_1, X_2, \ldots, X_n).
\end{aligned}
\tag{7.6.1}
$$

To obtain the new distribution, as in the two-dimensional case, we must assume that the functions $g_1, g_2, \ldots, g_n$ define a one-to-one transformation that maps an n-dimensional set E_n of the Euclidean n-space, $x_1, x_2 \ldots, x_n$, onto an n-dimensional set E^* in the $y_1, y_2, \ldots, y_n$ space; and we must have continuous first partial derivatives with respect to $x_1, x_2, \ldots, x_n$. These conditions imply that we can solve for the inverses of $g_1, g_2, \ldots, g_n$:

$$
\begin{aligned}
x_1 &= z_1^{-1}(y_1, y_2, \ldots, y_n) \\
x_2 &= z_2^{-1}(y_1, y_2, \ldots, y_n) \\
&\;\;\vdots \qquad \vdots \\
x_n &= z_n^{-1}(y_1, y_2, \ldots, y_n).
\end{aligned}
$$

Thus, the functions $z_1^{-1}, z_2^{-1}, \ldots, z_n^{-1}$ are one-to-one and have continuous first partial derivatives with respect to $y_1, y_2, \ldots, y_n$. Having made the above assumptions, we can obtain the multivariate probability density function as follows:

$$
z(y_1, y_2, \ldots, y_n) = f[z_1^{-1}(y_1, y_2, \ldots, y_n),
$$
$$
z_2^{-1}(y_1, y_2, \ldots, y_n), \ldots, z_n^{-1}(y_1, y_2, \ldots, y_n)]\,|J|,
$$

where $|J|$ denotes the absolute value of the Jacobian of the transformation, defined by the n by n determinant

$$
J = \begin{vmatrix}
\dfrac{\partial x_1}{\partial y_1} & \dfrac{\partial x_1}{\partial y_2} & \cdots & \dfrac{\partial x_1}{\partial y_n} \\[2ex]
\dfrac{\partial x_2}{\partial y_1} & \dfrac{\partial x_2}{\partial y_2} & \cdots & \dfrac{\partial x_2}{\partial y_n} \\[2ex]
\vdots & & & \\[1ex]
\dfrac{\partial x_n}{\partial y_1} & \dfrac{\partial x_n}{\partial y_2} & \cdots & \dfrac{\partial x_n}{\partial y_n}
\end{vmatrix},
$$

which cannot be equal to zero.

The above discussion can be intuitively presented as follows: Let $E_n \subset E$ be an n-dimensional subset (an event of E that consists of n-tuples) in the $x_1, x_2, \ldots, x_n$ space, and let $E_n^* \subset E^*$ be a subset (an event of E^* that consists of n-tuples) in the $y_1, y_2, \ldots, y_n$ space. Thus, under the condition of one-to-one transformation, the events

$$(X_1, X_2, \ldots, X_n) \in E_n \quad \text{and} \quad (Y_1, Y_2, \ldots, Y_n) \in E_n^*$$

are equivalent, and

$$Pr[(X_1, X_2, \ldots, X_n) \in E_n] = \iint_{E_n} \cdots \int f(x_1, x_2, \ldots, x_n) \, dx_1 \, dx_2 \cdots dx_n$$

$$= Pr[(Y_1, Y_2, \ldots, Y_n) \in E_n^*]$$

$$= \iint_{E_n^*} \cdots \int f[z_1^{-1}(y_1, y_2, \ldots, y_n),$$

$$\times z_2^{-1}(y_1, y_2, \ldots, y_n), z_n^{-1}(y_1, y_2, \ldots, y_n)]$$

$$\times |J| \, dy_1 \, dy_2 \cdots dy_n.$$

Hence, we summarize the above discussion by generalizing Theorem 6.6.1 to the n-dimensional case.

Theorem 7.6.1 Let $f(x_1, x_2, \ldots, x_n)$ be the multivariate probability density function of the continuous random variable $(X_1, X_2, \ldots, X_n)$. Suppose that

$$Y_1 = g_1(X_1, X_2, \ldots, X_n)$$
$$Y_2 = g_2(X_1, X_2, \ldots, X_n)$$
$$\vdots$$
$$Y_n = g_n(X_1, X_2, \ldots, X_n)$$

are such that $g_1, g_2, \ldots, g_n$ define a one-to-one transformation of the random variable $(X_1, X_2, \ldots, X_n)$ and that the variable has continuous first partial derivatives with respect to $x_1, x_2, \ldots, x_n$. Then the joint probability density function of the random variable $(Y_1, Y_2, \ldots, Y_n)$ is given by

$$z(y_1, y_2, \ldots, Y_n) = f[z_1^{-1}(y_1, y_2, \ldots, y_n),$$
$$z_2^{-1}(y_1, y_2, \ldots, y_n), \ldots, z_n^{-1}(y_1, y_2, \ldots, y_n)]|J|, \, (y_1, y_2, \ldots, y_n) \in S_n^*,$$

and zero elsewhere.

Example 7.6.1   Dirichlet Distribution   Let the multivariate probability density function of the $n + 1$-dimensional random variable $(X_1, X_2, \ldots, X_n, X_{n+1})$ be given by

$$(x_1, x_2, \ldots, x_n, x_{n+1}, \alpha_1, \alpha_2, \ldots, \alpha_n, \alpha_{n+1})$$

$$= \begin{cases} \prod_{i=1}^{n+1} \frac{1}{\Gamma(\alpha_i)} x_i^{\alpha_i - 1} e^{-x_i}, & x_i \geq 0, \ i = 1, 2, \ldots, n, n + 1, \\ 0, & \text{elsewhere.} \end{cases}$$

$$(7.6.2)$$

Suppose that

$$Y_1 = \frac{X_1}{X_1 + X_2 + \cdots + X_{n+1}}$$

$$Y_2 = \frac{X_2}{X_1 + X_2 + \cdots + X_{n+1}}$$

$$\vdots$$

$$Y_n = \frac{X_n}{X_1 + X_2 + \cdots + X_{n+1}}$$

$$Y_{n+1} = X_1 + X_2 + \cdots + X_{n+1},$$

and we wish to obtain the probability density function of the random variable $(Y_1, Y_2, \ldots, Y_n, Y_{n+1})$. Here the above transformation maps the set

$$E_n = \{(x_1, x_2, \ldots, x_{n+1}), \quad x_i \geq 0, \ i = 1, 2, \ldots, n + 1\}$$

onto the set

$$E_n^* = \{(y_1, y_2, \ldots, y_n, y_{n+1}), \quad y_i \geq 0, \ i = 1, 2, \ldots, n + 1,$$
$$y_1 + y_2 + \cdots + y_n < 1\}.$$

The single-valued inverse functions are

$$x_1 = y_1 y_{n+1}, \quad x_2 = y_2 y_{n+1}, \ldots, \quad x_n = y_n y_{n+1}, \quad x_{n+1}$$
$$= y_{n+1}(1 - y_1 - y_2 - \cdots - y_n),$$

and the Jacobian of transformation is

$$J = \begin{vmatrix} y_{n+1} & 0 & 0 & \cdots & 0 & y_1 \\ 0 & y_{n+1} & 0 & \cdots & 0 & y_2 \\ 0 & 0 & y_{n+1} & \cdots & 0 & y_3 \\ \vdots & \vdots & \vdots & & \vdots & \vdots \\ 0 & 0 & 0 & & y_{n+1} & y_n \\ -y_{n+1} & -y_{n+1} & -y_{n+1} & \cdots & -y_{n+1} & (1 - y_1 - y_2 - \cdots - y_n) \end{vmatrix} = y_{n+1}^n.$$

Thus,

$$z(y_1, y_2, \ldots, y_n, y_{n+1})$$

$$= f[y_1 y_{n+1}, y_2 y_{n+1}, \ldots, y_n y_{n+1}, y_{n+1}(1 - y_1 - y_2 - \cdots - y_n)] |J|$$

$$= \frac{1}{\Gamma(\alpha_1)} (y_1 y_{n+1})^{\alpha_1 - 1} e^{-y_1 y_{n+1}} \frac{1}{\Gamma(\alpha_2)} (y_2 y_{n+1})^{\alpha_2 - 1} e^{-y_2 y_{n+1}} \cdots$$

$$\frac{1}{\Gamma(\alpha_n)} (y_n y_{n+1})^{\alpha_n - 1} e^{-y_n y_{n+1}} \frac{1}{\Gamma(\alpha_{n+1})} [y_{n+1}(1 - y_1 - y_2 - \cdots - y_n]^{\alpha_{n+1} - 1}$$

$$e^{-[y_{n+1}(1 - y_1 - y_2 - \cdots - y_n)]} y_{n+1}^n$$

or

$$= \begin{cases} \dfrac{y_1^{\alpha_1 - 1} y_2^{\alpha_2 - 1} \cdots y_n^{\alpha_n - 1} y_{n+1}^{\sum_{i=1}^{n+1} \alpha_i - 1} (1 - y_1 - y_2 - \cdots - y_n)^{\alpha_{n+1} - 1} e^{-y_{n+1}}}{\prod_{i=1}^{n+1} \Gamma(\alpha_i)}, \\ \hspace{6cm} (y_1, y_2, \ldots, y_n, y_{n+1}) \in S_n^* \subset S^*, \\ 0, \quad \text{elsewhere.} \end{cases}$$

The marginal probability density function of the *n*-dimensional random variable $(Y_1, Y_2, \ldots, Y_n)$ is obtained by

$$z_n(y_1, y_2, \ldots, y_n) = \int_{-\infty}^{\infty} z(y_1, y_2, \ldots, y_n, y_{n+1}) dy_{n+1}$$

$$= \frac{y_1^{\alpha_1 - 1} y_2^{\alpha_2 - 1} \cdots y_n^{\alpha_n - 1} (1 - y_1 - y_2 - \cdots - y_n)^{\alpha_{n+1} - 1}}{\prod_{i=1}^{n+1} \Gamma(\alpha_i)}$$

$$= \int_0^{\infty} y_{n+1}^{\sum_{i+1}^{n+1} \alpha_i - 1} e^{-y_{n+1}} dy_{n+1}.$$

Thus, because

$$\left\{ \frac{1}{\Gamma(\sum_{i=1}^{n+1} \alpha_i)} \int_0^{\infty} y_{n+1}^{\sum_{i=1}^{n+1} \alpha_i - 1} e^{-y_{n+1}} dy_{n+1} \right\} = 1,$$

we have

$$z_n(y_1, y_2, \ldots, y_n)$$

$$= \begin{cases} \dfrac{\Gamma(\sum_{i=1}^{n+1} \alpha_i)}{\prod_{i=1}^{n+1} \Gamma(\alpha_i)} y_1^{\alpha_1 - 1} y_2^{\alpha_2 - 1} \cdots y_n^{\alpha_n - 1} (1 - y_1 - y_2 - \cdots - y_n)^{\alpha_{n+1} - 1}, \\ \hspace{6cm} (y_1, y_2, \ldots, y_n) \in S_n^*, \\ 0, \quad \text{elsewhere.} \end{cases}$$

$$(7.6.3)$$

The probability density function $z_n(y_1, y_2, \ldots, y_n)$ is called the *Dirichlet distribution*, with parameters $\alpha_i > 0$, $i = 1, 2, \ldots, n + 1$. This distribution has been used extensively in mathematical biology. It should be noted that the multivariate probability density (7.6.2) is simply the product of $n + 1$ independent random variables having a gamma distribution with $\beta_i = 1$ and $\alpha_i > 0$, $i = 1, 2, \ldots, n + 1$. Also, if we let $n = 1$ in Equation (7.6.3), the Dirichlet density reduces to the beta distribution, with parameters $\alpha > 0$ and $\beta = 1$.

If the n-dimensional random variable $(X_1, X_2, \ldots, X_n)$ is discrete, then the multivariate probability density function of the sequence of variates $(Y_1, Y_2, \ldots, Y_n)$, as defined in Equation (7.6.1), is

$$p(y_1, y_2, \ldots, y_n) = Pr(Y = y_1, Y = y_2, \ldots, Y = y_n)$$
$$= Pr[X_1 = z_1^{-1}(y_1, y_2, \ldots, y_n), X_2 = z_2^{-1}(y_1, y_2, \ldots, y_n),$$
$$\ldots, X_n = z_n^{-1}(y_1, y_2, \ldots, y_n)].$$

In the above discussion, we derived the joint probability density function of a sequence of n functional forms, $g_1, g_2, \ldots, g_n$, of the n-dimensional random variable $(X_1, X_2, \ldots, X_n)$. However, in many problems, the number of functional forms is less than the dimension of the given sequence of random variables. In such cases, in order to be able to apply Theorem 7.6.1, we must introduce *auxiliary* variables, as was illustrated for the two-dimensional case.

A problem often arises in deriving distributions when the transformation involved is not one-to-one. For example, suppose the transformation (7.6.1), considered above, which maps E_n in the $x_1, x_2, \ldots, x_n$ space onto E_n^* in the $y_1, y_2, \ldots, y_n$ space, is not one-to-one; that is, to each point in E_n there corresponds one point in E_n^*, but to some point in E_n^* there may correspond more than one point of E_n. In such a situation, we partition E_n into a finite number of mutually exclusive sets $E_{n_1}, E_{n_2}, \ldots, E_{n_r}$, with $\bigcup_{i=1}^r E_{n_i} = E_n$ such that the transformation (7.6.1) defines a one-to-one transformation of each E_{n_i}, $i = 1, 2, \ldots, n$ onto E_n^*. That is, for each point (n-tuple) in E_n^*, there will correspond at most one point in each E_{n_i}. Thus, we will have r sets of n inverse functions, with one set for each of the transformations given by

$$x_1 = z_{1_i}^{-1}(y_1, y_2, \ldots, y_n)$$
$$x_2 = z_{2_i}^{-1}(y_1, y_2, \ldots, y_n)$$
$$\vdots$$
$$x_n = z_{n_i}^{-1}(y_1, y_2, \ldots, y_n)$$

$i = 1, 2, \ldots, r$. We shall assume that the transformation will have continuous first partial derivatives, and the Jacobian for each i, $i = 1, 2, \ldots, r$ is

$$J_i = \begin{vmatrix} \dfrac{\partial z_{1_i}^{\,-1}}{\partial y_1} & \dfrac{\partial z_{1_i}^{\,-1}}{\partial y_2} & \cdots & \dfrac{\partial z_{1_i}^{\,-1}}{\partial y_n} \\[2ex] \dfrac{\partial z_{2_i}^{\,-1}}{\partial y_1} & \dfrac{\partial z_{2_i}^{\,-1}}{\partial y_2} & \cdots & \dfrac{\partial z_{2_i}^{\,-1}}{\partial y_n} \\[2ex] \vdots & & & \\[2ex] \dfrac{\partial z_{n_i}^{\,-1}}{\partial y_1} & \dfrac{\partial z_{n_i}^{\,-1}}{\partial y_2} & \cdots & \dfrac{\partial z_{n_i}^{\,-1}}{\partial y_n} \end{vmatrix},$$

which cannot be equal to zero. Thus, we can obtain the joint probability density function of the n-dimensional random variable $(Y_1, Y_2, \ldots Y_n)$, as defined by Equation (7.6.1), for each partition of the set E_n; and, because the r partitions are mutually exclusive, the sum of the probability density functions defined in each partition is the desired joint probability density function:

$$z(y_1, y_2, \ldots, y_n) = \begin{cases} \displaystyle\sum_{i=1}^{r} f[z_{1_i}^{-1}(y_1, y_2, \ldots, y_n), z_{2_i}^{-1}(y_1, y_2, \ldots, y_n), \ldots, \\ \qquad z_{n_i}^{-1}(y_1, y_2, \ldots, y_n)]|J_i|, \; (y_1, y_2, \ldots, y_n) \in S_n{}^*, \\[1ex] 0, \quad \text{elsewhere.} \end{cases}$$

When the given sequence of random variables $(Y_1, Y_2, \ldots, Y_n)$ is discrete and the n-dimensional random variable $(X_1, X_2, \ldots, X_n)$, as given in Equation (7.6.1), is continuous, its discrete probability mass function is

$$p(y_1, y_2, \ldots, y_n) = Pr(Y_1 = y_1, Y_2 = y_2, \ldots, Y_n = y_n)$$

$$= \sum_{i=1}^{r} Pr[X_1 = z_{1_i}^{-1}(y_1, y_2, \ldots, y_n), X_2 = z_{2_i}^{-1}(y_1, y_2, \ldots, y_n)$$

$$\times \ldots, X_n = z_{n_i}^{-1}(y_1, y_2, \ldots, y_n)].$$

7.7 Expected Value, Moments, and Characteristic Functions

The extension of Section 6.7 to the n-dimensional case is straightforward; thus, our discussion will be brief.

Definition 7.7.1 *Let $(X_1, X_2, \ldots, X_n)$ be an n-dimensional continuous random variable, with joint probability density function $f(x_1, x_2, \ldots, x_n)$. The multiple integral*

$$\int_{-\infty}^{\infty} \cdots \int_{-\infty}^{\infty} \int_{-\infty}^{\infty} x_1 x_2 \cdots x_n f(x_1, x_2, \ldots, x_n) dx_1 \, dx_2 \cdots dx_n$$

is called the expected value of the product of the variates $X_1, X_2, \ldots, X_n$ *if the following inequality is satisfied:*

$$\int_{-\infty}^{\infty} \cdots \int_{-\infty}^{\infty} \int_{-\infty}^{\infty} |x_1 x_2 \cdots x_n| f(x_1, x_2, \ldots, x_n) dx_1 \, dx_2 \cdots dx_n < \infty.$$

The generalized version of the properties of expectation, discussed in Section 5.2, are given below.

Theorem 7.7.1   Let $(X_1, X_2, \ldots, X_n)$ be an n-dimensional random variable of the continuous type, with joint probability density function $f(x_1, x_2, \ldots, x_n)$. If $U = g(X_1, X_2, \ldots, X_n)$, then the expected value of U is

$$E(U) = E[g(X_1, X_2, \ldots, X_n)]$$

$$\int_{-\infty}^{\infty} \cdots \int_{-\infty}^{\infty} \int_{-\infty}^{\infty} g(x_1, x_2, \ldots, x_n) f(x_1, x_2, \ldots, x_n) dx_1 \, dx_2 \cdots dx_n.$$

We omit the proof because it is similar to that of Theorem 5.2.2. However, understand that the multiple integral must be absolutely convergent in order for $E(U)$ to exist.

Theorem 7.7.2   Let $(X_1, X_2, \ldots, X_n)$ be an n-dimensional random variable with probability density $f(x_1, x_2, \ldots, x_n)$. If $Y_1 = g_1(X_i)$, $Y_2 = g_2(X_i)$, $\ldots, Y_n = g_n(X_i)$, $i = 1, 2, \ldots, n$, then

$$E(Y_1 Y_2 \cdots Y_n)$$

$$= E[g_1(x_i) g_2(x_i) \cdots g_n(x_i)]$$

$$= \int_{-\infty}^{\infty} \cdots \int_{-\infty}^{\infty} \int_{-\infty}^{\infty} g_1(x_i) g_2(x_i) \cdots g_n(x_i) f(x_1, x_2, \ldots, x_n) dx_1 \, dx_2 \cdots dx_n$$

if the variate $(X_1, X_2, \ldots, X_n)$ is continuous. Of course, we can also obtain the $E(Y_1 Y_2 \cdots Y_n)$ by first finding, if possible, the multivariate distribution of $(Y_1, Y_2, \ldots, Y_n)$, $z(y_1, y_2, \ldots, y_n)$, as discussed in the previous section, and then applying Definition 7.7.1 to obtain

$$E(Y_1 Y_2 \cdots Y_n)$$

$$= \int_{-\infty}^{\infty} \cdots \int_{-\infty}^{\infty} \int_{-\infty}^{\infty} y_1 y_2 \cdots y_n z(y_1, y_2, \ldots, y_n) dy_1 \, dy_2 \cdots dy_n.$$

Theorem 7.7.3   Let $(X_1, X_2, \ldots, X_n)$ be an n-dimensional random variable. If the variates in the sequence $(X_1, X_2, \ldots, X_n)$ are mutually independent, then

(1) $E(X_1 X_2 \cdots X_n) = \prod_{i=1}^{n} E(X_i);$

(2) $\mathrm{Var}(X_1 + X_2 + \cdots + X_n) = \sum_{i=1}^{n} \mathrm{Var}(X_i).$

Definition 7.7.2   *Let* $(X_1, X_2, \ldots, X_n)$ *be an n-dimensional random variable of the continuous type, with probability density function* $f(x_1, x_2, \ldots, x_n)$. *The moment of order* $k_1 + k_2 + \cdots + k_n$ *of the multivariate distribution of the variate* $(X_1, X_2, \ldots, X_n)$ *is*

$$E(X_1^{k_1} X_2^{k_2} \cdots X_n^{k_n})$$

$$= \int_{-\infty}^{\infty} \cdots \int_{-\infty}^{\infty} \int_{-\infty}^{\infty} x_1^{k_1} x_2^{k_2} \cdots x_n^{k_n} f(x_1, x_2, \ldots, x_n) dx_1 \, dx_2 \cdots dx_n$$

$$= \mu_{k_1, k_2, \ldots, k_n}.$$

The central moment of order $k_1 + k_2 + \cdots + k_n$ *is*

$$E[(X_1 - \mu_1)^{k_1}(X_2 - \mu_2)^{k_2} \cdots (X_n - \mu_n)^{k_n}]$$

$$= \int_{-\infty}^{\infty} \cdots \int_{-\infty}^{\infty} \int_{-\infty}^{\infty} (x_1 - \mu_1)^{k_1}(x_2 - \mu_2)^{k_2} \cdots (x_n - x_n)^{k_n} f(x_1, x_2, \ldots, x_n)$$

$$dx_1 \, dx_2 \cdots dx_n$$

$$= \eta_{k_1, k_z, \ldots, k_n},$$

where $E(X_i) = \mu_i$, $i = 1, 2, \ldots, n.$

Thus, if $k_i = k_j = 1$, $1 \le i < j \le n$, with the remaining k's equal to zero, then

$$\eta_{0, 0, \ldots, 0, 1, 0, \ldots, 0, 1, 0, \ldots, 0} = E[(X_i - \mu_i)(X_j - \mu_j)]$$

$$= \mathrm{Cov}(X_i, X_j).$$

Definition 7.7.3   *The* characteristic function *of the n-dimensional random variable* $(X_1, X_2, \ldots, X_n)$ *is given by*

$$\phi_{X_1 X_2 \cdots X_n}(t_1, t_2, \ldots, t_n)$$

$$= E[e^{i(t_1 X_1 + t_2 X_2 + \cdots + t_n X_n)}}$$

$$= \int_{-\infty}^{\infty} \cdots \int_{-\infty}^{\infty} \int_{-\infty}^{\infty} e^{i(t_1 X_1 + t_2 X_2 + \cdots + t_n X_n)} f(x_1, x_2, \ldots, x_n) dx_1 \, dx_2 \cdots dx_n,$$

where $f(x_1, x_2, \ldots, x_n)$ *is the joint probability density function of the given continuous variate.*

Example 7.7.1   The characteristic function of the multinomial distribution, the probability density function of which is given by Equation (7.1.3), is computed as follows:

$$\phi_{X_1 X_2 \cdots X_k}(t_1, t_2, \ldots, t_k) = E[e^{i(t_1 X_1 + t_2 X_2 + \cdots + t_k X_k)}]$$

$$= \sum_{x_1, x_2, \ldots, x_k} e^{i(t_1 x_1 + t_2 x_2 + \cdots + t_k x_k)} f(x_1, \ldots, x_k; p_1, \ldots, p_k, n)$$

$$= \sum_{x_1, x_2, \ldots, x_k} \frac{n!}{x_1! x_2! \cdots x_k!} e^{i(t_1 x_1 + t_2 x_2 + \cdots + t_k x_k)} p_1^{x_1} \cdots p_k^{x_k}$$

$$= \sum_{x_1, x_2, \ldots, x_k} \frac{n!}{x_1! x_2! \cdots x_k!} (e^{it_1} p_1)^{x_1} (e^{it_2} p_2)^{x_2} \cdots (e^{it_k} p_k)^{x_k}.$$

Thus, applying the multinomial theorem, we have

$$\phi_{X_1 X_2 \cdots X_k}(t_1, t_2, \ldots, t_k) = (p_1 e^{it_1} + p_2 e^{it_2} + \cdots + p_k e^{it_k})^n$$

$$= \left[\sum_{j=1}^{k} p_j e^{it_j} \right]^n.$$

Note:

(a) $\phi_{X_1 X_2 \cdots X_k}(0, 0, \ldots, 0) = 1,$

(b) $|\phi_{X_1 X_2 \cdots X_k}(t_1, t_2, \ldots, t_k)| = \left| \sum_{j=1}^{k} p_j e^{it_j} \right|$

$$\leq \sum_{j=1}^{k} p_j |e^{it_j}|$$

$$= \sum_{j=1}^{k} p_j |\cos t_j + i \sin t_j|$$

$$= \sum_{j=1}^{k} p_j.$$

Thus,

$$|\phi_{X_1 X_2 \cdots X_k}(t_1, t_2, \ldots, t_k)| \leq 1.$$

(c) $\phi_{X_1 X_2 \cdots X_k}(-t_1, -t_2, \ldots, -t_k) = \sum_{j=1}^{k} p_j e^{-it_j}$

$$= \sum_{j=1}^{k} p_j (\cos t_j - i \sin t_j)$$

$$= \overline{\phi_{X_1 X_2 \cdots X_k}(t_1, t_2, \ldots, t_k)}.$$

(d) The marginal characterisitic function of the marginal distribution of the random variable X_l is obtained by setting $t_r = 0, r \neq l$:

$$\phi_{X_l}(t_l) = \left(p_l e^{it_l} + \sum_{r \neq l} p_r \right)^n$$

$$= (p_l e^{it_l} + 1 - p_l)^n$$

$$= [p_l(e^{it_l} - 1) + 1]^n$$

which, of course, is the characteristic function of the binomial distribution.

(e) If the variates in the sequence, $X_1, X_2, \ldots, X_k$ are mutually independent, then

$$\phi_{X_1 X_2 \cdots X_k}(t_1, t_2, \ldots, t_k) = \phi_{X_1}(t_1)\phi_{X_2}(t_2) \cdots \phi_{X_k}(t_k)$$

$$= \prod_{l=1}^{k} \{[p_l(e^{it_l} - 1) + 1]^n\}.$$

As we have seen, one of the main features of the characteristic function is that we can obtain moments of order $k_1 + k_2 + \cdots + k_n$ of an n-dimensional variate. Assume that

$$\frac{\partial^{k_1 + k_2 + \cdots + k_n}}{\partial t_1^{k_1} \partial t_2^{k_2} \cdots \partial t_n^{k_n}} \phi_{X_1 X_2 \cdots X_n}(t_1, t_2, \ldots, t_n)$$

$$= \frac{\partial^{k_1 + k_2 + \cdots + k_n}}{\partial t_1^{k_1} \partial t_2^{k_2} \cdots \partial t_n^{k_n}} E[e^{i(t_1 X_1 + t_2 X_2 + \cdots + t_n X_n)}]$$

$$= E\left\{ \frac{\partial^{k_1 + k_2 + \cdots + k_n}}{\partial t_1^{k_1} \partial t_2^{k_2} \cdots \partial t_n^{k_n}} \right\} [e^{i(t_1 X_1 + t_2 X_2 + \cdots + t_n X_n)}].$$

Then

$$\frac{\partial^{k_1 + k_2 + \cdots + k_n}}{\partial t_1^{k_1} \partial t_2^{k_2} \cdots \partial t_n^{k_n}} \phi_{X_1 X_2 \cdots X_n}(t_1, t_2, \ldots, t_n)$$

$$= E[i^{k_1 + k_2 + \cdots + k_n} X_1^{k_1} X_2^{k_2} \cdots X_n^{k_n} e^{i(t_1 X_1 + t_2 X_2 + \cdots + t_n X_n)}]$$

$$= i^{k_1 + k_2 + \cdots + k_n} E[X_1^{k_1} X_2^{k_2} \cdots X_n^{k_n} e^{i(t_1 X_1 + t_2 X_2 + \cdots + t_n X_n)}].$$

Thus, the ordinary moment of order $k_1 + k_2 + \cdots + k_n$ is given by

$$\frac{\partial^{k_1 + k_2 + \cdots + k_n}}{i^{k_1 + k_2 + \cdots + k_n} \partial t_1^{k_1} \partial t_2^{k_2} \cdots \partial t_n^{k_n}} \phi_{X_1 X_2 \cdots X_n}(t_1, t_2, \ldots, t_n) \Bigg|_{\substack{t_1 = 0 \\ t_2 = 0 \\ \vdots \\ t_n = 0}} = \mu_{k_1, k_2, \cdots, k_n},$$

provided that the operations may be interchanged and that the required partial derivatives exist.

Example 7.7.2   Using the characteristic function of the multinomial distribution, we will compute the following moments:

(a) $E(X_l) = \dfrac{\partial}{i\partial t_l}\, \phi_{X_1 X_2 \cdots X_l}(t_1, t_2, \ldots, t_k) \Big|_{\substack{t_1 = 0 \\ t_2 = 0 \\ \vdots \\ t_k = 0}}$

$\qquad = \dfrac{\partial}{i\partial t_l} [p_1 e^{it_1} + p_2 e^{it_2} + \cdots + p_k e^{it_k}]^n \Big|_{\substack{t_1 = 0 \\ t_2 = 0 \\ \vdots \\ t_k = 0}}$

$\qquad = n p_l e^{it_l} [p_1 e^{it_1} + p_2 e^{it_2} + \cdots + p_k e^{it_k}]^{n-1} \Big|_{\substack{t_1 = 0 \\ t_2 = 0 \\ \vdots \\ t_k = 0}}$

$\qquad = n p_l, \quad l = 1, 2, \ldots, k;$

(b) $E(X_l X_m) = \dfrac{\partial^2}{i^2 \partial t_l \partial t_m}\, \phi_{X_1 X_2 \cdots X_k}(t_1, t_2, \ldots, t_k) \Big|_{\substack{t_1 = 0 \\ t_2 = 0 \\ \vdots \\ t_k = 0}}$

$\qquad = \dfrac{\partial^2}{i^2 \partial t_l \partial t_m} [p_1 e^{it_1} + p_2 e^{it_2} + \cdots + p_k e^{it_k}]^n \Big|_{\substack{t_1 = 0 \\ t_2 = 0 \\ \vdots \\ t_k = 0}}$

$\qquad = n(n-1) p_l p_m e^{it_l} e^{it_m} [p_1 e^{it_1} + p_2 e^{it_2} + \cdots + p_k e^{it_k}]^{n-2} \Big|_{\substack{t_1 = 0 \\ t_2 = 0 \\ \vdots \\ t_k = 0}}$

$\qquad = n(n-1) p_l p_m (p_1 + p_2 + \cdots + p_k)^{n-2} \quad l \neq m$

$\qquad = n(n-1) p_l p_m, \quad l \neq m = 1, 2, \cdots, k;$

(c) $\mathrm{Cov}(X_m, X_l) = E[X_m - n p_m)(X_l - n p_l)], \quad l \neq m$

$\qquad = E(X_m X_l) - n p_m E(X_l) - n p_l E(X_m) + n^2 p_m p_l$

$\qquad = n(n-1) p_l p_m - n^2 p_m p_l - n^2 p_m p_l + n^2 p_m p_l$

$\qquad = - n p_l p_m.$

Thus, if $l = m$, we have

$$
\begin{aligned}
\text{Var}(X_m) &= E[(X_m - np_m)^2] \\
&= E(X_m^2) - n^2 p_m^2 \\
&= n(n-1)p_m^2 + np_m - n^2 p_m^2 \\
&= np_m(1 - p_m), \quad m = 1, 2, \ldots, k.
\end{aligned}
$$

Note that $E(X_m^2)$ is obtained by

$$
\frac{\partial^2}{i^2 \partial t_m^2} \phi_{X_1 X_2 \cdots X_k}(t_1, t_2, \ldots, t_k) \Bigg|_{\substack{t_1 = 0 \\ t_2 = 0 \\ \vdots \\ t_k = 0}}
$$

$$
= [n(n-1)p_m^2 e^{2it_m}(p_1 e^{it_1} + p_2 e^{it_2} + \cdots + p_k e^{it_k})^{n-2}
$$

$$
+ np_m e^{it_m}(p_1 e^{it_1} + p_2 e^{it_2} + \cdots + p_k e^{it_k})^{n-1}] \Bigg|_{\substack{t_1 = 0 \\ t_2 = 0 \\ \vdots \\ t_k = 0}}
$$

$$
= n(n-1)p_m^2 + np_m.
$$

Properties (a) through (e) of the characteristic function, which we have studied for the one- and two-dimensional cases, hold also for the multivariate case. We shall state the extension of property (d).

Theorem 7.7.4   If the sequence of random variables, $X_1, X_2, \ldots, X_n$, is mutually independent, then

$$
\phi_{X_1 X_2 \cdots X_n}(t_1, t_2, \ldots, t_n) = \phi_{X_1}(t_1)\phi_{X_2}(t_2) \cdots \phi_{X_n}(t_n).
$$

Proof $\phi_{X_1 X_2 \cdots X_n}(t_1, t_2, \ldots, t_n) = E[e^{i(t_1 X_1 + t_2 X_2 + \cdots + t_n X_n)}]$

$$
\begin{aligned}
&= E[e^{it_1 X_1} e^{it_2 X_2} \cdots e^{it_n X_n}] \\
&= E[e^{it_1 X_1}]E[e^{it_2 X_2}] \cdots E[e^{it_n X_n}] \\
&= \phi_{X_1}(t_1)\phi_{X_2}(t_2) \cdots \phi_{X_n}(t_n).
\end{aligned}
$$

The converse of the above theorem is also true. That is, the n random variables $X_1, X_2, \ldots, X_n$ are mutually independent if

$$
\phi_{X_1 X_2 \cdots X_n}(t_1, t_2, \ldots, t_n) = \prod_{i=1}^{n} \phi_{X_i}(t_i),
$$

that is, if the characteristic function is equal to the product of the characteristic functions of the marginal distributions of each of the random variables.

In this chapter, we did not discuss the generalization of the moment generating function introduced in Section 5.4, which exists under certain conditions because the characteristic function always exists and can be used to generate those moments which exist. Furthermore, Theorem 6.7.11 (inversion formula) holds for the multivariate case. That is, if the characteristic function

$$\phi_{X_1 X_2 \cdots X_n}(t_1, t_2, \ldots, t_n)$$

of the n-dimensional random variable $(X_1, X_2, \ldots X_n)$ is known, we can uniquely determine its multivariate distribution function. Another useful technique in deriving distributions is the generalized version of Theorem 5.4.3, using characteristic functions instead of moment generating functions.

Theorem 7.7.5   Let $(X_1, X_2, \ldots, X_n)$ be an n-dimensional random variable with joint probability density function $f(x_1, x_2, \ldots, x_n)$, and let $U = g(X_1, X_2, \ldots, X_n)$ have probability density $z(u)$. If $\phi_{X_1 X_2 \cdots X_n}(t_1, t_2, \ldots, t_n)$ and $\phi_U(t)$ are equal, then $(X_1, X_2, \ldots, X_n)$ and $U = g(X_1, X_2, \ldots, X_n)$ have the same probability distributions,

$$f(x_1, x_2, \ldots, x_n) = z(u).$$

We shall use this theorem to derive some distributions that are useful and extremely important in the area of statistics.

Theorem 7.7.6   Let the sequence of random variables $X_1, X_2, \ldots, X_n$ be mutually independent and each normally distributed, with parameters $(\mu_1, \sigma_1^2), (\mu_2, \sigma_2^2), \ldots, (\mu_n, \sigma_n^2)$, respectively. If α_i, $i = 1, 2, \ldots, n$ are real constants, then the random variable

$$U = \sum_{j=1}^{n} \alpha_j X_j$$

is normally distributed, with mean $\sum_{j=1}^{n} \alpha_j \mu_j$ and variance $\sum_{j=1}^{n} \alpha_j^2 \sigma_j^2$.

Proof   Since the sequence of random variables $X_1, X_2, \ldots, X_n$ is mutually independent, we can apply Theorem 7.7.4 and have, for $t_j = t, j = 1, \ldots, n$:

$$\phi_{X_1 X_2 \cdots X_n}(t, t, \ldots, t) = E[e^{it(\alpha_1 X_1 + \alpha_2 X_2 + \cdots + \alpha_n X_n)}]$$

$$= E[e^{it\alpha_1 X_1}]E(e^{it\alpha_2 X_2}) \cdots E[e^{it\alpha_n X_n}].$$

We know (Example 5.5.6) that the characteristic function for any X_j is

$$\phi_{X_j}(t) = E[e^{itX_j}] = e^{\mu_j it - (1/2)t^2\sigma_j^2}, \quad j = 1, 2, \ldots, n.$$

In view of property (e) of Section 5.5, we have

$$\phi_{X_j}(\alpha_j t) = E[e^{it\alpha_j X_j}]$$
$$= e^{\mu_j i(\alpha_j t) - (1/2)\sigma_j^2(\alpha_j t)^2}, \quad j = 1, 2, \ldots, n.$$

Thus, the characteristic function of the random variable U is

$$\phi_U(t) = E[e^{itU}]$$
$$= E[e^{it(\alpha_1 X_1 + \alpha_2 X_2 + \cdots + \alpha_n X_n)}]$$
$$= E[e^{it\alpha_1 X_1}]E[e^{it\alpha_2 X_2}] \cdots E[e^{it\alpha_n X_n}]$$
$$= \prod_{j=1}^{n} E[e^{it\alpha_j X_j}]$$
$$= \prod_{j=1}^{n} e^{\mu_j i(\alpha_j t) - (1/2)\sigma_j^2(\alpha_j t)^2}$$
$$= e^{\sum_{j=1}^{n}(\alpha_j \mu_j)it - \frac{1}{2}\sum_{j=1}^{n}(\alpha_j^2 \sigma_j^2)t^2}$$

Therefore, $\phi_U(t)$ is the characteristic function of a normal distribution, with parameters $\sum_{j=1}^{n}\alpha_j \mu_j$ and $\sum_{j=1}^{n}\alpha_j^2\sigma_j^2$, and, thus, is the proof of Theorem 7.7.6.

A random variable X is *chi-square distributed*, $\chi^2(k)$, with k-degrees of freedom if its probability density function is

$$f(x; k) = \begin{cases} \dfrac{1}{\Gamma\left(\dfrac{k}{2}\right)2^{k/2}} x^{k/2 - 1}e^{-x/2}, & x \geq 0, \\ \\ 0, & \text{elsewhere.} \end{cases}$$

Thus, the $\chi^2(k)$ distribution is simply the gamma distribution, with parameters $\alpha = k/2$ and $\beta = 2$.

Theorem 7.7.7   Let the sequence of random variables $X_1, X_2, \ldots, X_n$ be mutually independent and each chi-square distributed, $\chi^2(k_1), \chi^2(k_2), \ldots,$ $\chi^2(k_n)$, with $k_1, k_2, \ldots, k_n$ degrees of freedom, respectively (see Example 4.2.11). If $U = X_1 + X_2 + \cdots + X_n$, then U is chi-square distributed, with r degrees of freedom, $\chi^2(r)$, $r = k_1 + k_2 + \cdots + k_n$.

Proof   The characteristic function of U is

$$\phi_U(t) = E[e^{itU}]$$
$$= E[e^{it(X_1 + X_2 + \cdots + X_n)}]$$
$$= E[e^{itX_1}]E[e^{itX_2}] \cdots E[e^{itX_n}].$$

It can easily be shown (see Example 5.4.4) that the characteristic function for any $X_j, j = 1, 2, \ldots, n$, is

$$\phi_{X_j}(t) = E[e^{itX_j}] = (1 - 2it)^{-(k_j/2)}$$

Thus,

$$\phi_U(t) = \prod_{j=1}^{n} (1 - 2it)^{-(k_j/2)}$$
$$= (1 - 2it)^{-(1/2)(k_1 + k_2 + \cdots + k_n)}$$

is the characteristic function of a distribution that is $\chi^2(k_1 + k_2 + \cdots + k_n)$. In view of Theorem 7.7.5, U is $\chi^2(r)$, $r = k_1 + k_2 + \cdots + k_n$.

The above result can also be obtained as follows: Let the sequence of random variables $X_1, X_2, \ldots, X_n$ be mutually independent and each one normally distributed, with mean μ and variance σ^2. Then the random variable

$$U = \sum_{j=1}^{n} \left(\frac{X_j - \mu}{\sigma}\right)^2$$

is $\chi^2(n)$. (See Problem 7.4.3.)

Example 7.7.3   Let the sequence of random variables $X_1, X_2, \ldots, X_n$ be mutually independent and each normally distributed, with parameters μ and σ^2. The distribution of the random variable

$$U = \frac{1}{n} \sum_{j=1}^{n} X_j,$$

applying Theorem 7.7.6, is also normally distributed, with parameters

$$\mu = \sum_{j=1}^{n} \left(\frac{1}{n}\mu\right) \quad \text{and} \quad \frac{\sigma^2}{n} = \sum_{j=1}^{n} \left(\frac{1}{n}\sigma\right)^2.$$

The random variable U is the *sample mean*, and it is usually denoted by $\overline{X}$.

Thus,

$$f\left(\bar{x};\ \mu, \frac{\sigma^2}{n}\right) = \frac{\sqrt{n}}{\sqrt{2\pi}\sigma} \exp\left\{-\frac{1}{2}\left(\frac{\bar{x}-\mu}{\sigma/\sqrt{n}}\right)^2\right\},$$

$$-\infty < \bar{x} < \infty,\ n = 1, 2, 3, \ldots, \sigma > 0.$$

Furthermore, if $\bar{X} = (1/n)\sum_{i=1}^{n} X_i$, then the distribution of $\{(n-1)S^2/\sigma^2\}$,

$$S^2 = \frac{1}{n-1}\sum_{i=1}^{n}(X_i - \bar{X})^2$$

is $\chi^2(n-1)$. The variate S^2 is called the *sample variance*, and it is used to estimate the variance of a given distribution function.

7.8   Conditional Expectation

We have seen in the study of two-dimensional random variables that conditional expectation is simply the expected value of a variate computed with respect to a conditional distribution and that its geometrical interpretation is a regression curve. The extension of conditional expectation to the multivariate case is briefly discussed below.

Definition 7.8.1   Let $f(x_1, x_2, \ldots, x_n)$ be the joint probability density function of the continuous n-dimensional random variable $(X_1, X_2, \ldots, X_n)$. The conditional expected value of the variate $(X_1 X_2 \cdots X_r)$, $r < n$, given that $X_{r+1} = x_{r+1}, X_{r+2} = x_{r+2}, \ldots, X_n = x_n$, is

$$E(X_1 X_2 \cdots X_r | X_{r+1} = x_{r+1}, X_{r+2} = x_{r+2}, \ldots, X_n = x_n)$$

$$= \int_{-\infty}^{\infty} \int_{-\infty}^{\infty} \cdots \int_{-\infty}^{\infty} x_1 x_2 \cdots x_r h(x_1, x_2, \ldots,$$

$$x_r | x_{r+1}, x_{r+2}, \ldots, x_n) dx_1\, dx_2 \cdots dx_r. \tag{7.8.1}$$

Thus, the above definition is interpreted as the average value of $(X_1 X_2 \cdots X_r)$, when it is known that $X_{r+1} = x_{r+1}, X_{r+2} = x_{r+2}, \ldots, X_n = x_n$. Of course, in order for the conditional expectation to exist, the right-hand side of Equation (7.8.1) must be absolutely convergent.

The conditional expectation of $(X_1 X_2 \cdots X_r)$, given $X_{r+1} = x_{r+1}, X_{r+2} = x_{r+2}, \ldots, X_n = x_n$, $r < n$, is *constant* if $x_{r+1}, x_{r+2}, \ldots, x_n$ are fixed values.

However, in general, the $E(X_1 X_2 \cdots X_r | X_{r+1} = x_{r+1}, X_{r+2} = x_{r+2}, \ldots,$ $X_n = x_n)$ is a function of $x_{r+1}, x_{r+2}, \ldots, x_n$, values of the $(n - r)$-dimensional random variable $(X_{r+1}, X_{r+2}, \ldots, X_n)$; and, thus, it is a random variable.

If the random variables in the sequence $(X_1, X_2, \ldots, X_n)$ are mutually independent, then

$$E(X_1 X_2 \cdots X_r | X_{r+1} = x_{r+1}, X_{r+2} = x_{r+2}, \ldots, X_n = x_n)$$

$$= \int_{-\infty}^{\infty} \int_{-\infty}^{\infty} \cdots \int_{-\infty}^{\infty} x_1 x_2 \cdots x_r \frac{f(x_1, x_2, \ldots, x_n)}{f_{n-r}(x_{r+1}, x_{r+2}, \ldots, x_n)} dx_1 dx_2 \cdots dx_r$$

$$= \int_{-\infty}^{\infty} \int_{-\infty}^{\infty} \cdots \int_{-\infty}^{\infty} x_1 x_2 \cdots x_r \frac{f_r(x_1, x_2, \ldots, x_r) f_{n-r}(x_{r+1}, x_{r+2}, \ldots, x_n)}{f_{n-r}(x_{r+1}, x_{r+2}, \ldots, x_n)}$$

$$dx_1 dx_2 \cdots dx_r$$

$$= \int_{-\infty}^{\infty} \int_{-\infty}^{\infty} \cdots \int_{-\infty}^{\infty} x_1 x_2 \cdots x_r f_r(x_1, x_2, \ldots, x_r) dx_1 dx_2 \cdots dx_r$$

$$= \int_{-\infty}^{\infty} x_1 f_1(x_1) dx_1 \int_{-\infty}^{\infty} x_2 f_2(x_2) dx_2 \cdots \int_{-\infty}^{\infty} x_r f(x_r) dx_r$$

$$= E(X_1) E(X_2) \cdots E(X_r).$$

Theorem 7.8.1   Let $(X_1, X_2, \ldots, X_n)$ be an n-dimensional random variable. If the conditional expectation

$$E(X_1 X_2 \cdots X_r | X_{r+1} = x_{r+1}, X_{r+2} = x_{r+2}, \ldots, X_n = x_n), r < n,$$

exists, then

$$E\{E(X_1 X_2 \cdots X_r | X_{r+1} = x_{r+1}, X_{r+2} = x_{r+2}, \ldots, X_n = x_n)\}$$

$$= E(X_1 X_2 \cdots X_r).$$

Proof   Let $f(x_1, x_2, \ldots, x_n)$, $h_{n-r}(x_{r+1}, x_{r+2}, \ldots, x_n)$ and $h(x_1, x_2, \ldots, x_r | x_{r+1}, x_{r+2}, \ldots, x_n)$ be the probability density function of the continuous random variable $(X_1, X_2, \ldots, X_n)$, the marginal probability density of the variate $(X_{r+1}, X_{r+2}, \ldots, X_n)$, and the conditional probability density function of the random variable $(X_1, X_2, \ldots, X_r | X_{r+1} = x_{r+1}, X_{r+2} = x_{r+2}, \ldots, X_n = x_n)$, respectively. Thus,

$$E[E(X_1 X_2 \cdots X_r | X_{r+1} = x_{r+1}, X_{r+2} = x_{r+2}, \ldots, X_n = x_n)]$$

$$= \int_{-\infty}^{\infty} \int_{-\infty}^{\infty} \cdots \int_{-\infty}^{\infty} E(X_1 X_2 \cdots X_r$$

$$| X_{r+1} = x_{r+1}, X_{r+2} = x_{r+2}, \ldots, X_n = x_n) \cdot$$

$$h_{n-r}(x_{r+1}, x_{r+2}, \ldots, x_n) dx_{r+1} dx_{r+2} \cdots dx_n$$

$$= \int_{-\infty}^{\infty} \int_{-\infty}^{\infty} \cdots \int_{-\infty}^{\infty} \left\{ \int_{-\infty}^{\infty} \int_{-\infty}^{\infty} \cdots \int_{-\infty}^{\infty} x_1 x_2 \cdots x_r h \right.$$

$$\times (x_1, x_2, \ldots, x_r | x_{r+1}, x_{r+2}, \ldots, x_n) dx_1 \, dx_2 \cdots dx_r \bigg\}$$

$$h_{n-r}(x_{r+1}, x_{r+2}, \ldots, x_n) dx_{r+1} \, dx_{r+2} \cdots dx_n$$

$$= \int_{-\infty}^{\infty} \int_{-\infty}^{\infty} \cdots \int_{-\infty}^{\infty} \left\{ \int_{-\infty}^{\infty} \int_{-\infty}^{\infty} \cdots \int_{-\infty}^{\infty} x_1 x_2 \cdots x_r \frac{f(x_1, x_2, \ldots, x_n)}{h_{n-r}(x_{r+1}, x_{r+2}, \ldots, x_n)} \right.$$

$$\left. dx_1 \, dx_2 \cdots dx_r \right\} h_{n-r}(x_{r+1}, x_{r+2}, \ldots, x_n) dx_{r+1} \, dx_{r+2} \cdots dx_n.$$

Since the expected value exists, we can change the order of integration and have

$$E[E(X_1 X_2 \cdots X_r | X_{r+1} = x_{r+1}, X_{r+2} = x_{r+2}, \ldots, X_n = x_n)]$$

$$= \int_{-\infty}^{\infty} \int_{-\infty}^{\infty} \cdots \int_{-\infty}^{\infty} x_1 x_2 \cdots x_r \left\{ \int_{-\infty}^{\infty} \int_{-\infty}^{\infty} \cdots \int_{-\infty}^{\infty} \frac{f(x_1, x_2, \ldots, x_n)}{h_{n-r}(x_{r+1}, x_{r+2}, \ldots, x_n)} \right.$$

$$\left. h_{n-r}(x_{r+1}, x_{r+2}, \ldots, x_n) dx_{r+1} \, dx_{r+2} \cdots dx_n \right\} dx_1 \, dx_2 \cdots dx_r$$

$$= \int_{-\infty}^{\infty} \int_{-\infty}^{\infty} \cdots \int_{-\infty}^{\infty} x_1 x_2 \cdots x_r h_r(x_1, x_2, \ldots, x_r) dx_1 dx_2 \cdots dx_r$$

$$= E(X_1 X_2 \cdots X_r).$$

Thus, the expected value of the conditional expected value is equal to the unconditional expectation.

If $g(X_1, X_2, \ldots X_n)$ is some functional form of the n-dimensional random variable $(X_1, X_2, \ldots, X_n)$, the joint probability density function of which is $f(x_1, x_2, \ldots, x_n)$, then

$$E[g(X_1, X_2, \ldots, X_n) | x_{11} \le X_1 \le x_{12}, x_{21} \le X_2 \le x_{22}, \ldots, x_{r1} \le X_r \le x_{r2}]$$

$$= \int_{-\infty}^{\infty} \int_{-\infty}^{\infty} \cdots \int_{-\infty}^{\infty} g(x_1, x_2, \ldots, x_n)$$

$$\times \frac{f(x_1, x_2, \ldots, x_n)}{Pr(x_{11} \le X_1 \le x_{12}, x_{21} \le X_2 \le x_{22}, \ldots, x_{r1} \le X_r \le x_{r2})}$$

$$dx_1 \, dx_2 \cdots dx_n,$$

provided $Pr(x_{11} \le X_1 \le x_{12}, x_{21} \le X_2 \le x_{22}, \ldots, x_{r1} \le X_r \le x_{r2}) \ne 0$ and the multiple integral is absolutely convergent. Applying the mathematical method used in Section 6.8, the above expression reduces to

$$E[g(X_1, X_2, \ldots, X_n) | x_{11} \leq X_1 \leq x_{12}, x_{21} \leq X_2 \leq x_{22}, \ldots, x_{r1} \leq X_r \leq x_{r2}]$$

$$= \int_{-\infty}^{\infty} \int_{-\infty}^{\infty} \cdots \int_{-\infty}^{\infty} g(x_1, x_2, \ldots, x_n) \frac{f(x_1, x_2, \ldots, x_n)}{h_r(x_1, x_2, \ldots, x_r)}$$

$$\times \, dx_{r+1} dx_{r+2} \cdots dx_n, \text{ with } h_r(x_1, x_2, \ldots, x_r) > 0.$$

7.9 Summary

Let S be a sample space and $X_1(s), X_2(s), \ldots, X_n(s)$ real valued functions (defined on S), each assigning a number to each element of the sample space. Then we call $(X_1(s) = X_1, X_2(s) = X_2, \ldots, X_n(s) = X_n)$ an *n-dimensional random variable*.

Let $(X_1, X_2, \ldots, X_n)$ be an *n*-dimensional random variable. If $(X_1, X_2, \ldots, X_n)$ can assume all values in some noncountable (nondenumerable) set of the *n*-dimensional Euclidean space, than we call $(X_1, X_2, \ldots, X_n)$ an *n-dimensional continuous random variable*.

Let $(X_1, X_2, \ldots, X_n)$ be an *n*-dimensional continuous random variable. A function $f(x_1, x_2, \ldots, x_n)$ is called a *multivariate or joint probability density function* of the random variable $(X_1, X_2, \ldots, X_n)$ if the following conditions are satisfied:

(1) $f(x_1, x_2, \ldots, x_n) \geq 0$ for all $(x_1, x_2, \ldots, x_n) \in R_{X_1, X_2, \ldots, X_n}$

(2) $\underset{R_{X_1, X_2, \cdots, X_n}}{\int\int \cdots \int} f(x_1, x_2, \ldots, x_n) \, dx_1 \, dx_2 \cdots dx_n = 1,$

where the integration is performed over $R_{X_1, X_2, \ldots, X_n}$, in which $(X_1, X_2, \ldots, X_n)$ assumes all values.

The *multinomial* and *multivariate normal* probability density functions have been discussed.

The *multivariate cumulative distribution function* of the continuous *n*-dimensional random variable $(X_1, X_2, \ldots, X_n)$, having joint probability density function function $f(x_1, x_2, \ldots, x_n)$, is given by

$$F(x_1, x_2, \ldots, x_n) = P_r(X_1 \leq x_1, X_2 \leq x_2, \ldots, X_n \leq x_n)$$

$$= \int_{-\infty}^{x_n} \int_{-\infty}^{x_{n-1}} \cdots \int_{-\infty}^{x_1} f(y_1, y_2, \ldots, y_n) dy_1, \ldots dy_{n-1} dy_n.$$

It possesses the following properties:

(1) $F(\infty, \infty, \ldots, \infty) = 1$;

(2) $F(x_1, x_2, \ldots, x_n) = 0$, if at least one of the x_i's is $-\infty$;

(3) $F(x_1, x_2, \ldots, x_n)$ is monotone nondecreasing in each variate separately;

(4) $F(x_1, x_2, \ldots, x_n)$ is continuous from the right in each variate separately;

(5) if $F(x_1, x_2, \ldots, x_n)$ is continuous and if its partial derivatives exist for all x_i's, then

$$\frac{\partial^n}{\partial x_1 \, \partial x_2 \cdots \partial x_n} F(x_1, x_2, \ldots, x_n) = f(x_1, x_2, \ldots, x_n).$$

Let $f(x_1, x_2, \ldots, x_n)$ be the joint probability density function of the variate $(X_1, X_2, \ldots, X_n)$. The *marginal probability density function* of $(X_1, X_2, \ldots, X_r), r < n$ is

$$h_r(x_1, x_2, \ldots, x_r) = \int_{-\infty}^{\infty} \cdots \int_{-\infty}^{\infty} f(x_1, x_2, \ldots, x_n) dx_{r+1} \cdots dx_n.$$

The *conditional probability density function* of the random variable $(X_1, X_2, \ldots, X_r), r < n$, given

$$(X_{r+1}, X_{r+2}, \ldots, X_n),$$

is

$$g_r(x_1, x_2, \ldots, x_r \,|\, x_{r+1}, \ldots, x_n)$$
$$= \frac{f(x_1, x_2, \ldots x_n)}{h_{n-r}(x_{r+1}, x_{r+2}, \ldots, x_n)}, \quad h_{n-r}(x_{r+1}, x_{r+2}, \ldots, x_n) > 0.$$

The random variables of the sequence $(X_1, X_2, \ldots, X_n)$ are said to be *mutually independent* if

$$F(x_1, x_2, \ldots, x_n) = F_1(x_1) F_2(x_2) \cdots F_n(x_n)$$

for all real n-tuples $(x_1, x_2, \ldots, x_n)$.

The method of deriving probability distributions of a sequence of functions of the n-dimensional random variable is given by Theorem 7.6.1.

The study of *expected value, moments,* and *characteristic functions* is discussed for n random variables.

The *conditional expected value of the variate* $(X_1 X_2 \cdots X_r), r < n$, given $X_{r+1} = x_{r+1}, X_{r+2} = x_{r+2}, \ldots, X_n = x_n$, is given by

$$E(X_1 X_2 \cdots X_r \,|\, X_{r+1} = x_{r+1}, X_{r+2} = x_{r+2}, \ldots, X_n = x_n)$$
$$= \int_{-\infty}^{\infty} \cdots \int_{-\infty}^{\infty} x_1, x_2, \ldots, x_r h(x_1, x_2, \ldots, x_r \,|\, x_{r+1}, x_{r+2}, \ldots, x_n)$$
$$dx_1 dx_2 \cdots dx_r.$$

Problems

7.1.   A die is rolled 10 times. If X, Y, and Z are random variables representing the number of sixes, fives, and fours, respectively, that turn up, derive the joint probability density function $f(x, y, z)$.

7.2.   Fifteen cards are drawn from an ordinary deck of cards. Let X, Y, and Z be random variables representing the number of spades, hearts, and diamonds, respectively, that are drawn. Exhibit the joint probability density function $f(x, y, z)$ if (a) there is replacement (b) there is no replacement.

7.3.   Five coins are tossed n times. Write the probability density of W, the number of times no heads appear; X, the number of times one head appears; Y, the number of times two heads appear; and Z, the number of times three heads appear.

7.4.   Five cards are drawn n times from a deck of cards containing five aces, four kings, and three queens. Find the probability density of W, the number of times no aces appear; X, the number of times one ace appears; Y, the number of times three aces appear; and Z, the number of times four aces appear if

   (a)   there is replacement   (b)   there is no replacement.

7.5.   The probability density function of X, Y, and Z is uniform throughout a cube that has vertices of $(3, 2, 0)$, $(3, 2, 1)$, $(3, 3, 0)$, $(3, 3, 1)$, $(4, 2, 0)$, $(4, 2, 1)$, $(4, 3, 0)$, and $(4, 3, 1)$. Obtain the joint probability density function of the random variable (X, Y, Z).

7.6.   If the probability density of X, Y, and Z is uniform throughout $0 \le x \le y \le z \le 1$, find the joint probability density function $f(x, y, z)$.

7.7.   If $f(x, y, z) = k$ for $0 \le x^2 \le y \le z \le 2$ and equals zero elsewhere, find k so that the function $f(x, y, z)$ is the joint probability density function of the random variable (X, Y, Z).

7.8.   If

$$f(w, x, y, z) = \begin{cases} kwxyz, & \text{for} \quad 1 \le w \le 7, 2 \le x \le 4, \\ & \qquad 3 \le y \le 5, 6 \le z \le 8, \\ 0, & \text{elsewhere,} \end{cases}$$

   find k so that the function $f(w, x, y, z)$ is a probability density function of the four-dimensional random variable (W, X, Y, Z).

7.9. Write the joint probability density function for W, X, Y, Z if it is uniform throughout a four-dimensional figure that has the following sixteen vertices: (a, b, c, d), where $a = 0, 1,\ \ b = 1, 3/2,\ \ c = 1, 2,$ and $d = 2, 5/2$.

7.10. If

$$f(w, x, y, z) = \begin{cases} kwxyz(z - y)(y - x)(x - w) & 0 \le w \le x \le y \le z \le 1, \\ 0, & \text{elsewhere,} \end{cases}$$

find k so that $f(w, x, y, z)$ is the joint probability density function of the random variable (W, X, Y, Z).

7.11. Find the cumulative distributions of the probability densities in Problems 7.5 through 7.7.

7.12. In Problems 7.8 through 7.10, find the cumulative distributions of the joint probability density functions.

7.13. Find the marginal probability densities of

(a) X (b) Y (c) XZ (d) YZ

in Problems 7.1, 7.2, 7.5, 7.6, and 7.7.

7.14. Find the marginal probability densities of

(a) W (b) (W, Z) (c) (X, Y) (d) (X, Z)
(e) (W, X, Y) (f) (W, X, Z) (g) (W, Y, Z) (h) (X, Y, Z)

for Problems 7.3, 7.4, 7.8, 7.9, and 7.10.

7.15. Find the following conditional probability density functions:

(a) $f(x|y)$ (b) $g(y|z)$ (c) $k_1(z|x, y)$ (d) $k_2(z|x, y)$
(e) $l(x, y|z)$

for Problems 7.1, 7.2, 7.5, 7.6, and 7.7, respectively.

7.16. Find the following conditional cumulative distribution functions:

(a) $F(x|y, z)$ (b) $G(y|x, z)$ (c) $H(z|x)$ (d) $L(x, z|y)$
(e) $M(y, z|x)$

for Problems 7.1, 7.2, 7.5, 7.6, and 7.7, respectively.

7.17. Find the following conditional probability density functions:

(a) $h(w|x)$ (b) $f(x|w, y)$ (c) $g(y|w, x, z)$ (d) $l(w, z|y)$
(e) $m(w, x, y|z)$

for Problems 7.3, 7.4, 7.8, 7.9, and 7.10, respectively.

7.18. Find the following conditional cumulative distribution functions:

    (a) $G(w|x, y, z)$ (b) $F(x|y, z)$ (c) $H(z|x)$
    (d) $L(x, z|w, y)$ (e) $M(x, y, z|w)$

for Problems 7.3, 7.4, 7.8, 7.9, and 7.10, respectively.

7.19. Determine whether the random variables involved in Problems 7.1 through 7.5 are mutually independent.

7.20. Determine whether the random variables involved in Problems 7.6 through 7.10 are mutually independent.

7.21. Let X_1 and X_2 be two independent random variables that have the same probability distribution: for $i = 1, 2$

$$Pr(X_i = -1) = \frac{1}{2} \quad \text{and} \quad Pr(X_i = 1) = \frac{1}{2}.$$

Further, let $X_3 = X_1 X_2$. Show that (X_1, X_3) and (X_2, X_3) are independent but that (X_1, X_2, X_3) are not independent.

7.22. Show that, for $n = 2, P^{-1} = \begin{bmatrix} \sigma_{11}{}^2 & \sigma_{12}{}^2 \\ \sigma_{21}{}^2 & \sigma_{22}{}^2 \end{bmatrix}$,

and $\rho = \sigma_{12}/\sigma_1\sigma_2$, the multivariate normal probability density function is given by

$$f(x) = \frac{1}{(2\pi)^{n/2}\sqrt{|p^{-1}|}} e^{-(1/2)(x-\mu)^T P(x-\mu)},$$

which reduces to

$$f(x_1, x_2) =$$

$$\frac{1}{(2\pi), \sigma_1\sigma_2\sqrt{1-\rho^2}} e^{-[1/2(1-\rho^2)]\left[\left(\frac{x_1-\mu_1}{\sigma_1}\right)^2\right.}$$

$$\left. + 2\rho\left(\frac{x_1-\mu_1}{\sigma_1}\right)\left(\frac{x_2-\mu_2}{\sigma_2}\right) + \left(\frac{x_2-\mu_2}{\sigma_2}\right)^2\right].$$

7.23. Let $Y_j = \sum_{i=1}^{j} X_i$ for $j = 1, 2, \ldots, n$. Find the joint probability density of $Y_1, Y_2, \ldots, Y_n$ if the joint probability density function of the n-dimensional random variable $(X_1, X_2, \ldots, X_n)$ is given by

    (a) $f(x_1, x_2, \ldots, x_n) = \dfrac{1}{(2\pi)^{n/2}\sigma^n} e^{-(1/2\sigma^2)\sum_{i=1}^{n}(x_i-\mu)^2}, \quad -\infty < x_i < \infty$

    (b) $f(x_1, x_2, \ldots, x_n) = \dfrac{1}{\beta^{n\alpha}[\Gamma(\alpha)]^n} \prod_{i=1}^{n} x_i^{\alpha-1} e^{-(1/\beta)\sum_{i=1}^{n} x_i}, \quad x_i > 0$

    (c) $f(x_1, x_2, \ldots, x_n) = \dfrac{\lambda^{\sum_{i=1}^{n} x_i} e^{-\lambda}}{\prod_{i=1}^{n} x_i!}, \quad x_i = 0, 1, 2, \ldots$

7.24. Do parts (a), (b), and (c) of Problem 7.23 if

(a) $Y_j = j \sum_{i=1}^{j} X_i$ (b) $Y_j = j \sum_{i=1}^{n} X_i$ (c) $Y_j = \dfrac{X_j}{\sum_{i=1}^{n} X_i}$.

7.25. Find

(a) $E(XYZ)$ (b) $E(XYZ)$ (c) $E(X^2 Y^3 Z^4)$
(d) $E(3X - Y^2 + 4Z)$ (e) $E(X + Y + Z)^2$

for the respective probability densities of Problems 7.1, 7.2, 7.5, 7.6, and 7.7.

7.26. Find

(a) $E(WXYZ)$ (b) $E(WXYZ)$
(c) $E(W^2 X^3 Y^4 Z^5)$ (d) $E(W + 2X^2 - 3Y + 4Z^2)$
(e) $E(W + X + Y + Z)^2$

for the respective probability densities of Problems 7.3, 7.4, 7.8, 7.9, and 7.10.

7.27. Let X_1, X_2, and X_3 be independent normally distributed random variables, with means 1, 2, 5 and standard deviations 2, 2, 4, respectively.

(a) Find the moment generating function of $Y = (X_1 - 2X_2 + X_3)$.
(b) Determine the probability that Y exceeds eight.

7.28. Find the moment of order

(a) $1 + 2 + 3$ (b) $3 + 3 + 3$ (c) $n_1 + n_2 + n_3$

for the respective probability densities of Problems 7.5, 7.6, and 7.7.

7.29. Do Problem 7.28 for central moments.

7.30. Find the moment of order

(a) $1 + 2 + 3 + 4$ (b) $3 + 3 + 3 + 3$ (c) $n_1 + n_2 + n_3 + n_4$

for the respective probability densities of Problems 7.8, 7.9, and 7.10.

7.31. Do Problem 7.30 for central moments.

7.32. Let $X_1, X_2, \ldots, X_n$ be a sequence of random variables having the same variance σ^2. If $\bar{X}$ is the sample mean, $\bar{X} = (1/n) \sum_{i=1}^{n} X_i$, show that

(a) $\mathrm{Var}(\bar{X}) = \dfrac{\sigma^2}{n}$ (b) $E\left[\sum_{i=1}^{n} (X_i - \bar{X})^2 \right] = (n-1)\sigma^2$

7.33. Let $X_1, X_2, \ldots, X_n$ be a sequence of random variables having a common standard deviation, σ. The coefficient of correlation between any two of them is ρ. Show that:

(a) the variance of their mean is given by

$$\frac{\sigma^2}{n} + \left(1 - \frac{1}{n}\right)\sigma^2,$$

(b) $E\left[\sum_{i=1}^{n} (X_i - \bar{X})^2\right] = (n-1)(1-\rho)\sigma^2$

7.34. Find the characteristic function for the probability densities of Problems 7.1, 7.2 (a), 7.3, and 7.4 (a).

7.35. Determine the characteristic function for the probability densities of Problems 7.5 through 7.10.

7.36. Using the results of Problems 7.34 and 7.35, find the marginal characteristic functions of

(a) Y (b) (X, Y) (c) (Y, Z) (d) W (e) (W, Z)
(f) (X, Y, Z)

for the respective probability densities of Problems 7.1, 7.3, 7.5, 7.7, 7.8, and 7.9.

7.37. Find the probability density function of

$$\frac{1}{n}\sum_{i=1}^{n} X_i$$

if, for $i = 1, 2, \ldots, n$:

(a) X_i is binomially distributed with parameters m and p
(b) X_i has the Poisson distribution with parameter λ
(c) X_i has the geometric probability density function with parameter p
(d) X_i has the negative binomial distribution with parameters k and p
(e) X_i has the gamma probability density with parameters α and β

(f) $f(x_i) = \frac{1}{2}e^{-|x_i|}$ $-\infty < x_i < \infty$

(g) $f(x_i) = \begin{cases} x_i, & 0 \le x_i \le 1, \\ 2 - x_i, & 1 < x_i \le 2, \\ 0, & \text{elsewhere.} \end{cases}$

7.38. Find the following conditional expectations:

(a) $E(X|Y=y)$ (b) $E(X|y, z)$ (c) $E(XY|Z=z)$

for the probability densities of Problems 7.1, 7.2, 7.5, 7.6, and 7.7

7.39. Find

(a) $E(W|X=x)$ (b) $E(W|X=x, Y=y)$
(c) $E(W|x, y, z)$ (d) $E(WX|Y=y)$
(e) $E(WX|y, z)$ (f) $E(WXY|Z=z)$

for the probability densities of Problems 7.3, 7.4, 7.8, 7.9, and 7.10.

7.40. Find

(a) $E(X+Y+Z|X, Y, Z > 2)$ for the probability densities of Problems 7.1 and 7.2

(b) $E\left(X+Y+Z|X>\frac{7}{2}, Y>\frac{5}{2}, Z>\frac{1}{2}\right)$ for Problem 7.5

(c) $E(X+Y+Z|X, Y, Z > 2)$ for the probability densities of Problems 7.6 and 7.7

7.41. Find

(a) $E(W+X+Y|W, X, Y, Z > k)$ for the probability densities of Problems 7.3 and 7.4
(b) $E(W+X+Y+Z|W, X > 3, Y > 4, Z > 7)$ for the probability density of Problem 7.8

7.42. Find

(a) $E\left(W+X+Y+Z|W>\frac{1}{2}, X>\frac{5}{4}, Y>\frac{3}{2}, Z>\frac{9}{4}\right)$

(b) $E\left(W+X+Y+Z|W, X, Y, Z>\frac{1}{2}\right)$

for Problem 7.10.

7.43. Let $X_1, X_2, \ldots, X_n$ be a sequence of mutually independent random variables, each of which is normally distributed with mean μ and variance σ^2. Show that

$$U = \sum_{i=1}^{n}\left(\frac{x_i - \mu}{\sigma}\right)^2$$

is chi-square distributed with n degrees of freedom.

References

[1] Anderson, T. W. *An Introduction to Multivariate Statistical Analysis.* New York: John Wiley and Sons, Inc., 1958.

Suggested Supplementary Reading

Feller, W. *An Introduction to Probability Theory and Its Applications.* Vol. 1, Second Edition. New York: John Wiley and Sons, Inc., 1960.

Fisz, M. *Probability Theory and Mathematical Statistics.* Third Edition. New York: John Wiley and Sons, Inc., 1962.

Harris, B. *Theory of Probability.* Reading, Massachusetts: Addison-Wesley Publishing Company, Inc., 1966.

Papoulis, A. *Probability Random Variables and Stochastic Processes.* New York: McGraw-Hill Book Company, Inc., 1965.

Parzen, E. *Modern Probability Theory and Its Applications.* New York: John Wiley and Sons, Inc., 1960.

Limit Theorems

8

8.0 Introduction

We shall begin this chapter with the classical inequality, derived by *Chebyshev*, which justifies the role that the standard deviation plays as a measure of variability. Following the discussion, we shall, in Section 8.2 and 8.3, expound and clarify the relative frequency interpretation of probability that was introduced in Chapter 1. Beginning our study is an introduction to the *Law of Large Numbers*, determined by *Bernoulli*; we shall continue our discussion into more general forms of this law. Specifically, we shall distinguish between the *Weak* and the *Strong Laws of Large Numbers* and shall illustrate their meanings with various examples.

The remainder of the chapter is devoted to the *Central Limit Theorem*, which is one of the most important theorems in the whole of mathematics. In a sequence of mutually independent random variables, $X_1, X_2, \ldots, X_n$, their sum, for sufficiently large n, is *approximately normally distributed* under certain conditions. To be practical, we shall confine our study to two versions of the Central Limit Theorem. To conclude, we shall prove the asymptotic normality of the binomial, Poisson, gamma, and $\chi^2(n)$ probability distributions and illustrate their usefulness by means of several problems.

8.1 Chebyshev's Inequality

In this section, we shall discuss a well-known inequality that was derived by the great Russian probabilist P. L. Chebyshev (Tchebysheff) (1821–1894). The Chebyshev inequality will justify our previous statement that the variance measures variability about the expected value of a random variable.

Theorem 8.1.1 (Chebyshev's Inequality)   Let X be a discrete or continuous random variable, with $E(X) = \mu$ and $\text{Var}(X) = \sigma^2$. Then, for any positive number k, we have

$$Pr(|X - \mu| \geq k\sigma) \leq \frac{1}{k^2}. \tag{8.1.1}$$

Note that an equivalent of expression (8.1.1) is

$$Pr(|X - \mu| < k\sigma) \geq 1 - \frac{1}{k^2}. \tag{8.1.2}$$

Proof   Let $f(x)$ be the probability density function of the continuous random variable X. We know that the definition of variance is

$$\text{Var}(X) = \sigma^2 = \int_{-\infty}^{\infty} (x - \mu)^2 f(x)\, dx. \tag{8.1.3}$$

For some $c > 0$, we can break up the range of integration of (8.1.3) into three parts, as shown in Figure 8.1.1.

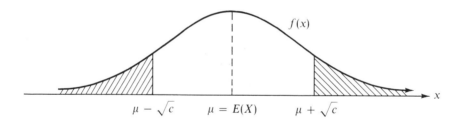

Figure 8.1.1

Accordingly,

$$\sigma^2 = \int_{-\infty}^{\mu-\sqrt{c}} (x-\mu)^2 f(x)\, dx + \int_{\mu-\sqrt{c}}^{\mu+\sqrt{c}} (x-\mu)^2 f(x)\, dx + \int_{\mu+\sqrt{c}}^{\infty} (x-\mu)^2 f(x)\, dx$$

$$\geq \int_{-\infty}^{\mu-\sqrt{c}} (x-\mu)^2 f(x)\, dx + \int_{\mu+\sqrt{c}}^{\infty} (x-\mu)^2 f(x)\, dx \tag{8.1.3}$$

because the middle term is nonnegative. We shall replace the factor $(x - \mu)^2$ by c. Note that $(x - \mu)^2 \geq c$ if and only if $x \geq \mu + \sqrt{c}$ or $x \leq \mu - \sqrt{c}$. Thus, inequality (8.1.2) still holds, and

$$\sigma^2 \geq \int_{-\infty}^{\mu-\sqrt{c}} cf(x)\,dx + \int_{\mu+\sqrt{c}}^{\infty} cf(x)\,dx = c\{Pr(X \leq \mu - \sqrt{c}) + Pr(X \geq \mu + \sqrt{c})\}$$

or

$$Pr\{(X - \mu) \leq -\sqrt{c}\} + Pr\{(X - \mu) \geq \sqrt{c}\} \leq \frac{\sigma^2}{c}.$$

It follows that

$$Pr(|X - \mu| \geq \sqrt{c}) \leq \frac{\sigma^2}{c}. \tag{8.1.4}$$

If we let $c = k^2\sigma^2$ in Equation (8.1.4), we have the desired result

$$Pr(|X - \mu| \geq k\sigma) \leq \frac{1}{k^2}.$$

The proof is analogous when the random variable is discrete.

What is important about Chebyshev's Inequality is that we can compute upper (or lower) bounds for quantities such as $Pr(|X - \mu| \geq k)$ from the knowledge of σ^2 and μ without knowing the probability density function of the random variable X. Of course, if the probability distribution of the variate X *is* known, we can compute $E(X)$ and $Var(X)$ and, thus, be able to compute the above probabilities exactly. However, in many instances involving physical phenomena, the distribution is not known; in such cases, inequality (8.1.1) gives us important information about the random variable.

In order to justify our initial remark that the variance measures (or controls) the spread or dispersion of the distribution of the variate X, with respect to its $E(X)$, we can write Inequality (8.1.2) as

$$Pr(\mu - k\sigma \leq X \leq \mu + k\sigma) \geq 1 - \frac{1}{k^2}.$$

Thus, the values of X falling in the interval from $\mu - k\sigma$ to $\mu + k\sigma$, inclusive, account for at least $1 - 1/k^2$ of the total probability. That is, the probability that the variate assumes a value within two standard deviations of its expected value is at least 3/4, the probability that it assumes a value within three standard deviations of μ is at least 8/9, the probability that it assumes a value within four standard deviations of the μ is at least 15/16, and so on. Therefore, it is clear that, if the variance is small, most of the probability distribution of X is concentrated near the $E(X)$. Note that $Var(X) = 0$ (random variable is *degenerate*) implies that all the probability is concentrated at the point $E(X)$. This condition is obvious in inequality 8.1.4 for $c > 0$:

$$Pr(|X - \mu| \geq \sqrt{c}) = 0,$$

or

$$Pr(|X - \mu| < \sqrt{c}) = 1.$$

A generalization of Chebyshev's Inequality is the important inequality developed by A. N. Kolmogorov.

Theorem 8.1.2 (Kolmogorov's Inequality).   Let $X_1, X_2, \ldots, X_n$ be a sequence of independent random variables (discrete or continuous), with $E(X_i^2) < \infty, i = 1, 2, \ldots, n$, and $Y_r = X_1 + X_2 + \cdots + X_r, r \leq n$. Then, for any positive number α, we have

$$Pr\left(\max_{1 \leq i \leq r} |Y_i - E(Y_i)| \geq \alpha\right) \leq \frac{1}{\alpha^2} [\mathrm{Var}(Y_n)], \ \mathrm{Var}(Y_n) = \mathrm{Var}\left(\sum_{i=1}^{n} X_i\right).$$

It is clear that, when $n = 1$ and $k = \alpha/\sqrt{\mathrm{Var}(Y_n)}$, we obtain the Chebyshev Inequality. For the proof of the theorem, we suggest Harris' book on the *Theory of Probability* (Suggested Supplementary Reading).

8.2   Bernoulli's Law of Large Numbers

In Section 1.1, we defined the relative frequency interpretation of probability as

$$\lim_{n \to \infty} \frac{S_n^*}{n} = p,$$

where n is the total number of trials in a given problem, S_n^* is the number of occurrences of the event S^*, and p is the probability of the event. The limit in the definition suggests that its applicability to various scientific problems where n is almost always finite will not be very extensive. However, despite this limitation, the frequency interpretation of probability is one of the most popular definitions among scientists. From a practical point of view, the limitation affects the accuracy of measuring p; the accuracy increases as the number of trials becomes very large. This convergence is stated more precisely as the *Law of Large Numbers*, which was first discovered by Jacob Bernoulli (1654-1705).

Theorem 8.2.1 (The Bernoulli Law of Large Numbers).   Let S_n^* be the observed number of successes in n independent repeated trials; p is the probability of success, and $1 - p$ is the probability of failure at each trial. Let

$$f_n = \frac{S_n^*}{n}$$

be the relative frequency of the observed number of successes in n trials. Then, for every $\varepsilon > 0$, we have

$$Pr(|f_n - p| < \varepsilon) \to 1 \quad \text{as} \quad n \to \infty \tag{8.2.1}$$

or, equivalently,

$$Pr(|f_n - p| \geq \varepsilon) \to 0 \quad \text{as} \quad n \to \infty. \tag{8.2.2}$$

Proof   The number of times the event S^* occurs, S_n^*, is a random variable binomially distributed, with $E(S_n^*) = np$ and $\text{Var}(S_n^*) = np(1 - p)$. It follows that

$$E(f_n) = E\left(\frac{S_n^*}{n}\right) = \frac{1}{n} E(S_n^*) = p \quad \text{and} \quad \text{Var}(f_n) = \text{Var}\left(\frac{S_n^*}{n}\right)$$

$$= \frac{1}{n^2} \text{Var}(S_n^*) = \frac{p(1 - p)}{n}.$$

The conditions of Chebyshev's Inequality are satisfied. Thus, applying Equation (8.1.1), we have

$$Pr\left(\left|f_n - p\right| \geq k\sqrt{\frac{p(1 - p)}{n}}\right) \leq \frac{1}{k^2}. \tag{8.2.3}$$

Choosing

$$\varepsilon = k\sqrt{\frac{p(1 - p)}{n}}, \quad \text{which implies} \quad k^2 = \frac{n\varepsilon^2}{p(1 - p)},$$

inequality (8.2.3) can be written as

$$Pr(|f_n - p| \geq \varepsilon) \leq \frac{p(1 - p)}{n\varepsilon^2}. \tag{8.2.4}$$

Thus, for any $\varepsilon > 0$, no matter how small,

$$Pr(|f_n - p| \geq \varepsilon) \leq \frac{p(1 - p)}{n\varepsilon^2} \to 0 \quad \text{as} \quad n \to \infty,$$

or

$$Pr(|f_n - p| < \varepsilon) = 1 - Pr(|f_n - p| \geq \varepsilon)$$

$$= 1 - \frac{p(1 - p)}{n\varepsilon^2} \to 1 \quad \text{as} \quad n \to \infty.$$

Therefore, expressions (8.2.1) and (8.2.2) simply state that, as n, the number of trials, tends to infinity, the relative frequency of successes in the n trials converges to the true value of p, the probability of a success on any individual trial. However, from the practical point of view, n is finite, and we are interested in determining the number of trials needed to place the observed relative frequency within a specified distance ε from the true value p, with a high probability. Thus, for a preassigned $\varepsilon > 0$, we want to determine n so that

$$Pr(|f_n - p| < \varepsilon) \geq 1 - \alpha, \quad 0 < \alpha < 1. \tag{8.2.5}$$

The value of n that satisfies the above inequality is obtained as follows: Inequality (8.2.4) can be written as

$$Pr(|f_n - p| < \varepsilon) \geq 1 - \frac{p(1-p)}{n\varepsilon^2}. \tag{8.2.6}$$

Using the fact that $p(1-p) \leq 1/4$ for all p, $0 \leq p \leq 1$, inequality (8.2.6) becomes

$$Pr(|f_n - p| < \varepsilon) \geq 1 - \frac{1}{4n\varepsilon^2}. \tag{8.2.7}$$

Choosing $n \geq 1/4\alpha\varepsilon^2$, $0 < \alpha < 1$, inequality (8.2.5) is satisfied. Thus, with this choice of n, we can conclude that, with probability at least $1 - \alpha$, the relative frequency is within ε units of the true value of p. Note that the validity of $p(1-p) \leq 1/4$ follows from the fact that

$$y = p(1-p), \quad 0 \leq p \leq 1$$

attains its maximum when $p = 1/2$, which implies that $y = 1/4$, and, thus, that $p(1-p) \leq 1/4$.

Example 8.2.1   Suppose that the failure of a certain component follows the binomial probability distribution, with unknown mean value, p. That is, $f(x) = p^x(1-p)^{1-x}$ for $x = 0$, 1, and zero, elsewhere. How many components must one test in order that the sample mean, $\overline{X}$, will lie within .4 of the true state of nature with probability at least as great as .95?

Solution: Here $\varepsilon = .4$; and, using inequality (8.2.7), we have

$$Pr(|\overline{X} - p| < .4) \geq 1 - \frac{1}{4n(.4)^2} = .95$$

or

$$n \geq \frac{1}{4(.05)(.4)^2} = \frac{1}{.032} = 31.25 .$$

Thus, with a sample of $n \geq 32$ components, we can conclude that

$$Pr(-.4 < (\overline{X} - p) < .4) \geq .95.$$

8.3 Weak and Strong Laws of Large Numbers

In this section, we will continue our discussion into more general forms of the *Law of Large Numbers*.

Let $X_1, X_2, \ldots, X_n$ be a sequence of mutually independent random variables, with a common probability density function, $E(X_i) = \mu$; and

$$S_n = X_1 + X_2 + \cdots + X_n.$$

Assume that the random variable $X_i = 1$ or 0, with respective probabilities p and $1 - p$ depending upon whether the ith trial results in a success or a failure. Then S_n is binomially distributed, with $E(S_n) = np$ and $Var(S_n) = np(1 - p)$. Applying the results of the previous section, we can write

$$Pr\left(\left|\frac{S_n}{n} - p\right| < \varepsilon\right) \to 1 \quad \text{as} \quad n \to \infty.$$

That is, for large n, the average portion of successes S_n/n is likely to lie near p, with high probability.

The above connection of Bernoulli trials and the theory of random variables is a special case of the *Weak Law of Large Numbers (WLLN)*.

Theorem 8.3.1 (WLLN)   Let $X_1, X_2, \ldots, X_n$ be a sequence of mutually independent random variables, with a common distribution. If $\mu = E(X_i)$ exists, then, for every $\varepsilon > 0$,

$$Pr\left(\left|\frac{S_n}{n} - \mu\right| < \varepsilon\right) \to 1 \quad \text{as} \quad n \to \infty. \tag{8.3.1}$$

Thus, without any knowledge of the probability distribution function of the variate S_n, the WLLN states that the sample mean, $\overline{X} = S_n/n = (1/n)\sum_1^n x_i$, will differ from the population mean by less than an arbitrary constant, $\varepsilon > 0$, with a probability that tends to 1 as n tends to ∞. Of course, if we assume the existence of a common variance, $\sigma^2 = Var(X_i)$, applying Chebyshev's Inequality to the proof of Theorem (8.3.1) is trivial.

The theorem of the WLLN was first proved, in 1929, by the Russian mathematician A. Khintchine. See Feller's book, *An Introduction to Probability Theory and Its Applications* (Suggested Supplementary Reading), for a further discussion. We shall, however, prove the WLLN for discrete random variables.

Proof   For an $i = 1, 2, \ldots, n$ and fixed $\delta > 0$, we will define two new sequences of random variables, which are functions of X_i, as follows:

$$Y_i = \begin{cases} X_i, & \text{if } |X_i| \leq \delta n, \\ 0, & \text{if } |X_i| > \delta n \end{cases} \quad \text{and} \quad Z_i = \begin{cases} 0, & \text{if } |X_i| \leq \delta n, \\ X_i, & \text{if } |X_i| > \delta n. \end{cases} \quad (8.3.2)$$

Let $p(x_j)$ be the common probability density function of X_i, $i = 1, 2, \ldots, n$. Since $E(X_i) = \mu$ is assumed to exist, then

$$\sum_j |x_j| p(x_j) = C < \infty.$$

The expected value of Y_i is

$$\mu_n = E(Y_i) = \sum_{|x_j| \leq \delta n} x_j p(x_j),$$

where the summation is over those j's for which $|x_j| \leq \delta n$. Then, as $n \to \infty$, $|x_j| \leq \delta n$ for all j so that $\mu_n \to \mu$. This condition implies that for all $\gamma > 0$, there exists a k_1 such that, for all $n \geq k_1$,

$$|\mu_n - \mu| < \gamma. \quad (8.3.3)$$

The variance of Y_i is

$$\begin{aligned} \text{Var}(Y_i) &= E(Y_i^2) - [E(Y_i)]^2 \\ &\leq E(Y_i^2) \\ &= \sum_{|x_j| \leq \delta n} x_j^2 p(x_j) \\ &= \sum_{|x_j| \leq \delta n} |x_j| |x_j| p(x_j) \\ &\leq \sum_{|x_j| \leq \delta n} n |x_j| p(x_j). \end{aligned}$$

But

$$n\delta \sum_{|x_j| \leq \delta n} |x_j| p(x_j) \leq n\delta \sum_{\text{all } j} |x_j| p(x_j) = n\delta C.$$

Thus, $\text{Var}(Y_i) \leq n\delta C$.

The Y_i's are mutually independent random variables because the X_i's were defined as such. Therefore,

$$\text{Var}(Y_1 + Y_2 + \cdots + Y_n) = \sum_{i=1}^{n} \text{Var}(Y_i)$$

$$\leq \sum_{i=1}^{n} n\delta C$$

$$= n^2 \delta C < \infty.$$

Since the variance exists and is finite, we apply Chebyshev's Inequality and have

$$Pr\left(\left|\frac{Y_1 + Y_2 + \cdots + Y_n}{n} - \mu_n\right| \geq \gamma\right) \leq \frac{\text{Var}\left(\dfrac{Y_1 + Y_2 + \cdots + Y_n}{n}\right)}{\gamma^2}$$

$$\leq \frac{n^2 \delta C}{n^2 \gamma^2} = \frac{\delta C}{\gamma^2}. \qquad (8.3.4)$$

Inequality (8.3.4) can be written as

$$Pr\left(\left|\left(\frac{Y_1 + Y_2 + \cdots + Y_n}{n} - \mu\right) + (\mu - \mu_n)\right| < \gamma\right) \geq 1 - \frac{\delta C}{\gamma^2}. \qquad (8.3.5)$$

Using the facts that $|a + b| \leq |a| + |b|$ and $|a - b| \geq |a| - |b|$ and $|\mu_n - \mu| < \gamma$ for $n \geq k_1$, we can write

$$\gamma > \left|\frac{Y_1 + Y_2 + \cdots + Y_n}{n} - \mu - (\mu_n - \mu)\right|$$

$$\geq \left|\frac{Y_1 + Y_2 + \cdots + Y_n}{n} - \mu\right| - |\mu - \mu_n|$$

$$> \left|\frac{Y_1 + Y_2 + \cdots + Y_n}{n} - \mu\right| - \gamma.$$

Then

$$2\gamma > \left|\frac{Y_1 + Y_2 + \cdots + Y_n}{n} - \mu\right| \quad \text{if} \quad \gamma > \left|\frac{Y_1 + Y_2 + \cdots + Y_n}{n} - \mu_n\right|,$$

and inequality (8.3.5) becomes

$$Pr\left(\left|\frac{Y_1 + Y_2 + \cdots + Y_n}{n} - \mu\right| < 2\gamma\right) = Pr\left(\left|\frac{Y_1 + Y_2 + \cdots + Y_n}{n} - \mu_n\right| < \gamma\right)$$

$$\geq 1 - \frac{\delta C}{\gamma^2},$$

or

$$Pr\left(\left|\frac{Y_1 + Y_2 + \cdots + Y_n}{n} - \mu\right| \ge 2\gamma\right) \le \frac{\delta C}{\gamma^2}. \tag{8.3.6}$$

Also, $Z_i = 0$ if $Y_i = X_i$ and

$$Pr(Z_i \ne 0) = Pr(Y_i = 0) = Pr(|X_i| > \delta n)$$

$$= \sum_{|x_j| > \delta n} p(x_j)$$

$$= \sum_{|x_j| > \delta n} \frac{|x_j|}{|x_j|} p(x_j)$$

$$\le \frac{1}{\delta n} \sum_{|x_j| > \delta n} |x_j| p(x_j) \to 0 \quad \text{as} \quad n \to \infty.$$

Hence, for an arbitrary $\delta_1 > 0$, there exists a k_2 such that, for $n \ge k_2$, $Pr(Z_i \ne 0) \le \delta_1$.
Thus,

$$Pr(Z_1 + Z_2 + \cdots + Z_n \ne 0) \le Pr(Z_1 \ne 0 \quad \text{or} \quad Z_2 \ne 0 \quad \text{or} \quad \cdots \quad \text{or} \quad Z_n \ne 0)$$

$$\le \sum_{i=1}^{n} Pr(Z_i \ne 0)$$

$$\le \sum_{i=1}^{n} \delta_1 = n\delta_1.$$

However,

$$S_n = X_1 + X_2 + \cdots + X_n$$
$$= (Y_1 + Z_1) + (Y_2 + Z_2) + \cdots + (Y_n + Z_n)$$
$$= (Y_1 + Y_2 + \cdots + Y_n) + (Z_1 + Z_2 + \cdots + Z_n)$$

and

$$Pr\left(\left|\frac{S_n}{n} - \mu\right| \ge 2\gamma\right)$$

$$= Pr\left(\left|\frac{Y_1 + Y_2 + \cdots + Y_n}{n} + \frac{Z_1 + Z_2 + \cdots + Z_n}{n} - \mu\right| \ge 2\gamma\right)$$

$$\le Pr\left(\left|\frac{Y_1 + Y_2 + \cdots + Y_n}{n} - \mu\right| \ge 2\gamma\right)$$

$$+ Pr\left(\left|\frac{Z_1 + Z_2 + \cdots + Z_n}{n}\right| \ne 0\right)$$

$$= Pr\left(\left|\frac{Y_1 + Y_2 + \cdots + Y_n}{n} - \mu\right| \ge 2\gamma\right)$$

$$+ Pr(Z_1 + Z_2 + \cdots + Z_n \ne 0).$$

Now, for $k = \max(k_1, k_2)$, $n > k$, the above inequality becomes

$$Pr\left(\left|\frac{S_n}{n} - \mu\right| > 2\gamma\right) \leq \frac{\delta C}{\gamma^2} + n\delta_1 = \gamma_1;$$ (8.3.7)

and, because δ, δ_1, and γ are arbitrary, the right-hand side of Equation (8.3.7) can be made as small as we wish. Therefore,

$$Pr\left(\left|\frac{S_n}{n} - \mu\right| \geq 2\gamma\right) \to 0 \quad \text{as} \quad n \to \infty.$$

The assumption of a common probability distribution for the X_i's in the above discussion can be eliminated. Let the sequence $X_1, X_2, \ldots, X_n$ of random variables be mutually independent, but not necessarily identically distributed, with finite means $\mu_i = E(X_i)$ and variances $\sigma_i^2 = \text{Var}(X_i)$. If

$$m_n = E(S_n) = E(X_1 + X_2 + \cdots + X_n)$$
$$= \mu_1 + \mu_2 + \cdots + \mu_n$$

and

$$s_n^2 = \text{Var}(S_n) = \text{Var}(X_1 + X_2 + \cdots + X_n)$$
$$= \text{Var}(X_1) + \text{Var}(X_2) + \cdots + \text{Var}(X_n)$$
$$= \sigma_1^2 + \sigma_2^2 + \cdots + \sigma_n^2,$$

then the WLLN holds for the sequence of variates $X_1, X_2, \ldots, X_n$. That is,

$$Pr\left(\left|\frac{S_n - m_n}{n}\right| < \varepsilon\right) \to 1 \quad \text{as} \quad n \to \infty.$$

Theorem 8.3.2   A sufficient condition for the sequence of random variables $X_1, X_2, \ldots, X_n, \ldots$, to satisfy the WLLN is

$$\frac{s_n}{n} \to 0 \quad \text{as} \quad n \to \infty.$$

Proof   Here

$$E\left(\frac{S_n}{n}\right) = \frac{m_n}{n}, \quad \text{and} \quad \text{Var}\left(\frac{S_n}{n}\right) = \frac{1}{n^2}\text{Var}(S_n) = \frac{s_n^2}{n^2}.$$

Applying Chebyshev's Inequality to S_n/n, we have

$$Pr\left(\left|\frac{S_n}{n} - \frac{m_n}{n}\right| \geq k\frac{s_n}{n}\right) \leq \frac{1}{k^2}$$

or

$$Pr\left(\left|\frac{S_n}{n} - \frac{m_n}{n}\right| \geq \varepsilon\right) \leq \frac{s_n^2}{n^2\varepsilon^2}. \tag{8.3.8}$$

If $s_n/n \to 0$ as $n \to \infty$, then, for $\varepsilon > 0$, $s_n^2/n^2\varepsilon^2 \to 0$ as $n \to \infty$, and we have

$$Pr\left(\left|\frac{S_n - m_n}{n}\right| < \varepsilon\right) \to 1 \quad \text{as} \quad n \to \infty.$$

Example 8.3.1   Let $X_1, X_2, \ldots, X_n$ represent the sales of a particular product per operating day, respectively. We will assume that the random variables are independent, and, due to various seasonal variations, they have different probability distributions. Past experience suggests that a good approximation for the expected sales, m_n, is \$2000; a good approximation for the variance, s_n^2, is \$1600. If we assume that $n = 320$ and $\varepsilon = 10$, we have, using inequality (8.3.8):

$$Pr\left(\left|\frac{S_n}{n} - 2000\right| \geq 10\right) \leq \frac{1600}{(10)^2 320}$$

or

$$Pr\left(1990 < \frac{S_n}{n} < 2010\right) \geq .95.$$

Example 8.3.2 (Feller)   Let $X_1, X_2, \ldots, X_n$ be a sequence of mutually independent random variables, with probability distributions defined below:

(a) $Pr(X_j = \sqrt{j}) = \frac{1}{2}$ and $Pr(X_j = -\sqrt{j}) = \frac{1}{2};$

(b) $Pr(X_j = 2^j) = 2^{-(2j+1)}$, $Pr(X_j = -2^j) = 2^{-(2j+1)}$

and $Pr(X_j = 0) = 1 - 2^{-2j};$

(c) $Pr(X_j = 2^j) = \frac{1}{2}$ and $Pr(X_j = -2^j) = \frac{1}{2}.$

We will show that the sequence of variates with probability distributions given by (b) satisfies the WLLN, but the sequence with probability distribution given by (a) and (c) does not satisfy the condition for the WLLN.

Solution: (a) $E(X_j) = \frac{1}{2}\sqrt{j} + \frac{1}{2}(-\sqrt{j}) = 0.$

$$\text{Var}(X_j) = E(X_j^2) - [E(X_j)]^2$$

$$= \frac{1}{2}(\sqrt{j})^2 + \frac{1}{2}(-\sqrt{j})^2$$

$$= j.$$

Thus,

$$s^2 = \sum_{j=1}^{n} j = \frac{n(n+1)}{2}$$

or

$$\frac{s_n^2}{n^2} = \frac{(n+1)}{2n} \to \frac{1}{2}, \quad \text{as} \quad n \to \infty$$

and the sufficient condition, stated in Theorem 8.3.2, for the WLLN is not satisfied.

(b) $E(X_j) = 2^{-(2j+1)}(2^j) + 2^{-(2j+1)}(-2^j) = 0;$

$\quad\quad \mathrm{Var}(X_j) = E(X_j^2) = 2^{-(2j+1)}(2^j)^2 + 2^{-(2j+1)}(-2^j)^2 = 1.$

Thus,

$$s_n^2 = \sum_{j=1}^{n} \mathrm{Var}(X_j) = n.$$

Therefore,

$$\frac{s_n^2}{n^2} = \frac{1}{n} \to 0 \quad \text{as} \quad n \to \infty,$$

which implies that the sequence of variates obeys the WLLN.

(c) $E(X_j) = \frac{1}{2}(2^j) + \frac{1}{2}(-2^j) = 0.$

$$\mathrm{Var}(X_j) = E(X_j^2) = \frac{1}{2}(2^j)^2 + \frac{1}{2}(-2^j)^2$$

$$= 2^{2j}.$$

Now

$$s_n^2 = \sum_{j=1}^{n} \mathrm{Var}(X_j) = 2^2 + 2^4 + \cdots + 2^{2n}$$

$$= \frac{4(4^n - 1)}{3}$$

or

$$\frac{s_n^2}{n^2} = \frac{4(4^n - 1)}{3n^2},$$

which diverges as $n \to \infty$; and again the condition for the WLLN is not satisfied.

Example 8.3.3   Let $X_1, X_2, \ldots, X_n$ be a sequence of mutually independent random variables, with probability distributions given by

(a) $Pr(X_i = i) = \dfrac{1}{2}$ and $Pr(X_i = -i) = \dfrac{1}{2}$

and

(b) $Pr(X_i = \sqrt{\ln(i + \alpha)}) = \dfrac{1}{2}$ and $Pr(X_i = -\sqrt{\ln(i + \alpha)}) = \dfrac{1}{2}$, α being a

positive integer.

The sequence of variates $X_1, X_2, \ldots, X_n$, the probability distribution of which is given by (a), does not satisfy the condition for the WLLN:

$$E(X_i) = 0, \quad \text{Var}(X_i) = \frac{1}{2}i^2 + \frac{1}{2}i^2 = i^2$$

and

$$\frac{s_n^2}{n^2} = \frac{\text{Var}(S_n)}{n^2} = \frac{n(n + 1)(2n + 1)}{6n^2},$$

which diverges as $n \to \infty$. However, in part (b), we have

$$E(X_i) = \frac{1}{2}\sqrt{\ln(i + \alpha)} - \frac{1}{2}\sqrt{\ln(i + \alpha)} = 0,$$

and

$$\text{Var}(X_i) = \frac{1}{2}\ln(i + \alpha) + \frac{1}{2}\ln(i + \alpha) = \ln(i + \alpha).$$

Also,

$$\text{Var}(S_n) = \sum_{i=1}^{n} \text{Var}(X_i) = \sum_{i=1}^{n} \ln(i + \alpha) = \ln \prod_{i=1}^{n}(i + \alpha)$$

$$= \ln[(1 + \alpha)(2 + \alpha) \cdots (n + \alpha)]$$

$$= \ln \frac{(n + \alpha)!}{\alpha!}$$

$$= \ln(n + \alpha)! - \ln \alpha!.$$

Applying Stirling's formula, we can write $\text{Var}(S_n)$ as

$$\text{Var}(S_n) \approx \ln\left[\sqrt{2\pi}\, e^{-(n+\alpha)}(n+\alpha)^{n+\alpha+1/2}\right] - \ln\alpha!$$

or

$$\frac{\text{Var}(S_n)}{n^2} \approx \frac{\ln\sqrt{2\pi}}{n^2} - \frac{(n+\alpha)}{n^2} - \frac{\ln\alpha!}{n^2} + \frac{(n+\alpha+1/2)\ln(n+\alpha)}{n^2}.$$

Thus, $s_n/n \to 0$ as $n \to \infty$; and the sequence of variates $X_1, X_2, \ldots, X_n$ obeys the WLLN.

An equivalent way of stating the WLLN Theorem (8.3.1) is

$$\lim_{n \to \infty} Pr\left(\left|\frac{S_n}{n} - \mu\right| < \varepsilon\right) = 1$$

for $\varepsilon > 0$, which means that S_n/n converges to μ *in probability* or *stochastically* as n increases indefinitely.

There are instances where the WLLN does not convey any information concerning the probability of convergence of S_n/n to μ. For example, inequality (8.2.7) can be written as

$$Pr\left(\left|\frac{S_n^{\;*}}{n} - p\right| \geq \varepsilon\right) \leq \frac{1}{4\varepsilon^2 n},$$

which tends to zero as $n \to \infty$. However, we can choose an r such that

$$Pr\left(\left|\frac{S_r^{\;*}}{r} - p\right| \geq \varepsilon + \left|\frac{S_{r+1}^*}{r+1} - p\right| \geq \varepsilon + \cdots +\right)$$

$$\leq Pr\left(\left|\frac{S_r^{\;*}}{r} - p\right| \geq \varepsilon\right) + Pr\left(\left|\frac{S_r^{\;*}}{r} - p\right| \geq \varepsilon\right) + \cdots +$$

$$\leq \frac{1}{4\varepsilon^2 r} + \frac{1}{4\varepsilon^2(r+1)} + \cdots +$$

$$= \frac{1}{4\varepsilon^2}\left(\frac{1}{r} + \frac{1}{r+1} + \cdots +\right),$$

which diverges and tells nothing about the probability. To overcome this difficulty, we have a stronger form of the WLLN, which is called the *Strong Law of Large Numbers* (SLLN) and is defined as follows:

Definition 8.3.0   *The sequence $X_1, X_2, \ldots, X_m, \ldots, X_n$ of mutually independent and identically distributed random variables with finite second* moments, $E(X_i^2) < \infty$, is said to obey the SLLN if, for $\varepsilon > 0$, $E(X_i) = \mu$, $\text{Var}(X_i) = \sigma^2$, and $S_r = X_1 + X_2 + \cdots + X_r$, we have

$$Pr\left(\left|\frac{S_r}{r} - \mu\right| \geq \varepsilon\right) \leq \frac{2\sigma^2}{\varepsilon^2 m} \tag{8.3.9}$$

for at least one r, $m \leq r \leq n$.

Note that the bound of the SLLN is twice that of the bound that one can obtain by using the WLLN. Also, inequality (8.3.9) is independent of n, even though we think of it as a very large number. The condition in which the random variables have a common probability density function can be eliminated, and the SLLN still holds. (See the book by Thomasian, *The Structure of Probability Theory with Applications*, listed in Suggested Supplementary Reading.)

An equivalent form of the SLLN is

$$Pr\left(\lim_{n \to \infty} S_n/n = \mu\right) = 1, \tag{8.3.10}$$

which states that, in almost every infinite sequence of variates, $S_1, S_2, \ldots, S_r$, $\ldots$, where $S_n = X_1 + X_2 + \cdots + X_n$, the sequence tends to a limit μ. More precisely, the sequence S_n/n converges to μ, with probability one, if Equation (8.3.10) holds.

A sufficient condition for the SLLN to apply to the above sequence of mutually independent random variables that are not necessarily identically distributed is given by the *Kolmogorov Criterion*.

Theorem 8.3.3 (Kolmogorov Criterion)   The convergence of the series

$$\sum_{r=1}^{\infty} \frac{\sigma_r^2}{r^2}$$

is a sufficient condition for the SLLN to apply to a sequence of mutually independent random variables, with $\text{Var}(X_r) = \sigma_r^2$.

The SLLN for Bernoulli trials can be stated as follows: Let $X_1, X_2, \ldots, X_m, \ldots, X_n$ be n Bernoulli trials, with probability p of success on each trial. If $S_r = X_1 + X_2 + \cdots + X_r$ and $\varepsilon > 0$, we have

$$Pr\left(\left|\frac{S_r}{r} - p\right| < \varepsilon\right) \geq 1 - \frac{2p(1-p)}{\varepsilon^2 m} \tag{8.3.11}$$

whenever $m \leq r \leq n$. Using the fact that $p(1-p) \leq 1/4$, inequality (8.3.11) becomes

$$Pr\left(\left|\frac{S_r}{r} - p\right| < \varepsilon\right) \geq 1 - \frac{1}{2\varepsilon^2 m}.$$

Example 8.3.4 Let $X_1, X_2, \ldots, X_n$ be a sequence of mutually independent random variables whose probability distribution is defined by

$$Pr(X_n = 0) = 1 - \frac{1}{n} \quad \text{and} \quad Pr(X_n = 1) = \frac{1}{n},$$

Here

$$E(X_r) = \frac{1}{r} \quad \text{and} \quad \text{Var}(X_r) = \frac{r-1}{r^2}.$$

Thus, the series

$$\sum_{r=1}^{\infty} \frac{\text{Var}(X_r)}{r^2} = \sum_{r=1}^{\infty} \frac{r-1}{r^4}$$

converges, and the above sequence of random variables obeys the SLLN.

8.4   The Central Limit Theorem

In Section 4.3, we mentioned that very few random phenomena precisely obey a normal probability law; however, the laws that they do follow can often, under certain conditions, be closely approximated by the normal probability law. In this sense, the normal distribution is of paramount importance. Of particular importance is the fact that, if a random variable X is represented by the sum of n *independent identically distributed random variables*, $X_1, X_2, \ldots, X_n$,

$$S_n = X_1 + X_2 + \cdots + X_n,$$

then S_n, for sufficiently large n, *is approximately normally distributed*, provided that the random variables possess finite means and variances. This remarkable result is known as the (classical) *Central Limit Theorem*. The Central Limit Theorem is one of the most important theorems in the whole of mathematics; the efforts that scientists have expended on it, especially in the area of statistics, are certainly justified.

There are two main versions of the Central Limit Theorem that you should be familiar with at this level of mathematical maturity: one is when the random variables in the sequence, $X_1, X_2, \ldots, X_n, \ldots$ are independent and identically distributed; the other is when the random variables in the sequence $X_1, X_2, \ldots, X_n \ldots$ are independent but not identically distributed. There are some additional conditions that we shall include in the theorem; however, from the practical point of view, the above distinction is of significant importance. The original formulation of the Central Limit Theorem was the work, in the early 19th century, of Laplace and Gauss. However, no formal presentation was made until 1901, when Lyapunov gave a rigorous mathematical proof of the theorem.

There are a number of different versions and extensions of the Central Limit Theorem; but, as we indicated above, we shall restrict ourselves to the versions represented by Theorems 8.4.1 and 8.4.2.

Theorem 8.4.1   Let $X_1, X_2, \ldots, X_n$ be a sequence of n independent and identically distributed random variables. Let $\mu = E(X_i)$ and $\sigma^2 = \mathrm{Var}(X_i)$ be the common expectation and variance. Let

$$S_n = X_1 + X_2 + \cdots + X_n.$$

Then $E(S_n) = n\mu$ and $\mathrm{Var}(S_n) = n\sigma^2$. Let the random variable Z_n be defined by

$$Z_n = \frac{S_n - n\mu}{\sqrt{n}\,\sigma}.$$

Then the variate Z_n is approximately normally distributed, with mean zero and variance one as $n \to \infty$. That is,

$$\lim_{n\to\infty} Pr(Z_n \leq z) = \frac{1}{\sqrt{2\pi}} \int_{-\infty}^{z} e^{-(1/2)t^2}\, dt = F(z)$$

or, equivalently, the distribution of the random variable $\overline{X}$ may be approximated as

$$\overline{X} \sim N\left(\mu, \frac{\sigma^2}{n}\right) \quad \text{as} \quad n \to \infty.$$

Proof   A rigorous proof of this theorem requires advanced mathematical techniques and is beyond the scope of this book. However, we shall give a proof of the theorem under a more restricted situation in which we use the characteristic function of the common probability distribution. The argument of the proof depends upon the application of Theorem 7.7.5 while indicating that, as n increases without bound, the characteristic function of the random variable Z_n approaches the characteristic function of the normal distribution, with mean 0 and variance 1.

Let the characteristic function of the X_i's be $\phi_X(t) = E[e^{itX}]$. Because the random variables X_1, X_2, ..., X_n are independent, the characteristic function of S_n is

$$\phi_{S_n}(t) = E[e^{itS_n}] = E[e^{it(X_1 + X_2 + \cdots + X_n)}]$$

$$= E[e^{itX_1}]E[e^{itX_2}] \cdots E[e^{itX_n}]$$

$$= \phi_{X_1}(t)\phi_{X_2}(t) \cdots \phi_{X_n}(t)$$

$$= [\phi_X(t)]^n.$$

The characteristic function of Z_n is

$$\phi_{Z_n}(t) = E[e^{itZ_n}] = E[e^{it(S_n - n\mu)/\sqrt{n}\sigma}]$$

$$= e^{-it\sqrt{n}\mu/\sigma}E[e^{itS_n/\sqrt{n}\sigma}]$$

$$= e^{-it\sqrt{n}\mu/\sigma}\phi_{S_n}(t/\sqrt{n}\sigma)$$

$$= e^{-it\sqrt{n}\mu/\sigma}[\phi_X(t/\sqrt{n}\sigma)]^n. \tag{8.4.1}$$

Equation (8.4.1) can be written as

$$\ln \phi_{Z_n}(t) = \frac{-it\sqrt{n}\mu}{\sigma} + n \ln \phi_X\left(\frac{t}{\sqrt{n}\sigma}\right). \tag{8.4.2}$$

Expanding $\phi_X(t/\sqrt{n}\sigma)$ as a power series in t, we have

$$n \ln \phi_X\left(\frac{t}{\sqrt{n}\sigma}\right) = n \ln E[e^{i(t/\sqrt{n}\sigma)X}]$$

$$= n \ln E\left[1 + i\frac{t}{\sqrt{n}\sigma}X + \frac{i^2t^2}{2!n\sigma^2}X^2 + \frac{i^3t^3}{3!n\sqrt{n}\sigma^3}X^3 + \cdots\right]$$

$$= n \ln\left[1 + \frac{it\mu_1}{\sqrt{n}\sigma} + \frac{i^2t^2\mu_2}{2!n\sigma^2} + \frac{i^3t^3\mu_3}{3!n\sqrt{n}\sigma^3} + \cdots\right]. \tag{8.4.3}$$

Thus, Equation (8.4.2) becomes

$$\ln \phi_{Z_n}(t) = \frac{-it\sqrt{n}\mu}{\sigma} + n \ln\left[1 + \frac{i\mu_1 t}{\sqrt{n}\sigma} + \frac{i^2t^2\mu_2}{2!n\sigma^2} + \frac{i^3t^3\mu_3}{3!n\sqrt{n}\sigma^3} + \cdots\right].$$

$$\tag{8.4.4}$$

Recall that the Maclaurin expansion for $\ln(1 + y)$ is

$$\ln(1 + y) = y - \frac{y^2}{2} + \frac{y^3}{3} - \cdots, \quad |y| < 1.$$

For

$$y = \left(\frac{i\mu_1 t}{\sqrt{n\mu}} + \frac{i^2 t^2 \mu_2}{2! n\sigma^2} + \frac{i^3 t^3 \mu_3}{3! n \sqrt{n\sigma^3}} + \cdots \right),$$

its absolute value, is less than one for sufficiently large n. Expression (8.4.4) can then be written as

$$\ln \phi_{Z_n}(t) = \frac{-it\sqrt{n\mu}}{\sigma} + n\left\{ \left[\frac{i\mu_1 t}{\sqrt{n\sigma}} + \frac{i^2 t^2 \mu_2}{2! n\sigma^2} + \frac{i^3 t^3 \mu_3}{3! n \sqrt{n\sigma^3}} + \cdots \right] \right.$$

$$- \frac{1}{2}\left[\frac{i\mu_1 t}{\sqrt{n\sigma}} + \frac{i^2 t^2 \mu_2}{2! n\sigma^2} + \frac{i^3 t^3 \mu_3}{3! n \sqrt{n\sigma^3}} + \cdots \right]^2$$

$$+ \frac{1}{3}\left[\frac{i\mu_1 t}{\sqrt{n\sigma}} + \frac{i^2 t^2 \mu_2}{2! n\sigma^2} + \frac{i^3 t^3 \mu_3}{3! n \sqrt{n\sigma^3}} + \cdots \right]^3$$

$$\left. - \cdots\cdots\cdots \right\}. \tag{8.4.5}$$

Collecting powers of it in Equation (8.4.5), we have

$$\ln \phi_{Z_n}(t) = \left(\frac{-\sqrt{n\mu}}{\sigma} + \frac{\mu_1 \sqrt{n}}{\mu\sigma} \right) it + \left(\frac{\mu_2}{2\sigma^2} - \frac{\mu_1^2}{2\sigma^2} \right) i^2 t^2$$

$$+ \left(\frac{\mu_3}{6\sigma^3 \sqrt{n}} - \frac{\mu_1 \mu_2}{2\sigma^3 \sqrt{n}} + \frac{\mu_1^3}{3\sigma^3 \sqrt{n}} \right) i^3 t^3 + \cdots. \tag{8.4.6}$$

Because $\mu = \mu_1$ and $\mu_2 - \mu_1^2 = \sigma^2$, Equation (8.4.6) reduces to

$$\ln \phi_{Z_n}(t) = -\frac{1}{2} t^2 + \left(\frac{\mu_3}{6} - \frac{\mu_1 \mu_2}{2} + \frac{\mu_1^3}{3} \right) \frac{i^3 t^3}{\sigma^3 \sqrt{n}} + \cdots. \tag{8.4.7}$$

Thus, the coefficient of t^3 is a constant times $1/\sqrt{n}$, and, in general, the coefficient of t^k will be a constant times $n^{1-k/2}$. Taking the limit as $n \to \infty$ on both sides of Equation (8.4.7), we have

$$\lim_{n \to \infty} \ln \phi_{Z_n}(t) = -\frac{1}{2} t^2.$$

Because the limit of the log equals the log of the limit, we obtain

$$\lim_{n \to \infty} \phi_{Z_n}(t) = e^{-(1/2)t^2}.$$

Therefore, the limiting characteristic function is that of the standard normal probability distribution; and, in view of the uniqueness theorem for characteristic functions, the proof of the theorem is completed.

Thus, we may conclude that, for any sequence $X_1, X_2, \ldots, X_n$ of independent identically distributed random variables with finite means and variances, we can approximate the probability that S_n lies between any two real numbers, a_1 and a_2, as shown below:

$$Pr(a_1 \leq S_n \leq a_2) = Pr\left(\frac{a_1 - n\mu}{\sqrt{n\sigma}} \leq \frac{S_n - n\mu}{\sqrt{n\sigma}} \leq \frac{a_2 - n\mu}{\sqrt{n\sigma}}\right)$$

$$\approx \frac{1}{\sqrt{2\pi}} \int_{\frac{a_1 - n\mu}{\sqrt{n\sigma}}}^{\frac{a_2 - n\mu}{\sqrt{n\sigma}}} e^{-(1/2)t^2} dt$$

$$= F\left(\frac{a_2 - n\mu}{\sqrt{n\sigma}}\right) - F\left(\frac{a_1 - n\mu}{\sqrt{n\sigma}}\right).$$

One of the astonishing things about the Central Limit Theorem is the fact that nothing is said about the common distribution of the random variables, except that they have finite variance. The distribution of $Z_n, f(z)$ may be approximated by the $N(0, 1)$ as $n \to \infty$. From the applied point of view, the assumption of finite variance is not a critical restriction because, in almost all practical situations, the range of the variate will be finite, which makes the variance finite.

The Central Limit Theorem also justifies a result important for its practical applications; by using the theorem, we can approximate the probability distribution of the sample mean,

$$\overline{X}_n = \frac{1}{n} \sum_{i=1}^{n} X_i,$$

with a normal distribution having mean μ and variance σ^2/n, when n is sufficiently large. Note that it is not correct to state that the distribution of $\overline{X}_n$ approaches that of a normal distribution as $n \to \infty$ because, under the condition of the Central Limit Theorem, the variance of $\overline{X}_n$ approaches 0 as $n \to \infty$. Therefore, if

$$\overline{X}_n = \frac{1}{n} \sum_{i=1}^{n} X_i,$$

then the variate Y_n,

$$Y_n = \frac{\overline{X}_n - E(\overline{X}_n)}{\sqrt{\text{Var } \overline{X}_n}} \tag{8.4.8}$$

is approximately normally distributed with mean 0 and variance 1 when n is sufficiently large. Here $E(\overline{X}_n) = \mu$ and $\text{Var}(\overline{X}_n) = \sigma^2/n$.

Example 8.4.1   Let X_1, X_2, ..., X_n be independent discrete random variables identically distributed as

$$f(x_i) = \begin{cases} .2, & x_i = 0, 1, 2, 3, 4, \\ 0, & \text{elsewhere} \quad \text{for} \quad i = 1, 2, \ldots, n. \end{cases}$$

Here we have

$$\mu = E(X_n) = \frac{1}{5} \sum_{r=0}^{4} r = \frac{1}{5}(0 + 1 + 2 + 3 + 4) = 2.0$$

and

$$\sigma^2 = \text{Var}(X_n) = \frac{1}{5} \sum_{r=0}^{4} (r - \mu)^2 = \frac{1}{5} \sum_{r=0}^{4} r^2 - \mu^2$$

$$= \frac{1}{5}(30) - 4 = 6 - 4 = 2.0.$$

Let the random variable $\bar{X}_{100}$ be defined by

$$\bar{X}_{100} = \frac{1}{100} \sum_{i=1}^{100} X_i.$$

What is the probability that $\bar{X}_{100}$ will exceed 2?

Solution: Applying Equation (8.4.8), we have

$$Pr(\bar{X}_{100} > 2) = 1 - Pr(\bar{X}_{100} \leq 2)$$

$$= 1 - Pr\left(\frac{\bar{X}_{100} - 2.0}{1.414/10} \leq \frac{2.0 - 2.0}{1.414/10}\right) = 1 - Pr(Z \leq 0),$$

where $Z \sim N(0, 1)$. Thus, we get

$$Pr(\bar{X}_{100} > 2) \approx 1 - \frac{1}{\sqrt{2\pi}} \int_{-\infty}^{0} e^{-z^2/2} \, dz$$

$$= 1 - F(0)$$

$$= 0.5.$$

Theorem 8.4.2   Let X_1, X_2, ..., X_n be a sequence of n independent random variables with finite means $E(X_i)$; and, for some $\beta > 0$, let

$$E[|X_r - E(X_r)|]^{2+\beta}$$

be finite. If

$$S_n = X_1 + X_2 + \cdots + X_n,$$

then

$$Z_n = \frac{S_n - n\mu}{\sqrt{n}\sigma}$$

may be approximately distributed as an $N(0, 1)$ variate as $n \to \infty$, provided that

$$\lim_{n \to \infty} [\text{Var}(S_n)]^{-(1+\beta/2)} \sum_{r=1}^{n} E[|X_r - E(X_r)|^{2+\beta}] = 0.$$

Theorem 8.4.2 is due to Lyapunov, and we will not prove it. It is important because the random variables need not be identically distributed. For additional extensions of the Central Limit Theorem and the proof of Theorem 8.4.2, we refer the reader to *Probability Theory and Mathematical Statistics*, by Fisz (Suggested Supplementary Reading).

Example 8.4.2 Let $X_1, X_2, \ldots, X_n$ be a sequence of independent random variables identically distributed as

$$f(x_i) = \begin{cases} \dfrac{1}{\alpha - \beta}, & \alpha \le x_i \le \beta, \\ 0, & \text{elsewhere} \quad \text{for} \quad i = 1, 2, \ldots, n. \end{cases}$$

Then

$$E(X_i) = \frac{\alpha + \beta}{2} \quad \text{and} \quad \text{Var}(X_i) = \frac{(\beta - \alpha)^2}{12}, \quad i = 1, 2, \ldots, n.$$

Let $Y_n = X_1 + X_2 + \cdots + X_n$. Applying the Central Limit Theorem, we obtain

$$Pr(y_1 \le Y_n \le y_2) =$$

$$= Pr\left[\frac{y_1 - n\left(\dfrac{\alpha + \beta}{2}\right)}{\sqrt{n}\,\dfrac{\beta - \alpha}{2\sqrt{3}}} \le \frac{Y_n - n\left(\dfrac{\alpha + \beta}{2}\right)}{\sqrt{n}\,\dfrac{\beta - \alpha}{2\sqrt{3}}} \le \frac{y_2 - n\left(\dfrac{\alpha + \beta}{2}\right)}{\sqrt{n}\,\dfrac{\beta - \alpha}{2\sqrt{3}}} \right]$$

$$\approx \frac{1}{\sqrt{2\pi}} \int_a^b e^{-(1/2)y_n^2} dy_n$$

$$= F(b) - F(a),$$

where

$$a = \frac{y_1 - n\left(\frac{\alpha + \beta}{2}\right)}{\sqrt{n}\,\dfrac{\beta - \alpha}{2\sqrt{3}}}, \quad b = \frac{y_2 - n\left(\frac{\alpha + \beta}{2}\right)}{\sqrt{n}\,\dfrac{\beta - \alpha}{2\sqrt{3}}}, \quad \text{and} \quad \alpha < y_1 < y_2 < \beta.$$

8.5   The DeMoivre-Laplace Theorem

Let $X_1, X_2, \ldots, X_n$ be a sequence of independent random variables. If we assume that the random variable X_i equals 1 if the ith trial results in a success, with probability p, and 0 otherwise, with probability $1 - p$, that is, for every i, $i = 1, 2, \ldots, n$

$$Pr(X_i = 1) = p \quad \text{and} \quad Pr(X_i = 0) = 1 - p, \quad 0 < p < 1,$$

then the sum $Y_n = X_1 + X_2 + \cdots + X_n$ is binomially distributed with mean np and variance $np(1 - p)$. Applying Theorem 8.4.1, the variate Z_n, defined by

$$Z_n = \frac{Y_n - np}{\sqrt{np(1 - p)}},$$

is asymptotically normally distributed, with mean 0 and variance 1. Thus, for n sufficiently large, we can approximate the binomial probability distribution with the normal probability law. This special case of the Central Limit Theorem is known as the *DeMoivre-Laplace Theorem*, which was first formulated in 1733. This theorem is of considerable theoretical and practical importance. We shall state it and prove it, using an approach different from that in our introductory discussion.

Theorem 8.5.1   Let $X_1, X_2, \ldots, X_n$ be a sequence of independent random variables, with the distribution

$$f(x_i) = \begin{cases} p, & x_i = 1, \\ 1 - p, & x_i = 0 \end{cases} \quad \text{for} \quad i = 1, 2, \ldots, n,$$

so that $Y_n = X_1 + X_2 + \cdots + X_n$ is binomially distributed, with parameters n and p. Then, for sufficiently large n,

$$\binom{n}{y_n} p^{y_n}(1 - p)^{n - y_n} \approx \frac{1}{\sqrt{2\pi}\sqrt{np(1 - p)}} \exp\left\{-\frac{1}{2}\left(\frac{y_n - np}{\sqrt{np(1 - p)}}\right)^2\right\}.$$

$$(8.5.1)$$

Proof   Recall that Stirling's approximation is given by

$$n! \approx n^{n+1/2}e^{-n}\sqrt{2\pi}. \qquad (8.5.2)$$

We can then write $\binom{n}{y_n}$ of expression (8.5.1) as follows:

$$\binom{n}{y_n} = \frac{n!}{y_n!(n - y_n)!}$$

$$\approx \frac{n^{n+1/2}e^{-n}\sqrt{2\pi}}{y_n^{y_n+1/2}e^{-y_n}\sqrt{2\pi}(n - y_n)^{n-y_n+1/2}e^{-(n-y_n)}\sqrt{2\pi}}$$

$$\approx \frac{1}{\sqrt{2\pi}} \frac{n^{n+1/2}e^{-n}}{y_n^{y_n+1/2}(n - y_n)^{n-y_n+1/2}e^{-y_n-n+y_n}}. \qquad (8.5.3)$$

Multiplying the denominator of Equation (8.5.3) by $n^{1/2}$ and the numerator by $n^{1/2+y_n-y_n}$, we have

$$\binom{n}{y_n} \approx \frac{1}{\sqrt{2\pi}} \frac{n^{y_n+1/2}n^{n-y_n+1/2}}{n^{1/2}y_n^{y_n+1/2}(n - y_n)^{n-y_n+1/2}}. \qquad (8.5.4)$$

Equation (8.5.4) becomes

$$\binom{n}{y_n} \approx \frac{1}{\sqrt{2\pi}\sqrt{n}} \left(\frac{n}{y_n}\right)^{y_n+1/2} \left(\frac{n}{n - y_n}\right)^{n-y_n+1/2}. \qquad (8.5.5)$$

The quantity $p^{y_n}(1 - p)^{n-y_n}$ in expression (8.5.1) can be written as

$$p^{y_n}(1 - p)^{n-y_n} = \frac{p^{y_n+1/2}(1 - p)^{n-y_n+1/2}}{p^{1/2}(1 - p)^{1/2}}. \qquad (8.5.6)$$

Substituting Equations (8.5.5) and (8.5.6) in expression (8.5.1), we have

$$\binom{n}{y_n}p^{y_n}(1 - p)^{n-y_n}$$

$$\approx \frac{1}{\sqrt{2\pi}\sqrt{np(1 - p)}} \frac{p^{y_n+1/2}}{\left(\dfrac{y_n}{n}\right)^{y_n+1/2}} \frac{(1 - p)^{n-y_n+1/2}}{\left[\dfrac{(n - y_n)}{n}\right]^{n-y_n+1/2}}$$

$$= \frac{1}{\sqrt{2\pi}\sqrt{np(1 - p)}} \left[\left(\frac{y_n}{np}\right)^{y_n+1/2}\right]^{-1} \left\{\left[\frac{n - y_n}{n(1 - p)}\right]^{n-y_n+1/2}\right\}^{-1}.$$

$$(8.5.7)$$

Letting

$$f(y_n; p, n) = \binom{n}{y_n} p^{y_n}(1 - p)^{n - y_n}$$

and taking the ln of both sides of Equation (8.5.7) results in

$$\ln f(y_n; p, n)$$

$$\approx \ln\left[\frac{1}{\sqrt{2\pi}\sqrt{np(1 - p)}}\right] - \ln\left(\frac{y_n}{np}\right)^{y_n + 1/2} - \ln\left[\frac{n - y_n}{n(1 - p)}\right]^{n - y_n + 1/2}$$

$$= -\ln(\sqrt{2\pi}\sqrt{np(1 - p)}) - \left(y_n + \frac{1}{2}\right)\ln\left(\frac{y_n}{np}\right) - \left(n - y_n + \frac{1}{2}\right)\ln\left[\frac{n - y_n}{n(1 - p)}\right].$$

$$(8.5.8)$$

Let

$$t = \frac{y_n - np}{\sqrt{np(1 - p)}},$$

which implies that

$$\frac{y_n}{np} = 1 + t\frac{\sqrt{1 - p}}{\sqrt{np}} \quad \text{and} \quad \frac{n - y_n}{n(1 - p)} = 1 - t\frac{\sqrt{p}}{\sqrt{n(1 - p)}}.$$

Thus, Equation (8.5.8) becomes

$$\ln f(y_n; p, n) \approx -\ln\left[\sqrt{2\pi}\sqrt{np(1 - p)}\right] - \left[np + t\sqrt{np(1 - p)} + \frac{1}{2}\right] \cdot$$

$$\ln\left[1 + t\frac{\sqrt{1 - p}}{\sqrt{np}}\right] - \left[n + \frac{1}{2} - (np + t\sqrt{np(1 - p)})\right] \cdot$$

$$\ln\left[1 - t\frac{\sqrt{p}}{\sqrt{n(1 - p)}}\right]. \qquad (8.5.9)$$

We shall make use of the expansion

$$\ln(1 + z) = z - \frac{z^2}{2} + \frac{z^3}{3} - \cdots,$$

which is valid for $|z| < 1$. Such a power series is permissible to use because $(t\sqrt{1 - p})/\sqrt{np} \to 0$ for large values of n. Also, the manner in which t is defined suggests that large values will occur only with very small probabilities. Thus, two of the terms in Equation (8.5.9) can be expanded, as in Equation 8.5.10 and 8.5.11.

$$\ln\left[1 + t\sqrt{\frac{1-p}{np}}\right] \approx t\sqrt{\frac{1-p}{np}} - \frac{t^2(1-p)}{2np} + \frac{t^3(1-p)\sqrt{1-p}}{3np\sqrt{np}} - \cdots.$$

$$(8.5.10)$$

$$\ln\left[1 - t\sqrt{\frac{p}{n(1-p)}}\right]$$

$$= -t\sqrt{\frac{p}{n(1-p)}} - \frac{t^2 p}{2n(1-p)} - \frac{t^3 p\sqrt{p}}{3n(1-p)\sqrt{n(1-p)}} - \cdots. \quad (8.5.11)$$

Substituting Equations (8.5.10) and (8.5.11) in (8.5.9), we have

$$\ln f(y_n; n, p)$$

$$\approx -\ln\left[\sqrt{2\pi}\sqrt{np(1-p)}\right] - \left[np + t\sqrt{np(1-p)} + \frac{1}{2}\right]$$

$$\times \left[t\sqrt{\frac{1-p}{np}} - \frac{t^2(1-p)}{2np} + \frac{t^3(1-p)\sqrt{1-p}}{3np\sqrt{np}} - \cdots\right]$$

$$- \left[n(1-p) - t\sqrt{np(1-p)} + \frac{1}{2}\right]\left[-t\sqrt{\frac{p}{n(1-p)}} - \frac{t^2 p}{2n(1-p)}\right.$$

$$\left. - \frac{t^3 p\sqrt{p}}{3n(1-p)\sqrt{n(1-p)}} - \cdots\right]. \quad (8.5.12)$$

Collecting powers of t in (8.5.12), we have

$$\ln f(y_n; n, p)$$

$$\approx -\ln\left[\sqrt{2\pi}\sqrt{np(1-p)}\right]$$

$$- \left[np\sqrt{\frac{1-p}{np}} + \frac{1}{2}\sqrt{\frac{1-p}{np}} - n(1-p)\sqrt{\frac{p}{n(1-p)}} - \frac{1}{2}\sqrt{\frac{p}{n(1-p)}}\right]t$$

$$- \left[-\frac{(1-p)}{2} + (1-p) - \frac{(1-p)}{4np} - \frac{p}{2} + p - \frac{p}{4n(1-p)}\right]t^2 - \cdots.$$

$$(8.5.13)$$

Equation (8.5.13) reduces to

$$\ln f(y_n; n, p) \approx -\ln[\sqrt{2\pi}\sqrt{np(1-p)}] + \frac{1}{2\sqrt{n}}\left[\sqrt{\frac{p}{1-p}} - \sqrt{\frac{1-p}{p}}\right]t - \frac{1}{2}t^2$$

$$+ \frac{1}{4n}\left[\frac{p}{1-p} + \frac{1-p}{p}\right]t^2 + \cdots, \tag{8.5.14}$$

where, as $n \to \infty$, the coefficients of t and t^2 tend to zero. Also, coefficients of higher powers of t will tend to zero so that

$$\ln f(y_n; n, p) \approx -\ln[\sqrt{2\pi}\sqrt{np(1-p)}] - \frac{1}{2}t^2$$

or

$$f(y_n; n, p) \approx \frac{1}{\sqrt{2\pi}\sqrt{np(1-p)}}e^{-t^2/2}. \tag{8.5.15}$$

Therefore, substituting $t = (y_n - np)/\sqrt{np(1-p)}$ in Equation (8.5.15), we have

$$f(y_n; n, p) = \binom{n}{y_n}p^{y_n}(1-p)^{n-y_n}$$

$$\approx \frac{1}{\sqrt{2\pi}\sqrt{np(1-p)}}\exp\left\{-\frac{1}{2}\left(\frac{y_n - np}{\sqrt{np(1-p)}}\right)^2\right\}.$$

Thus, the probability that a random phenomenon obeying the binomial probability distribution, with parameters n and p, will have an observed value between two arbitrary integers y_1, y_2 ($y_1 < y_2$) is given by applying the DeMoivre-Laplace theorem as follows:

$$Pr(y_1 < Y_n < y_2) = \sum_{r=y_1}^{y_2} \binom{n}{r}p^r(1-p)^{n-r}$$

$$= Pr\left(\frac{y_1 - np}{\sqrt{np(1-p)}} < \frac{Y_n - np}{\sqrt{np(1-p)}} < \frac{y_2 - np}{\sqrt{np(1-p)}}\right)$$

$$\approx \frac{1}{\sqrt{2\pi}}\int_{\frac{y_1-np}{\sqrt{np(1-p)}}}^{\frac{y_2-np}{\sqrt{np(1-p)}}} e^{-(1/2)z^2}dz$$

$$= F\left(\frac{y_2 - np}{\sqrt{np(1-p)}}\right) - F\left(\frac{y_1 - np}{\sqrt{np(1-p)}}\right).$$

$$\tag{8.5.16}$$

However, in the above discussion, we are approximating probabilities of a *discrete* density with a *continuous* probability distribution; and we need to introduce the conventional *correction for continuity*. In the discrete case, the probability is concentrated at the integers; but, when we approximate such probabilities with a continuous distribution, the corresponding probability is spread over a rectangle with base stretching from $-(1/2)$ to $1/2$ on either side of the integer involved. (See Figure 8.5.1.)

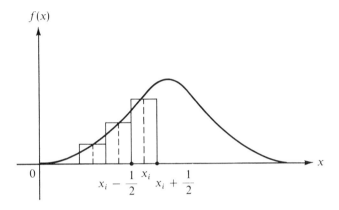

Figure 8.5.1

That is, if we were to approximate the probability up to point x_i, we would integrate $f(x)$ from $-\infty$ to x_i, in which case we would omit the area from x_i to $x_i + 1/2$. Thus, we need

$$Pr(X \leq x_i) \approx \int_{-\infty}^{x_i+1/2} f(x)\, dx. \qquad (8.5.17)$$

However, if we were to approximate the probability that $X < x_i$, we would integrate $f(x)$ from $-\infty$ to x_i; and we would improperly include the area from $x_i - 1/2$ to x_i. Thus, we must change our upper limit:

$$Pr(X < x_i) \approx \int_{-\infty}^{x_i-1/2} f(x)\, dx. \qquad (8.5.18)$$

Combining Equations (8.5.17) and (8.5.18), we obtain

$$Pr(X = x_i) = Pr(X \leq x_i) - Pr(X < x_i)$$

$$= \int_{x_i-1/2}^{x_i+1/2} f(x)\, dx.$$

Therefore, to improve our approximation of the binomial distribution, we include the *correction for continuity* in Equation (8.5.16):

$$Pr(y_1 \leq Y_n \leq y_2) \approx \frac{1}{\sqrt{2\pi}} \int_{\frac{y_1-np-1/2}{\sqrt{np(1-p)}}}^{\frac{y_2-np+1/2}{\sqrt{np(1-p)}}} e^{-(1/2)y_n^2} dy_n$$

$$= F\left(\frac{y_2 - np + 1/2}{\sqrt{np(1-p)}}\right) - F\left(\frac{y_1 - np - 1/2}{\sqrt{np(1-p)}}\right).$$

$$(8.5.19)$$

For example, in a random phenomenon where the binomial law is applicable with $p = 1/2$, $n = 10$, the normal approximation with the correction factor is significantly closer to the exact probabilities, as shown in Table 8.5.1.

Table 8.5.1. *Comparison of Binomial Probabilities with Normal Approximation $p = 1/2$, $n = 10$*

y	Exact Binomial Probabilities: Eq. (2.3.2)	Normal Approximation: Eq. (8.5.16)	Normal Approximation: Eq. (8.5.19)
0	0.00098	0.00079	0.00219
1	0.00977	0.00491	0.01136
2	0.04395	0.02302	0.04350
3	0.11719	0.07508	0.11405
4	0.20508	0.16050	0.20340
5	0.24609	0.23570	0.25100
6	0.20508	0.23570	0.20340
7	0.11719	0.16050	0.11405
8	0.04395	0.07508	0.04350
9	0.00977	0.02302	0.01136
10	0.00098	0.00491	0.00219

A geometrical illustration of the correctional factor for the above example is shown in Figure 8.5.2.

Example 8.5.1 illustrates the fruitfulness of the normal approximation from the computational point of view.

Example 8.5.1   Suppose that a "loaded" coin is tossed 2000 times. If the probability of a head's occurring at any given toss is .75, what is the probability that the number of tosses on which heads will occur is between 1475 and 1535?

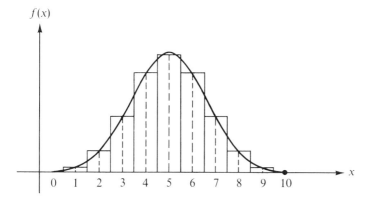

$f(x)$

$$0 \quad 1 \quad 2 \quad 3 \quad 4 \quad 5 \quad 6 \quad 7 \quad 8 \quad 9 \quad 10$$

x

Figure 8.5.2

Solution: An exact probability to this question is given by

$$Pr(1475 \le y_n \le 1535) = \sum_{y=1475}^{1535} \binom{2000}{y}\left(\frac{3}{4}\right)^y\left(\frac{1}{4}\right)^{2000-y}.$$

The calculation of the above probability is quite laborious, but an acceptable approximation to the sum is given by Equation (8.5.19).

$$Pr(1475 \le Y_n \le 1535)$$

$$= Pr\left(\frac{1475 - 1500 - 1/2}{\sqrt{375}} \le \frac{Y_n - 1500}{\sqrt{375}} \le \frac{1535 - 1500 + 1/2}{\sqrt{375}}\right)$$

$$\approx \frac{1}{\sqrt{2\pi}}\int_{-\frac{51\sqrt{15}}{150}}^{\frac{71\sqrt{15}}{150}} e^{-(1/2)z^2}dz = \frac{1}{\sqrt{2\pi}}\int_{-1.32}^{1.83} e^{-(1/2)z^2}dz$$

$$= F(1.83) - F(-1.27)$$

$$= .8730.$$

Example 8.5.2   In a certain industrial complex, we inspect 100 components of an electrical system. Each component is classified as being either operable or defective. We assign the value 1 if the component is operable and the value 0 if the component is defective. From previous experience, we know that the probability of finding an operable component is $p = .8$. What is the probability that the number of operable components will be more than 70 and less than 80?

Solution: Here the variate Y_n in Theorem 8.5.1 can assume values from 0 to 100. Also,

$$E[Y_n] = np = 80, \qquad \text{Var}(Y_n) = np(1-p) = 16$$

and

$$Pr(70 < Y_n < 80) = Pr\left(\frac{70 - 80 + 1/2}{4} < \frac{Y_n - 80}{4} < \frac{80 - 80 - 1/2}{4}\right)$$

$$= Pr\left(-2.38 < \frac{Y_n - 80}{4} < -.13\right)$$

$$\approx \frac{1}{\sqrt{2\pi}} \int_{-2.38}^{-.13} e^{-(1/2)z^2} dz$$

$$= F(-.13) - F(-2.38).$$

From tables of the standardized normal distribution, we find the above probability to be 0.4396.

Example 8.5.3 A shirt manufacturer knows that, on the average, 2% of his product will not meet quality specifications. Find the greatest number of shirts constituting a lot that will have, with a probability of .95, less than five defectives.

Solution: If we let the random variable X be the number of defectives in the lot, then $E(Y_n) = .02n$ and $\text{Var}(Y_n) = .196n$, where

$$Y_n = \sum_{i=1}^{n} X_i.$$

Using Theorem 8.5.1, we obtain

$$.95 \le Pr(X < 5) = Pr\left(\frac{Y_n - .02n}{\sqrt{.0196n}} < \frac{5 - 1/2 - .02n}{\sqrt{.0196n}}\right)$$

$$\approx \frac{1}{\sqrt{2\pi}} \int_{-\infty}^{\frac{5 - 1/2 - .02n}{\sqrt{.0196n}}} e^{-(1/2)z^2} dz$$

$$= F\left(\frac{5 - 1/2 - .02n}{\sqrt{.0196n}}\right),$$

which implies that $(5 - \frac{1}{2} - .02n)/\sqrt{.0196n} \ge 1.645$
or

$$.0004n^2 - .23271616n + 20.25 \ge 0.$$

Two solutions result:

$$n \leq 106.5176 \quad \text{and} \quad n \geq 475.2728.$$

The second solution, however, does not satisfy the original relationship

$$\frac{5 - 1/2 - .02n}{\sqrt{.0196n}} \geq 1.645;$$

so we disregard it and accept the first one. Our solution, then, is $n = 106$.

8.6 Normal Approximation to the Poisson Distribution

In Chapter 3, we derived the Poisson distribution as a limit of a sequence of binomial distributions: many of the properties of the binomial probability density also apply to the Poisson probability distribution, and we can approximate the Poisson probability density function with the normal distribution. One can illustrate this approximation by showing that, if $X_1, X_2, \ldots, X_n$ is a sequence of independent identically Poisson-distributed random variables, with parameters λ, then $Y_n = X_1 + X_2 + \cdots + X_n$ has the Poisson distribution with mean and variance $n\lambda$; in view of the Central Limit Theorem, we obtain the desired result. We shall, however, derive this important result by means of characteristic functions.

Theorem 8.6.1   If $X_1, X_2, \ldots, X_n$ is a sequence of independent identically Poisson-distributed random variables, with parameters λ, then the distribution of the variate Z_n,

$$Z_n = \frac{Y_n - E(Y_n)}{\sqrt{\text{Var}(Y_n)}} = \frac{Y_n - n\lambda}{\sqrt{n\lambda}},$$

may be approximated by a normal distribution with mean 0 and variance 1 as $n \to \infty$, where

$$Y_n = X_1 + X_2 + \cdots + X_n.$$

Proof   From the table at the end of Chapter 5, the characteristic function of any Poisson distributed variate X is

$$\phi_X(t) = e^{\lambda(e^{it} - 1)}.$$

Applying Theorem 7.7.4, we can write the characteristic function of the random variable Y_n as

$$\phi_{Y_n}(t) = [\phi_X(t)]^n$$
$$= [e^{\lambda(e^{it}-1)}]^n$$
$$= e^{n\lambda(e^{it}-1)}. \tag{8.6.1}$$

Also,

$$\phi_{Z_n}(t) = E[e^{itZ_n}]$$
$$= E[e^{itY_n/\sqrt{n\lambda} - itn\lambda/\sqrt{n\lambda}}]$$
$$= e^{-it\sqrt{n\lambda}} E[e^{itY_n/\sqrt{n\lambda}}]$$
$$= e^{-it\sqrt{n\lambda}} \exp\{n\lambda(e^{it/\sqrt{n\lambda}} - 1)\}. \tag{8.6.2}$$

Equation (8.6.2) can be written as

$$\ln \phi_{Z_n}(t) = -it\sqrt{n\lambda} + n\lambda(e^{it/\sqrt{n\lambda}} - 1). \tag{8.6.3}$$

Expanding $e^{it/\sqrt{n\lambda}}$ in Equation (8.6.3) in Taylor's series, we have

$$\ln \phi_{Z_n}(t) = -it\sqrt{n\lambda} + n\lambda\left(1 + \frac{it}{\sqrt{n\lambda}} + \frac{1}{2}\frac{i^2t^2}{n\lambda} + \frac{1}{6}\frac{i^3t^3}{n\lambda\sqrt{n\lambda}} + \cdots - 1\right)$$
$$= -it\sqrt{n\lambda} + \frac{n\lambda it}{\sqrt{n\lambda}} + \frac{1}{2}i^2t^2 + \frac{1}{6}\frac{i^3t^3}{\sqrt{n\lambda}} + \cdots. \tag{8.6.4}$$

Thus,

$$\lim_{n \to \infty} \ln \phi_{Z_n}(t) = t^2/2$$

because every other term of Equation (8.6.4) goes to zero as $n \to \infty$; thus,

$$\lim_{n \to \infty} \phi_{Z_n}(t) = e^{-t^2/2}.$$

Therefore, because of the property of the uniqueness of the characteristic function, the random variable $Z_n = (Y_n - n\lambda)/\sqrt{n\lambda}$ is asymptotically normally distributed, with mean 0 and variance 1.

In this case, we shall also employ the conventional correction factor of $1/2$ for continuity because we are approximating probabilities of a discrete distribution with a continuous probability density function, as discussed in the previous section. Hence, for a random phenomenon obeying the Poisson law, with parameter λ, the probability that we will have an observed value less than or equal to an arbitrary integer y is given by

$$Pr(Y_n \le y) = \sum_{r=0}^{y} \frac{e^{-\lambda}\lambda^r}{r!}$$

$$= Pr\left(\frac{Y_n - n\lambda}{\sqrt{n\lambda}} \le \frac{y - n\lambda + 1/2}{\sqrt{n\lambda}}\right)$$

$$\approx \frac{1}{\sqrt{2\pi}} \int_{-\infty}^{\frac{y - n\lambda + 1/2}{\sqrt{n\lambda}}} e^{-(1/2)t^2}dt$$

$$= F\left(\frac{y - n\lambda + 1/2}{\sqrt{n\lambda}}\right).$$

Note that, from the above discussion, any Poisson-distributed random variable with parameter λ is asymptotically normally distributed as $\lambda \to \infty$, due to the additive property of the independent identically Poisson-distributed random variables. The above approximation can also be shown by using Stirling's formula.

Example 8.6.1   A drug manufacturer receives a shipment of 10,000 calibrated "eyedroppers" for administering Sabin Poliovirus Vaccine. If the calibration mark is missing on 500 droppers, which are scattered randomly throughout the shipment, what is the probability that, at most, two defective droppers will be detected in a random sample of 125?

Solution: Here the population of 10,000 droppers is very large, and the Poisson law seems to be applicable. The probability that a dropper is defective is $500/10,000 = .05$, and the probability of finding at most two defectives is

$$Pr(Y_n \le 2) = \sum_{y_n=0}^{2} \frac{e^{-6.25}(6.25)^{Y_n}}{Y_n!}$$

$$\approx Pr\left(\frac{0 - 1/2 - 6.25}{2.5} \le \frac{Y_n - 6.25}{2.5} \le \frac{2 + 1/2 - 6.25}{2.5}\right)$$

$$= \int_{\frac{.5 + 6.25}{2.5}}^{\frac{2.5 - 6.25}{2.5}} e^{-z^2/2} dz$$

$$= F(-1.5) - F(-2.70)$$
$$= F(2.70) - F(1.5)$$
$$= .9965 - .9332$$
$$= .0633.$$

The probability that the number of defectives falls between one and three inclusively is

$$Pr(1 \le Y_n \le 3) = \sum_{y_n=1}^{2} \frac{e^{-6.25}(6.25)^{Y_n}}{y_n!}$$

$$\approx Pr\left(\frac{1 - 1/2 - 6.25}{2.5} \le \frac{Y_n - 6.25}{2.5} \le \frac{3 + 1/2 - 6.25}{2.5}\right)$$

$$= \frac{1}{\sqrt{2\pi}\, 2.5} \int_{1-1/2}^{3+1/2} \exp\left\{-\frac{1}{2}\left(\frac{y_n - 6.25}{2.5}\right)^2\right\} dy_n$$

$$= \frac{1}{\sqrt{2\pi}} \int_{\frac{1-1/2-6.25}{2.5}}^{\frac{3+1/2-6.25}{2.5}} e^{-(1/2)z^2} dz$$

$$= F(-1.1) - F(-2.3)$$
$$= F(2.3) - F(1.1)$$
$$= .9893 - .8643$$
$$= .1250.$$

8.7   Normal Approximation to the Gamma Distribution

In Section 3.3, we introduced the *gamma probability density function* and illustrated its usefulness. We shall now show that this distribution can be approximated by the normal probability density for sufficiently large n. As one might expect, as a consequence of this approximation, the $\chi^2(n)$-distribution is asymptotically normally distributed with mean n and variance $2n$. This last result is of significant importance in the study of statistics.

Theorem 8.7.1   Let $X_1, X_2, \ldots, X_n$ be a sequence of independent identically gamma-distributed random variables, with parameters α, β. If $Y_n = X_1 + X_2 + \cdots + X_n$, then the random variable Z_n,

$$Z_n = \frac{Y_n - E(Y_n)}{\sqrt{\mathrm{Var}(Y_n)}} = \frac{Y_n - n\alpha\beta}{\beta\sqrt{\alpha n}}$$

is normally distributed, with mean 0 and variance 1 as $n \to \infty$. Note that $E(X_i) = \alpha\beta$, $\mathrm{Var}(X_i) = \alpha\beta^2$, $i = 1, 2, \ldots, n$, and

$$E(Y_n) = E\left(\sum_{i=1}^{n} X_i\right) = \sum_{i=1}^{n} E(X_i) = n\alpha\beta \quad \text{and} \quad \mathrm{Var}(Y_n) = \mathrm{Var}\left(\sum_{i=1}^{n} X_i\right)$$

$$= \sum_{i=1}^{n} \mathrm{Var}(X_i) = n\alpha\beta^2.$$

Proof   It can easily be shown that the characteristic function of any gamma variate X is given by

$$\phi_X(t) = E(e^{itX}) = (1 - it\beta)^{-\alpha}.$$

In view of Theorem 7.7.4, we have

$$\phi_{Y_n}(t) = E(e^{itY_n}) = (1 - it\beta)^{-\alpha n}.$$

The characteristic function of the random variable z_n is

$$\phi_{z_n}(t) = E(e^{itz_n})$$

$$= E[e^{itY_n/\beta\sqrt{\alpha n} - it\alpha n/\sqrt{\alpha n}}]$$

$$= e^{-it\alpha n/\sqrt{\alpha n}} E(e^{itY_n/\beta\sqrt{\alpha n}})$$

$$= e^{it\alpha n/\sqrt{\alpha n}}\left(1 - \frac{it}{\sqrt{\alpha n}}\right)^{-\alpha n}. \tag{8.7.1}$$

Taking logs of both sides of Equation (8.7.1) gives

$$\ln \phi_{z_n}(t) = -\frac{it\alpha n}{\sqrt{\alpha n}} - \alpha n \ln\left(1 - \frac{it}{\sqrt{\alpha n}}\right)$$

$$= -\frac{it\alpha n}{\sqrt{\alpha n}} - \alpha n\left[-\frac{it}{\sqrt{\alpha n}} - \frac{i^2 t^2}{2\alpha n} - \frac{i^3 t^3}{3\alpha n\sqrt{\alpha n}} - \frac{i^4 t^4}{4\alpha^2 n^2} - \cdots\right]$$

$$= -\frac{it\alpha n}{\sqrt{\alpha n}} + \frac{it\alpha n}{\sqrt{\alpha n}} + \frac{i^2 t^2}{2} + \frac{i^3 t^3}{3\sqrt{\alpha n}} + \frac{i^4 t^4}{4\alpha n} + \cdots$$

$$= \frac{i^2 t^2}{2} + \sum_{j=3}^{\infty} \frac{(it)^j}{j(\alpha n)^{(j-2)/2}}. \tag{8.7.2}$$

Taking the limit of Equation (8.7.2) as $n \to \infty$, we obtain

$$\lim_{n \to \infty} \ln \phi_{z_n}(t) = -t^2/2.$$

Recalling that the limit of the log equals the log of the limit, we obtain

$$\lim_{n \to \infty} \ln \phi_{z_n}(t) = \ln \lim_{n \to \infty} \phi_{z_n}(t) = -t^2/2$$

or

$$\lim_{n \to \infty} \phi_{z_n}(t) = e^{-t^2/2},$$

which is the characteristic function of the standardized normal distribution.

Thus, the probability that a gamma-distributed random variable Y_n will assume a value between y_1 and y_2, $0 \le Y_1 < Y_2$, is

$$Pr(y_1 \le Y_n \le y_2) = \int_{y_1}^{y_2} \frac{1}{\Gamma(\alpha)\beta^2} y_n^{\alpha-1} e^{-(y_n/\beta)} dy_n$$

$$= Pr\left(\frac{y_1 - \alpha\beta n}{\beta\sqrt{\alpha n}} \le \frac{Y_n - \alpha\beta n}{\beta\sqrt{\alpha\beta}} \le \frac{y_2 - \alpha\beta n}{\beta\sqrt{\alpha n}}\right)$$

$$\approx \frac{1}{\sqrt{2\pi}} \int_{\frac{y_1 - \alpha\beta n}{\beta\sqrt{\alpha n}}}^{\frac{y_2 - \alpha\beta n}{\beta\sqrt{\alpha n}}} e^{-(1/2)z^2} dz.$$

Example 8.7.1   Suppose that the life of a certain electrical component follows the gamma distribution, with parameters $\alpha = 1$ and $\beta = 10$. A firm purchases 100 such components. What is the probability that the total life of these components will be between 850 and 1090 units?

Solution: Because the additive property of the gamma probability distribution holds, applying Theorem 8.7.1 with $Y_{100} = X_1 + X_2 + \cdots + X_{100}$, $E(Y_{100}) = n\alpha\beta = (100)(1)(10) = 1{,}000$ and $\text{Var}(Y_{100}) = (100)(1)(100) = 10{,}000$, we obtain

$$Pr(850 \le Y_{100} \le 1090) = Pr\left(\frac{850 - 1000}{100} \le \frac{Y_{100} - 1000}{100} \le \frac{1090 - 1000}{100}\right)$$

$$= Pr\left(-1.5 \le \frac{Y_{100} - 1000}{100} \le .9\right)$$

$$\approx \frac{1}{\sqrt{2\pi}} \int_{-1.5}^{.9} e^{-z^2/2} dz$$

$$= F(.9) - F(-1.5)$$

$$= 0.7491.$$

The exact probability is given by

$$Pr(850 \le Y_{100} \le 1090) = \frac{1}{10} \int_{850}^{1090} y^{99} e^{-(y/10)} dy$$

$$= 0.7561.$$

Example 8.7.2   Let $X_1, X_2, \ldots, X_n$ be a sequence of independent identically *chi-square distributed*, random variables, each with one degree of freedom. It was shown by Theorem 7.7.7 that the sum $Y_n = X_1 + X_2 + \cdots + X_n$ is $\chi^2(n)$-distributed, with n-degrees of freedom; that is, the additive property of the Central Limit Theorem holds. The expected value and variance of $\chi^2(n)$ are n and $2n$, respectively. Thus, in view of the Central Limit Theorem, the distribution of the random variable

$$Z_n = \frac{Y_n - n}{\sqrt{2n}}$$

may be approximated by a normal distribution with mean 0 and variance 1 for effectively large n. It is also clear that, since $\chi^2(n)$ is a special form of the gamma distribution $(\alpha = n/2, \ \beta = 2)$, the normal approximation is evident from Theorem 8.7.1. Thus, for $0 \le y_1 < y_2$,

$$Pr(y_1 \le Y_n \le y_2) = \int_{y_1}^{y_2} \frac{1}{\Gamma\left(\frac{n}{2}\right) 2^{n/2}} \, y_n^{(n/2)-1} e^{-(y_n/2)} dy_n$$

$$= Pr\left(\frac{y_1 - n}{\sqrt{2n}} \le \frac{Y_n - n}{\sqrt{2n}} \le \frac{y_2 - n}{\sqrt{2n}}\right)$$

$$\approx \frac{1}{\sqrt{2\pi}} \int_{\frac{y_1 - n}{\sqrt{2n}}}^{\frac{y_2 - n}{\sqrt{2n}}} e^{-(1/2)z^2} dz$$

$$= F\left(\frac{y_2 - n}{\sqrt{2n}}\right) - F\left(\frac{y_1 - n}{\sqrt{2n}}\right).$$

8.8   Summary

The important *Chebyshev Inequality*, which justifies the fact that the variance measures variability about the expected value of a random variable, states that, for any variate X with $E(X) = \mu$ and $\mathrm{Var}(X) = \sigma^2$, we have

$$Pr(|X - \mu| \ge k\sigma) \le \frac{1}{k^2},$$

where k is a positive number. A generalization of Chebyshev's Inequality is given by *Kolmogorov's Inequality*.

The *Bernoulli Law of Large Numbers* was discussed. Let $S_n{}^*$ be the observed number of successes in n independent repeated trials, with probability p of success and probability $1 - p$ of failure at each trial. Let

$$f_n = \frac{S_n{}^*}{n}$$

be the relative frequency of the observed number of successes in n trials. Then, for every $\varepsilon > 0$, we have

$$Pr(|f_n - p| < \varepsilon) \to 1 \quad \text{as} \quad n \to \infty.$$

A more general law is given by the *Weak Law of Large Numbers*. Let $X_1, X_2, \ldots, X_n$ be a sequence of mutually independent random variables, with a common distribution, let $E(X_i) = \mu$ exist. Then, for every $\varepsilon > 0$,

$$Pr\left(\left|\frac{S_n}{n} - \mu\right| < \varepsilon\right) \to 1 \quad \text{as} \quad n \to \infty,$$

where S_n is the number of successes in n trials. A stronger form of the WLLN is the *Strong Law of Large Numbers* (SLLN). A sufficient condition for the SLLN to apply to a sequence of mutually independent random variables not necessarily identically distributed is given by the *Kolmogorov Criterion*.

There are two main versions of the *Central Limit Theorem*: one in which the sequence of random variables $X_1, X_2, \ldots, X_n, \ldots$ is independent and has the same probability distribution, and one in which the random variables $X_1, X_2, \ldots, X_n, \ldots$ are independent but not identically distributed.

The *DeMoivre-Laplace Theorem* was discussed. For n sufficiently large, we can approximate the binomial probability distribution with the normal probability law. Also, the normal approximation to the Poisson and gamma distributions was studied.

Problems

8.1. Suppose that the number of cars arriving at a busy intersection in a large city has a Poisson distribution with mean 120. Determine a lower bound for the probability that the number of cars arriving in a given 20-minute period will be between 100 and 140, using *Chebyshev's Inequality*.

8.2. If a random variable X has mean 24 and variance 9, obtain a bound on the probability that the random variable X assumes a value between 16 and 28.

8.3.   Find the smallest value of n in a binomial distribution for which we can assert that

$$Pr\left(\left|\frac{X}{n} - P\right| < 0.1\right) \geq .90.$$

8.4.   How large should the size of a random sample be so that we can be 90% certain that the sample mean $\overline{X}$ will not deviate from the true mean by more than $\sigma/2$?

8.5.   Prove Chebyshev's Inequality for the discrete case.

8.6.   Consider a random sample of size 100, taken from a normal population with mean 0.5 and variance 0.04; that is, $X_1, X_2, \ldots, X_{100}$ are independent and identically distributed as $N(0.5, 0.4)$. Prove without the use of tables that

$$Pr(.42 \leq \overline{X} \leq .58) \geq 0.9375,$$

where

$$\overline{x} = \frac{1}{100}\sum_{i=1}^{100} x_i.$$

8.7.   The failure of a certain type of light bulb is characterized by the Poisson probability density function, with parameter $\lambda = .08n$. That is,

$$f(x) = \begin{cases} \dfrac{e^{-.08n}(.08n)^x}{x!}, & x = 0, 1, 2, \ldots, \\ 0, & \text{elsewhere.} \end{cases}$$

How many light bulbs must one test in order that the sample mean will lie within 0.6 of the true mean, with probability at least as great as 0.90?

8.8.   A random sample of size n is to be taken to determine the true proportion of cancer victims in a certain country. Determine the sample size n required to have probability of at least 0.95 that the observed proportion of cancer victims will differ from the true proportion by more than

(a) 1%   (b) 5%

8.9.   Color blindness appears in 2% of the people of a certain population. How large must a random sample be in order to obtain a probability of 0.99 or more that a color-blind person will be in the sample?

8.10. Let $Pr(X \le 0) = 0$. Show that, if $\mu = E(X)$ exists, then

$$Pr(X \ge 2\mu) \le 1/2.$$

8.11. Let $X_1, X_2, \ldots, X_n$ be a sequence of mutually independent random variables, with probability distribution given by

$$Pr\left(X_j = -\frac{1}{j}\right) = \frac{j^2}{1 + j^2} \quad \text{and} \quad Pr(X_j = j) = \frac{1}{1 + j^2},$$

$j = 1, 2, \ldots, n$. Show that the sequence of random variables satisfies Theorem 8.3.2.

8.12. Let $X_1, X_2, \ldots, X_n$ be a sequence of mutually independent random variables, with probability distribution defined by

$$Pr\left(X_r = \frac{1}{\sqrt{r}}\right) = \frac{1}{2} \quad \text{and} \quad Pr\left(X_r = -\frac{1}{\sqrt{r}}\right) = \frac{1}{2}, \quad r = 1, 2, \ldots, n$$

Does the sequence of random variables obey the *Weak Law of Large Numbers*?

8.13. Let $X_1, X_2, \ldots, X_n$ be a sequence of mutually independent random variables, with probability density function given by

$$Pr\left(X_k = \frac{1}{2^k}\right) = \frac{1}{2} \quad \text{and} \quad Pr\left(X_k = -\frac{1}{2^k}\right) = \frac{1}{2},$$

$k = 1, 2, \ldots, n$.
Does the sequence of random variables obey the WLLN?

8.14. Let $Y_1, Y_2, \ldots, Y_n$ be a sequence of mutually independent random variables, whose probability density is defined by

$$Pr(X_r = 0) = \frac{1}{r} \quad \text{and} \quad Pr(X_r = 1) = 1 - \frac{1}{r}, \quad r = 1, 2, \ldots, n.$$

Show that the sequence of random variables obeys the *Strong Law of Large Numbers*.

8.15. Prove or disprove that the sequence of mutually independent random variables $X_1, X_2, \ldots, X_n$, satisfies the Weak Law of Large Numbers, where

$$Pr(X_j = c^{-j}) = \frac{1}{2}, \qquad Pr(X_i = -c^{-j}) = \frac{1}{2},$$

$j = 1, 2, \ldots, n$ and $c > 1$ a constant.

8.16. A random sample of size 144 is taken from an infinite population with mean $\mu = 53$ and variance $\sigma^2 = 324$. What is the probability that $\overline{X}_{144}$ is between 51 and 55?

8.17. Find the approximate probability that the mean of a random sample of size 25, taken from a distribution, the probability density function of which is given by

$$f(x) = \begin{cases} 3x^2, & 0 \le x \le 1, \\ 0, & \text{elsewhere}, \end{cases}$$

lies between 2/5 and 3/5. Repeat the question for a sample of size 64.

8.18. Suppose that the lifetime X in hours of a certain type of electrical component has the exponential distribution

$$f(x) = \begin{cases} \dfrac{1}{3} e^{-(1/3)x}, & x > 0, \\ 0, & \text{elsewhere}. \end{cases}$$

If a random sample of size 36 is taken from these components, what is the probability that the mean $\overline{X}_{36}$ is less than two hours?

8.19. Consider a game of chance in which a man may win five dollars or lose 1, 2, 3 dollars with probability 0.25 each. After 36 plays of the game, what is the probability that the man will have an average gain or loss between -2 and $+2$ dollars?

8.20. During tests of reliability of a certain item, the probability of failure is 0.1. What is the probability that, during tests of 100 items, the number of failures will be (a) less than three hours (b) between three and five hours (c) more than four hours?

8.21. If a condenser fails during a time T, with probability 0.2, what is the probability that, among 144 condensers during time T, (a) at least 15 will fail (b) less than 10 will fail (c) between 16 and 24 will fail?

8.22. Given that an event occurs with probability 0.4, how many trials are necessary for at least 25 occurrences, with probability ≥ 0.90?

8.23. (Feller) Let $X_1, X_2, \ldots, X_n$ be a sequence of mutually independent random variables such that

$$Pr(X_n = -1) = Pr(X_n = +1) = \frac{(1 - 2^{-n})}{2}$$

and

$$Pr(X_n = -2^n) = Pr(X_n = +2^n) = 2^{-(n+1)}.$$

Show that both the WLLN and the SLLN apply to the sequence.

8.24. Suppose that a "loaded" coin is tossed a large number of times. If the probability of a head occurring at any given toss is 0.60, find the number of tosses required so that the experiment will reveal less than 20 tails, with a probability of at least 0.95.

8.25. The probability that a gunner will hit a target is $1/30$. How many times must he fire at the target so that he will be 95% certain of hitting the target at least once? Solve the problem using the Poisson distribution and Normal Approximation to the Poisson distribution, and compare your answers.

8.26. Suppose that 2500 customers subscribe to a telephone exchange. There are 80 trunklines available. Any one customer has a probability of 0.03 of needing a trunkline on a given call. Considering the situation as 2500 trials with probability of "success" $p = 0.03$, what is the approximate probability that the 2500 customers will "tie up" the 80 trunklines at any given time?

8.27. The exponential distribution is a special case of the gamma distribution when $\alpha = 1$, $\beta > 0$. Suppose the lifetime of a certain brand of light bulb is exponentially distributed, with mean 100 hours. If a person buys 50 bulbs for his apartment house, what is the approximate probability that the total of the lifetimes is greater than 4000 hours?

8.28. Let $X_1, X_2, \ldots, X_n$ be a sequence of independent identically distributed random variables with mean μ and variance σ^2. Show that

$$Z_n = \frac{\overline{X}_n - E(\overline{X})}{\sqrt{\operatorname{Var}(\overline{X})}}$$

is approximately normally distributed with mean 0 and variance 1 for sufficiently large n.

8.29. Let $X_1, X_2, \ldots, X_n$ be a sequence of independent identically chi-square-distributed random variables, each with one degree of freedom. Show using the technique employed in Theorem 8.4.1 that

$$Z_n = \frac{Y_n - E(Y_n)}{\sqrt{\text{Var}(Y_n)}},$$

where $Y_n = X_1 + X_2 + \cdots + X_n$ is approximately normally distributed with mean 0 and variance 1 for sufficiently large n.

8.30. Let $X_1, X_2, \ldots, X_n$ be a sequence of independent identically normally distributed random variables with mean 0 and variance 1. Show that

$$S_n = \sum_{i=1}^{n} X_i^2$$

has the chi-square distribution, with n degrees of freedom. Then prove that

$$Z_n = \frac{S_n - E(S_n)}{\sqrt{\text{Var}(S_n)}}$$

is approximately normally distributed with mean 0 and variance 1 as $n \to \infty$.

8.31. Let $X_1, X_2, \ldots, X_n$ be a sequence of independent identically normally distributed random variables with mean μ and variance σ^2. Show that

$$D_n = \frac{(n-1)S^2}{\sigma^2},$$

where $S^2 = [1/(n-1)] \sum_{i=1}^{n} (x_i - \bar{x})^2$ has a chi-square distribution, with $n - 1$ degrees of freedom. Then prove that

$$Z_n = \frac{D_n - E(D_n)}{\sqrt{\text{Var}(D_n)}}$$

is approximately normally distributed with mean 0 and variance 1 for sufficiently large n, using characteristic functions.

8.32. Let $X_1, X_2, \ldots, X_n$ be a sequence of independent identically normally distributed r.v.'s, with parameters μ and σ^2. Show that the probability density of

$$t_n = \frac{(\bar{X} - \mu)\sqrt{n}}{\sqrt{s}}$$

is given by

$$f(t_n) = \frac{\Gamma\left(\dfrac{n}{2}\right)}{\sqrt{n-1}\,\sqrt{\pi}\,\Gamma\left(\dfrac{n-1}{2}\right)} \left(1 + \frac{t_n^{\,2}}{n-1}\right)^{-n/2}, \quad -\infty < t < \infty$$

(*Student-t distribution* with $n - 1$ degrees of freedom). Prove that

$$Z_n = \frac{t_n - E(t_n)}{\sqrt{\text{Var}(t_n)}}$$

is approximately normally distributed, with mean 0 and variance 1 for sufficiently large n.

8.33. Let X_1, X_2, ..., X_n be a sequence of random variables that are characterized by the binomial probability density

$$Pr(X_n = k) = \binom{n}{k} p^k (1 - p)^{n-k}, \quad k = 0, 1, 2, \ldots, n$$

$0 < p < 1$. Use the *DeMoivre-Laplace Limit Theorem* to obtain an analogous result for the sequence of random variables defined by

$$V_n = \frac{X_n}{n}.$$

8.34. Of a large lot of a certain type of an electrical component, 18% are defective. A component is selected at random and is marked defective or nondefective. Before choosing the next component, we return the first one to the lot so that the probability of selecting a defective component remains 0.18. In this manner, we inspect n of the components. What should the value of n be so that the probability will be 0.90 that the frequency of the defective components will lie between 0.16 and 0.20?

8.35. Let X_1, X_2, ..., X_n be a sequence of mutually independent random variables that are uniformly distributed; that is, let

$$(x_i) = \begin{cases} \dfrac{1}{\beta - \alpha}, & \alpha \le x_i \le \beta, \\ 0, & \text{elsewhere,} \end{cases}$$

$i = 1, 2, \ldots, n$. Show, using characteristic functions, that

$$Z_n = \frac{Y_n - E(Y_n)}{\sqrt{\text{Var}(Y_n)}},$$

where $Y_n = (X_1 + X_2 + \cdots + X_n)/n$, is approximately normally distributed, with mean 0 and variance 1 as $n \to \infty$.

8.36. Let $X_1, X_2, \ldots, X_n$ be a sequence of mutually independent Poisson-distributed random variables, with a common parameter λ. Using the technique employed in Theorem 8.5.1, show that

$$Z_n = \frac{Y_n - E(Y_n)}{\sqrt{\text{Var}(Y_n)}},$$

where $Y_n = X_1 + X_2 + \cdots + X_n$ is approximately normally distributed with mean 0 and variance 1 as $n \to \infty$.

Suggested Supplementary Reading

Feller, W. *An Introduction to Probability Theory and Its Applications*. Vol. 1, 2nd ed. New York: John Wiley and Sons, Inc., 1960.

Fisz, M. *Probability Theory and Mathematical Statistics*. 3rd ed. New York: John Wiley and Sons, Inc., 1962.

Harris, B. *Theory of Probability*. Reading, Massachusetts: Addison-Wesley, Publishing Company, Inc., 1966.

Papoulis, A. *Probability Random Variables and Stochastic Processes*. New York: McGraw-Hill Book Company, Inc., 1965.

Parzen, E. *Modern Probability Theory and Its Applications*. New York: John Wiley and Sons, Inc., 1960.

Thomasian, A. J. *The Structure of Probability Theory with Applications*. New York: McGraw-Hill Book Company, Inc., 1969.

Finite Markov Chains

9

9.0 Introduction

One important concept in probability theory is known as the *stochastic process*. A *stochastic or random process* is defined as a family of random variables, $\{X(t)\}$, describing an empirical process, the development of which in time is governed by probabilistic laws. The parameter t is often interpreted as time and may be either discrete or continuous. Some examples of stochastic processes are provided by the growth of populations, such as bacteria colonies, the paths traced by moving particles in Brownian motion, and the fluctuating particles emitted by a radioactive source. Applications of stochastic processes occur in many fields; in particular, they appear in agriculture, biology, economics, engineering, medicine, oceanography, and psychology. A complete treatment of the subject may be found in the suggested readings at the end of the chapter.

In this chapter, we shall be concerned with a special class of stochastic processes, termed *Markov processes or chains*, which has been investigated quite extensively. The basic concepts of Markov chains were introduced in 1907 by the Russian mathematician A. A. Markov. A Markov chain may be defined as a random process, the development of which is treated as a series of transitions between certain values, called the *states*, of the process, which are finite or countably infinite and which possess the property that the future probabilistic behavior of the process depends only on the present (given) state and not on the method by which the process arrived in that state.

Markov-chain theory is of great importance in many branches of science and engineering. In this chapter, we shall give a brief introduction to the basic concepts of a special class of Markov chains: namely, finite Markov chains having a discrete parameter. A complete treatment of the other three basic classifications of Markov processes:

(1)   discrete state space and continuous parameter,
(2)   continuous state space and discrete parameter,
(3)   continuous state space and continuous parameter,

can be found in Parzen's *Stochastic Processes* (Suggested Supplementary Reading).

9.1   Basic Concepts in Markov Chains

Consider a random process that is represented by a sequence of random variables $X_1, X_2, X_3, \ldots$, defined on the space T of all possible values that the variates can assume. The space T is called the *state space* of the sequence, and the different values that the variates can assume are called the *states*. Thus, if we denote the states of the space by $i_1, i_2, i_3, \ldots, i_{n-1}, i_n$, one can pose the following question: What is the probability that the random variable $X_n = i_k$, given that $X_1 = i_1, X_2 = i_2, \ldots, X_{n-1}, = i_{n-1}$? If the structure of the random process is such that the conditional probabilities of the question depend only on the value that the random variable X_{n-1} assumes and are independent of all previous values, then we call such a process a *Markov chain*.

Definition 9.1.1   *Let $i_{k_1}, i_{k_2}, i_{k_3}, \ldots, i_{k_n}$ be any sequence of states. The sequence of variates $X_1, X_2, X_3, \ldots$ will be called a* Markov chain *if*

$$Pr(X_n = i_{k_n} | X_1 = i_{k_1}, \ldots, X_{n-1} = i_{k_{n-1}}) = Pr(X_n = i_{k_n} | X_{n-1} = i_{k_{n-1}}).$$

$$(9.1.1)$$

Thus, an intuitive interpretation of a Markov chain is simply that the probability of going from the k_{n-1}st state, $i_{k_{n-1}}$, to the k_nth state, i_{k_n}, does *not* depend on how we got to the k_{n-1}st state. That is, only the present state of the process determines its future.

One, of course, can interpret the *state space* as the set of outcomes of a given process; and, if the outcome on the $(n-1)$st trial is $i_{k_{n-1}}$, we may use the terminology that the process is in state $i_{k_{n-1}}$ at the $(n-1)$st step or at time $(n-1)$. Thus, in a Markovian sense, the outcome of any trial depends upon the outcome of the immediately preceding trial.

With each Markov chain, we associate a set of *transition probabilities*.

Definition 9.1.2   *The conditional probabilities that the process moves to state j at time n, given that it was in state i at time n − 1, are called* transition probabilities *and are denoted by p_{ij},*

$$p_{ij} = Pr(X_n = j \mid X_{n-1} = i), \qquad (9.1.2)$$

with the subscript of p indicating the direction of transition $i \rightarrow j$. The transition probabilities satisfy the conditions

$$p_{ij} \geq 0 \quad \text{for all} \quad i \quad \text{and} \quad j; \qquad (9.1.3)$$

and, for every i,

$$\sum_{j=1}^{n} p_{ij} = 1. \qquad (9.1.4)$$

Definition 9.1.3   *If the transition probabilities p_{ij} depend only on the states i and j and not on the time n − 1, then the conditional probabilities are* stationary *or* constant.

Markov chains with stationary transition probabilities are called *homogeneous Markov chains.* Stationary transition probabilities mean that, if the process is in a state i_k at time zero and in state i_r at time t_2, then, if the process starts in state i_k at time t_1, the probability of being in state i_r at time $t_1 + t_2$ is the same as the probability would be if the process had started in state i_k at time zero. That is, no matter when the process arrived at state i_k, the probability of transition to state i_r remains the same. In this chapter, we shall be concerned only with Markov chains that have stationary transition probabilities.

The behavior of such Markov chains is described by the transition or *stochastic matrices* of the processes.

Definition 9.1.4   *The transition or stochastic matrix of a process having states $i_1, i_2, i_3, \ldots, i_n$ and transition probabilities $p_{ij}, i, j = 1, 2, 3, \ldots, n$ is*

$$P = \begin{pmatrix}
p_{11} & p_{12} & p_{13} & \cdots & p_{1j} & \cdots & p_{1n} \\
p_{21} & p_{22} & p_{23} & \cdots & p_{2j} & \cdots & p_{2n} \\
\vdots & \vdots & \vdots & & \vdots & & \vdots \\
p_{i1} & p_{i2} & p_{i3} & \cdots & p_{ij} & \cdots & p_{in} \\
\vdots & \vdots & \vdots & & \vdots & & \vdots \\
p_{n1} & p_{n2} & p_{n3} & \cdots & p_{nj} & \cdots & p_{nn}
\end{pmatrix}. \qquad (9.1.5)$$

Clearly, P is a square matrix. Each entry of the transition matrix P, p_{ij}, $i, j = 1, 2, \ldots, n$ must be nonnegative and each row must sum to one; that is, conditions (9.1.3) and (9.1.4),

$$p_{ij} \geq 0, \, i, j = 1, 2, \ldots, n \quad \text{and} \quad \sum_{j=1}^{n} p_{ij} = 1, \quad \text{for all} \quad i,$$

hold. The ith row of the stochastic matrix, P,

$$(p_{i1}, p_{i2}, p_{i3}, \ldots, p_{ij}, \ldots, p_{in}),$$

is called a *probability vector*. It represents the probabilities of all possible outcomes of the next trial. If, in addition to the rows, the columns of P sum to unity, the matrix is called *doubly stochastic*.

State or transition diagrams are quite helpful in order to gain insight into the behavior of Markov chains that have stationary transition probabilities. For example, let the transition matrix of a certain process that has Markovian states be given by

$$P = \begin{array}{c} \\ i_1 \\ i_2 \\ i_3 \\ i_4 \end{array} \begin{array}{c} i_1 \quad i_2 \quad i_3 \quad i_4 \\ \begin{pmatrix} \dfrac{1}{3} & \dfrac{1}{3} & 0 & \dfrac{1}{3} \\ 0 & \dfrac{1}{2} & 0 & \dfrac{1}{2} \\ \dfrac{1}{4} & \dfrac{1}{2} & 0 & \dfrac{1}{4} \\ \dfrac{1}{4} & \dfrac{1}{6} & \dfrac{1}{3} & \dfrac{1}{4} \end{pmatrix} \end{array}.$$

The state diagram of such a transition matrix is shown in Figure 9.1.1, in

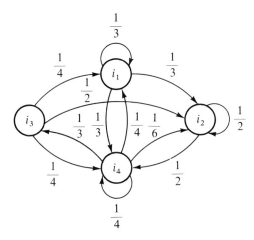

Figure 9.1.1

which circles denote the states of the process and arrows denote the transition probabilities from state i to state j in *single steps*. Conversely, looking at a state diagram of the form (Figure 9.1.2), we can write its transition probability matrix as

$$
P = \begin{array}{c} \\ \\ i_1 \\ \\ i_2 \\ \\ i_3 \\ \\ i_4 \\ \\ i_5 \end{array}
\begin{array}{c} i_1 \quad i_2 \quad i_3 \quad i_4 \quad i_5 \\
\begin{pmatrix}
\dfrac{1}{2} & \dfrac{1}{4} & 0 & 0 & \dfrac{1}{4} \\[2mm]
0 & \dfrac{1}{6} & \dfrac{1}{2} & 0 & \dfrac{1}{3} \\[2mm]
0 & 0 & \dfrac{1}{3} & \dfrac{1}{3} & \dfrac{1}{3} \\[2mm]
\dfrac{1}{2} & 0 & 0 & \dfrac{3}{8} & \dfrac{1}{8} \\[2mm]
\dfrac{1}{4} & \dfrac{1}{6} & \dfrac{1}{3} & \dfrac{1}{4} & 0
\end{pmatrix}
\end{array}
$$

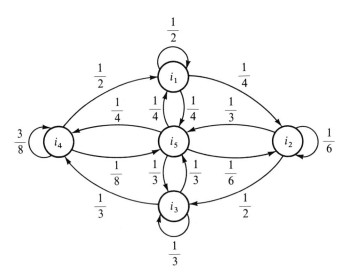

Figure 9.1.2

Example 9.1.1 (Random-Walk Problem)   A man is standing at one of six states arranged in a straight path

$$i_1 - i_2 - i_3 - i_4 - i_5 - i_6,$$

where i_1 and i_6 will be referred to as the boundary states. Assume that the man moves only in steps of one full unit and moves to the right, with probability p, or to the left, with probability $q = 1 - p$. He moves until he reaches one of the two boundary states. The transition matrix for this random walk is

$$P = \begin{array}{c} \\ i_1 \\ i_2 \\ i_3 \\ i_4 \\ i_5 \\ i_6 \end{array} \begin{array}{c} \begin{array}{cccccc} i_1 & i_2 & i_3 & i_4 & i_5 & i_6 \end{array} \\ \left(\begin{array}{cccccc} 1 & 0 & 0 & 0 & 0 & 0 \\ q & 0 & p & 0 & 0 & 0 \\ 0 & q & 0 & p & 0 & 0 \\ 0 & 0 & q & 0 & p & 0 \\ 0 & 0 & 0 & q & 0 & p \\ 0 & 0 & 0 & 0 & 0 & 1 \end{array} \right) \end{array}.$$

The first and last row of the matrix correspond to the boundary states. The second row corresponds to the fact that the man moves from state i_2 to i_3, with probability p, or to state i_1, with probability q; the third row corresponds to the fact that the man moves from state i_3 to i_4, with probability p, or to state i_2, with probability q, and so on.

Example 9.1.2   Four quarterbacks are warming up by throwing a football to one another. Let i_1, i_2, i_3, and i_4 denote the four quarterbacks. It has been observed that i_1 is as likely to throw the ball to i_2 as to i_3 and i_4. Player i_2 never throws to i_3 but splits his throws between i_1 and i_4. Quarterback i_3 throws twice as many passes to i_1 as to i_4 and never throws to i_2, but i_4 throws only to i_1. This process forms a Markov chain because the player who is about to throw the ball is not influenced by the player who had the ball before him. The one-step transition probability matrix is

$$P = \begin{array}{c} \\ i_1 \\ \\ i_2 \\ \\ i_3 \\ \\ i_4 \end{array} \begin{array}{c} \begin{array}{cccc} i_1 & i_2 & i_3 & i_4 \end{array} \\ \left(\begin{array}{cccc} 0 & \frac{1}{3} & \frac{1}{3} & \frac{1}{3} \\ \\ \frac{1}{2} & 0 & 0 & \frac{1}{2} \\ \\ \frac{2}{3} & 0 & 0 & \frac{1}{3} \\ \\ 1 & 0 & 0 & 0 \end{array} \right) \end{array}.$$

The state diagram of the process is shown in Figure 9.1.3.

Example 9.1.3   **(Gambler's-Ruin Problem)**   Suppose that an individual named Nick is playing a game of chance against an adversary. Let each player begin the game with $3.00. On each play, it is possible for Nick to win $1.00

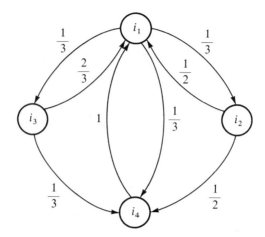

Figure 9.1.3

from his opponent or to lose \$1.00 to his opponent. The game is stopped either when Nick loses all of his money or when he wins all of his opponent's money, that is, when Nick's fortune reaches either \$0.00 or \$6.00. Assume that the probability of Nick's winning on each play of the game is equal to p and that the probability of his losing on each play is equal to $q = 1 - p$. Thus, the probability of his fortune's remaining the same is zero. When $p > q$, the game is advantageous to Nick; when $p = q$, the game is fair; and when $p < q$, the game is advantageous to Nick's opponent.

If $i_1, i_2, i_3, i_4, i_5, i_6$, and i_7 represent the possible states of Nick's fortune, where $i_1 = 0$, $i_2 = 1, \ldots, i_7 = 6$, then his fortune may be represented by a random walk among these possible states. The probability of a step to the right (Nick's winning \$1.00) is p, and the probability of a step to the left (Nick's losing \$1.00) is q, for each play. The transition probability matrix for this Markov chain is given by

$$
P =
\begin{array}{c}
\\ i_1 \\ i_2 \\ i_3 \\ i_4 \\ i_5 \\ i_6 \\ i_7
\end{array}
\begin{array}{c}
\begin{array}{ccccccc} i_1 & i_2 & i_3 & i_4 & i_5 & i_6 & i_7 \end{array} \\
\begin{pmatrix}
1 & 0 & 0 & 0 & 0 & 0 & 0 \\
q & 0 & p & 0 & 0 & 0 & 0 \\
0 & q & 0 & p & 0 & 0 & 0 \\
0 & 0 & q & 0 & p & 0 & 0 \\
0 & 0 & 0 & q & 0 & p & 0 \\
0 & 0 & 0 & 0 & q & 0 & p \\
0 & 0 & 0 & 0 & 0 & 0 & 1
\end{pmatrix}
\end{array}.
$$

Example 9.1.4 (*Biological Population Problem*)   Suppose a finite biological population of N (fixed) individuals consists of individuals of either type A or type a. The population undergoes a birth and death process such that N remains fixed: At discrete instants of time, $t_1 < t_2 \ldots < t_n < \ldots$, one individual dies and is replaced by another individual of type A or a. If, just before time instant t_k when an individual is replaced, there are m individuals of type A and $N - m$ of type a present in the population, we assume that the probability that an A individual dies (or will be replaced) is mp_1/Q_m and the probability that an a individual dies is $[(N - m)p_2]/Q_m$, where $Q_m = p_1m + p_2(N - m)$. This assumption is based on the premise that a single type A individual dies at each time instant, with probability $p_1/(p_1 + p_2)$, and a single type a individual dies at each time instant, with probability $p_2/(p_1 + p_2)$, so that, for m of type A and $N - m$ of type a at each instant, the above probabilities apply. No difference in the birth pattern of the types is assumed; and, thus, the new individual has probability m/N of being type A and probability $(N - m)/N$ of being type a. The Markov chain $X_1, X_2, \ldots, X_n, \ldots$, where X_n is the number of individuals of type A in the population at time instant t_n, $n = 1, 2, \ldots$, describes the population growth process. The possible states for the Markov chain are $i_1 = 0$, $i_2 = 1$, $i_3 = 2, \ldots, i_{N+1} = N$, (that is, $i_{m+1} = m$), with transition probabilities given by

$$p_{m, m-1} = \frac{p_1 m(N - m)}{Q_m N}, \quad p_{m, m+1} = \frac{p_2 m(N - m)}{Q_m N},$$

$$p_{mm} = 1 - p_{m, m-1} - p_{m, m+1}, \quad \text{and} \quad p_{mk} = 0 \quad \text{if} \quad |k - m| > 1.$$

Therefore, the one-step transition probability matrix is given by

$$P = \begin{pmatrix} 1 & 0 & 0 & 0 & 0 & \cdots & 0 & 0 \\ \dfrac{p_1(N-1)}{Q_1 N} & 1 - (p_1 + p_2)\dfrac{N-1}{Q_1 N} & \dfrac{p_2(N-1)}{Q_1 N} & 0 & 0 & \cdots & 0 & 0 \\ 0 & \dfrac{2p_1(N-2)}{Q_2 N} & 1 - (p_1 + p_2)\dfrac{2(N-2)}{Q_2 N} & \dfrac{2p_2(N-2)}{Q_2 N} & 0 & \cdots & 0 & 0 \\ \vdots & \vdots & \vdots & \vdots & \vdots & & \vdots & \vdots \\ 0 & 0 & 0 & 0 & 0 & \cdots & 0 & 0 \\ 0 & 0 & 0 & 0 & 0 & \cdots & 0 & 1 \end{pmatrix}.$$

Example 9.1.5 Suppose that a signal is received that consists of only the digits 0, 1, 7, and 9 such that the next digit in the signal depends on the previous one received, one digit being received at each of the time instants t_n, $n = 1, 2, \ldots$. Assume that, if a 0 is received at time instant t_k, then only a 1 may be received at time t_{k+1}; if a 1 is received at time t_k, then, at t_{k+1}, a 0 is received, with probability 1/2, and a 9 is received, with probability 1/2; if a 7 is received at the kth instant, then, at the $(k + 1)$th instant, a 0 is received, with probability 1/2, and a 1 with probability of 1/2, and, if a 9 is received, then, with probability one, a 7 follows. This process constitutes a Markov chain $X_1, X_2, \ldots, X_n, \ldots$, where $X_n, n = 1, 2, \ldots$, takes the value of the digit received at time t_n. The states of the process are $i_1 = 0$, $i_2 = 1$, $i_3 = 7$, and $i_4 = 9$. The one-step transition probability matrix is given by

$$
P = \begin{array}{c} \\ i_1 \\ i_2 \\ \\ i_3 \\ \\ i_4 \end{array}
\begin{pmatrix}
\begin{array}{cccc} i_1 & i_2 & i_3 & i_4 \end{array} \\
\begin{pmatrix}
0 & 1 & 0 & 0 \\
\frac{1}{2} & 0 & 0 & \frac{1}{2} \\
\frac{1}{2} & \frac{1}{2} & 0 & 0 \\
0 & 0 & 1 & 0
\end{pmatrix}
\end{pmatrix}.
$$

That is,

$$
p_{12} = 1, \; p_{21} = \frac{1}{2}, \; p_{24} = \frac{1}{2}, \; p_{31} = \frac{1}{2}, \; p_{32} = \frac{1}{2}, \; p_{43} = 1,
$$

and all other p_{ij}'s are zero.

Of considerable importance in a random process that has Markovian states is to obtain the probability that the process will move through a given sequence of states. In general, the probability that the process will move through a sequence of states

$$
i_1 \rightsquigarrow i_2 \rightsquigarrow i_3 \rightsquigarrow \cdots \rightsquigarrow i_{n-1} \rightsquigarrow i_n
$$

is the product of the probability of starting at state i_1 and the one-step transition probabilities up to the boundary state i_n. Applying the *General Law of Compound Probability*, Theorem 1.3.1, we can verify the above statement as follows: We can write

$$
Pr(X_1 = i_1, X_2 = i_2, X_3 = i_3, \ldots, X_{n-1} = i_{n-1}, X_n = i_n)
$$
$$
= Pr(X_1 = i_1)Pr(X_2 = i_2 | X_1 = i_1)Pr(X_3 = i_3 | X_1 = i_1, X_2 = i_2) \cdots
$$
$$
Pr(X_n = i_n | X_1 = i_1, X_2 = i_2, \ldots, X_{n-1} = i_{n-1}); \quad (9.1.6)
$$

and, since the sequence of states is Markovian, Equation (9.1.6) becomes

$$
Pr(X_1 = i_1, X_2 = i_2, X_3 = i_3, \ldots, X_{n-1} = i_{n-1}, X_n = i_n)
$$
$$
= Pr(X_1 = i_1)Pr(X_2 = i_2 | X_1 = i_1)Pr(X_3 = i_3 | X_2 = i_2) \cdots
$$
$$
Pr(X_n = i_n | X_{n-1} = i_{n-1})
$$
$$
= Pr(X_1 = i_1)p_{i_1 i_2}p_{i_2 i_3} \cdots p_{i_{n-1} i_n}, \quad (9.1.7)
$$

where $Pr(X_1 = i_1)$ is the probability that the process is initially in state i_1. In a given Markov chain, the probability given by expression (9.1.7) is called the *initial probability density* because we are concerned with the probability distribution at the starting set of observations. Of course, the process does not necessarily have to start at state i_1, but it must begin at one of the states $i_1, i_2, \ldots, i_n$ so that

$$p_{i_k} \geq 0 \quad \text{for all} \quad k$$

and

$$\sum_{k=1}^{n} p_{i_k} = 1.$$

Thus, the initial probability distribution will generate a sequence of initial probabilities

$$\pi_0 = (p_{i_1} p_{i_2} p_{i_3} \cdots p_{i_{n-1}} p_{i_n}),$$

which we refer to as the *initial probability vector* of the process and denote by π_0.

In many applications of random Markovian processes, we are given the initial probability distribution and the transition matrix. The question that we would like to answer with this information is the following: What is the probability that, at a particular time, the process is at a certain state? Before giving the theoretical formulation of the above question, we shall illustrate the method with an example that uses the concept of a *tree diagram*.

Example 9.1.6 Consider the random-walk problem formulated in Example 9.1.1. Assuming $p = q = 1/2$, the transition matrix becomes

$$
P = \quad
\begin{array}{c}
 \\
i_1 \\
i_2 \\
i_3 \\
i_4 \\
i_5 \\
i_6
\end{array}
\begin{array}{c}
\begin{array}{cccccc}
i_1 & i_2 & i_3 & i_4 & i_5 & i_6
\end{array} \\
\begin{pmatrix}
1 & 0 & 0 & 0 & 0 & 0 \\
\frac{1}{2} & 0 & \frac{1}{2} & 0 & 0 & 0 \\
0 & \frac{1}{2} & 0 & \frac{1}{2} & 0 & 0 \\
0 & 0 & \frac{1}{2} & 0 & \frac{1}{2} & 0 \\
0 & 0 & 0 & \frac{1}{2} & 0 & \frac{1}{2} \\
0 & 0 & 0 & 0 & 0 & 1
\end{pmatrix}
\end{array}.
$$

A tree diagram of the transition matrix is shown in Figure 9.1.4. The starting point of the process is assumed to be in state i_4.

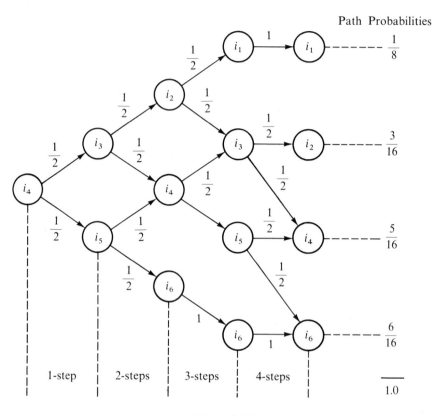

Path Probabilities

Figure 9.1.4

Suppose we want to obtain the probability that the process, at time $n = 3$ or at the third step, is in state i_3. This probability is determined by adding all the path probabilities that lead to state i_3 : $1/8 + 1/8 = 1/4$. Similarly, the probability that we are in state i_1 at the fourth step is $1/2 + 1/8 = 5/8$. Clearly, starting at state i_4, the probability of being in state i_5 after two steps is zero.

One can also obtain the various steps of probability distribution vectors from a tree diagram. For the above example, the probability distribution vectors are given below:

$$
\begin{array}{cccccc}
i_1 & i_2 & i_3 & i_4 & i_5 & i_6
\end{array}
$$

$$
\pi_0 = (0 \quad 0 \quad 0 \quad 1 \quad 0 \quad 0)
$$

$$
\pi_1 = \left(0 \quad 0 \quad \frac{1}{2} \quad 0 \quad \frac{1}{2} \quad 0\right)
$$

$$\pi_2 = \begin{pmatrix} 0 & \dfrac{1}{4} & 0 & \dfrac{1}{2} & 0 & \dfrac{1}{4} \end{pmatrix}$$

$$\pi_3 = \begin{pmatrix} \dfrac{1}{8} & 0 & \dfrac{3}{8} & 0 & \dfrac{1}{4} & \dfrac{1}{4} \end{pmatrix}$$

$$\pi_4 = \begin{pmatrix} \dfrac{1}{8} & \dfrac{3}{16} & 0 & \dfrac{5}{16} & 0 & \dfrac{3}{8} \end{pmatrix}.$$

Thus, from π_3, we can conclude that, starting from state i_4, the process will be at states i_1, i_2, i_3, i_4, i_5, and i_6 at the third step, with probabilities 1/8, 0, 3/8, 0, 1/4, and 1/4, respectively.

The mathematical formulation of the above question is given by

$$Pr(X_k = j) = \sum_i Pr(X_{k-1} = i) Pr(X_k = j \mid X_{k-1} = i)$$

$$= \sum_i p_j^{(k-1)} p_{ij}$$

$$= p_j^{(k)}; \tag{9.1.8}$$

that is, the probability that the process is in state j at the kth step is equal to the sum over all probabilties that the process is in state i at the $(k-1)$st step; on the next step, the process moves from state i to state j.

Note that $p_j^{(k-1)}$ is the $(k-1)$st step probability. Thus, for $k = 1$, we get

$$p_j^{(1)} = \sum_i p_j^{(0)} p_{ij},$$

where $p_j^{(0)}$ is the initial ($n = 0$ steps) probability, which constitutes the probability vector

$$\pi_0 = (p_1^{(0)} p_2^{(0)} \cdots p_m^{(0)});$$

for $k = 2$,

$$p_j^{(2)} = \sum_i p_j^{(1)} p_{ij},$$

where $p_j^{(1)}$ is the jth element of the first-step probability, which constitutes the probability vector

$$\pi_1 = (p_1^{(1)} p_2^{(1)} \cdots p_m^{(1)}).$$

Equation (9.1.8), which can easily be shown to be true by induction on k, is precisely the product of a row vector (probability distribution vector) and a matrix (the transition matrix). Thus, Equation (9.1.8) can be written in the form

$$\pi_k = \pi_{k-1} P \tag{9.1.9}$$

for $k \geq i$. This situation can be seen as follows:

$$(p_1^{(k-1)} p_2^{(k-1)} \cdots p_i^{(k-1)} \cdots p_m^{(k-1)}) \begin{pmatrix} p_{11} & p_{12} & \cdots & p_{1j} & \cdots & p_{1m} \\ p_{21} & p_{22} & \cdots & p_{2j} & \cdots & p_{2m} \\ \vdots & \vdots & & \vdots & & \\ p_{i1} & p_{i2} & \cdots & p_{ij} & \cdots & p_{im} \\ \vdots & \vdots & & \vdots & & \\ p_{m1} & p_{m2} & \cdots & p_{mj} & \cdots & p_{mm} \end{pmatrix}$$

$$= \left(\sum_{i=1}^{m} p_i^{(k-1)} p_{i1}, \sum_{i=1}^{m} p_i^{(k-1)} p_{i2} \cdots, \sum_{i=1}^{m} p_i^{(k-1)} p_{ij}, \ldots, \sum_{i=1}^{m} p_i^{(k-1)} p_{im} \right) = \pi_k.$$

By successive iteration of Equation (9.1.9), the kth step probability distribution vector π_k results in

$$\pi_k = \pi_{k-1} P$$
$$= \pi_{k-2} P^2 = \pi_{k-3} P^3 = \cdots = \pi_1 P^{k-1} = \pi_0 P^k. \qquad (9.1.10)$$

Thus, to obtain the kth step probability distribution vector, we multiply the initial probability distribution vector by the one-step transition probability matrix, raised to the kth power. Therefore, given the initial probability distribution and the transition matrix of a Markov chain and using Equation (9.1.9) or (9.1.10), we can obtain the probability distribution vector at any given time.

Example 9.1.7   Here we shall use Equation (9.1.9) to calculate the one-, two-, three-, and four-step probability distribution vectors for the transition matrix given in Example 9.1.6.

(a)

$$\pi_1 = \pi_0 P = (0\ 0\ 0\ 1\ 0\ 0) \begin{pmatrix} 1 & 0 & 0 & 0 & 0 & 0 \\ \frac{1}{2} & 0 & \frac{1}{2} & 0 & 0 & 0 \\ 0 & \frac{1}{2} & 0 & \frac{1}{2} & 0 & 0 \\ 0 & 0 & \frac{1}{2} & 0 & \frac{1}{2} & 0 \\ 0 & 0 & 0 & \frac{1}{2} & 0 & \frac{1}{2} \\ 0 & 0 & 0 & 0 & 0 & 1 \end{pmatrix}$$

$$= \left(0\ 0\ \frac{1}{2}\ 0\ \frac{1}{2}\ 0 \right);$$

(b)

$$\pi_2 = \pi_1 P = \begin{pmatrix} 0 & 0 & \dfrac{1}{2} & 0 & \dfrac{1}{2} & 0 \end{pmatrix} \begin{pmatrix} 1 & 0 & 0 & 0 & 0 & 0 \\ \dfrac{1}{2} & 0 & \dfrac{1}{2} & 0 & 0 & 0 \\ 0 & \dfrac{1}{2} & 0 & \dfrac{1}{2} & 0 & 0 \\ 0 & 0 & \dfrac{1}{2} & 0 & \dfrac{1}{2} & 0 \\ 0 & 0 & 0 & \dfrac{1}{2} & 0 & \dfrac{1}{2} \\ 0 & 0 & 0 & 0 & 0 & 1 \end{pmatrix}$$

$$= \begin{pmatrix} 0 & \dfrac{1}{4} & 0 & \dfrac{1}{2} & 0 & \dfrac{1}{4} \end{pmatrix};$$

(c)

$$\pi_3 = \pi_2 P = \begin{pmatrix} 0 & \dfrac{1}{4} & 0 & \dfrac{1}{2} & 0 & \dfrac{1}{4} \end{pmatrix} \begin{pmatrix} 1 & 0 & 0 & 0 & 0 & 0 \\ \dfrac{1}{2} & 0 & \dfrac{1}{2} & 0 & 0 & 0 \\ 0 & \dfrac{1}{2} & 0 & \dfrac{1}{2} & 0 & 0 \\ 0 & 0 & \dfrac{1}{2} & 0 & \dfrac{1}{2} & 0 \\ 0 & 0 & 0 & \dfrac{1}{2} & 0 & \dfrac{1}{2} \\ 0 & 0 & 0 & 0 & 0 & 1 \end{pmatrix}$$

$$= \begin{pmatrix} \dfrac{1}{8} & 0 & \dfrac{3}{8} & 0 & \dfrac{1}{4} & \dfrac{1}{4} \end{pmatrix};$$

(d)

$$\pi_4 = \pi_3 P = \begin{pmatrix} \dfrac{1}{8} & 0 & \dfrac{3}{8} & 0 & \dfrac{1}{4} & \dfrac{1}{4} \end{pmatrix} \begin{pmatrix} 1 & 0 & 0 & 0 & 0 & 0 \\ \dfrac{1}{2} & 0 & \dfrac{1}{2} & 0 & 0 & 0 \\ 0 & \dfrac{1}{2} & 0 & \dfrac{1}{2} & 0 & 0 \\ 0 & 0 & \dfrac{1}{2} & 0 & \dfrac{1}{2} & 0 \\ 0 & 0 & 0 & \dfrac{1}{2} & 0 & \dfrac{1}{2} \\ 0 & 0 & 0 & 0 & 0 & 1 \end{pmatrix}$$

$$= \begin{pmatrix} \dfrac{1}{8} & \dfrac{3}{16} & 0 & \dfrac{5}{16} & 0 & \dfrac{3}{8} \end{pmatrix}.$$

Hence, the probability distribution vectors that we calculate using Equation (9.1.9) are the same as those obtained from the tree diagram.

It is, thus, clear that a random process that results in a sequence of states that are Markovian, with stationary transition probabilities, is completely specified (defined) when we know the initial probability density and the transition probabilities.

9.2   N-Step Transition Probabilities

The entry p_{ij} in the transition matrix P of a Markov chain is the probability that the process changes from state i to state j in a single step. There are many processes, however, in which it is impossible to change from state i to state j in one step. For instance, in the state diagram shown by Figure 9.1.1, it is impossible for the process to change from state i_2 to i_1 in one step, but it can make the change in two steps, via state i_4.

We know that the one-step transition probability, $i \rightsquigarrow j$, is given by

$$p_{ij} = Pr[X_n = j \mid X_{n-1} = i].$$

For a two-step transition, $i \rightsquigarrow r \rightsquigarrow j$, the transition probabilities that the process changes from state $i \rightsquigarrow r$ and $r \rightsquigarrow j$ are independent. Thus,

$$Pr[X_{n-1} = r \mid X_{n-2} = i] \cdot Pr[X_n = j \mid X_{n-1} = r] = p_{ir} p_{rj}.$$

Summing over all possible intermediate states, we obtain the two-step transition probability

$$p_{ij}^{(2)} = \sum_r p_{ir} p_{rj}.$$

Similarly, the three-step transition probability is given recursively by

$$p_{ij}^{(3)} = \sum_r p_{ir}^{(2)} p_{rj};$$

and, in general, the $(n + 1)$-step transition probabilities are given by

$$p_{ij}^{(n+1)} = \sum_r p_{ir}^{(n)} p_{rj}. \tag{9.2.1}$$

We proceed to show that, for all r,

$$Pr(X_{m+r} = j \mid X_m = i) = p_{ij}^{(r)}. \tag{9.2.2}$$

For $r = 1$, Equation (9.2.2) is true, by the definition of a Markov chain.

Assume that Equation (9.2.2) is true for $r = n$. We have

$$Pr(X_{m+n+1} = j \,|\, X_m = i) = \sum_k Pr(X_{m+n} = k, X_{m+n+1} = j \,|\, X_m = i). \quad (9.2.3)$$

Recall that

$$Pr(AB \,|\, C) = Pr(A \,|\, C)Pr(B \,|\, AC).$$

Thus, Equation (9.2.3) can be written as

$$Pr(X_{m+n+1} = j \,|\, X_m = i)$$
$$= \sum_k Pr(X_{m+n} = k \,|\, X_m = i)Pr(X_{m+n+1} = j \,|\, X_m = i, X_{m+n} = k).$$

Applying the Markov property, the above equation becomes

$$Pr(X_{m+n+1} = j \,|\, X_m = i) = \sum_k Pr(X_{m+n} = k \,|\, X_m = i)Pr(X_{m+n+1} = j \,|\, X_{m+n} = k)$$
$$= \sum_k p_{ik}^{(n)} p_{kj}$$
$$= p_{ij}^{(n+1)}.$$

Therefore, by induction, we have shown that Equation (9.2.2) is true for all r.

A generalization of Equation (9.2.1) can be formulated as follows: Suppose that a process is to move from state i into state j in $m + n$ steps, and we wish to obtain the transition probability $p_{ij}^{(m+n)}$. The first m steps will take the process from state i into some intermediate state k, and the second n steps will take the process from state k to state j. The product of these two transition probabilities, $p_{ik}^{(m)} p_{kj}^{(n)}$, summed over all possible intermediate states that the process may visit, gives the desired $(m + n)$-step transition probability

$$p_{ij}^{(m+n)} = \sum_k p_{ik}^{(m)} p_{kj}^{(n)}, \quad (9.2.4)$$

where

$$p_{ij}^{(0)} = \begin{cases} 1 & \text{for } i = j, \\ 0 & \text{for } i \neq j. \end{cases}$$

Note that, for $m = 1$, Equation (9.2.4) reduces to Equation (9.2.1). It can be shown by induction that Equation (9.2.4) is true for all m.

In Section 9.1, we have defined a one-step transition matrix, which describes the behavior of a Markov chain. Similarly, for n-step transition probabilities, we shall define an *n-step transition matrix* in Definition 9.2.1.

Definition 9.2.1   *The n-step transition matrix of a process, with states* $i_1, i_2, \ldots, i_k$ *and n-step transition probabilities* $p_{ij}^{(n)}$, $i, j = 1, 2, \ldots, k$, *is defined as*

$$P^{(n)} = \begin{pmatrix} p_{11}^{(n)} & p_{12}^{(n)} & p_{13}^{(n)} & \cdots & p_{1j}^{(n)} & \cdots & p_{1k}^{(n)} \\ p_{21}^{(n)} & p_{22}^{(n)} & p_{23}^{(n)} & \cdots & p_{2j}^{(n)} & \cdots & p_{2k}^{(n)} \\ \vdots & \vdots & \vdots & & \vdots & & \vdots \\ p_{i1}^{(n)} & p_{i2}^{(n)} & p_{i3}^{(n)} & \cdots & p_{ij}^{(n)} & \cdots & p_{ik}^{(n)} \\ \vdots & \vdots & \vdots & & \vdots & & \vdots \\ p_{k1}^{(n)} & p_{k2}^{(n)} & p_{k3}^{(n)} & \cdots & p_{kj}^{(n)} & \cdots & p_{kk}^{(n)} \end{pmatrix},$$

where

$$p_{ij}^{(n)} \geq 0, \quad i, j = 1, 2, \ldots, k$$

and

$$\sum_j p_{ij}^{(n)} = 1, \quad \text{for all} \quad i.$$

Clearly, $P^{(n)}$ is a square matrix; and $p_{ij}^{(n)}$ denotes the transition probability that the process moves from state i to state j in n steps.

Equation (9.2.4) is, by definition (see Section 0.8),

$$P^{(m+n)} = P^{(m)}P^{(n)}. \tag{9.2.5}$$

Equation (9.2.5) is the matrix form of the well-known *Equation of Chapman-Kolmogorov*, which is of significant importance in the theory of Markov Chains. Also, from the applications point of view, Equation (9.2.5) is a very useful result. We should mention that matrices do not commute, in general, but that transition matrices do satisfy the condition

$$P^{(m+n)} = P^{(m)}P^{(n)} = P^{(n)}P^{(m)}.$$

A fundamental property of the transition matrix P is that the n-step transition matrix is equal to the nth power of P,

$$P^{(n)} = P^n. \tag{9.2.6}$$

To verify Equation (9.2.6), consider the process to be in state i at time k; we are interested in obtaining the probability, $p_{ij}^{(n)}$, that the process is in state j at time $k + n$. Because the process is in state i at time k, the initial probability distribution vector, $\pi_i = (0 \quad 0 \quad 0 \quad \cdots \quad 1 \quad \cdots \quad 0 \quad 0 \quad 0)$, has a one at the ith state and zeros everywhere else. As a consequence of Equation (9.1.9), we have

$$\pi_n = \pi_0 P^n = (0\,0\,0 \cdots 1 \cdots 0\,0\,0) \begin{pmatrix} p_{11} & p_{12} & \cdots & p_{1j} & \cdots & p_{1k} \\ p_{21} & p_{22} & \cdots & p_{2j} & \cdots & p_{2k} \\ \vdots & \vdots & & \vdots & & \vdots \\ p_{i1} & p_{i2} & \cdots & p_{ij} & \cdots & p_{ik} \\ \vdots & \vdots & & \vdots & & \vdots \\ p_{k1} & p_{k2} & & p_{kj} & & p_{kk} \end{pmatrix}$$

$$= (p_{i1} p_{i2} \cdots p_{ij} \cdots p_{ik})^n,$$

$$= (p_{i1}^{(n)} p_{i2}^{(n)} \cdots p_{ij}^{(n)} \cdots p_{ik}^{(n)}),$$

that is, the ith row of the transition matrix P^n. Thus, $p_{ij}^{(n)}$ is the jth component of the ith row of P^n; and, hence, $P^{(n)} = P^n$.

Example 9.2.1   Consider the one-step transition matrix given in Example 9.1.2,

$$P = \begin{array}{c} \\ i_1 \\ i_2 \\ i_3 \\ i_4 \end{array} \begin{array}{c} \begin{array}{cccc} i_1 & i_2 & i_3 & i_4 \end{array} \\ \begin{pmatrix} 0 & \frac{1}{3} & \frac{1}{3} & \frac{1}{3} \\ \frac{1}{2} & 0 & 0 & \frac{1}{2} \\ \frac{2}{3} & 0 & 0 & \frac{1}{3} \\ 1 & 0 & 0 & 0 \end{pmatrix} \end{array}.$$

The two-step transition matrix, P^2, is

$$P^2 = P \cdot P = \begin{pmatrix} 0 & \frac{1}{3} & \frac{1}{3} & \frac{1}{3} \\ \frac{1}{2} & 0 & 0 & \frac{1}{2} \\ \frac{2}{3} & 0 & 0 & \frac{1}{3} \\ 1 & 0 & 0 & 0 \end{pmatrix} \begin{pmatrix} 0 & \frac{1}{3} & \frac{1}{3} & \frac{1}{3} \\ \frac{1}{2} & 0 & 0 & \frac{1}{2} \\ \frac{2}{3} & 0 & 0 & \frac{1}{3} \\ 1 & 0 & 0 & 0 \end{pmatrix}$$

$$= \begin{pmatrix} \frac{13}{18} & 0 & 0 & \frac{5}{18} \\ \frac{1}{2} & \frac{1}{6} & \frac{1}{6} & \frac{1}{6} \\ \frac{1}{3} & \frac{2}{9} & \frac{2}{9} & \frac{2}{9} \\ 0 & \frac{1}{3} & \frac{1}{3} & \frac{1}{3} \end{pmatrix}.$$

The three-step transition matrix, P^3, is

$$P^3 = P^2 \cdot P = \begin{pmatrix} \frac{13}{18} & 0 & 0 & \frac{5}{18} \\ \frac{1}{2} & \frac{1}{6} & \frac{1}{6} & \frac{1}{6} \\ \frac{1}{3} & \frac{2}{9} & \frac{2}{9} & \frac{2}{9} \\ 0 & \frac{1}{3} & \frac{1}{3} & \frac{1}{3} \end{pmatrix} \begin{pmatrix} 0 & \frac{1}{3} & \frac{1}{3} & \frac{1}{3} \\ \frac{1}{2} & 0 & 0 & \frac{1}{2} \\ \frac{2}{3} & 0 & 0 & \frac{1}{3} \\ 1 & 0 & 0 & 0 \end{pmatrix}$$

$$= \begin{pmatrix} \frac{5}{18} & \frac{13}{54} & \frac{13}{54} & \frac{13}{54} \\ \frac{13}{36} & \frac{1}{6} & \frac{1}{6} & \frac{11}{36} \\ \frac{13}{27} & \frac{1}{9} & \frac{1}{9} & \frac{8}{27} \\ \frac{13}{18} & 0 & 0 & \frac{5}{18} \end{pmatrix}.$$

The third row of P^3,

$$\left(\frac{13}{27} \quad \frac{1}{9} \quad \frac{1}{9} \quad \frac{8}{27} \right),$$

denotes that, after three throws, the ball is in the hands of players i_1, i_2, i_3, and i_4, with respective probabilities 13/27, 1/9, 1/9, and 8/27.

Example 9.2.2   In the *Gambler's-Ruin Problem*, the three-step transition probability matrix, the entries of which are $p_{jk}^{(3)}$, the probability of being in state i_k after three plays, given that the fortune was in state i_j, is given by

$$P^3 = \begin{pmatrix} 1 & 0 & 0 & 0 & 0 & 0 & 0 \\ q+pq^2 & 0 & 2p^2q & 0 & p^3 & 0 & 0 \\ q^2 & 2pq^2 & 0 & 3p^2q & 0 & p^3 & 0 \\ q^3 & 0 & 3pq^2 & 0 & 3p^2q & 0 & p^3 \\ 0 & q^3 & 0 & 3pq^2 & 0 & 2p^2q & p^2 \\ 0 & 0 & q^3 & 0 & 2pq^2 & 0 & p+p^2q \\ 0 & 0 & 0 & 0 & 0 & 0 & 1 \end{pmatrix}.$$

Example 9.2.3   In Example 9.1.5, we may find the probabilities of receiving certain combinations of n digits by considering the n-step transition probabilities and the n-step transition probability matrix P^n. For example, because

$$p_{22}^{(3)} = \sum_{j=1}^{4} \sum_{k=1}^{4} p_{2k} p_{kj} p_{j2} = p_{24} p_{43} p_{32},$$

from the above values of p_{jk}, $j, k = 1, 2, 3, 4$, we may find the probability that the combination 1971 will be received in the next three transitions, given that the first 1 was received at the last time instant, that is, that the process is in state $i_2 = 1$.

$$P^3 = \begin{pmatrix} 0 & \dfrac{1}{2} & \dfrac{1}{2} & 0 \\[2mm] \dfrac{1}{2} & \dfrac{1}{4} & 0 & \dfrac{1}{4} \\[2mm] \dfrac{1}{4} & \dfrac{1}{4} & \dfrac{1}{4} & \dfrac{1}{4} \\[2mm] \dfrac{1}{4} & \dfrac{1}{2} & 0 & \dfrac{1}{4} \end{pmatrix},$$

so that $p_{22}^{(3)} = 1/4$.

Thus, the probability for a transition in n-steps may simply be obtained by raising the one-step transition matrix to the nth power.

When n is fairly large, computing P^n is laborious; but, in the following section, we present a shorter method for accomplishing such calculations.

9.3   Evaluation of P^n

Before we proceed with this section, we will discuss some preliminary concepts concerning matrices. These notions will be essential to the understanding of what follows.

9.3.1   The Characteristic Equation   The characteristic equation of any square $k \times k$ matrix A is

$$|A - \lambda I| = 0,$$

and its k solutions are called the *eigenvalues* of the matrix A. For every distinct eigenvalue of the matrix A, there exists an eigenvector, $\mathbf{x}$, such that

$$(A - \lambda I)\mathbf{x} = \mathbf{0}.$$

We now give some illustrative examples:

Example 9.3.1   Let the matrix A be given by

$$A = \begin{bmatrix} 0 & 1 \\ 1-d & d \end{bmatrix}.$$

Then the characteristic equation is

$$0 = |A - \lambda I| = \left\| \begin{bmatrix} 0 & 1 \\ 1-d & d \end{bmatrix} - \begin{bmatrix} \lambda & 0 \\ 0 & \lambda \end{bmatrix} \right\| = \begin{vmatrix} -\lambda & 1 \\ 1-d & d-\lambda \end{vmatrix}$$

$$= -\lambda(d - \lambda) - (1 - d) = \lambda^2 - d\lambda - 1 + d.$$

Thus, the characteristic equation of the matrix A is

$$\lambda^2 - d\lambda - 1 + d = 0.$$

To solve the characteristic equation, we write

$$\lambda = \frac{d \pm \sqrt{d^2 + 4(1-d)}}{2} = \frac{d \pm \sqrt{(d-2)^2}}{2} = \frac{d \pm (d-2)}{2} = d-1, 1.$$

Therefore, the eigenvalues of the matrix A are $\lambda_1 = d - 1$ and $\lambda_2 = 1$. The eigenvector corresponding to the eigenvalue λ_1 is $\mathbf{x}_1$ such that

$$0 = (A - \lambda_1 I)\mathbf{x}_1 = \left(\begin{bmatrix} 0 & 1 \\ 1-d & d \end{bmatrix} - \begin{bmatrix} d-1 & 0 \\ 0 & d-1 \end{bmatrix} \right)\mathbf{x}_1 = \begin{bmatrix} 1-d & 1 \\ 1-d & 1 \end{bmatrix}\mathbf{x}_1.$$

At this point, we express the eigenvector $\mathbf{x}_1$ as $\begin{bmatrix} a \\ b \end{bmatrix}$ and solve for the components of $\mathbf{x}_1$, namely a and b:

$$\begin{bmatrix} 1-d & 1 \\ 1-d & 1 \end{bmatrix}\begin{bmatrix} a \\ b \end{bmatrix} = \begin{bmatrix} (1-d)a + b \\ (1-d)a + b \end{bmatrix} = \begin{bmatrix} 0 \\ 0 \end{bmatrix}.$$

This implies that

$$b = (d-1)a.$$

Thus,

$$\mathbf{x}_1 = \begin{bmatrix} a \\ (d-1)a \end{bmatrix}.$$

We let a equal any convenient number, say one; and we determine that the eigenvector corresponding to $\lambda_1 = d - 1$ is

$$\mathbf{x}_1 = \begin{bmatrix} 1 \\ d - 1 \end{bmatrix}.$$

We can easily check to see that $(A - \lambda_1 I)\mathbf{x}_1 = 0$. The eigenvector corresponding to λ_2 is $\mathbf{x}_2$, such that

$$0 = (A - \lambda_2 I)\mathbf{x}_2 = \left(\begin{bmatrix} 0 & 1 \\ 1 - d & d \end{bmatrix} - \begin{bmatrix} 1 & 0 \\ 0 & 1 \end{bmatrix} \right)\mathbf{x}_2 = \begin{bmatrix} -1 & 1 \\ 1 - d & d - 1 \end{bmatrix}\mathbf{x}_2.$$

Expressing $\mathbf{x}_2$ as $\begin{bmatrix} a \\ b \end{bmatrix}$ and solving for a and b gives

$$\begin{bmatrix} -1 & 1 \\ 1 - d & d - 1 \end{bmatrix}\begin{bmatrix} a \\ b \end{bmatrix} = \begin{bmatrix} -(a - b) \\ (1 - d)(a - b) \end{bmatrix} = \begin{bmatrix} 0 \\ 0 \end{bmatrix}.$$

This implies that $a = b$; so $\mathbf{x}_2 = \begin{bmatrix} b \\ b \end{bmatrix}$. Letting b equal any convenient number, say one, we see that the eigenvector corresponding to $\lambda_2 = 1$ is

$$\mathbf{x}_2 = \begin{bmatrix} 1 \\ 1 \end{bmatrix}.$$

If we construct a matrix B, the columns of which are the eigenvectors of A (A having distinct eigenvalues), then $B^{-1}AB = \Lambda$, where Λ is a diagonal matrix of the eigenvalues of A. (A diagonal matrix is a square matrix, the nonzero elements of which appear only on the upper left to lower right main diagonal.) To illustrate, we immediately can construct B from $\mathbf{x}_1$ and $\mathbf{x}_2$, getting

$$B = \begin{bmatrix} 1 & 1 \\ d - 1 & 1 \end{bmatrix} \quad \text{and} \quad B^{-1} = \frac{1}{2 - d}\begin{bmatrix} 1 & -1 \\ 1 - d & 1 \end{bmatrix}.$$

$$B^{-1}AB = \frac{1}{2 - d}\begin{bmatrix} 1 & -1 \\ 1 - d & 1 \end{bmatrix}\begin{bmatrix} 0 & 1 \\ 1 - d & d \end{bmatrix}\begin{bmatrix} 1 & 1 \\ d - 1 & 1 \end{bmatrix}$$

$$= \frac{1}{2 - d}\begin{bmatrix} d - 1 & 1 - d \\ 1 - d & 1 \end{bmatrix}\begin{bmatrix} 1 & 1 \\ d - 1 & 1 \end{bmatrix}$$

$$= \frac{1}{2 - d}\begin{bmatrix} (d - 1)(2 - d) & 0 \\ 0 & 2 - d \end{bmatrix} = \begin{bmatrix} d - 1 & 0 \\ 0 & 1 \end{bmatrix}.$$

Thus, we have that

$$B^{-1}AB = \Lambda$$

or

$$\frac{1}{2 - d}\begin{bmatrix} 1 & -1 \\ 1 - d & 1 \end{bmatrix}\begin{bmatrix} 0 & 1 \\ 1 - d & d \end{bmatrix}\begin{bmatrix} 1 & 1 \\ d - 1 & 1 \end{bmatrix} = \begin{bmatrix} d - 1 & 0 \\ 0 & 1 \end{bmatrix}.$$

Example 9.3.2   Let the matrix A be given by

$$A = \begin{bmatrix} 1 & 0 & 0 \\ \dfrac{3}{4} & \dfrac{1}{4} & 0 \\ \dfrac{1}{4} & \dfrac{1}{4} & \dfrac{1}{2} \end{bmatrix}.$$

The characteristic equation is

$$\begin{vmatrix} 1-\lambda & 0 & 0 \\ \dfrac{3}{4} & \dfrac{1}{4}-\lambda & 0 \\ \dfrac{1}{4} & \dfrac{1}{4} & \dfrac{1}{2}-\lambda \end{vmatrix} = 0.$$

Solving it gives $\lambda_1 = 1$, $\lambda_2 = 1/4$, and $\lambda_3 = 1/2$. To obtain the eigenvector for $\lambda_1 = 1$, we write

$$\begin{bmatrix} 0 & 0 & 0 \\ \dfrac{3}{4} & -\dfrac{3}{4} & 0 \\ \dfrac{1}{4} & \dfrac{1}{4} & -\dfrac{1}{2} \end{bmatrix} \begin{bmatrix} a \\ b \\ c \end{bmatrix} = \begin{bmatrix} 0 \\ \dfrac{3}{4}(a-b) \\ \dfrac{1}{4}(a+b-2c) \end{bmatrix} = \begin{bmatrix} 0 \\ 0 \\ 0 \end{bmatrix},$$

which implies that $a = b = c$; so we get that

$$\mathbf{x}_1 = \begin{bmatrix} 1 \\ 1 \\ 1 \end{bmatrix}.$$

For $\lambda_2 = 1/4$, we have

$$\begin{bmatrix} \dfrac{3}{4} & 0 & 0 \\ \dfrac{3}{4} & 0 & 0 \\ \dfrac{1}{4} & \dfrac{1}{4} & \dfrac{1}{4} \end{bmatrix} \begin{bmatrix} a \\ b \\ c \end{bmatrix} = \begin{bmatrix} \dfrac{3}{4}a \\ \dfrac{3}{4}a \\ \dfrac{1}{4}(a+b+c) \end{bmatrix} = \begin{bmatrix} 0 \\ 0 \\ 0 \end{bmatrix},$$

which implies that $a = 0$ and $b = -c$. Therefore,

$$\mathbf{x}_2 = \begin{bmatrix} 0 \\ -1 \\ 1 \end{bmatrix}.$$

And, finally, for $\lambda_3 = 1/2$, we have

$$\begin{bmatrix} \dfrac{1}{2} & 0 & 0 \\ \dfrac{3}{4} & -\dfrac{1}{4} & 0 \\ \dfrac{1}{4} & \dfrac{1}{4} & 0 \end{bmatrix} \begin{bmatrix} a \\ b \\ c \end{bmatrix} = \begin{bmatrix} \dfrac{1}{2}a \\ \dfrac{1}{4}(3a - b) \\ \dfrac{1}{4}(a + b) \end{bmatrix} = \begin{bmatrix} 0 \\ 0 \\ 0 \end{bmatrix},$$

which implies that $a = b = 0$. Thus,

$$\mathbf{x}_3 = \begin{bmatrix} 0 \\ 0 \\ 1 \end{bmatrix}.$$

Constructing B gives

$$B = \begin{bmatrix} 1 & 0 & 0 \\ 1 & -1 & 0 \\ 1 & 1 & 1 \end{bmatrix}, \quad \text{and} \quad B^{-1} = \begin{bmatrix} 1 & 0 & 0 \\ 1 & -1 & 0 \\ -2 & 1 & 1 \end{bmatrix}.$$

Thus,

$$B^{-1}AB = \begin{bmatrix} 1 & 0 & 0 \\ 1 & -1 & 0 \\ -2 & 1 & 1 \end{bmatrix} \begin{bmatrix} 1 & 0 & 0 \\ \dfrac{3}{4} & \dfrac{1}{4} & 0 \\ \dfrac{1}{4} & \dfrac{1}{4} & \dfrac{1}{2} \end{bmatrix} \begin{bmatrix} 1 & 0 & 0 \\ 1 & -1 & 0 \\ 1 & 1 & 1 \end{bmatrix}$$

$$= \begin{bmatrix} 1 & 0 & 0 \\ \dfrac{1}{4} & -\dfrac{1}{4} & 0 \\ -1 & \dfrac{1}{2} & \dfrac{1}{2} \end{bmatrix} \begin{bmatrix} 1 & 0 & 0 \\ 1 & -1 & 0 \\ 1 & 1 & 1 \end{bmatrix} = \begin{bmatrix} 1 & 0 & 0 \\ 0 & \dfrac{1}{4} & 0 \\ 0 & 0 & \dfrac{1}{2} \end{bmatrix}.$$

In the previous section, we showed how to calculate the probability distribution vectors at any stage n of a Markov process by using the relationship $\pi_n = \pi_0 P^n$. But the calculation of P^n could be prohibitive if the order of P were large and/or n were large. So, instead of multiplying P by itself n times, we describe an alternative method for computing P^n.

Suppose P is an $m \times m$ transition matrix, and further suppose that all of its eigenvalues are distinct. One can then theoretically calculate m eigenvectors of P. If we let C be the matrix that has columns that are the m eigenvectors, then $C^{-1}PC = \Lambda$, where Λ is a matrix on whose main diagonal appear the m eigenvalues and everywhere else are zeros. Thus, $P = C\Lambda C^{-1}$; and we have that $P^n = C\Lambda^n C^{-1}$. We state this result in Theorem 9.3.1.

Theorem 9.3.1   Let P be an $m \times m$ matrix with distinct eigenvalues, and let P equal $C\Lambda C^{-1}$, where C is a matrix whose columns are the eigenvectors of P and Λ is a diagonal matrix of the eigenvalues of P. Then $P^n = C\Lambda^n C^{-1}$.

Proof   The proof will be by induction. For $n = 1$, we have $P = C\Lambda C^{-1}$, which is given. If we assume $P^n = C\Lambda^n C^{-1}$ to be true for $n = k$, then $P^{k+1} = P^k \cdot P = (C\Lambda^k C^{-1})(C\Lambda C^{-1}) = C\Lambda^{k+1} C^{-1}$, and the theorem is proved.

Example 9.3.3   Let

$$P = \begin{bmatrix} \alpha & 1 - \alpha \\ 1 - \beta & \beta \end{bmatrix}.$$

We wish to find P^n. In the first step, we find the eigenvalues of P:

$$0 = |P - \lambda I| = \begin{bmatrix} \alpha - \lambda & 1 - \alpha \\ 1 - \beta & \beta - \lambda \end{bmatrix} = (\alpha - \lambda)(\beta - \lambda) - (1 - \alpha)(1 - \beta)$$

$$= \alpha\beta - (\alpha + \beta)\lambda + \lambda^2 - 1 + (\alpha + \beta) - \alpha\beta$$

$$= \lambda^2 - (\alpha + \beta)\lambda - (1 - \alpha - \beta).$$

Solving for λ, we get

$$\lambda = \frac{\alpha + \beta \pm \sqrt{(\alpha + \beta)^2 + 4(1 - \alpha - \beta)}}{2} = \frac{\alpha + \beta \pm \sqrt{(\alpha + \beta)^2 - 4(\alpha + \beta) + 4}}{2}$$

$$= \frac{\alpha + \beta \pm \sqrt{(\alpha + \beta - 2)^2}}{2}$$

$$= \frac{\alpha + \beta \pm (\alpha + \beta - 2)}{2} = 1, \quad \alpha + \beta - 1.$$

Thus, the eigenvalues of P are 1 and $\alpha + \beta - 1$. The second step is to find the eigenvectors of P: For $\lambda = 1$,

$$0 = (P - \lambda I)\mathbf{x} = \begin{bmatrix} \alpha - 1 & 1 - \alpha \\ 1 - \beta & \beta - 1 \end{bmatrix} \begin{bmatrix} x_1 \\ x_2 \end{bmatrix} = \begin{bmatrix} (\alpha - 1)x_1 + (1 - \alpha)x_2 \\ (1 - \beta)x_1 + (\beta - 1)x_2 \end{bmatrix}$$

$$= \begin{bmatrix} (1 - \alpha)(x_2 - x_1) \\ -(1 - \beta)(x_2 - x_1) \end{bmatrix} = \begin{bmatrix} 0 \\ 0 \end{bmatrix}.$$

Since $1 - \alpha$, $1 - \beta \neq 0$, we conclude that $x_2 = x_1$; and, therefore, an eigenvector is $\begin{bmatrix} 1 \\ 1 \end{bmatrix}$. For $\lambda = \alpha + \beta - 1$,

$$0 = (P - \lambda I)\mathbf{x} = \begin{bmatrix} 1 - \beta & 1 - \alpha \\ 1 - \beta & 1 - \alpha \end{bmatrix} \begin{bmatrix} x_1 \\ x_2 \end{bmatrix} = \begin{bmatrix} (1 - \beta)x_1 + (1 - \alpha)x_2 \\ (1 - \beta)x_1 + (1 - \alpha)x_2 \end{bmatrix} = \begin{bmatrix} 0 \\ 0 \end{bmatrix}.$$

The solution is that $x_1 = 1 - \alpha$ and $x_2 = -(1 - \beta)$. Thus, the other eigenvector is $\begin{bmatrix} 1 - \alpha \\ -(1 - \beta) \end{bmatrix}$. We can now determine the matrix C, the columns of which are the eigenvectors. Thus,

$$C = \begin{bmatrix} 1 & 1 - \alpha \\ 1 & -(1 - \beta) \end{bmatrix};$$

and

$$C^{-1} = -\frac{1}{2 - \alpha - \beta} \begin{bmatrix} -(1 - \beta) & -(1 - \alpha) \\ -1 & 1 \end{bmatrix} = \frac{1}{2 - \alpha - \beta} \begin{bmatrix} 1 - \beta & 1 - \alpha \\ 1 & -1 \end{bmatrix}.$$

We can now find

$$P^n = C\Lambda^n C^{-1} = \frac{1}{2 - \alpha - \beta} \begin{bmatrix} 1 & 1 - \alpha \\ 1 & -(1 - \beta) \end{bmatrix} \begin{bmatrix} 1 & 0 \\ 0 & (\alpha + \beta - 1)^n \end{bmatrix} \begin{bmatrix} 1 - \beta & 1 - \alpha \\ 1 & -1 \end{bmatrix}$$

$$= \frac{1}{2 - \alpha - \beta} \begin{bmatrix} 1 & (1 - \alpha)(\alpha + \beta - 1)^n \\ 1 & -(1 - \beta)(\alpha + \beta - 1)^n \end{bmatrix} \begin{bmatrix} 1 - \beta & 1 - \alpha \\ 1 & -1 \end{bmatrix}$$

$$= \frac{1}{2 - \alpha - \beta} \begin{bmatrix} 1 - \beta + (1 - \alpha)(\alpha + \beta - 1)^n & (1 - \alpha)[1 - (\alpha + \beta - 1)^n] \\ (1 - \beta)[1 - (\alpha + \beta - 1)^n] & 1 - \alpha + (1 - \beta)(\alpha + \beta - 1)^n \end{bmatrix}$$

Example 9.3.4   Let

$$P = \begin{bmatrix} 1 & 0 & 0 \\ \dfrac{1}{2} & \dfrac{1}{2} & 0 \\ \dfrac{1}{3} & \dfrac{1}{2} & \dfrac{1}{6} \end{bmatrix}.$$

To find the eigenvalues, we write

$$0 = |P - \lambda I| = \begin{vmatrix} 1 - \lambda & 0 & 0 \\ \dfrac{1}{2} & \dfrac{1}{2} - \lambda & 0 \\ \dfrac{1}{3} & \dfrac{1}{2} & \dfrac{1}{6} - \lambda \end{vmatrix} = (1 - \lambda)\left(\frac{1}{2} - \lambda\right)\left(\frac{1}{6} - \lambda\right) = 0,$$

which implies that $\lambda = 1, 1/2, 1/6$. To find the eigenvector for $\lambda = 1$, we must solve

$$\mathbf{0} = (P - \lambda I)\mathbf{x} = \begin{bmatrix} 0 & 0 & 0 \\ \dfrac{1}{2} & -\dfrac{1}{2} & 0 \\ \dfrac{1}{3} & \dfrac{1}{2} & -\dfrac{5}{6} \end{bmatrix} \begin{bmatrix} x_1 \\ x_2 \\ x_2 \end{bmatrix} = \begin{bmatrix} 0 \\ \dfrac{1}{2}x_1 - \dfrac{1}{2}x_2 \\ \dfrac{1}{3}x_1 + \dfrac{1}{2}x_2 - \dfrac{5}{6}x_3 \end{bmatrix} = \begin{bmatrix} 0 \\ 0 \\ 0 \end{bmatrix},$$

which implies that $x_1 = x_2$ and $x_2 = x_3$. Therefore, an eigenvector corre-

sponding to $\lambda = 1$ is $\begin{bmatrix} 1 \\ 1 \\ 1 \end{bmatrix}$. For $\lambda = 1/2$, we have

$$\begin{bmatrix} \dfrac{1}{2} & 0 & 0 \\ \dfrac{1}{2} & 0 & 0 \\ \dfrac{1}{3} & \dfrac{1}{2} & -\dfrac{1}{3} \end{bmatrix} \begin{bmatrix} x_1 \\ x_2 \\ x_3 \end{bmatrix} = \begin{bmatrix} \dfrac{1}{2}x_1 \\ \dfrac{1}{2}x_1 \\ \dfrac{1}{3}x_1 + \dfrac{1}{2}x_2 - \dfrac{1}{3}x_3 \end{bmatrix} = \begin{bmatrix} 0 \\ 0 \\ 0 \end{bmatrix}.$$

This equation implies that $x_1 = 0$ and $3x_2 = 2x_3$. So, if we let $x_3 = 3$, then

$x_2 = 2$; and an eigenvector for $\lambda = 1/2$ is $\begin{bmatrix} 0 \\ 2 \\ 3 \end{bmatrix}$. And, finally, for $\lambda = 1/6$, we

write

$$\begin{bmatrix} \dfrac{5}{6} & 0 & 0 \\ \dfrac{1}{2} & \dfrac{1}{3} & 0 \\ \dfrac{1}{3} & \dfrac{1}{2} & 0 \end{bmatrix} \begin{bmatrix} x_1 \\ x_2 \\ x_3 \end{bmatrix} = \begin{bmatrix} \dfrac{5}{6}x_1 \\ \dfrac{1}{2}x_1 + \dfrac{1}{3}x_2 \\ \dfrac{1}{3}x_1 + \dfrac{1}{2}x_2 \end{bmatrix} = \begin{bmatrix} 0 \\ 0 \\ 0 \end{bmatrix},$$

which requires that $x_1 = x_2 = 0$. Thus, an eigenvector for $\lambda = 1/6$ is $\begin{bmatrix} 0 \\ 0 \\ 1 \end{bmatrix}$.

The matrix C then is

$$\begin{bmatrix} 1 & 0 & 0 \\ 1 & 2 & 0 \\ 1 & 3 & 1 \end{bmatrix}, \quad \text{and} \quad C^{-1} = \dfrac{1}{2}\begin{bmatrix} 2 & 0 & 0 \\ -1 & 1 & 0 \\ 1 & -3 & 2 \end{bmatrix}.$$

To find P^n, we write $P^n = C\Lambda^n C^{-1}$, or

$$P^n = \frac{1}{2}\begin{bmatrix} 1 & 0 & 0 \\ 1 & 2 & 0 \\ 1 & 3 & 1 \end{bmatrix}\begin{bmatrix} 1 & 0 & 0 \\ 0 & \dfrac{1}{2^n} & 0 \\ 0 & 0 & \dfrac{1}{6^n} \end{bmatrix}\begin{bmatrix} 2 & 0 & 0 \\ -1 & 1 & 0 \\ 1 & -3 & 2 \end{bmatrix}$$

$$= \frac{1}{2}\begin{bmatrix} 1 & 0 & 0 \\ 1 & \dfrac{2}{2^n} & 0 \\ 1 & \dfrac{3}{2^n} & \dfrac{1}{6^n} \end{bmatrix}\begin{bmatrix} 2 & 0 & 0 \\ -1 & 1 & 0 \\ 1 & -3 & 2 \end{bmatrix}$$

$$= \frac{1}{2}\begin{bmatrix} 2 & 0 & 0 \\ 2 - \dfrac{2}{2^n} & \dfrac{2}{2^n} & 0 \\ 2 - \dfrac{3}{2^n} + \dfrac{1}{6^n} & \dfrac{3}{2^n} - \dfrac{3}{6^n} & \dfrac{2}{6^n} \end{bmatrix}$$

$$= \begin{bmatrix} 1 & 0 & 0 \\ 1 - \dfrac{1}{2^n} & \dfrac{1}{2^n} & 0 \\ 1 - \dfrac{3}{2^{n+1}} + \dfrac{3}{6^{n+1}} & \dfrac{3}{2^{n+1}} - \dfrac{9}{6^{n+1}} & \dfrac{1}{6^n} \end{bmatrix}.$$

If the eigenvalues of P are not all distinct, then, in general, we cannot find a matrix B such that $B^{-1}PB = \Lambda$. Instead, we find a matrix C such that $C^{-1}PC = J$, where J is the *Jordan canonical form* of the matrix P, which has all the eigenvalues of P on its main diagonal, some ones on its first super-diagonal (the diagonal row of elements just above the main diagonal), and zeros elsewhere. The first super-diagonal of J can be made to consist of ones, located immediately above those eigenvalues on the main diagonal that are repetitions of eigenvalues having already occurred on the main diagonal (viewed from upper left to lower right), and zeros elsewhere. For example, suppose that the eigenvalues of P are 1/2, 1/4, 1/4, 1/4. Then the

Jordan canonical form can be made to look like any of the following four configurations:

$$
\begin{bmatrix} \frac{1}{2} & 0 & 0 & 0 \\ 0 & \frac{1}{4} & 1 & 0 \\ 0 & 0 & \frac{1}{4} & 1 \\ 0 & 0 & 0 & \frac{1}{4} \end{bmatrix},
\begin{bmatrix} \frac{1}{4} & 0 & 0 & 0 \\ 0 & \frac{1}{2} & 1 & 0 \\ 0 & 0 & \frac{1}{4} & 1 \\ 0 & 0 & 0 & \frac{1}{4} \end{bmatrix},
\begin{bmatrix} \frac{1}{4} & 1 & 0 & 0 \\ 0 & \frac{1}{4} & 0 & 0 \\ 0 & 0 & \frac{1}{2} & 1 \\ 0 & 0 & 0 & \frac{1}{4} \end{bmatrix}, \text{ or }
\begin{bmatrix} \frac{1}{4} & 1 & 0 & 0 \\ 0 & \frac{1}{4} & 1 & 0 \\ 0 & 0 & \frac{1}{4} & 0 \\ 0 & 0 & 0 & \frac{1}{2} \end{bmatrix}.
$$

$$\quad\text{(a)}\qquad\qquad\text{(b)}\qquad\qquad\text{(c)}\qquad\qquad\text{(d)}$$

We notice that a one never occurs on the first super-diagonal immediately above 1/2 because 1/2 is not repeated on the main diagonal. Thus, a zero always appears on the first super-diagonal immediately above 1/2. Viewing the main diagonal from upper left to lower right, we note that 1/4 appears three times. On the first super-diagonal, immediately above the first occurrence of 1/4, appears a zero; but on the first super-diagonal, immediately above the second and third occurrences of 1/4, there appears a one. Henceforth, when we speak of J, we shall mean the form of J as shown in (a) above, which can be obtained by the proper ordering of the columns of C. In general, then, the main diagonal of J, going from upper left to lower right, will have as its first elements the unrepeated eigenvalues of A. Then the repeating eigenvalues of A will appear in unbroken strings of lengths equal to their respective multiplicities. Finally, of course, the first super-diagonal of J will consist of ones and zeros, the location of which is described above.

We shall denote any square matrix having ones and zeros on its first super-diagonal and zeros elsewhere as the matrix M. Observe the important fact that M^2 will have ones and zeros only on its second super-diagonal (the diagonal row immediately above the first super-diagonal) and zeros elsewhere. Similarly, M^3 will have ones and zeros only on its third super-diagonal and zeros elsewhere. Thus, if M is a $k \times k$ matrix, $M^k = 0$.

According to the above paragraph, we can now express J as $J = \Lambda + M$ so that, if $C^{-1}PC = J$, we can write $C^{-1}PC = \Lambda + M$, which may be rewritten as $P = C(\Lambda + M)C^{-1}$; and, finally, by Theorem 9.3.1, we have

$$P^n = C(\Lambda + M)^n C^{-1}.$$

If P is a $k \times k$ matrix, then so is Λ and so is M. Accordingly,

$$(\Lambda + M)^n = \sum_{i=1}^{n} \binom{h}{i} M^i \Lambda^{n-i} = \Lambda^n + nM\Lambda^{n-1} + \frac{n(n-1)}{2} M^2 \Lambda^{n-2} + \cdots + M^n.$$

But, since $M^j = 0$ for $j \geq k$, we have

$$(\Lambda + M)^n = \Lambda^n + nM\Lambda^{n-1} + \frac{n(n-1)}{2} M^2\Lambda^{n-2} + \cdots$$

$$+ \frac{n(n-1)\cdots\cdots(n-k+2)}{(k-1)!} M^{k-1}\Lambda^{n-k+1},$$

or

$$(\Lambda + M)^n = \sum_{i=1}^{k-1} \binom{n}{i} M^i\Lambda^{n-i}.$$

To illustrate, suppose A is a 4×4 matrix with eigenvalues $1/2$, $1/4$, $1/4$, $1/4$. Then $J = \Lambda + M$ may be expressed as

$$\begin{bmatrix} \frac{1}{2} & 0 & 0 & 0 \\ 0 & \frac{1}{4} & 1 & 0 \\ 0 & 0 & \frac{1}{4} & 1 \\ 0 & 0 & 0 & \frac{1}{4} \end{bmatrix} = \begin{bmatrix} \frac{1}{2} & 0 & 0 & 0 \\ 0 & \frac{1}{4} & 0 & 0 \\ 0 & 0 & \frac{1}{4} & 0 \\ 0 & 0 & 0 & \frac{1}{4} \end{bmatrix} + \begin{bmatrix} 0 & 0 & 0 & 0 \\ 0 & 0 & 1 & 0 \\ 0 & 0 & 0 & 1 \\ 0 & 0 & 0 & 0 \end{bmatrix}$$

and $J^n = (\Lambda + M)^n$ may be written as

$$\begin{bmatrix} \frac{1}{2} & 0 & 0 & 0 \\ 0 & \frac{1}{4} & 1 & 0 \\ 0 & 0 & \frac{1}{4} & 1 \\ 0 & 0 & 0 & \frac{1}{4} \end{bmatrix}^n = \left(\begin{bmatrix} \frac{1}{2} & 0 & 0 & 0 \\ 0 & \frac{1}{4} & 0 & 0 \\ 0 & 0 & \frac{1}{4} & 0 \\ 0 & 0 & 0 & \frac{1}{4} \end{bmatrix} + \begin{bmatrix} 0 & 0 & 0 & 0 \\ 0 & 0 & 1 & 0 \\ 0 & 0 & 0 & 1 \\ 0 & 0 & 0 & 0 \end{bmatrix}\right)^n$$

$$= \begin{bmatrix} \frac{1}{2} & 0 & 0 & 0 \\ 0 & \frac{1}{4} & 0 & 0 \\ 0 & 0 & \frac{1}{4} & 0 \\ 0 & 0 & 0 & \frac{1}{4} \end{bmatrix}^n + n\begin{bmatrix} 0 & 0 & 0 & 0 \\ 0 & 0 & 1 & 0 \\ 0 & 0 & 0 & 1 \\ 0 & 0 & 0 & 0 \end{bmatrix}\begin{bmatrix} \frac{1}{2} & 0 & 0 & 0 \\ 0 & \frac{1}{4} & 0 & 0 \\ 0 & 0 & \frac{1}{4} & 0 \\ 0 & 0 & 0 & \frac{1}{4} \end{bmatrix}^{-1},$$

$$+\frac{n(n-1)}{2}\begin{bmatrix} 0 & 0 & 0 & 0 \\ 0 & 0 & 1 & 0 \\ 0 & 0 & 0 & 1 \\ 0 & 0 & 0 & 0 \end{bmatrix}^{2}\begin{bmatrix} \frac{1}{2} & 0 & 0 & 0 \\ 0 & \frac{1}{4} & 0 & 0 \\ 0 & 0 & \frac{1}{4} & 0 \\ 0 & 0 & 0 & \frac{1}{4} \end{bmatrix}^{n-2}+\frac{n(n-1)(n-2)}{6}\begin{bmatrix} 0 & 0 & 0 & 0 \\ 0 & 0 & 1 & 0 \\ 0 & 0 & 0 & 1 \\ 0 & 0 & 0 & 0 \end{bmatrix}^{3}\begin{bmatrix} \frac{1}{2} & 0 & 0 & 0 \\ 0 & \frac{1}{4} & 0 & 0 \\ 0 & 0 & \frac{1}{4} & 0 \\ 0 & 0 & 0 & \frac{1}{4} \end{bmatrix}^{n-3}$$

$$=\begin{bmatrix} \frac{1}{2^{n}} & 0 & 0 & 0 \\ 0 & \frac{1}{4^{n}} & 0 & 0 \\ 0 & 0 & \frac{1}{4^{n}} & 0 \\ 0 & 0 & 0 & \frac{1}{4^{n}} \end{bmatrix}+\begin{bmatrix} 0 & 0 & 0 & 0 \\ 0 & 0 & n & 0 \\ 0 & 0 & 0 & n \\ 0 & 0 & 0 & 0 \end{bmatrix}\begin{bmatrix} \frac{1}{2^{n-1}} & 0 & 0 & 0 \\ 0 & \frac{1}{4^{n-1}} & 0 & 0 \\ 0 & 0 & \frac{1}{4^{n-1}} & 0 \\ 0 & 0 & 0 & \frac{1}{4^{n-1}} \end{bmatrix}$$

$$+\begin{bmatrix} 0 & 0 & 0 & 0 \\ 0 & 0 & 0 & \frac{n(n-1)}{2} \\ 0 & 0 & 0 & 0 \\ 0 & 0 & 0 & 0 \end{bmatrix}\begin{bmatrix} \frac{1}{2^{n-2}} & 0 & 0 & 0 \\ 0 & \frac{1}{4^{n-2}} & 0 & 0 \\ 0 & 0 & \frac{1}{4^{n-2}} & 0 \\ 0 & 0 & 0 & \frac{1}{4^{n-2}} \end{bmatrix}+\begin{bmatrix} 0 & 0 & 0 & 0 \\ 0 & 0 & 0 & 0 \\ 0 & 0 & 0 & 0 \\ 0 & 0 & 0 & 0 \end{bmatrix}\begin{bmatrix} \frac{1}{2^{n-3}} & 0 & 0 & 0 \\ 0 & \frac{1}{4^{n-3}} & 0 & 0 \\ 0 & 0 & \frac{1}{4^{n-3}} & 0 \\ 0 & 0 & 0 & \frac{1}{4^{n-3}} \end{bmatrix}$$

$$=\begin{bmatrix} \frac{1}{2^{n}} & 0 & 0 & 0 \\ 0 & \frac{1}{4^{n}} & 0 & 0 \\ 0 & 0 & \frac{1}{4^{n}} & 0 \\ 0 & 0 & 0 & \frac{1}{4^{n}} \end{bmatrix}+\begin{bmatrix} 0 & 0 & 0 & 0 \\ 0 & 0 & \frac{n}{4^{n-1}} & 0 \\ 0 & 0 & 0 & \frac{n}{4^{n-1}} \\ 0 & 0 & 0 & 0 \end{bmatrix}+\begin{bmatrix} 0 & 0 & 0 & 0 \\ 0 & 0 & 0 & \frac{n(n-1)}{2\cdot 4^{n-2}} \\ 0 & 0 & 0 & 0 \\ 0 & 0 & 0 & 0 \end{bmatrix}+\begin{bmatrix} 0 & 0 & 0 & 0 \\ 0 & 0 & 0 & 0 \\ 0 & 0 & 0 & 0 \\ 0 & 0 & 0 & 0 \end{bmatrix}$$

$$=\begin{bmatrix} \frac{1}{2^{n}} & 0 & 0 & 0 \\ 0 & \frac{1}{4^{n}} & \frac{n}{4^{n-1}} & \frac{n(n-1)}{2\cdot 4^{n-2}} \\ 0 & 0 & \frac{1}{4^{n}} & \frac{n}{4^{n-1}} \\ 0 & 0 & 0 & \frac{1}{4^{n}} \end{bmatrix}.$$

Thus, if we premultiply this matrix by C and postmultiply it by C^{-1}, we obtain P^n.

We now indicate the procedure for obtaining C such that $C^{-1}PC = J$, where P has eigenvalues of multiplicity greater than or equal to one. Let P be a square $k \times k$ matrix, the ith eigenvalue of which occurs with multiplicity m_i, $i = 1, 2, \ldots, l$. Thus, P has l different eigenvalues, and $\sum_{i=1}^{l} m_i = k$. We wish to obtain a matrix C such that $C^{-1}PC = J$, where J is defined as above. To do so, we proceed as follows:

(1) Determine an eigenvector for λ_i; call it $\mathbf{x}_1$.
(2) Determine $\mathbf{x}_2$ such that $(A - \lambda_i I)\mathbf{x}_2 = \mathbf{x}_1$.
(3) Determine $\mathbf{x}_3$ such that $(A - \lambda_i I)\mathbf{x}_3 = \mathbf{x}_2$.
(4) In general, determine $\mathbf{x}_j$ such that $(A - \lambda_i I)\mathbf{x}_j = \mathbf{x}_{j-1}$.
(5) Continue in this manner until $j = m_i$, $i = 1, 2, \ldots, l$.
(6) The eigenvectors so derived, in the order of derivation, will make up the columns of C.

Examples 9.3.5 and 9.4.6 should illustrate the above procedure.

Example 9.3.5   Let

$$A = \begin{pmatrix} 1 & 0 & 0 & 0 \\ \dfrac{3}{4} & \dfrac{1}{4} & 0 & 0 \\ \dfrac{1}{2} & \dfrac{1}{4} & \dfrac{1}{4} & 0 \\ \dfrac{1}{4} & \dfrac{1}{4} & \dfrac{1}{4} & \dfrac{1}{4} \end{pmatrix}$$

so that $\lambda_1 = 1$, $\lambda_2 = 1/4$, $\lambda_3 = 1/4$, and $\lambda_4 = 1/4$.

The eigenvector for $\lambda_1 = 1$,

$$\begin{pmatrix} 0 & 0 & 0 & 0 \\ \dfrac{3}{4} & -\dfrac{3}{4} & 0 & 0 \\ \dfrac{1}{2} & \dfrac{1}{4} & -\dfrac{3}{4} & 0 \\ \dfrac{1}{4} & \dfrac{1}{4} & \dfrac{1}{4} & -\dfrac{3}{4} \end{pmatrix} \begin{pmatrix} a \\ b \\ c \\ d \end{pmatrix} = \begin{pmatrix} 0 \\ \dfrac{3}{4}(a - b) \\ \dfrac{1}{4}(2a + b - 3c) \\ \dfrac{1}{4}(a + b + c - 3d) \end{pmatrix} = \begin{pmatrix} 0 \\ 0 \\ 0 \\ 0 \end{pmatrix},$$

implies that $a = b = c = d$. Therefore,

$$\mathbf{x}_1 = \begin{pmatrix} 1 \\ 1 \\ 1 \\ 1 \end{pmatrix}.$$

The eigenvector for $\lambda_2 = 1/4$,

$$\begin{pmatrix} \frac{3}{4} & 0 & 0 & 0 \\ \frac{3}{4} & 0 & 0 & 0 \\ \frac{1}{2} & \frac{1}{4} & 0 & 0 \\ \frac{1}{4} & \frac{1}{4} & \frac{1}{4} & 0 \end{pmatrix} \begin{pmatrix} a \\ b \\ c \\ d \end{pmatrix} = \begin{pmatrix} \frac{3a}{4} \\ \frac{3a}{4} \\ \frac{1}{4}(2a + b) \\ \frac{1}{4}(a + b + c) \end{pmatrix} = \begin{pmatrix} 0 \\ 0 \\ 0 \\ 0 \end{pmatrix},$$

implies that $a = b = c = 0$. Therefore,

$$\mathbf{x}_2 = \begin{pmatrix} 0 \\ 0 \\ 0 \\ 1 \end{pmatrix}.$$

The eigenvector for $\lambda_3 = 1/4$,

$$\begin{pmatrix} \frac{3}{4} & 0 & 0 & 0 \\ \frac{3}{4} & 0 & 0 & 0 \\ \frac{1}{2} & \frac{1}{4} & 0 & 0 \\ \frac{1}{4} & \frac{1}{4} & \frac{1}{4} & 0 \end{pmatrix} \begin{pmatrix} a \\ b \\ c \\ d \end{pmatrix} = \begin{pmatrix} \frac{3a}{4} \\ \frac{3a}{4} \\ \frac{1}{4}(2a + b) \\ \frac{1}{4}(a + b + c) \end{pmatrix} = \begin{pmatrix} 0 \\ 0 \\ 0 \\ 1 \end{pmatrix},$$

implies that $a = b = 0$, and $c = 4$. Therefore,

$$\mathbf{x}_3 = \begin{pmatrix} 0 \\ 0 \\ 4 \\ 1 \end{pmatrix}.$$

The eigenvector for $\lambda_4 = 1/4$,

$$\begin{pmatrix} \dfrac{3}{4} & 0 & 0 & 0 \\[2mm] \dfrac{3}{4} & 0 & 0 & 0 \\[2mm] \dfrac{1}{2} & \dfrac{1}{4} & 0 & 0 \\[2mm] \dfrac{1}{4} & \dfrac{1}{4} & \dfrac{1}{4} & 0 \end{pmatrix} \begin{pmatrix} a \\ b \\ c \\ d \end{pmatrix} = \begin{pmatrix} \dfrac{3a}{4} \\[2mm] \dfrac{3a}{4} \\[2mm] \dfrac{1}{4}(2a + b) \\[2mm] \dfrac{1}{4}(a + b + c) \end{pmatrix} = \begin{pmatrix} 0 \\ 0 \\ 4 \\ 1 \end{pmatrix},$$

implies that $a = 0$, $b = 16$, and $c = -12$. Therefore,

$$\mathbf{x}_4 = \begin{pmatrix} 0 \\ 16 \\ -12 \\ 1 \end{pmatrix}.$$

Thus, we obtain

$$C = \begin{pmatrix} 1 & 0 & 0 & 0 \\ 1 & 0 & 0 & 16 \\ 1 & 0 & 4 & -12 \\ 1 & 1 & 1 & 1 \end{pmatrix}.$$

As an exercise, the student should calculate C^{-1} and then show that

$$C^{-1}PC = J = \begin{pmatrix} 1 & 0 & 0 & 0 \\[2mm] 0 & \dfrac{1}{4} & 1 & 0 \\[2mm] 0 & 0 & \dfrac{1}{4} & 0 \\[2mm] 0 & 0 & 0 & \dfrac{1}{4} \end{pmatrix};$$

finally, he should calculate $P^n = CJ^nC^{-1} = C(\Lambda + M)^nC^{-1}$, where

$$
\Lambda = \begin{pmatrix} 1 & 0 & 0 & 0 \\ 0 & \frac{1}{4} & 0 & 0 \\ 0 & 0 & \frac{1}{4} & 0 \\ 0 & 0 & 0 & \frac{1}{4} \end{pmatrix} \quad \text{and} \quad M = \begin{pmatrix} 0 & 0 & 0 & 0 \\ 0 & 0 & 1 & 0 \\ 0 & 0 & 0 & 1 \\ 0 & 0 & 0 & 0 \end{pmatrix}.
$$

Example 9.3.6   Let

$$
P = \begin{pmatrix} \frac{1}{2} & 0 & 0 & \frac{1}{2} \\ 0 & \frac{1}{2} & \frac{1}{2} & 0 \\ \frac{1}{2} & 0 & \frac{1}{2} & 0 \\ 0 & 0 & 0 & 1 \end{pmatrix}.
$$

Then the characteristic equation of P is

$$
0 = |P - \lambda I|
$$

$$
= \begin{vmatrix} \frac{1}{2} - \lambda & 0 & 0 & \frac{1}{2} \\ 0 & \frac{1}{2} - \lambda & \frac{1}{2} & 0 \\ \frac{1}{2} & 0 & \frac{1}{2} - \lambda & 0 \\ 0 & 0 & 0 & 1 - \lambda \end{vmatrix}
$$

$$
= (1 - \lambda) \begin{vmatrix} \frac{1}{2} - \lambda & 0 & 0 \\ 0 & \frac{1}{2} - \lambda & \frac{1}{2} \\ \frac{1}{2} & 0 & \frac{1}{2} - \lambda \end{vmatrix}
$$

$$= (1 - \lambda)\left(\frac{1}{2} - \lambda\right)\begin{vmatrix} \frac{1}{2} - \lambda & \frac{1}{2} \\ 0 & \frac{1}{2} - \lambda \end{vmatrix}$$

$$= (1 - \lambda)\left(\frac{1}{2} - \lambda\right)^3,$$

which implies that $\lambda_1 = 1$, $\lambda_2 = \lambda_3 = \lambda_4 = 1/2$.

The eigenvector for $\lambda_1 = 1$,

$$\begin{pmatrix} -\frac{1}{2} & 0 & 0 & \frac{1}{2} \\ 0 & -\frac{1}{2} & \frac{1}{2} & 0 \\ \frac{1}{2} & 0 & -\frac{1}{2} & 0 \\ 0 & 0 & 0 & 0 \end{pmatrix}\begin{pmatrix} a \\ b \\ c \\ d \end{pmatrix} = \begin{pmatrix} \frac{1}{2}(d - a) \\ \frac{1}{2}(c - b) \\ \frac{1}{2}(a - c) \\ 0 \end{pmatrix} = \begin{pmatrix} 0 \\ 0 \\ 0 \\ 0 \end{pmatrix},$$

implies that $a = b = c = d$. Therefore,

$$\mathbf{x}_1 = \begin{pmatrix} 1 \\ 1 \\ 1 \\ 1 \end{pmatrix}.$$

The eigenvector for $\lambda_2 = 1/2$,

$$\begin{pmatrix} 0 & 0 & 0 & \frac{1}{2} \\ 0 & 0 & \frac{1}{2} & 0 \\ \frac{1}{2} & 0 & 0 & 0 \\ 0 & 0 & 0 & \frac{1}{2} \end{pmatrix}\begin{pmatrix} a \\ b \\ c \\ d \end{pmatrix} = \begin{pmatrix} \frac{d}{2} \\ \frac{c}{2} \\ \frac{a}{2} \\ \frac{d}{2} \end{pmatrix} = \begin{pmatrix} 0 \\ 0 \\ 0 \\ 0 \end{pmatrix},$$

implies that $a = c = d = 0$. Therefore,

$$\mathbf{x}_2 = \begin{pmatrix} 0 \\ 1 \\ 0 \\ 0 \end{pmatrix}.$$

The eigenvector for $\lambda_3 = 1/2$,

$$\begin{pmatrix} \dfrac{d}{2} \\ \dfrac{c}{2} \\ \dfrac{a}{2} \\ \dfrac{d}{2} \end{pmatrix} = \begin{pmatrix} 0 \\ 1 \\ 0 \\ 0 \end{pmatrix},$$

implies that $a = d = 0$ and $c = 2$. Therefore,

$$\mathbf{x}_3 = \begin{pmatrix} 0 \\ 1 \\ 2 \\ 0 \end{pmatrix}.$$

The eigenvector for $\lambda_4 = 1/2$,

$$\begin{pmatrix} \dfrac{d}{2} \\ \dfrac{c}{2} \\ \dfrac{a}{2} \\ \dfrac{d}{2} \end{pmatrix} = \begin{pmatrix} 0 \\ 1 \\ 2 \\ 0 \end{pmatrix},$$

implies that $a = 4$, $c = 2$, and $d = 0$. Therefore,

$$\mathbf{x}_4 = \begin{pmatrix} 4 \\ 1 \\ 2 \\ 0 \end{pmatrix}.$$

Thus, we obtain

$$C = \begin{pmatrix} 1 & 0 & 0 & 4 \\ 1 & 1 & 1 & 1 \\ 1 & 0 & 2 & 2 \\ 1 & 0 & 0 & 0 \end{pmatrix} \quad \text{and} \quad C^{-1} = \begin{pmatrix} 0 & 0 & 0 & 1 \\ 0 & 1 & -\dfrac{1}{2} & -\dfrac{1}{2} \\ -\dfrac{1}{4} & 0 & \dfrac{1}{2} & -\dfrac{1}{4} \\ \dfrac{1}{4} & 0 & 0 & -\dfrac{1}{4} \end{pmatrix}.$$

As a check to see that $C^{-1}PC = J$, we write

$$\begin{pmatrix} 0 & 0 & 0 & 1 \\ 0 & 1 & -\dfrac{1}{2} & -\dfrac{1}{2} \\ -\dfrac{1}{4} & 0 & \dfrac{1}{2} & -\dfrac{1}{4} \\ \dfrac{1}{4} & 0 & 0 & -\dfrac{1}{4} \end{pmatrix} \begin{pmatrix} \dfrac{1}{2} & 0 & 0 & \dfrac{1}{2} \\ 0 & \dfrac{1}{2} & \dfrac{1}{2} & 0 \\ \dfrac{1}{2} & 0 & \dfrac{1}{2} & 0 \\ 0 & 0 & 0 & 1 \end{pmatrix} \begin{pmatrix} 1 & 0 & 0 & 4 \\ 1 & 1 & 1 & 1 \\ 1 & 0 & 2 & 2 \\ 1 & 0 & 0 & 0 \end{pmatrix}$$

$$= \begin{pmatrix} 0 & 0 & 0 & 1 \\ -\dfrac{1}{4} & \dfrac{1}{2} & \dfrac{1}{4} & -\dfrac{1}{2} \\ \dfrac{1}{8} & 0 & \dfrac{1}{4} & -\dfrac{3}{8} \\ \dfrac{1}{8} & 0 & 0 & -\dfrac{1}{8} \end{pmatrix} \begin{pmatrix} 1 & 0 & 0 & 4 \\ 1 & 1 & 1 & 1 \\ 1 & 0 & 2 & 2 \\ 1 & 0 & 0 & 0 \end{pmatrix} = \begin{pmatrix} 1 & 0 & 0 & 0 \\ 0 & \dfrac{1}{2} & 1 & 0 \\ 0 & 0 & \dfrac{1}{2} & 1 \\ 0 & 0 & 0 & \dfrac{1}{2} \end{pmatrix}.$$

To calculate P^n, we write $P^n = CJ^nC^{-1}$, or

$$P^n = C(\Lambda + M)^nC^{-1}. \tag{9.3.1}$$

First we must calculate $(\Lambda + M)^n$:

$$(\Lambda + M)^n = \left(\begin{pmatrix} 1 & 0 & 0 & 0 \\ 0 & \dfrac{1}{2} & 0 & 0 \\ 0 & 0 & \dfrac{1}{2} & 0 \\ 0 & 0 & 0 & \dfrac{1}{2} \end{pmatrix} + \begin{pmatrix} 0 & 0 & 0 & 0 \\ 0 & 0 & 1 & 0 \\ 0 & 0 & 0 & 1 \\ 0 & 0 & 0 & 0 \end{pmatrix}\right)^n$$

$$= \begin{pmatrix} 1 & 0 & 0 & 0 \\ 0 & \dfrac{1}{2^n} & 0 & 0 \\ 0 & 0 & \dfrac{1}{2^n} & 0 \\ 0 & 0 & 0 & \dfrac{1}{2^n} \end{pmatrix} + \begin{pmatrix} 0 & 0 & 0 & 0 \\ 0 & 0 & n & 0 \\ 0 & 0 & 0 & n \\ 0 & 0 & 0 & 0 \end{pmatrix}\begin{pmatrix} 1 & 0 & 0 & 0 \\ 0 & \dfrac{1}{2^{n-1}} & 0 & 0 \\ 0 & 0 & \dfrac{1}{2^{n-1}} & 0 \\ 0 & 0 & 0 & \dfrac{1}{2^{n-1}} \end{pmatrix}$$

$$+ \begin{pmatrix} 0 & 0 & 0 & 0 \\ 0 & 0 & 0 & \dfrac{n(n-1)}{2} \\ 0 & 0 & 0 & 0 \\ 0 & 0 & 0 & 0 \end{pmatrix}\begin{pmatrix} 1 & 0 & 0 & 0 \\ 0 & \dfrac{1}{2^{n-2}} & 0 & 0 \\ 0 & 0 & \dfrac{1}{2^{n-2}} & 0 \\ 0 & 0 & 0 & \dfrac{1}{2^{n-2}} \end{pmatrix}$$

$$+ \begin{pmatrix} 0 & 0 & 0 & 0 \\ 0 \cdot 0 & 0 & 0 & 0 \\ 0 & 0 & 0 & 0 \\ 0 & 0 & 0 & 0 \end{pmatrix}\begin{pmatrix} 1 & 0 & 0 & 0 \\ 0 & \dfrac{1}{2^{n-3}} & 0 & 0 \\ 0 & 0 & \dfrac{1}{2^{n-3}} & 0 \\ 0 & 0 & 0 & \dfrac{1}{2^{n-3}} \end{pmatrix}$$

$$
= \begin{pmatrix} 1 & 0 & 0 & 0 \\ 0 & \dfrac{1}{2^n} & 0 & 0 \\ 0 & 0 & \dfrac{1}{2^n} & 0 \\ 0 & 0 & 0 & \dfrac{1}{2^n} \end{pmatrix} + \begin{pmatrix} 0 & 0 & 0 & 0 \\ 0 & 0 & \dfrac{n}{2^{n-1}} & 0 \\ 0 & 0 & 0 & \dfrac{n}{2^{n-1}} \\ 0 & 0 & 0 & 0 \end{pmatrix} + \begin{pmatrix} 0 & 0 & 0 & 0 \\ 0 & 0 & 0 & \dfrac{n(n-1)}{2^{n-1}} \\ 0 & 0 & 0 & 0 \\ 0 & 0 & 0 & 0 \end{pmatrix} + 0
$$

$$
= \begin{pmatrix} 1 & 0 & 0 & 0 \\ 0 & \dfrac{1}{2^n} & \dfrac{n}{2^{n-1}} & \dfrac{n(n-1)}{2^{n-1}} \\ 0 & 0 & \dfrac{1}{2^n} & \dfrac{n}{2^{n-1}} \\ 0 & 0 & 0 & \dfrac{1}{2^n} \end{pmatrix}.
$$

Substituting this value into Equation (9.3.1) gives

$$
P^n = \begin{pmatrix} 1 & 0 & 0 & 4 \\ 1 & 1 & 1 & 1 \\ 1 & 0 & 2 & 2 \\ 1 & 0 & 0 & 0 \end{pmatrix} \begin{pmatrix} 1 & 0 & 0 & 0 \\ 0 & \dfrac{1}{2^n} & \dfrac{n}{2^{n-1}} & \dfrac{n(n-1)}{2^{n-1}} \\ 0 & 0 & \dfrac{1}{2^n} & \dfrac{n}{2^{n-1}} \\ 0 & 0 & 0 & \dfrac{1}{2^n} \end{pmatrix} \begin{pmatrix} 0 & 0 & 0 & 1 \\ 0 & 1 & -\dfrac{1}{2} & -\dfrac{1}{2} \\ -\dfrac{1}{4} & 0 & \dfrac{1}{2} & -\dfrac{1}{4} \\ \dfrac{1}{4} & 0 & 0 & -\dfrac{1}{4} \end{pmatrix}
$$

$$
= \begin{pmatrix} 1 & 0 & 0 & \dfrac{4}{2^n} \\ 1 & \dfrac{1}{2^n} & \dfrac{2n+1}{2^n} & \dfrac{2n^2+1}{2^n} \\ 1 & 0 & \dfrac{2}{2^n} & \dfrac{2(2n+1)}{2^n} \\ 1 & 0 & 0 & 0 \end{pmatrix} \begin{pmatrix} 0 & 0 & 0 & 1 \\ 0 & 1 & -\dfrac{1}{2} & -\dfrac{1}{2} \\ -\dfrac{1}{4} & 0 & \dfrac{1}{2} & -\dfrac{1}{4} \\ \dfrac{1}{4} & 0 & 0 & -\dfrac{1}{4} \end{pmatrix}
$$

$$
= \begin{pmatrix}
\dfrac{1}{2^n} & 0 & 0 & 1 - \dfrac{1}{2^n} \\[2ex]
\dfrac{n(n-1)}{2^{n+1}} & \dfrac{1}{2^n} & \dfrac{n}{2^n} & 1 - \dfrac{n^2 + n + 2}{2^{n+1}} \\[2ex]
\dfrac{n}{2^n} & 0 & \dfrac{1}{2^n} & 1 - \dfrac{n+1}{2^n} \\[2ex]
0 & 0 & 0 & 1
\end{pmatrix}.
$$

9.4   Classification of States

In this section, we shall discuss the classification of states of a given Markov chain. The classification of states is of importance in the physical interpretation of states and in the study of the asymptotic behavior of the n-step transition probabilities, $p_{ij}^{(n)}$.

Definition 9.4.1   *A transition matrix, P, all the entries of which are positive, is called a* positive transition matrix.

The importance of positive matrices is seen by considering an initial distribution, π_0, and a transition matrix, P, with P^γ positive for some integer $\gamma \geq 1$. For $\beta > \gamma$, we have

$$
\pi_\beta = \pi_0 P^\beta,
$$

which has only positive entries. This shows that, after the random process has continued for a certain number of steps, the probability that the process is in a particular state, i_k, $k = 1, 2, \ldots, n$, is positive.

Example 9.4.1   In Example 9.2.3, P^5 is a positive transition matrix:

$$
P^5 = \begin{pmatrix}
\dfrac{1}{8} & \dfrac{1}{2} & \dfrac{1}{4} & \dfrac{1}{8} \\[2ex]
\dfrac{3}{8} & \dfrac{1}{4} & \dfrac{1}{8} & \dfrac{1}{4} \\[2ex]
\dfrac{5}{16} & \dfrac{3}{8} & \dfrac{1}{8} & \dfrac{3}{16} \\[2ex]
\dfrac{1}{4} & \dfrac{1}{4} & \dfrac{1}{4} & \dfrac{1}{4}
\end{pmatrix}.
$$

Thus, no matter what the initial distribution is, after five steps there is a positive probability that the process is in each of the four states i_1, i_2, i_3, and i_4.

Definition 9.4.2   *A Markov chain is called* ergodic *if it is possible to move from every state to every other state. Some synonyms of the term ergodic are* nonnull *and* nonperiodic. *It is clear that a Markov chain with a positive transition matrix is ergodic.*

Definition 9.4.3   *A state i of a Markov chain is called an* absorbing state *if, for every positive integer* $k > 0$, $p_{ii}^{(k)} = 1$.

Hence, once a random process enters an *absorbing state*, it remains there forever. A Markov chain may have one or more such states, or it may have none. Clearly, if an ergodic set contains only one element, then that element is an absorbing state. In the random-walk example, the one-step transition matrix of which is given by

$$
P = \begin{array}{c} \\ i_1 \\ i_2 \\ i_3 \\ i_4 \\ i_5 \\ i_6 \end{array}
\begin{array}{c} \begin{array}{cccccc} i_1 & i_2 & i_3 & i_4 & i_5 & i_6 \end{array} \\
\begin{pmatrix} 1 & 0 & 0 & 0 & 0 & 0 \\ q & 0 & p & 0 & 0 & 0 \\ 0 & q & 0 & p & 0 & 0 \\ 0 & 0 & q & 0 & p & 0 \\ 0 & 0 & 0 & q & 0 & p \\ 0 & 0 & 0 & 0 & 0 & 1 \end{pmatrix} \end{array},
$$

states i_1 and i_6 are *absorbing states*. The chain is obviously not ergodic because it is impossible to leave states i_1 and i_6. However, there is a subset of the states which is *ergodic*, namely

$$
P_E = \begin{array}{c} \\ i_2 \\ i_3 \\ i_4 \\ i_5 \end{array}
\begin{array}{c} \begin{array}{cccc} i_2 & i_3 & i_4 & i_5 \end{array} \\
\begin{pmatrix} 0 & p & 0 & 0 \\ q & 0 & p & 0 \\ 0 & q & 0 & p \\ 0 & 0 & q & 0 \end{pmatrix} \end{array}.
$$

The fact that it is possible to move from every state to every other state in $\{i_2, i_3, i_4, i_5\}$ can be clearly seen from the state diagram of P_E (Figure 9.4.1). Thus, the set of states $G = \{i_k : k = 1, 2, \ldots, 6\}$ is not ergodic, but the subset $E = \{i_k : k = 2, 3, 4, 5\}$ is ergodic.

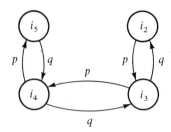

Figure 9.4.1

Definition 9.4.4   *A state, i, of a Markov chain is called* transient (non-recurrent) *if there exists a state, j, and an integer, k, such that* $p_{ij}^{(k)} > 0$ *and* $n_{ji}^{(k)} = 0$, $k = 0, 1, 2, \ldots$. *Otherwise, state i is called* nontransient. *Thus, a pontransient state is ergodic.*

The definition says that *i* is a transient state if there exists any other state *j* to which the process, in some number of steps, can get from state *i* but from which it can never return to state *i*. Thus, if *i* is a transient state, $p_{ii} < 1$.

Definition 9.4.5   *A Markov chain is called an* absorbing chain *if all the states of the chain are nontransient.*

Definition 9.4.6   *A state i is called* persistent (recurrent) *if, for every state j, the existence of an integer, k_i, such that $p_{ij}^{(k_i)} > 0$, implies the existence of an integer, k_j, such that $p_{ji}^{(k_j)} > 0$.*

This definition says that, no matter what state history may occur, once the process enters a persistent state it will always be able in some number of steps to return to that state. Thus, if *i* is a persistent state, $p_{ii} = 1$; the probability is one that, having started at *i*, the process will eventually return to *i*.

Definition 9.4.7   *A persistent state i is called* periodic *if there exists an integer, $d > 1$, such that $p_{ii}^{(k)} = 0$ for all values of k other than d, 2d, 3d, \ldots . A state that is not periodic is called* aperiodic.

We shall illustrate this definition by considering a random process shown by the state diagram in Figure 9.4.2.

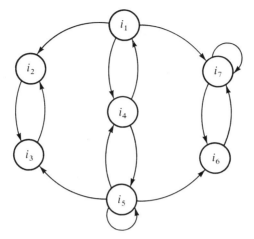

Figure 9.4.2

The only states that the process can leave in some way such that it may never return to them are states i_1, i_4, and i_5. Thus, states i_1, i_4, and i_5 are *transient* states. Clearly, states i_2, i_3, i_6, and i_7 are *persistent*. States i_2 and i_3 are the only *periodic* states.

9.4.1 Absorbing Markov Chains   An interesting question the student may ask regarding a Markov chain is the following: If a random process starts at a transient state, what is the mean number of times the process is in a given (transient) state? We shall answer this question by formulating the *undamental matrix* or *normal matrix N* (see Kemeny and Snell, Finite Markov Chains, Suggested Supplementary Reading) for absorbing Markov chains.

Given the transition matrix P for a Markov chain, we rearrange it by row and column operations so that we obtain a partition of P into four submatrices, one of which contains all ergodic sets and another of which contains all transient sets. The matrix P is then of the form

$$
P_{s \times s} = \begin{pmatrix} \overset{s-r}{\overbrace{E}} & \overset{r}{\overbrace{O}} \\ \hline G & T \end{pmatrix} \begin{matrix} \}s-r \\ \}r \end{matrix} \quad ,
$$

where

(1) E is an $(s-r) \times (s-r)$ matrix, which deals with the process after it has reached an ergodic set;

(2) O is an $(s-r) \times r$ zero matrix;

(3) G is an $r \times (s - r)$ matrix of transition probabilities from transient states to ergodic states;

(4) T is an $r \times r$ matrix of transition probabilities between transient states.

The above partition of the matrix P for a finite absorbing Markov chain becomes

$$P_{s \times s} = \begin{pmatrix} \overset{s-r}{\widetilde{I}} & \overset{r}{\widetilde{O}} \\ \hline G & T \end{pmatrix} \begin{matrix} \}s-r \\ \\ \}r \end{matrix} \,, \tag{9.4.1}$$

where I is the $(s - r) \times (s - r)$ identity matrix.

Definition 9.4.8   *The matrix N, given by*

$$N = (I - T)^{-1},$$

is called the fundamental matrix *or* normal matrix *for an absorbing Markov chain.*

The matrix N answers the question posed; that is, it yields the average number of times that a random process is in a given transient state, j, given that the process started at state i. The existence of such a matrix depends upon $(I - T)$ possessing an inverse. This dependence can be shown by proving that

$$(I - T)^{-1} = I + T + T^2 + \cdots + T^n + \cdots$$

$$= \sum_{n=0}^{\infty} T^n$$

converges.

We shall illustrate the above remarks in Example 9.4.2.

Example 9.4.2   Consider the random-walk example, the one-step transition probabilities of which are given as in Example 9.1.1. Here states i_1 and i_6 are absorbing states. Thus, the stochastic matrix P must be rearranged into the form (9.4.1):

$$
P = \begin{array}{c} \\ i_1 \\ i_6 \\ \\ i_2 \\ i_3 \\ i_4 \\ i_5 \end{array}
\begin{array}{c} \overset{i_1 \quad i_6}{} \quad \overset{i_2 \;\; i_3 \;\; i_4 \;\; i_5}{} \\
\left(\begin{array}{cc|cccc}
1 & 0 & 0 & 0 & 0 & 0 \\
0 & 1 & 0 & 0 & 0 & 0 \\
\hline
q & 0 & 0 & p & 0 & 0 \\
0 & 0 & q & 0 & p & 0 \\
0 & 0 & 0 & q & 0 & p \\
0 & p & 0 & 0 & q & 0
\end{array} \right),
\end{array}
$$

where

$$I = \begin{pmatrix} 1 & 0 \\ 0 & 1 \end{pmatrix}, \qquad O = \begin{pmatrix} 0 & 0 & 0 & 0 \\ 0 & 0 & 0 & 0 \end{pmatrix},$$

$$G = \begin{pmatrix} q & 0 \\ 0 & 0 \\ 0 & 0 \\ 0 & p \end{pmatrix}, \quad \text{and} \quad T = \begin{pmatrix} 0 & p & 0 & 0 \\ q & 0 & p & 0 \\ 0 & q & 0 & p \\ 0 & 0 & q & 0 \end{pmatrix}.$$

Here

$$(I - T) = \begin{pmatrix} 1 & -p & 0 & 0 \\ -q & 1 & -p & 0 \\ 0 & -q & 1 & -p \\ 0 & 0 & -q & 1 \end{pmatrix},$$

and the *normal matrix* is given by

$$N = (I - T)^{-1}$$

$$= \frac{1}{1 - 3pq + p^2 q^2} \begin{array}{cccc} i_2 & i_3 & i_4 & i_5 \\ \begin{pmatrix} 1 - 2pq & p(1 - pq) & p^2 & p^3 \\ q(1 - pq) & 1 - pq & p & p^2 \\ q^2 & q & 1 - pq & p(1 - pq) \\ q^3 & q^2 & q(1 - pq) & 1 - 2pq \end{pmatrix} \end{array}.$$

Thus, the mean of the total number of times the random walk is in a given transient state, i_2, i_3, i_4, or i_5, is given by the matrix N. If we assume $p = q = 1/2$, that is, if we assume that it is equally likely that the man will move to the right or to the left, the fundamental matrix becomes

$$N = (I - T)^{-1} = \frac{1}{5} \begin{array}{cccc} i_2 & i_3 & i_4 & i_5 \\ \begin{pmatrix} 8 & 6 & 4 & 2 \\ 6 & 12 & 8 & 4 \\ 4 & 8 & 12 & 6 \\ 2 & 4 & 6 & 8 \end{pmatrix} \end{array}.$$

Hence, the mean of the total number of times the process is in a given transient state is shown by the matrix N. For example, if the random walk starts in state i_2, then it will be in state i_3 an average of 6/5 times and in states i_4 and i_5 an average of 4/5 and 2/5 times, respectively. Note that, if the process starts in state i_5, it will be in state i_2 an average of 2/5 times, which is the minimum mean of the total number of times the process is in a transient state.

One can utilize the *normal matrix, N*, to answer a number of additional questions that concern absorbing Markov chains and that are of significant importance in applications. These questions are:

(1) What is the variance of the number of times that a process is in state j, given that it started in state i?
(2) Given that the process started in state i, what is the expected number of transitions before absorption?
(3) What is the variance of the number of transitions before absorption, given that the process started in a transient state?
(4) What is the probability that the process will be in an absorbing state, given that it started in a transient state?

As we mentioned above, we will not give a mathematically rigorous presentation as the answer to the above questions. We shall only indicate how one can utilize the fundamental matrix to answer them. We refer the reader to the book of Kemeny and Snell for an elegant presentation of the subject.

Theorem 9.4.1   The variance of the number of times, m, that a process is in a transient state, i, is given by

$$\text{Var}(m_{j|i}) = V_1 = N(2D - I) - S,$$

where

(1) $N_{r \times r} = (I - T)^{-1}$;
(2) D is an $r \times r$ diagonal matrix containing the main diagonal elements of the normal matrix;
(3) I is an $r \times r$ identity matrix; and
(4) S is an $r \times r$ matrix whose elements are the squares of the elements of the normal matrix.

Thus, V_1 is an $r \times r$ matrix of variances of the number of times the process is in state j, given that it started in state i.

Example 9.4.3   We shall compute V_1 for the random-walk problem, for which we obtained the normal matrix in the previous example. Here

$$D = \begin{pmatrix} \dfrac{1 - 2pq}{1 - 3pq + p^2q^2} & 0 & 0 & 0 \\ 0 & \dfrac{1 - pq}{1 - 3pq + p^2q^2} & 0 & 0 \\ 0 & 0 & \dfrac{1 - pq}{1 - 3pq + p^2q^2} & 0 \\ 0 & 0 & 0 & \dfrac{1 - 2pq}{1 - 3pq + p^2q^2} \end{pmatrix};$$

$$S = \frac{1}{(1 - 3pq + p^2q^2)^2}$$

$$\times \begin{pmatrix} (1 - 2pq)^2 & p^2(1 - pq)^2 & p^4 & p^6 \\ q^2(1 - pq)^2 & (1 - pq)^2 & p^2 & p^4 \\ q^4 & q^2 & (1 - pq)^2 & p^2(1 - pq)^2 \\ q^6 & q^4 & q^2(1 - pq)^2 & (1 - 2pq)^2 \end{pmatrix},$$

$$2D - I = \frac{1}{1 - 3pq + p^2q^2}$$

$$\times \begin{pmatrix} 1 - pq - p^2q^2 & 0 & 0 & 0 \\ 0 & 1 + pq - p^2q^2 & 0 & 0 \\ 0 & 0 & 1 + pq - p^2q^2 & 0 \\ 0 & 0 & 0 & 1 - pq - p^2q^2 \end{pmatrix},$$

$$N(2D - I) = \frac{1}{(1 - 3pq + p^2q^2)^2}$$

$$\times \begin{pmatrix} 1 - 3pq + p^2q^2 + 2p^3q^3 & p - 2p^3q^2 + p^4q^3 & p^2 + p^3q - p^4q^2 & p^3 - p^4q - p^5q^2 \\ q - 2pq^2 + p^3q^4 & 1 - 2p^2q^2 + p^3q^3 & p + p^2q - p^3q^2 & p^2 - p^3q - p^4q^2 \\ q^2 - pq^3 - p^2q^4 & q + pq^2 - p^2q^3 & 1 - 2p^2q^2 + p^3q^3 & p - 2p^2q + 4p^4q^3 \\ q^3 - pq^4 - p^2q^5 & q^2 + pq^3 - p^2q^4 & q - 2p^2q^3 + p^3q^4 & 1 - 3pq + p^2q^2 + 2p^3q^3 \end{pmatrix}.$$

Hence,

$$V_1 = N(2D - I) - S = \frac{1}{(1 - 3pq + p^2q^2)^2}$$

$$\begin{matrix} i_2 & i_3 & i_4 & i_5 \end{matrix}$$

$$\times \begin{pmatrix} pq - 3p^2q^2 + 2p^3q^3 & pq + 2p^4q - p^5q^2 & p^2q + 2p^3q - p^4q^2 & p^3q + p^6q \\ pq - 2p^2q^2 - p^2q^5 & 2pq - 3p^2q^2 + p^3q^3 & p - p^3 - p^3q^2 & p^2q - p^4q + p^5q \\ q^3 - 3pq^3 - p^2q^4 & q - q^3 - p^2q^3 & 2pq - 3p^2q^2 + p^3q^3 & pq - 2p^2q^2 - p^4q^3 \\ pq^3 + pq^6 & pq^2 + 2pq^3 - p^2q^4 & pq + 2pq^4 - p^2q^5 & pq - 3p^2q^2 + 2p^3q^3 \end{pmatrix}.$$

If $p = q = 1/2$, the variance of the number of times the process is in a given transient state is computed below:

$$D = \begin{pmatrix} \frac{8}{5} & 0 & 0 & 0 \\ 0 & \frac{12}{5} & 0 & 0 \\ 0 & 0 & \frac{12}{5} & 0 \\ 0 & 0 & 0 & \frac{8}{5} \end{pmatrix}, \quad S = \frac{1}{25} \begin{pmatrix} 64 & 36 & 16 & 4 \\ 36 & 144 & 64 & 16 \\ 16 & 64 & 144 & 36 \\ 4 & 16 & 36 & 64 \end{pmatrix},$$

and

$$V_1 = N(2D - I) - S$$

$$= \frac{1}{25} \begin{matrix} i_2 & i_3 & i_4 & i_5 \\ \begin{pmatrix} 24 & 78 & 60 & 18 \\ 30 & 84 & 88 & 28 \\ 28 & 88 & 84 & 30 \\ 18 & 60 & 78 & 24 \end{pmatrix} \end{matrix}.$$

Thus, if the initial state is i_3, the variances of the number of times the process is in states i_2, i_3, i_4, and i_5 are 6/5, 84/25, 88/25, and 28/25, respectively. Note that, no matter in what state the process starts, the variances are the largest in the middle states, that is, in states i_3 and i_4.

Theorem 9.4.2   Let $m(t)$ be the function that gives the number of steps that the process is in a transient state. If the process starts at state i, then

$$E[m(t)] = \psi = N\xi$$

and

$$\text{Var}[m(t)] = \psi_1 = (2N - I)\psi - \psi_{sq}$$

where

(1) $N_{r \times r} = (I - T)^{-1}$;
(2) ξ is an $r \times 1$ vector of ones;
(3) I is an $r \times r$ identity matrix; and
(4) ψ_{sq} is an $r \times 1$ vector, the elements of which are the square of the elements of the vector ψ.

Hence, ψ is an $r \times 1$ vector of the expected number of transitions before absorption; and ψ_1 is an $r \times 1$ vector of the variances of the number of transitions before absorption.

Example 9.4.4   Here we shall obtain the vectors ψ and ψ_1 for the random-walk problem given in Example 9.4.3.

$$\psi = N\xi$$

$$= \frac{1}{1 - 3pq + p^2q^2} \begin{pmatrix} 1 - 2pq & p(1 - pq) & p^2 & p^3 \\ q(1 - pq) & 1 - pq & p & p^2 \\ q^2 & q & 1 - pq & p(1 - pq) \\ q^3 & q^2 & q(1 - pq) & 1 - 2pq \end{pmatrix} \begin{pmatrix} 1 \\ 1 \\ 1 \\ 1 \end{pmatrix}$$

$$= \frac{1}{1 - 3pq + p^2q^2} \begin{matrix} \begin{pmatrix} q + 2p^2 + 2p^3 \\ 2q + 4p^2 - p^3 \\ 3q + p^2 + p^3 \\ p + 2q^2 + 2q^3 \end{pmatrix} & \begin{matrix} i_2 \\ i_3 \\ i_4 \\ i_5 \end{matrix} \end{matrix}.$$

The variance ψ_1 is obtained as follows:

$$2N - I = \frac{1}{1 - 3pq + p^2q^2}\begin{pmatrix} 1 - pq - p^2q^2 & 2p(1 - pq) & 2p^2 & 2p^3 \\ 2q(1 - pq) & 1 + pq - p^2q^2 & 2p & 2p^2 \\ 2q^2 & 2q & 1 + pq - p^2q^2 & 2p(1 - pq) \\ 2q^3 & 2q^2 & 2q(1 - pq) & 1 - pq - p^2q^2 \end{pmatrix},$$

and

$$\psi_1 = (2N - I)\psi - \psi_{sq} = \frac{1}{(1 - 3pq + p^2q^2)^2}$$

$$\times \begin{pmatrix} 2p^2 + 10p^3 - 2p^4 - 6p^5 - 4p^6 + 5pq - pq^2 \\ \quad + 2p^2q - 6p^3q - 10p^4q + 2p^6q - 5p^2q^3 - 2p^4q^2 + 4q^3p^3 \\ 4p^2 + 3p^3 - 14p^4 + 8p^5 - p^6 + 8pq \\ \quad - 12p^2q + 4p^2q^2 - 2pq^4 + 5p^4q - 8p^4q^2 + p^5q^2 \\ 3q - 5q^2 + 2q^3 + 3p^2 - 2p^5 - p^6 + 2p^2q + 7pq^2 + 4pq^3 \\ \quad - 8p^3q + p^4q + 4p^2q^2 + 4p^3q^2 + 7p^2q^3 - 4p^2q^4 - p^4q^2 - p^5q^2 \\ 8q^2 + 6q^3 - 2q^4 - 8q^5 - 4q^6 + pq - 4pq^2 - 12pq^3 - 2pq^4 - 2p^2q^4 \\ \quad - 2p^2q^5 + p^2q + 2p^3q + 8p^2q^2 + 4p^3q^3 + 4p^2q^3 - 5p^3q^2 - 2p^4q^2 \end{pmatrix} \begin{matrix} i_2 \\ \\ i_3 \\ \\ i_4 \\ \\ i_5 \end{matrix}.$$

If $p = q = 1/2$, we shall compute the expected number of transitions before absorption for the random-walk problem.

$$\psi = N\xi = \frac{1}{5}\begin{array}{c} \\ \\ \\ \end{array}\overset{\displaystyle i_2 \quad i_3 \quad i_4 \quad i_5}{\begin{pmatrix} 8 & 6 & 4 & 2 \\ 6 & 12 & 8 & 4 \\ 4 & 8 & 12 & 6 \\ 2 & 4 & 6 & 8 \end{pmatrix}}\begin{pmatrix} 1 \\ 1 \\ 1 \\ 1 \end{pmatrix}$$

$$= \begin{matrix} i_2 \\ i_3 \\ i_4 \\ i_5 \end{matrix}\begin{pmatrix} 4 \\ 6 \\ 6 \\ 4 \end{pmatrix}.$$

Hence, the process will reach an absorbing state more quickly from states i_2 or i_5, which is reasonable because it is easier to reach the boundary states from the outside states of the absorbing Markov chain. Note that the symmetry of the vector ψ is due to the fact that $p = q$.

The variance of the number of steps before absorption is computed below:

$$(2N - I) = \begin{pmatrix} \dfrac{11}{5} & \dfrac{12}{5} & \dfrac{8}{5} & \dfrac{4}{5} \\[2mm] \dfrac{12}{5} & \dfrac{19}{5} & \dfrac{16}{5} & \dfrac{8}{5} \\[2mm] \dfrac{8}{5} & \dfrac{16}{5} & \dfrac{19}{5} & \dfrac{12}{5} \\[2mm] \dfrac{4}{5} & \dfrac{8}{5} & \dfrac{12}{5} & \dfrac{11}{5} \end{pmatrix};$$

$$(2N - I)\psi = \frac{1}{5}\begin{pmatrix} 11 & 12 & 8 & 4 \\ 12 & 19 & 16 & 8 \\ 8 & 16 & 19 & 12 \\ 4 & 8 & 12 & 11 \end{pmatrix}\begin{pmatrix} 4 \\ 6 \\ 6 \\ 4 \end{pmatrix} = \begin{pmatrix} 36 \\ 58 \\ 58 \\ 36 \end{pmatrix};$$

and

$$\psi_1 = (2N - I)\psi - \psi_{sq} = \begin{pmatrix} 36 \\ 58 \\ 58 \\ 36 \end{pmatrix} - \begin{pmatrix} 16 \\ 36 \\ 36 \\ 16 \end{pmatrix} = \begin{matrix} i_2 \\ i_3 \\ i_4 \\ i_5 \end{matrix}\begin{pmatrix} 20 \\ 22 \\ 22 \\ 20 \end{pmatrix}.$$

Thus, the variance of the number of steps before the process enters an absorbing state is smallest for the outside states, as one would expect.

Theorem 9.4.3   Let the process start at transient state i. Then the probability that the process ends up in an absorbing state, j, is given by

$$A = NG,$$

where

$$N_{r \times r} = (I - T)^{-1}$$

and G is an $r \times (s - r)$ matrix of transition probabilities from the transient states to absorbing states. Thus, A is an $r \times (s - r)$ matrix of probabilities that the absorbing states will capture the random process.

Example 9.4.5   The absorbing probabilities for the random-walk problem are:

$$A = NG = \frac{1}{1 - 3pq + p^2q^2} \begin{pmatrix} (1 - 2pq) & p(1 - pq) & p^2 & p^3 \\ q(1 - pq) & (1 - pq) & p & p^2 \\ q^2 & q & (1 - pq) & p(1 - pq) \\ q^3 & q^2 & q(1 - pq) & (1 - 2pq) \end{pmatrix} \begin{pmatrix} q & 0 \\ 0 & 0 \\ 0 & 0 \\ 0 & p \end{pmatrix}$$

$$= \frac{1}{1 - 3pq + p^2q^2} \begin{pmatrix} q(1 - 2pq) & p^4 \\ q^2(1 - pq) & p^3 \\ q^3 & p^2(1 - pq) \\ q^4 & p(1 - 2pq) \end{pmatrix} \begin{matrix} i_1 & i_6 \\ \\ i_2 \\ i_3 \\ i_4 \\ i_5 \end{matrix}.$$

The probability that the process is completed in the absorbing states i_1 and i_6, given that it started in state i_5, is

$$\frac{q^4}{1 - 3pq + p^2q^2} \quad \text{and} \quad \frac{p(1 - 2pq)}{1 - 3pq + p^2q^2},$$

respectively.

Suppose that $p = q = 1/2$; then the matrix A becomes

$$A = \frac{1}{5} \begin{matrix} i_2 & i_3 & i_4 & i_5 \\ \begin{pmatrix} 8 & 6 & 4 & 2 \\ 6 & 12 & 8 & 4 \\ 4 & 8 & 12 & 6 \\ 2 & 4 & 6 & 8 \end{pmatrix} \end{matrix} \begin{pmatrix} \frac{1}{2} & 0 \\ 0 & 0 \\ 0 & 0 \\ 0 & \frac{1}{2} \end{pmatrix}$$

$$= \begin{matrix} & i_1 & i_6 \\ i_2 & \left(\frac{4}{5}\right. & \left.\frac{1}{5}\right. \\ i_3 & \frac{3}{5} & \frac{2}{5} \\ i_4 & \frac{2}{5} & \frac{3}{5} \\ i_5 & \left.\frac{1}{5}\right. & \left.\frac{4}{5}\right) \end{matrix}.$$

Thus, if the random walk starts at state i_3, the probability that it ends up in the absorbing states i_1 and i_6 is 3/5 and 2/5, respectively. Again, the symmetry exhibited by the matrix A is due to the fact that $p = q = 1/2$.

9.4.2 Regular Markov Chains   In this section we shall define the concept of a regular Markov chain and its fundamental property, and illustrate its meaning with an example.

Definition 9.4.9   *A Markov chain that consists of no transient states and has a single ergodic set is called a* regular Markov chain.

Definition 9.4.10   *A stochastic matrix of a regular Markov chain is called a* regular transition matrix.

It can be shown that a regular transition matrix is, in fact, a *positive transition matrix*. That is, a Markov chain is regular if and only if it is possible to be in any state after some number n of steps, no matter in what state the process started. However, the Markov chain given by the state diagram (Figure 9.4.3) consists of a transient set, states $\{i_1, i_3, i_6\}$, and an ergodic set, states $\{i_2, i_4, i_5\}$, where $\alpha, \beta > 0$ and $\alpha + \beta = 1$.

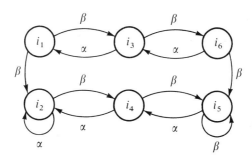

Figure 9.4.3

The single ergodic set constitutes a regular Markov chain, and its stochastic matrix P is regular for $n = 2$. That is, every entry of P^2 is positive:

$$
P = \begin{array}{c} \\ i_2 \\ i_4 \\ i_5 \end{array}
\begin{array}{c} \begin{array}{ccc} i_2 & i_4 & i_5 \end{array} \\
\begin{pmatrix} \alpha & \beta & 0 \\ \alpha & 0 & \beta \\ 0 & \alpha & \beta \end{pmatrix} \end{array}
$$

and

$$
P^2 = \begin{pmatrix} \alpha(\alpha + \beta) & \alpha\beta & \beta^2 \\ \alpha^2 & 2\alpha\beta & \beta^2 \\ \alpha^2 & \alpha\beta & \beta(\alpha + \beta) \end{pmatrix}.
$$

The fundamental property of regular transition matrices is given by Theorem 9.4.4, the proof of which is beyond the scope of this book.

Theorem 9.4.4   Let P be a regular transition matrix. Then

(1) P has a unique fixed probability vector $\gamma = (\gamma_1, \gamma_2, \ldots, \gamma_n)$, the components of which are positive, such that $\gamma P = \gamma$;

(2) the sequence $P, P^2, P^3, \ldots, P^n$ of powers of P approaches a probability matrix W, each of the rows of which have the same probability vector γ; and $PW = WP = W$; and

(3) if π is any probability vector, then the sequence of vectors, $\pi P, \pi P^2, \pi P^3, \ldots, \pi P^n$, approaches the vector γ as n tends to infinity.

By stating that the matrix P^n approaches the matrix W, we mean that each entry of P^n approaches the corresponding entry of W as n tends to infinity. Similarly, πP^n approaches the vector γ means that each component of πP^n approaches the corresponding component of γ. We shall refer to matrix W as the limiting matrix of a regular transition matrix. We have seen in Section 9.2 that, if the random process starts in each of the states with probabilities given by the vector π, then the probabilities of being in each of the states after n steps are given by πP. The above theorem states that, if P is a regular transition matrix, then, for large n, πP^n is approximately equal to the vector γ. In fact, the probability vector γ is unique. Thus, for a regular Markov chain, for large values of n, the probabilities of being in each of the states are independent of the initial probability vector.

Example 9.4.6   Consider the Markov chain generated by the four quarterbacks illustrated in Example 9.1.2. Here the Markov chain is regular, and its regular stochastic matrix is given by

$$P = \begin{array}{c} \\ i_1 \\ i_2 \\ i_3 \\ i_4 \end{array} \begin{array}{c} \begin{array}{cccc} i_1 & i_2 & i_3 & i_4 \end{array} \\ \left(\begin{array}{cccc} 0 & \dfrac{1}{3} & \dfrac{1}{3} & \dfrac{1}{3} \\[2mm] \dfrac{1}{2} & 0 & 0 & \dfrac{1}{2} \\[2mm] \dfrac{2}{3} & 0 & 0 & \dfrac{1}{3} \\[2mm] 1 & 0 & 0 & 0 \end{array} \right) \end{array}.$$

We seek a probability vector $\gamma = (\gamma_1, \gamma_2, \gamma_3, \gamma_4)$ such that $\gamma P = \gamma$:

$$(\gamma_1, \gamma_2, \gamma_3, \gamma_4) \begin{pmatrix} 0 & \frac{1}{3} & \frac{1}{3} & \frac{1}{3} \\ \frac{1}{2} & 0 & 0 & \frac{1}{2} \\ \frac{2}{3} & 0 & 0 & \frac{1}{3} \\ 1 & 0 & 0 & 0 \end{pmatrix} = \begin{pmatrix} \gamma_1 \\ \gamma_2 \\ \gamma_3 \\ \gamma_4 \end{pmatrix}$$

Solving the set of equations

$$\gamma_1 + \gamma_2 + \gamma_3 + \gamma_4 = 1$$

$$\frac{1}{2}\gamma_2 + \frac{2}{3}\gamma_3 + \gamma_4 = \gamma_1$$

$$\frac{1}{3}\gamma_1 = \gamma_2$$

$$\frac{1}{3}\gamma_1 = \gamma_3$$

$$\frac{1}{3}\gamma_1 + \frac{1}{2}\gamma_2 + \frac{1}{3}\gamma_3 = \gamma_4,$$

where the first equation comes from the fact that γ must be a probability vector, we have the unique solution

$$\gamma = \left(\frac{18}{41}, \frac{6}{41}, \frac{6}{41}, \frac{11}{41}\right).$$

In view of Theorem 9.4.4, the limiting matrix A is

$$W = \begin{array}{c} \\ i_1 \\ i_2 \\ i_3 \\ i_4 \end{array} \begin{array}{cccc} i_1 & i_2 & i_3 & i_4 \\ \begin{pmatrix} \frac{18}{41} & \frac{6}{41} & \frac{6}{41} & \frac{11}{41} \\ \frac{18}{41} & \frac{6}{41} & \frac{6}{41} & \frac{11}{41} \\ \frac{18}{41} & \frac{6}{41} & \frac{6}{41} & \frac{11}{41} \\ \frac{18}{41} & \frac{6}{41} & \frac{6}{41} & \frac{11}{41} \end{pmatrix} \end{array} = \begin{pmatrix} .4390 & .1463 & .1463 & .2683 \\ .4390 & .1463 & .1463 & .2683 \\ .4390 & .1463 & .1463 & .2683 \\ .4390 & .1463 & .1463 & .2683 \end{pmatrix}.$$

Each row of the probability matrix W gives the long-range prediction regarding to whom each of the four quarterbacks will throw the football. We also show that the convergence of P^n to the matrix W is fairly fast; that is, $n = 15$;

$$P^{15} = \begin{pmatrix} .43908 & .14629 & .14629 & .26832 \\ .43908 & .14630 & .14630 & .26829 \\ .43902 & .14634 & .14634 & .26827 \\ .43888 & .14642 & .14642 & .26824 \end{pmatrix}.$$

Thus, the first row gives the probabilities of the ball being thrown to each quarterback 15 throws after it begins with quarterback i_1.

A transition matrix with identical rows is called a *steady-state matrix*. In the previous example, we have illustrated the important property that transition matrices asymptotically approach a *steady-state matrix*. Two basic properties of steady-state matrices are given in Corollary 9.4.1.

Corollary 9.4.1   Let P_S be an $n \times n$ steady-state matrix, with rows $(s_1, s_2, s_3, \ldots, s_n)$. Then

(1)   for all $n \times n$ transition matrices P we have

$$P \times P_S = P_S,$$

and

(2)   for π a $1 \times n$ probability vector we have

$$\pi P_S = (s_1, s_2, s_3, \ldots, s_n).$$

We shall conclude our brief discussion of finite Markov chains by illustrating the method by which one can obtain the mean and variance of the number of steps necessary to go from state i to state j for the first time (first-passage times) for regular Markov chains. Corresponding to the fundamental matrix N for absorbing Markov chains, we shall define (Kemeny and Snell), a similar matrix for regular Markov chains.

Definition 9.4.11   *Let P be a regular transition matrix and W its limiting matrix. Then the matrix defined by*

$$L = [I - (P - W)]^{-1}$$

is called the fundamental matrix *for regular Markov chains.*

Definition 9.4.12   *The* first-passage time, t_k, *is the number of steps necessary before entering state i_k for the first time. The* mean first-passage matrix *is denoted by F and its entries are denoted by f_{ij}*:

$$F = E(t_{j|i})$$

The mean first-passage matrix for regular Markov chains is given by the Theorem 9.4.5.

Theorem 9.4.5   Let L be the fundamental matrix for a regular Markov chain. Then the mean first-passage matrix is given by

$$F = (I - L + HL_{dg})Q,$$

where

(1) $H = WQ$, W is the steady-state matrix;

(2) Q is a diagonal matrix with diagonal elements $d_{ii} = 1/\gamma_i$; and

(3) L_{dg} is a diagonal matrix containing the main diagonal elements of the fundamental matrix L.

Example 9.4.7   We shall compute the mean first-passage matrix for the regular stochastic matrix given in Example 9.4.6. We first compute the fundamental matrix:

$$[I - (P - W)] = \begin{pmatrix} 1.4390 & -.1870 & -.1870 & -.0650 \\ -.0610 & 1.1463 & .1463 & -.2317 \\ -.2276 & .1463 & 1.1463 & -.0650 \\ -.5610 & .1463 & .1463 & 1.2683 \end{pmatrix}$$

and

$$L = [I - (P - W)]^{-1} = \begin{pmatrix} .7388 & .0999 & .0999 & .0613 \\ .0803 & .8804 & -.1196 & .1588 \\ .1535 & -.0952 & .9048 & .0369 \\ .2998 & -.0464 & -.0464 & .7930 \end{pmatrix}.$$

Here

$$
H = WQ = \begin{pmatrix} \dfrac{18}{41} & \dfrac{6}{41} & \dfrac{6}{41} & \dfrac{11}{41} \\[6pt] \dfrac{18}{41} & \dfrac{6}{41} & \dfrac{6}{41} & \dfrac{11}{41} \\[6pt] \dfrac{18}{41} & \dfrac{6}{41} & \dfrac{6}{41} & \dfrac{11}{41} \\[6pt] \dfrac{18}{41} & \dfrac{6}{41} & \dfrac{6}{41} & \dfrac{11}{41} \end{pmatrix} \begin{pmatrix} \dfrac{41}{18} & 0 & 0 & 0 \\[6pt] 0 & \dfrac{41}{6} & 0 & 0 \\[6pt] 0 & 0 & \dfrac{41}{6} & 0 \\[6pt] 0 & 0 & 0 & \dfrac{41}{11} \end{pmatrix}
$$

$$
= \begin{pmatrix} 1 & 1 & 1 & 1 \\ 1 & 1 & 1 & 1 \\ 1 & 1 & 1 & 1 \\ 1 & 1 & 1 & 1 \end{pmatrix},
$$

and

$$
HL_{dg} = \begin{pmatrix} 1 & 1 & 1 & 1 \\ 1 & 1 & 1 & 1 \\ 1 & 1 & 1 & 1 \\ 1 & 1 & 1 & 1 \end{pmatrix} \begin{pmatrix} .7388 & 0 & 0 & 0 \\ 0 & .8804 & 0 & 0 \\ 0 & 0 & .9048 & 0 \\ 0 & 0 & 0 & .7930 \end{pmatrix}
$$

$$
= \begin{pmatrix} .7388 & .8804 & .9048 & .7930 \\ .7388 & .8804 & .9048 & .7930 \\ .7388 & .8804 & .9048 & .7930 \\ .7388 & .8804 & .9048 & .7930 \end{pmatrix}.
$$

Thus,

$$
F = (I - L + HL_{dg})Q
$$

$$
= \begin{pmatrix} 1.0000 & .7805 & .8049 & .7317 \\ .6585 & 1.0000 & 1.0244 & .6342 \\ .5853 & .9756 & 1.0000 & .6561 \\ .4390 & .9268 & .9512 & 1.0000 \end{pmatrix} \begin{pmatrix} \dfrac{41}{18} & 0 & 0 & 0 \\[6pt] 0 & \dfrac{41}{6} & 0 & 0 \\[6pt] 0 & 0 & \dfrac{41}{6} & 0 \\[6pt] 0 & 0 & 0 & \dfrac{41}{11} \end{pmatrix}
$$

$$
= \begin{matrix} \quad i_1 \quad & i_2 \quad & i_3 \quad & i_4 \end{matrix}
$$
$$
= \begin{pmatrix} 2.2778 & 5.3641 & 5.5000 & 2.7272 \\ 1.4999 & 6.8333 & 7.0000 & 2.3639 \\ 1.3332 & 6.6666 & 6.8333 & 2.4455 \\ .9999 & 6.3331 & 6.4999 & 3.7273 \end{pmatrix}.
$$

Therefore, we conclude that, if the ball is presently with quarterback i_2, the mean number of throws before the ball is with players i_1, i_3, and i_4 is 1.4999, 7.0000, and 2.3639 throws, respectively. The mean number of throws before the ball returns to player i_2 is 6.8333, and so on.

We shall also use the fundamental matrix L to obtain the variance of the first-passage time for regular Markov chains.

Theorem 9.4.6   Let L be the fundamental matrix and F the mean first-passage matrix for a regular Markov chain. Then the variance first-passage matrix, V_2, is given by

$$V_2 = F(2L_{dg}Q - I) + 2[LF - H(LF)_{dg}],$$

where

(1) L_{dg} is a diagonal matrix containing the main diagonal elements of the fundamental matrix L;

(2) Q is a diagonal matrix with diagonal elements $d_{ii} = 1/\gamma_i$;

(3) $H = WQ$, W being the limiting matrix of the regular transition matrix P; and

(4) $(LF)_{dg}$ is a diagonal matrix containing the main diagonal of the product of the matrices L and F.

Example 9.4.8   The variance for the first-passage matrix of Example 9.4.7 is given below.

$$LQ = \begin{pmatrix} 1.6828 & 0 & 0 & 0 \\ 0 & 6.0161 & 0 & 0 \\ 0 & 0 & 6.1828 & 0 \\ 0 & 0 & 0 & 2.9557 \end{pmatrix};$$

$$2LQ - I = \begin{pmatrix} 2.3656 & 0 & 0 & 0 \\ 0 & 11.0322 & 0 & 0 \\ 0 & 0 & 11.3656 & 0 \\ 0 & 0 & 0 & 4.9114 \end{pmatrix};$$

$$F(2LQ - I) = \begin{pmatrix} 5.3884 & 59.1778 & 62.5108 & 13.3944 \\ 3.5483 & 75.3863 & 79.5592 & 11.6101 \\ 3.1539 & 73.5480 & 77.6646 & 12.0108 \\ 2.3654 & 69.8680 & 73.8753 & 18.3063 \end{pmatrix};$$

$$LF = \begin{pmatrix} 1.6828 & 3.9630 & 4.0634 & 2.0149 \\ 1.3205 & 6.0160 & 6.1628 & 2.0812 \\ 1.2543 & 6.0319 & 6.1828 & 2.2127 \\ .7929 & 5.0221 & 5.1544 & 2.9557 \end{pmatrix};$$

$$H(LF)_{dg} = \begin{pmatrix} 1.6828 & 6.0160 & 6.1828 & 2.9557 \\ 1.6828 & 6.0160 & 6.1828 & 2.9557 \\ 1.6828 & 6.0160 & 6.1828 & 2.9557 \\ 1.6828 & 6.0160 & 6.1828 & 2.9557 \end{pmatrix}$$

$$2[LF - H(LF)_{dg}] = \begin{pmatrix} 0 & -4.1060 & -4.2388 & -1.8816 \\ -.7246 & 0 & -.0400 & -1.7490 \\ -.8570 & .0318 & 0 & -1.4860 \\ -1.7798 & -1.9878 & -2.0568 & 0 \end{pmatrix}.$$

Thus, the variance matrix is

$$V_2 = F(2L_{dg}\, Q - I) + 2[LF - H(LF)_{gd}]$$

$$\begin{array}{cccc} i_1 & i_2 & i_3 & i_4 \end{array}$$

$$= \begin{pmatrix} 5.3884 & 55.0718 & 58.2720 & 11.5128 \\ 2.8237 & 75.3863 & 79.5192 & 9.8611 \\ 2.2969 & 73.5798 & 77.6646 & 10.5248 \\ .5856 & 67.8802 & 71.8185 & 18.3063 \end{pmatrix}.$$

Therefore, the variance for the first-passage times is largest for the "middle states." The minimum variance for the mean first-passage time occurs when player i_4 is initiating the throwing to player i_1. In general, the variances are quite large for the given random process.

Problems

9.1. Draw the state diagram for each of the following transition matrices:

(a)
$$P = \begin{array}{c} \\ i_1 \\ i_2 \\ i_3 \\ i_4 \end{array} \begin{array}{cccc} i_1 & i_2 & i_3 & i_4 \\ \begin{pmatrix} 1 & 0 & 0 & 0 \\ \dfrac{1}{2} & \dfrac{1}{2} & 0 & 0 \\ \dfrac{1}{4} & \dfrac{1}{2} & 0 & \dfrac{1}{4} \\ \dfrac{1}{4} & \dfrac{1}{4} & \dfrac{1}{4} & \dfrac{1}{4} \end{pmatrix} \end{array}$$

(b)
$$P = \begin{array}{c} \\ i_1 \\ i_2 \\ i_3 \\ i_4 \end{array} \begin{array}{cccc} i_1 & i_2 & i_3 & i_4 \\ \begin{pmatrix} 0 & q & 0 & p \\ 0 & q & 0 & p \\ q & 0 & 0 & p \\ 0 & 0 & 1 & 0 \end{pmatrix} \end{array}, \quad p + q = 1$$

9.2. Write the transition matrix for each of the following state diagrams:

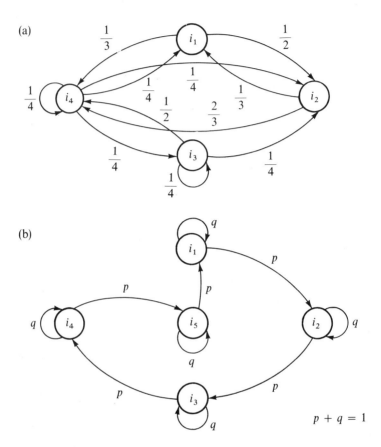

(a)

(b)

$p + q = 1$

9.3. A man can get to his office by car, train, or bus. He will take either the train or the bus on the day following a day on which he drives. If he takes the train to his office, then the next day he is just as likely to drive as to take the bus, but if he takes the bus, then the next day the chances are three to one that he will take the train rather than drive.

(a) What is the state space of the process?
(b) Write the transition matrix of the Markov chain.
(c) Draw the state diagram of the transition matrix.

9.4. A quarterback usually throws the ball to only three players, E_1, E_2, and E_3. He never throws the ball to the same player on successive plays. If he throws to player E_1, then on the next play he will throw to E_2. However, if he throws either to E_2 or E_3, then on the next play he is twice as likely to throw to player E_1 as to the other player. Does this process constitute a Markov chain?

9.5. A cage consists of seven compartments that open into each other, as shown in the accompanying diagram. A mouse is placed in one of the compartments, and it begins moving from compartment to compartment in search of food. If each exit of any given compartment has an equally likely chance of being selected by the mouse, find the transition probability matrix of the Markov chain.

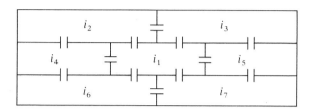

9.6. A player has three dollars with which to play a game. On each play of the game, it is possible for him to win $2.00, with probability .40, or lose $1.00, with probability .60. The game is stopped when he has either won $3.00 or lost $3.00. Determine the transition matrix for this special case of the gambler's-ruin problem.

9.7. (Random walk with reflecting barriers). Consider the *random-walk problem*, which was formulated in Section 9.1, under the following additional condition. When the man reaches a boundary state, he is required to take a step backwards to the state from which he came. Thus, in Example 9.1.1, when the man enters state i_1, he is on the next step "reflected" back to state i_2. Similarly, if he enters state i_6, he goes back to i_5 on the next step.

(a) Write the transition matrix of the random walk.
(b) Assume that the process starts with state i_3 ; draw a tree diagram showing the one-step, two-step, three-step, and four-step transitions.
(c) Write the first four probability distribution vectors directly from the tree diagram.
(d) Interpret the meaning of π_3.

9.8. Use Equation 9.1.9 to calculate the first four probability distribution vectors of Problem 9.7 and compare your answers with part (c).

9.9. In Problem 9.6, calculate the following:

(a) the probability that the player has lost his money at the end of at most four steps
(b) the probability that the game will last more than six plays, that is, that the process has not entered states i_1 or i_7.

9.10. Referring back to Problem 9.3, suppose that the process begins with the man's taking the train to his office. What is the probability that he will be taking the train again five days later?

9.11. Using mathematical induction, prove that Equation (9.2.4) is true for all m.

9.12. Matrices in general do not commute, but probability transition matrices do commute: Show that, if P is an $h \times h$ transition matrix and m and n are positive integers, then

$$P^{(m+n)} = P^{(m)} \cdot P^{(n)} = P^{(n)} P^{(m)}.$$

9.13. (a) Calculate the three-step transition matrix of Problem 9.5.
     (b) Suppose that the mouse is initially placed in compartment i_3. What are the probabilities that, after three steps, the mouse will be in states $i_1, i_2, i_3, i_4, i_5, i_6$, and i_7, respectively?

9.14. Consider a sequence of Bernoulli trials that generates a chain, the links of which are either a success, with probability p, or a failure, with probability $1 - p$. The transition matrix is given by

$$P = \begin{pmatrix} p & 1-p \\ p & 1-p \end{pmatrix}.$$

Find the eigenvalues of the matrix P.

9.15. Let the transition matrix of a simple random-walk problem be given by

$$P = \begin{pmatrix} \dfrac{1}{4} & \dfrac{1}{2} & \dfrac{1}{4} \\ 0 & \dfrac{3}{4} & \dfrac{1}{4} \\ 0 & 0 & 1 \end{pmatrix}.$$

Calculate the eigenvalues of the matrix P.

9.16. Apply Theorem 9.3.1 to find P^r of the transition matrix given in Problem 9.15, and evaluate the resulting matrix for $r = 10$. Interpret the third row of P^{10}.

9.17. Use the *Jordan canonical form* to raise the transition matrix P, given by

$$P = \begin{pmatrix} 1 & 0 & 0 & 0 \\ \dfrac{1}{3} & \dfrac{2}{3} & 0 & 0 \\ \dfrac{1}{3} & \dfrac{1}{3} & \dfrac{1}{3} & 0 \\ \dfrac{1}{6} & \dfrac{1}{4} & \dfrac{1}{4} & \dfrac{1}{3} \end{pmatrix},$$

to the kth power.

9.18. Are the eigenvalues of the transition matrix P, given by

$$P = \begin{pmatrix} \dfrac{1}{3} & 0 & \dfrac{1}{4} & \dfrac{5}{12} \\ 0 & \dfrac{1}{6} & \dfrac{1}{2} & \dfrac{1}{3} \\ 0 & 0 & \dfrac{1}{3} & \dfrac{2}{3} \\ 0 & 0 & 0 & 1 \end{pmatrix},$$

all distinct? Use accordingly either Theorem 9.3.1 or the *Jordan canonical form* to obtain P^{15} and to interpret the first and last row of the resulting matrix. Does the matrix P^{15} seem to be approaching a steady state?

9.19. Let the transition matrix P be given by

$$P = \begin{pmatrix} \dfrac{1}{2} & 0 & \dfrac{1}{2} \\ \dfrac{1}{2} & \dfrac{1}{2} & 0 \\ 0 & 0 & 1 \end{pmatrix}$$

Raise the matrix P to the n-th power, and evaluate the resulting matrix for $n = 20$.

9.20. Construct two 3×3 transition matrices so that one will have distinct eigenvalues and the other will have two or more identical eigenvalues.

9.21. Find the necessary number of steps that converts the transition matrix *P*, given by

$$
P = \begin{pmatrix}
0 & 1 & 0 & 0 & 0 \\
\dfrac{1}{3} & 0 & \dfrac{2}{3} & 0 & 0 \\
0 & \dfrac{1}{3} & 0 & \dfrac{2}{3} & 0 \\
0 & 0 & \dfrac{1}{3} & 0 & \dfrac{2}{3} \\
0 & 0 & 0 & 0 & 1
\end{pmatrix},
$$

into a positive transition matrix. What is the physical interpretation of the resulting matrix?

9.22. Consider a Markov chain, the transition probability matrix of which is given by

$$
P = \begin{array}{c}
\\ i_1 \\ i_2 \\ i_3 \\ i_4 \\ i_5 \\ i_6
\end{array}
\begin{array}{c}
\begin{array}{cccccc} i_1 & i_2 & i_3 & i_4 & i_5 & i_6 \end{array} \\
\begin{pmatrix}
0 & \dfrac{1}{3} & 0 & \dfrac{1}{3} & 0 & \dfrac{1}{3} \\
\dfrac{1}{4} & \dfrac{1}{4} & 0 & 0 & 0 & \dfrac{1}{2} \\
0 & \dfrac{1}{2} & 0 & 0 & \dfrac{1}{3} & \dfrac{1}{6} \\
0 & 0 & 0 & \dfrac{1}{2} & \dfrac{1}{2} & 0 \\
0 & 0 & 0 & \dfrac{1}{2} & \dfrac{1}{2} & 0 \\
0 & 0 & 0 & 0 & 0 & 1
\end{pmatrix}
\end{array}.
$$

Classify which state or states are absorbing, periodic, persistent, and transient.

9.23. Rearrange the transition matrix of the Markov chain given in Problem 9.7 into the form of Equation (9.4.1), and calculate the normal matrix of the random walk. What is the physical interpretation of the fundamental matrix?

9.24. Referring to Problem 9.6, find the mean of the total number of times the gambler is in a given transient state.

9.25. In Problem 9.7, let $p = 2/3$ and $q = 1/3$; that is, let the transition matrix of the Markov chain be given by

$$
P = \quad
\begin{array}{c}
\\
i_1 \\
i_2 \\
i_3 \\
i_4 \\
i_5 \\
i_6
\end{array}
\begin{array}{c}
\begin{array}{cccccc}
i_1 & i_2 & i_3 & i_4 & i_5 & i_6
\end{array} \\
\left(
\begin{array}{cccccc}
0 & 1 & 0 & 0 & 0 & 0 \\
\frac{1}{3} & 0 & \frac{2}{3} & 0 & 0 & 0 \\
0 & \frac{1}{3} & 0 & \frac{2}{3} & 0 & 0 \\
0 & 0 & \frac{1}{3} & 0 & \frac{2}{3} & 0 \\
0 & 0 & 0 & \frac{1}{3} & 0 & \frac{2}{3} \\
0 & 0 & 0 & 0 & 1 & 0
\end{array}
\right).
\end{array}
$$

(a) Find the mean of the total number of times that the random walk with reflecting barriers is in a given transient state, i_n, $n = 1, 3, 4, 6$.
(b) What is the variance of the number of times that the process (random walk) is in i_n, $n = 1, 3, 4, 6$, given that it started in one of the transient states?
(c) Given that the process started in one of the transient states, what is the expected number of transitions before absorption?
(d) What is the variance of the number of transitions before absorption, given that the process started in one of the following states: i_1, i_3, i_4, or i_6?
(e) What is the probability that the process will be in an absorbing state, given that it started in a transient state?

9.26. Answer questions (a) through (e) of Problem 9.25 for the transition of the Markov chain obtained in Problem 9.5.

9.27. Let T be an $n \times n$ matrix of transition probabilities between transient states. Show that

$$(I - T)^{-1} = I + T + T^2 + \cdots + T^n + \cdots$$

converges. This will assure the existence of the fundamental matrix of absorbing Markov chains.

9.28. Does the Markov chain given in Problem 9.3 constitute a regular Markov chain? What is the necessary number of transitions for the stochastic matrix to be regular?

9.29. Suppose that a mouse is placed in compartment i_1 in the process described in Problem 9.5.

(a)   Draw a state diagram of the Markov chain.
(b)   Which of the states form an ergodic set and which are transient?

9.30. Obtain the limiting matrix, W, of a Markov chain, the transition matrix, P, of which is given by

$$P = \begin{array}{c} \\ i_1 \\ i_2 \\ i_3 \\ i_4 \end{array} \begin{array}{cccc} i_1 & i_2 & i_3 & i_4 \\ \left(\begin{array}{cccc} 0 & \frac{1}{2} & \frac{1}{4} & \frac{1}{4} \\ \frac{1}{2} & 0 & \frac{1}{4} & \frac{1}{4} \\ \frac{1}{2} & \frac{1}{2} & 0 & 0 \\ \frac{1}{2} & \frac{1}{4} & \frac{1}{4} & 0 \end{array} \right) \end{array}.$$

What is the physical interpretation of the matrix W?

9.31. Using the methods discussed in Section 9.3, show that the probability transition matrix given in Problem 9.29 reaches a steady state after 10 transitions.

9.32. Prove Corollary 9.4.1.

9.33. Calculate the fundamental matrix for the regular transition matrix given in Problem 9.29.

9.34. Compute the mean first passage matrix for the regular stochastic matrix given in Problem 9.29. Give a physical interpretation of the resulting matrix.

9.35. Compute and interpret the variance of the first-passage time matrix of Problem 9.34.

Suggested Supplementary Reading

Bailey, N. T. J. *The Elements of Stochastic Process.* New York: John Wiley and Sons, Inc., 1964.

Bartlett, M. S. *An Introduction to Stochastic Processes.* New York: Cambridge University Press, 1955.

Bharucha-Reid, A. T. *Elements of the Theory of Markov Processes and Their Applications.* New York: McGraw-Hill Book Company, Inc., 1960.

Breiman, L. *Probability and Stochastic Process.* Boston: Houghton Mifflin Company, 1969.

Cox, D. R. and Miller, H. D. *The Theory of Stochastic Processes.* New York: John Wiley and Sons, Inc., 1965.

Feller, W. *An Introduction to Probability Theory and Its Applications.* 2nd ed. New York: John Wiley and Sons, Inc., 1957.

Kemeny, J. G. and Snell, J. L. *Finite Markov Chains.* New York: D. Van Nostrand Company Inc., 1960.

Parzen, E. *Stochastic Processes.* San Francisco: Holden-Day, Inc., 1962.

List of Tables

Individual Terms of the Binomial Distribution:

$$f(x) = \binom{n}{x} p^x q^{n-x}, x = 0, 1, 2, \ldots, n, q = 1 - p, p + q = 1$$

Cumulative Terms of the Binomial Distribution:

$$Pr(X \geq x') = \sum_{x=x'}^{n} \binom{n}{x} p^x q^{n-x}, x = 0, 1, 2, \ldots, n, p + q = 1$$

Individual Terms of the Poisson Distribution:

$$f(x) = \frac{e^{-m} m^x}{x!}, x = 0, 1, 2, \ldots, m > 0$$

Cumulative Terms of the Poisson Distribution:

$$Pr(X \geq x') = \sum_{x=x'}^{\infty} \frac{e^{-m} m^x}{x!}, x = 0, 1, 2, \ldots, m > 0$$

Hypergeometric Distribution:

$$f(x) = \frac{\binom{n}{x}\binom{N-n}{n-x}}{\binom{N}{n}} \cdot$$

Negative Binomial Distribution:

$$f(x) = \binom{x+r-1}{r-1} p^r q^x, x = 0, 1, 2, \ldots; p + q = 1$$

Exponential Functions

Normal Distribution

Table 1

Individual Terms of the Binomial Distribution

The $(x + 1)^{st}$ term in the expansion of the binomial $[\theta + (1 - \theta)]^n$ is given by

$$f(x;n,\theta) = \binom{n}{x} \theta^x (1 - \theta)^{n-x}, \qquad x = 0, 1, 2, \ldots , n.$$

This is the probability of exactly x successes in n independent binomial trials with probability of success on a single trial equal to θ. This table contains the individual terms of $f(x;n,\theta)$ for specified choices of x, n, and θ.

For $\theta > 0.5$, the value of $\binom{n}{x} \theta^x (1 - \theta)^{n-x}$ is found by using the table entry for

$$\binom{n}{n - x} (1 - \theta)^{n-x} \theta^x.$$

Source: William H. Beyer, ed. *Handbook of Tables for Probability and Statistics.* Cleveland: The Chemical Rubber Company, 1966. Reprinted by permission of the publisher.

n	x	.05	.10	.15	.20	θ .25	.30	.35	.40	.45	.50
1	0	.9500	.9000	.8500	.8000	.7500	.7000	.6500	.6000	.5500	.5000
	1	.0500	.1000	.1500	.2000	.2500	.3000	.3500	.4000	.4500	.5000
2	0	.9025	.8100	.7225	.6400	.5625	.4900	.4225	.3600	.3025	.2500
	1	.0950	.1800	.2550	.3200	.3750	.4200	.4550	.4800	.4950	.5000
	2	.0025	.0100	.0225	.0400	.0625	.0900	.1225	.1600	.2025	.2500
3	0	.8574	.7290	.6141	.5120	.4219	.3430	.2746	.2160	.1664	.1250
	1	.1354	.2430	.3251	.3840	.4219	.4410	.4436	.4320	.4084	.3750
	2	.0071	.0270	.0574	.0960	.1406	.1890	.2389	.2880	.3341	.3750
	3	.0001	.0010	.0034	.0080	.0156	.0270	.0429	.0640	.0911	.1250
4	0	.8145	.6561	.5220	.4096	.3164	.2401	.1785	.1296	.0915	.0625
	1	.1715	.2916	.3685	.4096	.4219	.4116	.3845	.3456	.2995	.2500
	2	.0135	.0486	.0975	.1536	.2109	.2646	.3105	.3456	.3675	.3750
	3	.0005	.0036	.0115	.0256	.0469	.0756	.1115	.1536	.2005	.2500
	4	.0000	.0001	.0005	.0016	.0039	.0081	.0150	.0256	.0410	.0625
5	0	.7738	.5905	.4437	.3277	.2373	.1681	.1160	.0778	.0503	.0312
	1	.2036	.3280	.3915	.4096	.3955	.3602	.3124	.2592	.2059	.1562
	2	.0214	.0729	.1382	.2048	.2637	.3087	.3364	.3456	.3369	.3125
	3	.0011	.0081	.0244	.0512	.0879	.1323	.1811	.2304	.2757	.3125
	4	.0000	.0004	.0022	.0064	.0146	.0284	.0488	.0768	.1128	.1562
	5	.0000	.0000	.0001	.0003	.0010	.0024	.0053	.0102	.0185	.0312
6	0	.7351	.5314	.3771	.2621	.1780	.1176	.0754	.0467	.0277	.0156
	1	.2321	.3543	.3993	.3932	.3560	.3025	.2437	.1866	.1359	.0938
	2	.0305	.0984	.1762	.2458	.2966	.3241	.3280	.3110	.2780	.2344
	3	.0021	.0146	.0415	.0819	.1318	.1852	.2355	.2765	.3032	.3125
	4	.0001	.0012	.0055	.0154	.0330	.0595	.0951	.1382	.1861	.2344
	5	.0000	.0001	.0004	.0015	.0044	.0102	.0205	.0369	.0609	.0938
	6	.0000	.0000	.0000	.0001	.0002	.0007	.0018	.0041	.0083	.0156
7	0	.6983	.4783	.3206	.2097	.1335	.0824	.0490	.0280	.0152	.0078
	1	.2573	.3720	.3960	.3670	.3115	.2471	.1848	.1306	.0872	.0547
	2	.0406	.1240	.2097	.2753	.3115	.3177	.2985	.2613	.2140	.1641
	3	.0036	.0230	.0617	.1147	.1730	.2269	.2679	.2903	.2918	.2734
	4	.0002	.0026	.0109	.0287	.0577	.0972	.1442	.1935	.2388	.2734
	5	.0000	.0002	.0012	.0043	.0115	.0250	.0466	.0774	.1172	.1641
	6	.0000	.0000	.0001	.0004	.0013	.0036	.0084	.0172	.0320	.0547
	7	.0000	.0000	.0000	.0000	.0001	.0002	.0006	.0016	.0037	.0078
8	0	.6634	.4305	.2725	.1678	.1001	.0576	.0319	.0168	.0084	.0039
	1	.2793	.3826	.3847	.3355	.2670	.1977	.1373	.0896	.0548	.0312
	2	.0515	.1488	.2376	.2936	.3115	.2965	.2587	.2090	.1569	.1094
	3	.0054	.0331	.0839	.1468	.2076	.2541	.2786	.2787	.2568	.2188
	4	.0004	.0046	.0185	.0459	.0865	.1361	.1875	.2322	.2627	.2734
	5	.0000	.0004	.0026	.0092	.0231	.0467	.0808	.1239	.1719	.2188
	6	.0000	.0000	.0002	.0011	.0038	.0100	.0217	.0413	.0703	.1094
	7	.0000	.0000	.0000	.0001	.0004	.0012	.0033	.0079	.0164	.0312
	8	.0000	.0000	.0000	.0000	.0000	.0001	.0002	.0007	.0017	.0039

Linear interpolations with respect to θ will in general be accurate at most to two decimal places.

n	x	.05	.10	.15	.20	θ .25	.30	.35	.40	.45	.50
9	0	.6302	.3874	.2316	.1342	.0751	.0404	.0207	.0101	.0046	.0020
	1	.2985	.3874	.3679	.3020	.2253	.1556	.1004	.0605	.0339	.0176
	2	.0629	.1722	.2597	.3020	.3003	.2668	.2162	.1612	.1110	.0703
	3	.0077	.0446	.1069	.1762	.2336	.2668	.2716	.2508	.2119	.1641
	4	.0006	.0074	.0283	.0661	.1168	.1715	.2194	.2508	.2600	.2461
	5	.0000	.0008	.0050	.0165	.0389	.0735	.1181	.1672	.2128	.2461
	6	.0000	.0001	.0006	.0028	.0087	.0210	.0424	.0743	.1160	.1641
	7	.0000	.0000	.0000	.0003	.0012	.0039	.0098	.0212	.0407	.0703
	8	.0000	.0000	.0000	.0000	.0001	.0004	.0013	.0035	.0083	.0176
	9	.0000	.0000	.0000	.0000	.0000	.0000	.0001	.0003	.0008	.0020
10	0	.5987	.3487	.1969	.1074	.0563	.0282	.0135	.0060	.0025	.0010
	1	.3151	.3874	.3474	.2684	.1877	.1211	.0725	.0403	.0207	.0098
	2	.0746	.1937	.2759	.3020	.2816	.2335	.1757	.1209	.0763	.0439
	3	.0105	.0574	.1298	.2013	.2503	.2668	.2522	.2150	.1665	.1172
	4	.0010	.0112	.0401	.0881	.1460	.2001	.2377	.2508	.2384	.2051
	5	.0001	.0015	.0085	.0264	.0584	.1029	.1536	.2007	.2340	.2461
	6	.0000	.0001	.0012	.0055	.0162	.0368	.0689	.1115	.1596	.2051
	7	.0000	.0000	.0001	.0008	.0031	.0090	.0212	.0425	.0746	.1172
	8	.0000	.0000	.0000	.0001	.0004	.0014	.0043	.0106	.0229	.0439
	9	.0000	.0000	.0000	.0000	.0000	.0001	.0005	.0016	.0042	.0098
	10	.0000	.0000	.0000	.0000	.0000	.0000	.0000	.0001	.0003	.0010
11	0	.5688	.3138	.1673	.0859	.0422	.0198	.0088	.0036	.0014	.0004
	1	.3293	.3835	.3248	.2362	.1549	.0932	.0518	.0266	.0125	.0055
	2	.0867	.2131	.2866	.2953	.2581	.1998	.1395	.0887	.0513	.0269
	3	.0137	.0710	.1517	.2215	.2581	.2568	.2254	.1774	.1259	.0806
	4	.0014	.0158	.0536	.1107	.1721	.2201	.2428	.2365	.2060	.1611
	5	.0001	.0025	.0132	.0388	.0803	.1321	.1830	.2207	.2360	.2256
	6	.0000	.0003	.0023	.0097	.0268	.0566	.0985	.1471	.1931	.2256
	7	.0000	.0000	.0003	.0017	.0064	.0173	.0379	.0701	.1128	.1611
	8	.0000	.0000	.0000	.0002	.0011	.0037	.0102	.0234	.0462	.0806
	9	.0000	.0000	.0000	.0000	.0001	.0005	.0018	.0052	.0126	.0269
	10	.0000	.0000	.0000	.0000	.0000	.0000	.0002	.0007	.0021	.0054
	11	.0000	.0000	.0000	.0000	.0000	.0000	.0000	.0000	.0002	.0005
12	0	.5404	.2824	.1422	.0687	.0317	.0138	.0057	.0022	.0008	.0002
	1	.3413	.3766	.3012	.2062	.1267	.0712	.0368	.0174	.0075	.0029
	2	.0988	.2301	.2924	.2835	.2323	.1678	.1088	.0639	.0339	.0161
	3	.0173	.0852	.1720	.2362	.2581	.2397	.1954	.1419	.0923	.0537
	4	.0021	.0213	.0683	.1329	.1936	.2311	.2367	.2128	.1700	.1208
	5	.0002	.0038	.0193	.0532	.1032	.1585	.2039	.2270	.2225	.1934
	6	.0000	.0005	.0040	.0155	.0401	.0792	.1281	.1766	.2124	.2256
	7	.0000	.0000	.0006	.0033	.0115	.0291	.0591	.1009	.1489	.1934
	8	.0000	.0000	.0001	.0005	.0024	.0078	.0199	.0420	.0762	.1208
	9	.0000	.0000	.0000	.0001	.0004	.0015	.0048	.0125	.0277	.0537
	10	.0000	.0000	.0000	.0000	.0000	.0002	.0008	.0025	.0068	.0161
	11	.0000	.0000	.0000	.0000	.0000	.0000	.0001	.0003	.0010	.0029
	12	.0000	.0000	.0000	.0000	.0000	.0000	.0000	.0000	.0001	.0002

n	x	.05	.10	.15	.20	θ .25	.30	.35	.40	.45	.50
13	0	.5133	.2542	.1209	.0550	.0238	.0097	.0037	.0013	.0004	.0001
	1	.3512	.3672	.2774	.1787	.1029	.0540	.0259	.0113	.0045	.0016
	2	.1109	.2448	.2937	.2680	.2059	.1388	.0836	.0453	.0220	.0095
	3	.0214	.0997	.1900	.2457	.2517	.2181	.1651	.1107	.0660	.0349
	4	.0028	.0277	.0838	.1535	.2097	.2337	.2222	.1845	.1350	.0873
	5	.0003	.0055	.0266	.0691	.1258	.1803	.2154	.2214	.1989	.1571
	6	.0000	.0008	.0063	.0230	.0559	.1030	.1546	.1968	.2169	.2095
	7	.0000	.0001	.0011	.0058	.0186	.0442	.0833	.1312	.1775	.2095
	8	.0000	.0000	.0001	.0011	.0047	.0142	.0336	.0656	.1089	.1571
	9	.0000	.0000	.0000	.0001	.0009	.0034	.0101	.0243	.0495	.0873
	10	.0000	.0000	.0000	.0000	.0001	.0006	.0022	.0065	.0162	.0349
	11	.0000	.0000	.0000	.0000	.0000	.0001	.0003	.0012	.0036	.0095
	12	.0000	.0000	.0000	.0000	.0000	.0000	.0000	.0001	.0005	.0016
	13	.0000	.0000	.0000	.0000	.0000	.0000	.0000	.0000	.0000	.0001
14	0	.4877	.2288	.1028	.0440	.0178	.0068	.0024	.0008	.0002	.0001
	1	.3593	.3559	.2539	.1539	.0832	.0407	.0181	.0073	.0027	.0009
	2	.1229	.2570	.2912	.2501	.1802	.1134	.0634	.0317	.0141	.0056
	3	.0259	.1142	.2056	.2501	.2402	.1943	.1366	.0845	.0462	.0222
	4	.0037	.0349	.0998	.1720	.2202	.2290	.2022	.1549	.1040	.0611
	5	.0004	.0078	.0352	.0860	.1468	.1963	.2178	.2066	.1701	.1222
	6	.0000	.0013	.0093	.0322	.0734	.1262	.1759	.2066	.2088	.1833
	7	.0000	.0002	.0019	.0092	.0280	.0618	.1082	.1574	.1952	.2095
	8	.0000	.0000	.0003	.0020	.0082	.0232	.0510	.0918	.1398	.1833
	9	.0000	.0000	.0000	.0003	.0018	.0066	.0183	.0408	.0762	.1222
	10	.0000	.0000	.0000	.0000	.0003	.0014	.0049	.0136	.0312	.0611
	11	.0000	.0000	.0000	.0000	.0000	.0002	.0010	.0033	.0093	.0222
	12	.0000	.0000	.0000	.0000	.0000	.0000	.0001	.0005	.0019	.0056
	13	.0000	.0000	.0000	.0000	.0000	.0000	.0000	.0001	.0002	.0009
	14	.0000	.0000	.0000	.0000	.0000	.0000	.0000	.0000	.0000	.0001
15	0	.4633	.2059	.0874	.0352	.0134	.0047	.0016	.0005	.0001	.0000
	1	.3658	.3432	.2312	.1319	.0668	.0305	.0126	.0047	.0016	.0005
	2	.1348	.2669	.2856	.2309	.1559	.0916	.0476	.0219	.0090	.0032
	3	.0307	.1285	.2184	.2501	.2252	.1700	.1110	.0634	.0318	.0139
	4	.0049	.0428	.1156	.1876	.2252	.2186	.1792	.1268	.0780	.0417
	5	.0006	.0105	.0449	.1032	.1651	.2061	.2123	.1859	.1404	.0916
	6	.0000	.0019	.0132	.0430	.0917	.1472	.1906	.2066	.1914	.1527
	7	.0000	.0003	.0030	.0138	.0393	.0811	.1319	.1771	.2013	.1964
	8	.0000	.0000	.0005	.0035	.0131	.0348	.0710	.1181	.1647	.1964
	9	.0000	.0000	.0001	.0007	.0034	.0116	.0298	.0612	.1048	.1527
	10	.0000	.0000	.0000	.0001	.0007	.0030	.0096	.0245	.0515	.0916
	11	.0000	.0000	.0000	.0000	.0001	.0006	.0024	.0074	.0191	.0417
	12	.0000	.0000	.0000	.0000	.0000	.0001	.0004	.0016	.0052	.0139
	13	.0000	.0000	.0000	.0000	.0000	.0000	.0001	.0003	.0010	.0032
	14	.0000	.0000	.0000	.0000	.0000	.0000	.0000	.0000	.0001	.0005
	15	.0000	.0000	.0000	.0000	.0000	.0000	.0000	.0000	.0000	.0000

n	x	.05	.10	.15	.20	θ .25	.30	.35	.40	.45	.50
16	0	.4401	.1853	.0743	.0281	.0100	.0033	.0010	.0003	.0001	.0000
	1	.3706	.3294	.2097	.1126	.0535	.0228	.0087	.0036	.0009	.0002
	2	.1463	.2745	.2775	.2111	.1336	.0732	.0353	.0150	.0056	.0018
	3	.0359	.1423	.2285	.2463	.2079	.1465	.0888	.0468	.0215	.0085
	4	.0061	.0514	.1311	.2001	.2252	.2040	.1553	.1014	.0572	.0278
	5	.0008	.0137	.0555	.1201	.1802	.2099	.2008	.1623	.1123	.0667
	6	.0001	.0028	.0180	.0550	.1101	.1649	.1982	.1983	.1684	.1222
	7	.0000	.0004	.0045	.0197	.0524	.1010	.1524	.1889	.1969	.1746
	8	.0000	.0001	.0009	.0055	.0197	.0487	.0923	.1417	.1812	.1964
	9	.0000	.0000	.0001	.0012	.0058	.0185	.0442	.0840	.1318	.1746
	10	.0000	.0000	.0000	.0002	.0014	.0056	.0167	.0392	.0755	.1222
	11	.0000	.0000	.0000	.0000	.0002	.0013	.0049	.0142	.0337	.0667
	12	.0000	.0000	.0000	.0000	.0000	.0002	.0011	.0040	.0115	.0278
	13	.0000	.0000	.0000	.0000	.0000	.0000	.0002	.0008	.0029	.0085
	14	.0000	.0000	.0000	.0000	.0000	.0000	.0000	.0001	.0005	.0018
	15	.0000	.0000	.0000	.0000	.0000	.0000	.0000	.0000	.0001	.0002
	16	.0000	.0000	.0000	.0000	.0000	.0000	.0000	.0000	.0000	.0000
17	0	.4181	.1668	.0631	.0225	.0075	.0023	.0007	.0002	.0000	.0000
	1	.3741	.3150	.1893	.0957	.0426	.0169	.0060	.0019	.0005	.0001
	2	.1575	.2800	.2673	.1914	.1136	.0581	.0260	.0102	.0035	.0010
	3	.0415	.1556	.2359	.2393	.1893	.1245	.0701	.0341	.0144	.0052
	4	.9076	.0605	.1457	.2093	.2209	.1868	.1320	.0796	.0411	.0182
	5	.0010	.0175	.0668	.1361	.1914	.2081	.1849	.1379	.0875	.0472
	6	.0001	.0039	.0236	.0680	.1276	.1784	.1991	.1839	.1432	.0944
	7	.0000	.0007	.0065	.0267	.0668	.1201	.1685	.1927	.1841	.1484
	8	.0000	.0001	.0014	.0084	.0279	.0644	.1134	.1606	.1883	.1855
	9	.0000	.0000	.0003	.0021	.0093	.0276	.0611	.1070	.1540	.1855
	10	.0000	.0000	.0000	.0004	.0025	.0095	.0263	.0571	.1008	.1484
	11	.0000	.0000	.0000	.0001	.0005	.0026	.0090	.0242	.0525	.0944
	12	.0000	.0000	.0000	.0000	.0001	.0006	.0024	.0081	.0215	.0472
	13	.0000	.0000	.0000	.0000	.0000	.0001	.0005	.0021	.0068	.0182
	14	.0000	.0000	.0000	.0000	.0000	.0000	.0001	.0004	.0016	.0052
	15	.0000	.0000	.0000	.0000	.0000	.0000	.0000	.0001	.0003	.0010
	16	.0000	.0000	.0000	.0000	.0000	.0000	.0000	.0000	.0000	.0001
	17	.0000	.0000	.0000	.0000	.0000	.0000	.0000	.0000	.0000	.0000
18	0	.3972	.1501	.0536	.0180	.0056	.0016	.0004	.0001	.0000	.0000
	1	.3763	.3002	.1704	.0811	.0338	.0126	.0042	.0012	.0003	.0001
	2	.1683	.2835	.2556	.1723	.0958	.0458	.0190	.0069	.0022	.0006
	3	.0473	.1680	.2406	.2297	.1704	.1046	.0547	.0246	.0095	.0031
	4	.0093	.0700	.1592	.2153	.2130	.1681	.1104	.0614	.0291	.0117
	5	.0014	.0218	.0787	.1507	.1988	.2017	.1664	.1146	.0666	.0327
	6	.0002	.0052	.0301	.0816	.1436	.1873	.1941	.1655	.1181	.0708
	7	.0000	.0010	.0091	.0350	.0820	.1376	.1792	.1892	.1657	.1214
	8	.0000	.0002	.0022	.0120	.0376	.0811	.1327	.1734	.1864	.1669
	9	.0000	.0000	.0004	.0033	.0139	.0386	.0794	.1284	.1694	.1855
	10	.0000	.0000	.0001	.0008	.0042	.0149	.0385	.0771	.1248	.1669
	11	.0000	.0000	.0000	.0001	.0010	.0046	.0151	.0374	.0742	.1214

n	x	.05	.10	.15	.20	θ .25	.30	.35	.40	.45	.50
18	12	.0000	.0000	.0000	.0000	.0002	.0012	.0047	.0145	.0354	.0708
	13	.0000	.0000	.0000	.0000	.0000	.0002	.0012	.0045	.0134	.0327
	14	.0000	.0000	.0000	.0000	.0000	.0000	.0002	.0011	.0039	.0117
	15	.0000	.0000	.0000	.0000	.0000	.0000	.0000	.0002	.0009	.0031
	16	.0000	.0000	.0000	.0000	.0000	.0000	.0000	.0000	.0001	.0006
	17	.0000	.0000	.0000	.0000	.0000	.0000	.0000	.0000	.0000	.0001
	18	.0000	.0000	.0000	.0000	.0000	.0000	.0000	.0000	.0000	.0000
19	0	.3774	.1351	.0456	.0144	.0042	.0011	.0003	.0001	.0000	.0000
	1	.3774	.2852	.1529	.0685	.0268	.0093	.0029	.0008	.0002	.0000
	2	.1787	.2852	.2428	.1540	.0803	.0358	.0138	.0046	.0013	.0003
	3	.0533	.1796	.2428	.2182	.1517	.0869	.0422	.0175	.0062	.0018
	4	.0112	.0798	.1714	.2182	.2023	.1491	.0909	.0467	.0203	.0074
	5	.0018	.0266	.0907	.1636	.2023	.1916	.1468	.0933	.0497	.0222
	6	.0002	.0069	.0374	.0955	.1574	.1916	.1844	.1451	.0949	.0518
	7	.0000	.0014	.0122	.0443	.0974	.1525	.1844	.1797	.1443	.0961
	8	.0000	.0002	.0032	.0166	.0487	.0981	.1489	.1797	.1771	.1442
	9	.0000	.0000	.0007	.0051	.0198	.0514	.0980	.1464	.1771	.1762
	10	.0000	.0000	.0001	.0013	.0066	.0220	.0528	.0976	.1449	.1762
	11	.0000	.0000	.0000	.0003	.0018	.0077	.0233	.0532	.0970	.1442
	12	.0000	.0000	.0000	.0000	.0004	.0022	.0083	.0237	.0529	.0961
	13	.0000	.0000	.0000	.0000	.0001	.0005	.0024	.0085	.0233	.0518
	14	.0000	.0000	.0000	.0000	.0000	.0001	.0006	.0024	.0082	.0222
	15	.0000	.0000	.0000	.0000	.0000	.0000	.0001	.0005	.0022	.0074
	16	.0000	.0000	.0000	.0000	.0000	.0000	.0000	.0001	.0005	.0018
	17	.0000	.0000	.0000	.0000	.0000	.0000	.0000	.0000	.0001	.0003
	18	.0000	.0000	.0000	.0000	.0000	.0000	.0000	.0000	.0000	.0000
	19	.0000	.0000	.0000	.0000	.0000	.0000	.0000	.0000	.0000	.0000
20	0	.3585	.1216	.0388	.0115	.0032	.0008	.0002	.0000	.0000	.0000
	1	.3774	.2702	.1368	.0576	.0211	.0068	.0020	.0005	.0001	.0000
	2	.1887	.2852	.2293	.1369	.0669	.0278	.0100	.0031	.0008	.0002
	3	.0596	.1901	.2428	.2054	.1339	.0716	.0323	.0123	.0040	.0011
	4	.0133	.0898	.1821	.2182	.1897	.1304	.0738	.0350	.0139	.0046
	5	.0022	.0319	.1028	.1746	.2023	.1789	.1272	.0746	.0365	.0148
	6	.0003	.0089	.0454	.1091	.1686	.1916	.1712	.1244	.0746	.0370
	7	.0000	.0020	.0160	.0545	.1124	.1643	.1844	.1659	.1221	.0739
	8	.0000	.0004	.0046	.0222	.0609	.1144	.1614	.1797	.1623	.1201
	9	.0000	.0001	.0011	.0074	.0271	.0654	.1158	.1597	.1771	.1602
	10	.0000	.0000	.0002	.0020	.0099	.0308	.0686	.1171	.1593	.1762
	11	.0000	.0000	.0000	.0005	.0030	.0120	.0336	.0710	.1185	.1602
	12	.0000	.0000	.0000	.0001	.0008	.0039	.0136	.0355	.0727	.1201
	13	.0000	.0000	.0000	.0000	.0002	.0010	.0045	.0146	.0366	.0739
	14	.0000	.0000	.0000	.0000	.0000	.0002	.0012	.0049	.0150	.0370
	15	.0000	.0000	.0000	.0000	.0000	.0000	.0003	.0013	.0049	.0148
	16	.0000	.0000	.0000	.0000	.0000	.0000	.0000	.0003	.0013	.0046
	17	.0000	.0000	.0000	.0000	.0000	.0000	.0000	.0000	.0002	.0011
	18	.0000	.0000	.0000	.0000	.0000	.0000	.0000	.0000	.0000	.0002
	19	.0000	.0000	.0000	.0000	.0000	.0000	.0000	.0000	.0000	.0000
	20	.0000	.0000	.0000	.0000	.0000	.0000	.0000	.0000	.0000	.0000

Table 2

Cumulative Terms of the Binomial Distribution

For the binomial probability function $f(x;n,\theta)$ the probability of observing x' or more successes is given by

$$\sum_{x=x'}^{n} \binom{n}{x} \theta^x (1 - \theta)^{n-x},$$

This table contains the values of $\displaystyle\sum_{x=x'}^{n} \binom{n}{x} \theta^x (1 - \theta)^{n-x}$ for specified values of n, x', and

θ. If $\theta > 0.5$, the values for $\displaystyle\sum_{x=x'}^{n} \binom{n}{x} \theta^x (1 - \theta)^{n-x}$ are obtained using the corresponding

results obtained from

$$1 - \sum_{x=n-x'+1}^{n} \binom{n}{x} (1 - \theta)^x \theta^{n-x}$$

The cumulative binomial distribution is related to the incomplete beta function as follows:

$$\sum_{x=x'}^{n} \binom{n}{x} \theta^x (1 - \theta)^{n-x} = I_\theta(x', n - x' + 1),$$

$$\sum_{x=0}^{x'-1} \binom{n}{x} \theta^x (1 - \theta)^{n-x} = 1 - I_\theta(x', n - x' + 1)$$

$$= 1 - \int_0^\theta u^{x'-1}(1 - u)^{n-x'} du \Big/ \int_0^1 u^{x'-1}(1 - u)^{n-x'} du.$$

The cumulative binomial distribution is related to the cumulative negative binomial distribution as follows:

$$1 - \sum_{x'=0}^{r-1} \binom{x + r}{x'} \theta^{x'}(1 - \theta)^{x+r-x'} = \sum_{x'=0}^{x} \binom{x' + r - 1}{r - 1} \theta^r (1 - \theta)^{x'}$$

or

$$\sum_{x'=r}^{x+r} \binom{x + r}{x'} \theta^{x'}(1 - \theta)^{x+r-x'} = \sum_{x'=0}^{x} \binom{x' + r - 1}{r - 1} \theta^r (1 - \theta)^{x'}.$$

Source: William H. Beyer, ed. *Handbook of Tables for Probability and Statistics.* Cleveland: The Chemical Rubber Company, 1966. Reprinted by permission of the publishers.

n	x'	.05	.10	.15	.20	θ .25	.30	.35	.40	.45	.50
2	1	.0975	.1900	.2775	.3600	.4375	.5100	.5775	.6400	.6975	.7500
	2	.0025	.0100	.0225	.0400	.0625	.0900	.1225	.1600	.2025	.2500
3	1	.1426	.2710	.3859	.4880	.5781	.6570	.7254	.7840	.8336	.8750
	2	.0072	.0280	.0608	.1040	.1562	.2160	.2818	.3520	.4252	.5000
	3	.0001	.0010	.0034	.0080	.0156	.0270	.0429	.0640	.0911	.1250
4	1	.1855	.3439	.4780	.5904	.6836	.7599	.8215	.8704	.9085	.9375
	2	.0140	.0523	.1095	.1808	.2617	.3483	.4370	.5248	.6090	.6875
	3	.0005	.0037	.0120	.0272	.0508	.0837	.1265	.1792	.2415	.3125
	4	.0000	.0001	.0005	.0016	.0039	.0081	.0150	.0256	.0410	.0625
5	1	.2262	.4095	.5563	.6723	.7627	.8319	.8840	.9222	.9497	.9688
	2	.0226	.0815	.1648	.2627	.3672	.4718	.5716	.6630	.7438	.8125
	3	.0012	.0086	.0266	.0579	.1035	.1631	.2352	.3174	.4069	.5000
	4	.0000	.0005	.0022	.0067	.0156	.0308	.0540	.0870	.1312	.1875
	5	.0000	.0000	.0001	.0003	.0010	.0024	.0053	.0102	.0185	.0312
6	1	.2649	.4686	.6229	.7379	.8220	.8824	.9246	.9533	.9723	.9844
	2	.0328	.1143	.2235	.3447	.4661	.5798	.6809	.7667	.8364	.8906
	3	.0022	.0158	.0473	.0989	.1694	.2557	.3529	.4557	.5585	.6562
	4	.0001	.0013	.0059	.0170	.0376	.0705	.1174	.1792	.2553	.3438
	5	.0000	.0001	.0004	.0016	.0046	.0109	.0223	.0410	.0692	.1094
	6	.0000	.0000	.0000	.0001	.0002	.0007	.0018	.0041	.0083	.0156
7	1	.3017	.5217	.6794	.7903	.8665	.9176	.9510	.9720	.9848	.9922
	2	.0444	.1497	.2834	.4233	.5551	.6706	.7662	.8414	.8976	.9375
	3	.0038	.0257	.0738	.1480	.2436	.3529	.4677	.5801	.6836	.7734
	4	.0002	.0027	.0121	.0333	.0706	.1260	.1998	.2898	.3917	.5000
	5	.0000	.0002	.0012	.0047	.0129	.0288	.0556	.0963	.1529	.2266
	6	.0000	.0000	.0001	.0004	.0013	.0038	.0090	.0188	.0357	.0625
	7	.0000	.0000	.0000	.0000	.0001	.0002	.0006	.0016	.0037	.0078
8	1	.3366	.5695	.7275	.8322	.8999	.9424	.9681	.9832	.9916	.9961
	2	.0572	.1869	.3428	.4967	.6329	.7447	.8309	.8936	.9368	.9648
	3	.0058	.0381	.1052	.2031	.3215	.4482	.5722	.6846	.7799	.8555
	4	.0004	.0050	.0214	.0563	.1138	.1941	.2936	.4059	.5230	.6367
	5	.0000	.0004	.0029	.0104	.0273	.0580	.1061	.1737	.2604	.3633
	6	.0000	.0000	.0002	.0012	.0042	.0113	.0253	.0498	.0885	.1445
	7	.0000	.0000	.0000	.0001	.0004	.0013	.0036	.0085	.0181	.0352
	8	.0000	.0000	.0000	.0000	.0000	.0001	.0002	.0007	.0017	.0039
9	1	.3698	.6126	.7684	.8658	.9249	.9596	.9793	.9899	.9954	.9980
	2	.0712	.2252	.4005	.5638	.6997	.8040	.8789	.9295	.9615	.9805
	3	.0084	.0530	.1409	.2618	.3993	.5372	.6627	.7682	.8505	.9102
	4	.0006	.0083	.0339	.0856	.1657	.2703	.3911	.5174	.6386	.7461
	5	.0000	.0009	.0056	.0196	.0489	.0988	.1717	.2666	.3786	.5000
	6	.0000	.0001	.0006	.0031	.0100	.0253	.0536	.0994	.1658	.2539
	7	.0000	.0000	.0000	.0003	.0013	.0043	.0112	.0250	.0498	.0898
	8	.0000	.0000	.0000	.0000	.0001	.0004	.0014	.0038	.0091	.0195
	9	.0000	.0000	.0000	.0000	.0000	.0000	.0001	.0003	.0008	.0020

Linear interpolation will be accurate at most to two decimal places.

n	x′	.05	.10	.15	.20	θ .25	.30	.35	.40	.45	.50
10	1	.4013	.6513	.8031	.8926	.9437	.9718	.9865	.9940	.9975	.9990
	2	.0861	.2639	.4557	.6242	.7560	.8507	.9140	.9536	.9767	.9893
	3	.0115	.0702	.1798	.3222	.4744	.6172	.7384	.8327	.9004	.9453
	4	.0010	.0128	.0500	.1209	.2241	.3504	.4862	.6177	.7340	.8281
	5	.0001	.0016	.0099	.0328	.0781	.1503	.2485	.3669	.4956	.6230
	6	.0000	.0001	.0014	.0064	.0197	.0473	.0949	.1662	.2616	.3770
	7	.0000	.0000	.0001	.0009	.0035	.0106	.0260	.0548	.1020	.1719
	8	.0000	.0000	.0000	.0001	.0004	.0016	.0048	.0123	.0274	.0547
	9	.0000	.0000	.0000	.0000	.0000	.0001	.0005	.0017	.0045	.0107
	10	.0000	.0000	.0000	.0000	.0000	.0000	.0000	.0001	.0003	.0010
11	1	.4312	.6862	.8327	.9141	.9578	.9802	.9912	.9964	.9986	.9995
	2	.1019	.3026	.5078	.6779	.8029	.8870	.9394	.9698	.9861	.9941
	3	.0152	.0896	.2212	.3826	.5448	.6873	.7999	.8811	.9348	.9673
	4	.0016	.0185	.0694	.1611	.2867	.4304	.5744	.7037	.8089	.8867
	5	.0001	.0028	.0159	.0504	.1146	.2103	.3317	.4672	.6029	.7256
	6	.0000	.0003	.0027	.0117	.0343	.0782	.1487	.2465	.3669	.5000
	7	.0000	.0000	.0003	.0020	.0076	.0216	.0501	.0994	.1738	.2744
	8	.0000	.0000	.0000	.0002	.0012	.0043	.0122	.0293	.0610	.1133
	9	.0000	.0000	.0000	.0000	.0001	.0006	.0020	.0059	.0148	.0327
	10	.0000	.0000	.0000	.0000	.0000	.0000	.0002	.0007	.0022	.0059
	11	.0000	.0000	.0000	.0000	.0000	.0000	.0000	.0000	.0002	.0005
12	1	.4596	.7176	.8578	.9313	.9683	.9862	.9943	.9978	.9992	.9998
	2	.1184	.3410	.5565	.7251	.8416	.9150	.9576	.9804	.9917	.9968
	3	.0196	.1109	.2642	.4417	.6093	.7472	.8487	.9166	.9579	.9807
	4	.0022	.0256	.0922	.2054	.3512	.5075	.6533	.7747	.8655	.9270
	5	.0002	.0043	.0239	.0726	.1576	.2763	.4167	.5618	.6956	.8062
	6	.0000	.0005	.0046	.0194	.0544	.1178	.2127	.3348	.4731	.6128
	7	.0000	.0001	.0007	.0039	.0143	.0386	.0846	.1582	.2607	.3872
	8	.0000	.0000	.0001	.0006	.0028	.0095	.0255	.0573	.1117	.1938
	9	.0000	.0000	.0000	.0001	.0004	.0017	.0056	.0153	.0356	.0730
	10	.0000	.0000	.0000	.0000	.0000	.0002	.0008	.0028	.0079	.0193
	11	.0000	.0000	.0000	.0000	.0000	.0000	.0001	.0003	.0011	.0032
	12	.0000	.0000	.0000	.0000	.0000	.0000	.0000	.0000	.0001	.0002
13	1	.4867	.7458	.8791	.9450	.9762	.9903	.9963	.9987	.9996	.9999
	2	.1354	.3787	.6017	.7664	.8733	.9363	.9704	.9874	.9951	.9983
	3	.0245	.1339	.2704	.4983	.6674	.7975	.8868	.9421	.9731	.9888
	4	.0031	.0342	.0967	.2527	.4157	.5794	.7217	.8314	.9071	.9539
	5	.0003	.0035	.0260	.0991	.2060	.3457	.4995	.6470	.7721	.8666
	6	.0000	.0009	.0053	.0300	.0802	.1654	.2841	.4256	.5732	.7095
	7	.0000	.0001	.0013	.0070	.0243	.0624	.1295	.2288	.3563	.5000
	8	.0000	.0000	.0002	.0012	.0056	.0182	.0462	.0977	.1788	.2905
	9	.0000	.0000	.0000	.0002	.0010	.0040	.0126	.0321	.0698	.1334
	10	.0000	.0000	.0000	.0000	.0001	.0007	.0025	.0078	.0203	.0461
	11	.0000	.0000	.0000	.0000	.0000	.0001	.0003	.0013	.0041	.0112
	12	.0000	.0000	.0000	.0000	.0000	.0000	.0000	.0001	.0005	.0017
	13	.0000	.0000	.0000	.0000	.0000	.0000	.0000	.0000	.0000	.0001

n	x'	.05	.10	.15	.20	θ .25	.30	.35	.40	.45	.50
14	1	.5123	.7712	.8972	.9560	.9822	.9932	.9976	.9992	.9998	.9999
	2	.1530	.4154	.6433	.8021	.8990	.9525	.9795	.9919	.9971	.9991
	3	.0301	.1584	.3521	.5519	.7189	.8392	.9161	.9602	.9830	.9935
	4	.0042	.0441	.1465	.3018	.4787	.6448	.7795	.8757	.9368	.9713
	5	.0004	.0092	.0467	.1298	.2585	.4158	.5773	.7207	.8328	.9102
	6	.0000	.0015	.0115	.0439	.1117	.2195	.3595	.5141	.6627	.7880
	7	.0000	.0002	.0022	.0116	.0383	.0933	.1836	.3075	.4539	.6047
	8	.0000	.0000	.0003	.0024	.0103	.0315	.0753	.1501	.2586	.3953
	9	.0000	.0000	.0000	.0004	.0022	.0083	.0243	.0583	.1189	.2120
	10	.0000	.0000	.0000	.0000	.0003	.0017	.0060	.0175	.0426	.0898
	11	.0000	.0000	.0000	.0000	.0000	.0002	.0011	.0039	.0114	.0287
	12	.0000	.0000	.0000	.0000	.0000	.0000	.0001	.0006	.0022	.0065
	13	.0000	.0000	.0000	.0000	.0000	.0000	.0000	.0001	.0003	.0009
	14	.0000	.0000	.0000	.0000	.0000	.0000	.0000	.0000	.0000	.0001
15	1	.5367	.7941	.9126	.9648	.9866	.9953	.9984	.9995	.9999	1.0000
	2	.1710	.4510	.6814	.8329	.9198	.9647	.9858	.9948	.9983	.9995
	3	.0362	.1841	.3958	.6020	.7639	.8732	.9383	.9729	.9893	.9963
	4	.0055	.0556	.1773	.3518	.5387	.7031	.8273	.9095	.9576	.9824
	5	.0006	.0127	.0617	.1642	.3135	.4845	.6481	.7827	.8796	.9408
	6	.0001	.0022	.0168	.0611	.1484	.2784	.4357	.5968	.7392	.8491
	7	.0000	.0003	.0036	.0181	.0566	.1311	.2452	.3902	.5478	.6964
	8	.0000	.0000	.0006	.0042	.0173	.0500	.1132	.2131	.3465	.5000
	9	.0000	.0000	.0001	.0008	.0042	.0152	.0422	.0950	.1818	.3036
	10	.0000	.0000	.0000	.0001	.0008	.0037	.0124	.0338	.0769	.1509
	11	.0000	.0000	.0000	.0000	.0001	.0007	.0028	.0093	.0255	.0592
	12	.0000	.0000	.0000	.0000	.0000	.0001	.0005	.0019	.0063	.0176
	13	.0000	.0000	.0000	.0000	.0000	.0000	.0001	.0003	.0011	.0037
	14	.0000	.0000	.0000	.0000	.0000	.0000	.0000	.0000	.0001	.0005
	15	.0000	.0000	.0000	.0000	.0000	.0000	.0000	.0000	.0000	.0000
16	1	.5599	.8147	.9257	.9719	.9900	.9967	.9990	.9997	.9999	1.0000
	2	.1892	.4853	.7161	.8593	.9365	.9739	.9902	.9967	.9990	.9997
	3	.0429	.2108	.4386	.6482	.8029	.9006	.9549	.9817	.9934	.9979
	4	.0070	.0684	.2101	.4019	.5950	.7541	.8661	.9349	.9719	.9894
	5	.0009	.0170	.0791	.2018	.3698	.5501	.7108	.8334	.9147	.9616
	6	.0001	.0033	.0235	.0817	.1897	.3402	.5100	.6712	.8024	.8949
	7	.0000	.0005	.0056	.0267	.0796	.1753	.3119	.4728	.6340	.7228
	8	.0000	.0001	.0011	.0070	.0271	.0744	.1594	.2839	.4371	.5982
	9	.0000	.0000	.0002	.0015	.0075	.0257	.0671	.1423	.2559	.4018
	10	.0000	.0000	.0000	.0002	.0016	.0071	.0229	.0583	.1241	.2272
	11	.0000	.0000	.0000	.0000	.0003	.0016	.0062	.0191	.0486	.1051
	12	.0000	.0000	.0000	.0000	.0000	.0003	.0013	.0049	.0149	.0384
	13	.0000	.0000	.0000	.0000	.0000	.0000	.0002	.0009	.0035	.0106
	14	.0000	.0000	.0000	.0000	.0000	.0000	.0000	.0001	.0006	.0021
	15	.0000	.0000	.0000	.0000	.0000	.0000	.0000	.0000	.0001	.0003
	16	.0000	.0000	.0000	.0000	.0000	.0000	.0000	.0000	.0000	.0000

n	x′	.05	.10	.15	.20	θ .25	.30	.35	.40	.45	.50
17	1	.5819	.8332	.9369	.9775	.9925	.9977	.9993	.9998	1.0000	1.0000
	2	.2078	.5182	.7475	.8818	.9499	.9807	.9933	.9979	.9994	.9999
	3	.0503	.2382	.4802	.6904	.8363	.9226	.9673	.9877	.9959	.9988
	4	.0088	.0826	.2444	.4511	.6470	.7981	.8972	.9536	.9816	.9936
	5	.0012	.0221	.0987	.2418	.4261	.6113	.7652	.8740	.9404	.9755
	6	.0001	.0047	.0319	.1057	.2347	.4032	.5803	.7361	.8529	.9283
	7	.0000	.0008	.0083	.0377	.1071	.2248	.3812	.5522	.7098	.8338
	8	.0000	.0001	.0017	.0109	.0402	.1046	.2128	.3595	.5257	.6855
	9	.0000	.0000	.0003	.0026	.0124	.0403	.0994	.1989	.3374	.5000
	10	.0000	.0000	.0000	.0005	.0031	.0127	.0383	.0919	.1834	.3145
	11	.0000	.0000	.0000	.0001	.0006	.0032	.0120	.0348	.0826	.1662
	12	.0000	.0000	.0000	.0000	.0001	.0007	.0030	.0106	.0301	.0717
	13	.0000	.0000	.0000	.0000	.0000	.0001	.0006	.0025	.0086	.0245
	14	.0000	.0000	.0000	.0000	.0000	.0000	.0000	.0005	.0019	.0064
	15	.0000	.0000	.0000	.0000	.0000	.0000	.0000	.0001	.0003	.0012
	16	.0000	.0000	.0000	.0000	.0000	.0000	.0000	.0000	.0000	.0001
	17	.0000	.0000	.0000	.0000	.0000	.0000	.0000	.0000	.0000	.0000
18	1	.6028	.8499	.9464	.9820	.9944	.9984	.9996	.9999	1.0000	1.0000
	2	.2265	.5497	.7759	.9009	.9605	.9858	.9954	.9987	.9997	.9999
	3	.0581	.2662	.5203	.7287	.8647	.9400	.9764	.9918	.9975	.9993
	4	.0109	.0982	.2798	.4990	.6943	.8354	.9217	.9672	.9880	.9962
	5	.0015	.0282	.1206	.2836	.4813	.6673	.8114	.9058	.9589	.9846
	6	.0002	.0064	.0419	.1329	.2825	.4656	.6450	.7912	.8923	.9519
	7	.0000	.0012	.0118	.0513	.1390	.2783	.4509	.6257	.7742	.8811
	8	.0000	.0002	.0027	.0163	.0569	.1407	.2717	.4366	.6085	.7597
	9	.0000	.0000	.0005	.0043	.0193	.0596	.1391	.2632	.4222	.5927
	10	.0000	.0000	.0001	.0009	.0054	.0210	.0597	.1347	.2527	.4073
	11	.0000	.0000	.0000	.0002	.0012	.0061	.0212	.0576	.1280	.2403
	12	.0000	.0000	.0000	.0000	.0002	.0014	.0062	.0203	.0537	.1189
	13	.0000	.0000	.0000	.0000	.0000	.0003	.0014	.0058	.0183	.0481
	14	.0000	.0000	.0000	.0000	.0000	.0000	.0003	.0013	.0049	.0154
	15	.0000	.0000	.0000	.0000	.0000	.0000	.0000	.0002	.0010	.0038
	16	.0000	.0000	.0000	.0000	.0000	.0000	.0000	.0000	.0001	.0007
	17	.0000	.0000	.0000	.0000	.0000	.0000	.0000	.0000	.0000	.0001
	18	.0000	.0000	.0000	.0000	.0000	.0000	.0000	.0000	.0000	.0000
19	1	.6226	.8649	.9544	.9856	.9958	.9989	.9997	.9999	1.0000	1.0000
	2	.2453	.5797	.8015	.9171	.9690	.9896	.9969	.9992	.9998	1.0000
	3	.0665	.2946	.5587	.7631	.8887	.9538	.9830	.9945	.9985	.9996
	4	.0132	.1150	.3159	.5449	.7369	.8668	.9409	.9770	.9923	.9978
	5	.0020	.0352	.1444	.3267	.5346	.7178	.8500	.9304	.9720	.9904
	6	.0002	.0086	.0537	.1631	.3322	.5261	.7032	.8371	.9223	.9682
	7	.0000	.0017	.0163	.0676	.1749	.3345	.5188	.6919	.8273	.9165
	8	.0000	.0003	.0041	.0233	.0775	.1820	.3344	.5122	.6831	.8204
	9	.0000	.0000	.0008	.0067	.0287	.0839	.1855	.3325	.5060	.6762
	10	.0000	.0000	.0001	.0016	.0089	.0326	.0875	.1861	.3290	.5000

						θ					
n	x'	.05	.10	.15	.20	.25	.30	.35	.40	.45	.50
19	11	.0000	.0000	.0000	.0003	.0023	.0105	.0347	.0885	.1841	.3238
	12	.0000	.0000	.0000	.0000	.0005	.0028	.0114	.0352	.0871	.1796
	13	.0000	.0000	.0000	.0000	.0001	.0006	.0031	.0116	.0342	.0835
	14	.0000	.0000	.0000	.0000	.0000	.0001	.0007	.0031	.0109	.0318
	15	.0000	.0000	.0000	.0000	.0000	.0000	.0001	.0006	.0028	.0096
	16	.0000	.0000	.0000	.0000	.0000	.0000	.0000	.0001	.0005	.0022
	17	.0000	.0000	.0000	.0000	.0000	.0000	.0000	.0000	.0001	.0004
	18	.0000	.0000	.0000	.0000	.0000	.0000	.0000	.0000	.0000	.0000
	19	.0000	.0000	.0000	.0000	.0000	.0000	.0000	.0000	.0000	.0000
20	1	.6415	.8784	.9612	.9885	.9968	.9992	.9998	1.0000	1.0000	1.0000
	2	.2642	.6083	.8244	.9308	.9757	.9924	.9979	.9995	.9999	1.0000
	3	.0755	.3231	.5951	.7939	.9087	.9645	.9879	.9964	.9991	.9998
	4	.0159	.1330	.3523	.5886	.7748	.8929	.9556	.9840	.9951	.9987
	5	.0026	.0432	.1702	.3704	.5852	.7625	.8818	.9490	.9811	.9941
	6	.0003	.0113	.0673	.1958	.3828	.5836	.7546	.8744	.9447	.9793
	7	.0000	.0024	.0219	.0867	.2142	.3920	.5834	.7500	.8701	.9423
	8	.0000	.0004	.0059	.0321	.1018	.2277	.3990	.5841	.7480	.8684
	9	.0000	.0001	.0013	.0100	.0409	.1133	.2376	.4044	.5857	.7483
	10	.0000	.0000	.0002	.0026	.0139	.0480	.1218	.2447	.4086	.5881
	11	.0000	.0000	.0000	.0006	.0039	.0171	.0532	.1275	.2493	.4119
	12	.0000	.0000	.0000	.0001	.0009	.0051	.0196	.0565	.1308	.2517
	13	.0000	.0000	.0000	.0000	.0002	.0013	.0060	.0210	.0580	.1316
	14	.0000	.0000	.0000	.0000	.0000	.0003	.0015	.0065	.0214	.0577
	15	.0000	.0000	.0000	.0000	.0000	.0000	.0003	.0016	.0064	.0207
	16	.0000	.0000	.0000	.0000	.0000	.0000	.0000	.0003	.0015	.0059
	17	.0000	.0000	.0000	.0000	.0000	.0000	.0000	.0000	.0003	.0013
	18	.0000	.0000	.0000	.0000	.0000	.0000	.0000	.0000	.0000	.0002
	19	.0000	.0000	.0000	.0000	.0000	.0000	.0000	.0000	.0000	.0000
	20	.0000	.0000	.0000	.0000	.0000	.0000	.0000	.0000	.0000	.0000
21	1	.6594	.8906	.9671	.9908	.9976	.9994	.9999	1.0000	1.0000	1.0000
	2	.2830	.6353	.8450	.9424	.9810	.9944	.9996	.9997	.9999	1.0000
	3	.0849	.3516	.6295	.8213	.9255	.9729	.9914	.9976	.9994	.9999
	4	.0189	.1520	.3887	.6296	.8083	.9144	.9669	.9890	.9969	.9993
	5	.0032	.0522	.1975	.4140	.6326	.8016	.9076	.9630	.9874	.9967
	6	.0004	.0144	.0827	.2307	.4334	.6373	.7991	.9043	.9611	.9867
	7	.0000	.0033	.0287	.1085	.2564	.4495	.6433	.7998	.9036	.9608
	8	.0000	.0006	.0083	.0431	.1299	.2770	.4635	.6505	.8029	.9054
	9	.0000	.0001	.0020	.0144	.0561	.1477	.2941	.4763	.6587	.8083
	10	.0000	.0000	.0004	.0041	.0206	.0676	.1632	.3086	.4883	.6682
	11	.0000	.0000	.0001	.0010	.0064	.0264	.0772	.1744	.3210	.5000
	12	.0000	.0000	.0000	.0002	.0017	.0087	.0313	.0849	.1841	.3318
	13	.0000	.0000	.0000	.0000	.0004	.0024	.0108	.0352	.0908	.1917
	14	.0000	.0000	.0000	.0000	.0001	.0006	.0031	.0123	.0379	.0946
	15	.0000	.0000	.0000	.0000	.0000	.0001	.0007	.0036	.0132	.0392
	16	.0000	.0000	.0000	.0000	.0000	.0000	.0001	.0008	.0037	.0133
	17	.0000	.0000	.0000	.0000	.0000	.0000	.0000	.0002	.0008	.0036
	18	.0000	.0000	.0000	.0000	.0000	.0000	.0000	.0000	.0001	.0007
	19	.0000	.0000	.0000	.0000	.0000	.0000	.0000	.0000	.0000	.0001

Table 3

Individual Terms of the Poisson Distribution

The Poisson probability function is given by

$$f(x;\lambda) = \frac{\lambda^x e^{-\lambda}}{x!}, \qquad \lambda > 0, \, x = 0, 1, 2, \ldots \ .$$

This table contains the individual terms of $f(x;\lambda)$ for specified values of x and λ.

Source: William H. Beyer, ed, *Handbook of Tables for Probability and Statistics.* Cleveland: The Chemical Rubber Company, 1966. Reprinted by permission of the publisher.

x	0.1	0.2	0.3	0.4	λ 0.5	0.6	0.7	0.8	0.9	1.0
0	.9048	.8187	.7408	.6703	.6065	.5488	.4966	.4493	.4066	.3679
1	.0905	.1637	.2222	.2681	.3033	.3293	.3476	.3595	.3659	.3679
2	.0045	.0164	.0333	.0536	.0758	.0988	.1217	.1438	.1647	.1839
3	.0002	.0011	.0033	.0072	.0126	.0198	.0284	.0383	.0494	.0613
4	.0000	.0001	.0003	.0007	.0016	.0030	.0050	.0077	.0111	.0153
5	.0000	.0000	.0000	.0001	.0002	.0004	.0007	.0012	.0020	.0031
6	.0000	.0000	.0000	.0000	.0000	.0000	.0001	.0002	.0003	.0005
7	.0000	.0000	.0000	.0000	.0000	.0000	.0000	.0000	.0000	.0001

x	1.1	1.2	1.3	1.4	λ 1.5	1.6	1.7	1.8	1.9	2.0
0	.3329	.3012	.2725	.2466	.2231	.2019	.1827	.1653	.1496	.1353
1	.3662	.3614	.3543	.3452	.3347	.3230	.3106	.2975	.2842	.2707
2	.2014	.2169	.2303	.2417	.2510	.2584	.2640	.2678	.2700	.2707
3	.0738	.0867	.0998	.1128	.1255	.1378	.1496	.1607	.1710	.1804
4	.0203	.0260	.0324	.0395	.0471	.0551	.0636	.0723	.0812	.0902
5	.0045	.0062	.0084	.0111	.0141	.0176	.0216	.0260	.0309	.0361
6	.0008	.0012	.0018	.0026	.0035	.0047	.0061	.0078	.0098	.0120
7	.0001	.0002	.0003	.0005	.0008	.0011	.0015	.0020	.0027	.0034
8	.0000	.0000	.0001	.0001	.0001	.0002	.0003	.0005	.0006	.0009
9	.0000	.0000	.0000	.0000	.0000	.0000	.0001	.0001	.0001	.0002

x	2.1	2.2	2.3	2.4	λ 2.5	2.6	2.7	2.8	2.9	3.0
0	.1225	.1108	.1003	.0907	.0821	.0743	.0672	.0608	.0550	.0498
1	.2572	.2438	.2306	.2177	.2052	.1931	.1815	.1703	.1596	.1494
2	.2700	.2681	.2652	.2613	.2565	.2510	.2450	.2384	.2314	.2240
3	.1890	.1966	.2033	.2090	.2138	.2176	.2205	.2225	.2237	.2240
4	.0992	.1082	.1169	.1254	.1336	.1414	.1488	.1557	.1622	.1680
5	.0417	.0476	.0538	.0602	.0668	.0735	.0804	.0872	.0940	.1008
6	.0146	.0174	.0206	.0241	.0278	.0319	.0362	.0407	.0455	.0504
7	.0044	.0055	.0068	.0083	.0099	.0118	.0139	.0163	.0188	.0216
8	.0011	.0015	.0019	.0025	.0031	.0038	.0047	.0057	.0068	.0081
9	.0003	.0004	.0005	.0007	.0009	.0011	.0014	.0018	.0022	.0027
10	.0001	.0001	.0001	.0002	.0002	.0003	.0004	.0005	.0006	.0008
11	.0000	.0000	.0000	.0000	.0000	.0001	.0001	.0001	.0002	.0002
12	.0000	.0000	.0000	.0000	.0000	.0000	.0000	.0000	.0000	.0001

x	3.1	3.2	3.3	3.4	λ 3.5	3.6	3.7	3.8	3.9	4.0
0	.0450	.0408	.0369	.0334	.0302	.0273	.0247	.0224	.0202	.0183
1	.1397	.1304	.1217	.1135	.1057	.0984	.0915	.0850	.0789	.0733
2	.2165	.2087	.2008	.1929	.1850	.1771	.1692	.1615	.1539	.1465
3	.2237	.2226	.2209	.2186	.2158	2125	.2087	.2046	.2001	.1954
4	.1734	.1781	.1823	.1858	.1888	.1912	.1931	.1944	.1951	.1954
5	.1075	.1140	.1203	.1264	.1322	.1377	.1429	.1477	.1522	.1563
6	.0555	.0608	.0662	.0716	.0771	.0826	.0881	.0936	.0989	.1042
7	.0246	.0278	.0312	.0348	.0385	.0425	.0466	.0508	.0551	.0595
8	.0095	.0111	.0129	.0148	.0169	.0191	.0215	.0241	.0269	.0298
9	.0033	.0040	.0047	.0056	.0066	.0076	.0089	.0102	.0116	.0132

x	3.1	3.2	3.3	3.4	3.5	3.6	3.7	3.8	3.9	4.0
10	.0010	.0013	.0016	.0019	.0023	.0028	.0033	.0039	.0045	.0053
11	.0003	.0004	.0005	.0006	.0007	.0009	.0011	.0013	.0016	.0019
12	.0001	.0001	.0001	.0002	.0002	.0003	.0003	.0004	.0005	.0006
13	.0000	.0000	.0000	.0000	.0001	.0001	.0001	.0001	.0002	.0002
14	.0000	.0000	.0000	.0000	.0000	.0000	.0000	.0000	.0000	.0001

x	4.1	4.2	4.3	4.4	4.5	4.6	4.7	4.8	4.9	5.0
0	.0166	.0150	.0136	.0123	.0111	.0101	.0091	.0082	.0074	.0067
1	.0679	.0630	.0583	.0540	.0500	.0462	.0427	.0395	.0365	.0337
2	.1393	.1323	.1254	.1188	.1125	.1063	.1005	.0948	.0894	.0842
3	.1904	.1852	.1798	.1743	.1687	.1631	.1574	.1517	.1460	.1404
4	.1951	.1944	.1933	.1917	.1898	.1875	.1849	.1820	.1789	.1755
5	.1600	.1633	.1662	.1687	.1708	.1725	.1738	.1747	.1753	.1755
6	.1093	.1143	.1191	.1237	.1281	.1323	.1362	.1398	.1432	.1462
7	.0640	.0686	.0732	.0778	.0824	.0869	.0914	.0959	.1002	.1044
8	.0328	.0360	.0393	.0428	.0463	.0500	.0537	.0575	.0614	.0653
9	.0150	.0168	.0188	.0209	.0232	.0255	.0280	.0307	.0334	.0363
10	.0061	.0071	.0081	.0092	.0104	.0118	.0132	.0147	.0164	.0181
11	.0023	.0027	.0032	.0037	.0043	.0049	.0056	.0064	.0073	.0082
12	.0008	.0009	.0011	.0014	.0016	.0019	.0022	.0026	.0030	.0034
13	.0002	.0003	.0004	.0005	.0006	.0007	.0008	.0009	.0011	.0013
14	.0001	.0001	.0001	.0001	.0002	.0002	.0003	.0003	.0004	.0005
15	.0000	.0000	.0000	.0000	.0001	.0001	.0001	.0001	.0001	.0002

x	5.1	5.2	5.3	5.4	5.5	5.6	5.7	5.8	5.9	6.0
0	.0061	.0055	.0050	.0045	.0041	.0037	.0033	.0030	.0027	.0025
1	.0311	.0287	.0265	.0244	.0225	.0207	.0191	.0176	.0162	.0149
2	.0793	.0746	.0701	.0659	.0618	.0580	.0544	.0509	.0477	.0446
3	.1348	.1293	.1239	.1185	.1133	.1082	.1033	.0985	.0938	.0892
4	.1719	.1681	.1641	.1600	.1558	.1515	.1472	.1428	.1383	.1339
5	.1753	.1748	.1740	.1728	.1714	.1697	.1678	.1656	.1632	.1606
6	.1490	.1515	.1537	.1555	.1571	.1584	.1594	.1601	.1605	.1606
7	.1086	.1125	.1163	.1200	.1234	.1267	.1298	.1326	.1353	.1377
8	.0692	.0731	.0771	.0810	.0849	.0887	.0925	.0962	.0998	.1033
9	.0392	.0423	.0454	.0486	.0519	.0552	.0586	.0620	.0654	.0688
10	.0200	.0220	.0241	.0262	.0285	.0309	.0334	.0359	.0386	.0413
11	.0093	.0104	.0116	.0129	.0143	.0157	.0173	.0190	.0207	.0225
12	.0039	.0045	.0051	.0058	.0065	.0073	.0082	.0092	.0102	.0113
13	.0015	.0018	.0021	.0024	.0028	.0032	.0036	.0041	.0046	.0052
14	.0006	.0007	.0008	.0009	.0011	.0013	.0015	.0017	.0019	.0022
15	.0002	.0002	.0003	.0003	.0004	.0005	.0006	.0007	.0008	.0009
16	.0001	.0001	.0001	.0001	.0001	.0002	.0002	.0002	.0003	.0003
17	.0000	.0000	.0000	.0000	.0000	.0000	.0001	.0001	.0001	.0001

x	6.1	6.2	6.3	6.4	6.5 λ	6.6	6.7	6.8	6.9	7.0
0	.0022	.0020	.0018	.0017	.0015	.0014	.0012	.0011	.0010	.0009
1	.0137	.0126	.0116	.0106	.0098	.0090	.0082	.0076	.0070	.0064
2	.0417	.0390	.0364	.0340	.0318	.0296	.0276	.0258	.0240	.0223
3	.0848	.0806	.0765	.0726	.0688	.0652	.0617	.0584	.0552	.0521
4	.1294	.1249	.1205	.1162	.1118	.1076	.1034	.0992	.0952	.0912
5	.1579	.1549	.1519	.1487	.1454	.1420	.1385	.1349	.1314	.1277
6	.1605	.1601	.1595	.1586	.1575	.1562	.1546	.1529	.1511	.1490
7	.1399	.1418	.1435	.1450	.1462	.1472	.1480	.1486	.1489	.1490
8	.1066	.1099	.1130	.1160	.1188	.1215	.1240	.1263	.1284	.1304
9	.0723	.0757	.0791	.0825	.0858	.0891	.0923	.0954	.0985	.1014
10	.0441	.0469	.0498	.0528	.0558	.0588	.0618	.0649	.0679	.0710
11	.0245	.0265	.0285	.0307	.0330	.0353	.0377	.0401	.0426	.0452
12	.0124	.0137	.0150	.0164	.0179	.0194	.0210	.0227	.0245	.0264
13	.0058	.0065	.0073	.0081	.0089	.0098	.0108	.0119	.0130	.0142
14	.0025	.0029	.0033	.0037	.0041	.0046	.0052	.0058	.0064	.0071
15	.0010	.0012	.0014	.0016	.0018	.0020	.0023	.0026	.0029	.0033
16	.0004	.0005	.0005	.0006	.0007	.0008	.0010	.0011	.0013	.0014
17	.0001	.0002	.0002	.0002	.0003	.0003	.0004	.0004	.0005	.0006
18	.0000	.0001	.0001	.0001	.0001	.0001	.0001	.0002	.0002	.0002
19	.0000	.0000	.0000	.0000	.0000	.0000	.0000	.0001	.0001	.0001

x	7.1	7.2	7.3	7.4	7.5 λ	7.6	7.7	7.8	7.9	8.0
0	.0008	.0007	.0007	.0006	.0006	.0005	.0005	.0004	.0004	.0003
1	.0059	.0054	.0049	.0045	.0041	.0038	.0035	.0032	.0029	.0027
2	.0208	.0194	.0180	.0167	.0156	.0145	.0134	.0125	.0116	.0107
3	.0492	.0464	.0438	.0413	.0389	.0366	.0345	.0324	.0305	.0286
4	.0874	.0836	.0799	.0764	.0729	.0696	.0663	.0632	.0602	.0573
5	.1241	.1204	.1167	.1130	.1094	.1057	.1021	.0986	.0951	.0916
6	.1468	.1445	.1420	.1394	.1367	.1339	.1311	.1282	.1252	.1221
7	.1489	.1486	.1481	.1474	.1465	.1454	.1442	.1428	.1413	.1396
8	.1321	.1337	.1351	.1363	.1373	.1382	.1388	.1392	.1395	.1396
9	.1042	.1070	.1096	.1121	.1144	.1167	.1187	.1207	.1224	.1241
10	.0740	.0770	.0800	.0829	.0858	.0887	.0914	.0941	.0967	.0993
11	.0478	.0504	.0531	.0558	.0585	.0613	.0640	.0667	.0695	.0722
12	.0283	.0303	.0323	.0344	.0366	.0388	.0411	.0434	.0457	.0481
13	.0154	.0168	.0181	.0196	.0211	.0227	.0243	.0260	.0278	.0296
14	.0078	.0086	.0095	.0104	.0113	.0123	.0134	.0145	.0157	.0169
15	.0037	.0041	.0046	.0051	.0057	.0062	.0069	.0075	.0083	.0090
16	.0016	.0019	.0021	.0024	.0026	.0030	.0033	.0037	.0041	.0045
17	.0007	.0008	.0009	.0010	.0012	.0013	.0015	.0017	.0019	.0021
18	.0003	.0003	.0004	.0004	.0005	.0006	.0006	.0007	.0008	.0009
19	.0001	.0001	.0001	.0002	.0002	.0002	.0003	.0003	.0003	.0004
20	.0000	.0000	.0001	.0001	.0001	.0001	.0001	.0001	.0001	.0002
21	.0000	.0000	.0000	.0000	.0000	.0000	.0000	.0000	.0001	.0001

					λ					
x	8.1	8.2	8.3	8.4	8.5	8.6	8.7	8.8	8.9	9.0
0	.0003	.0003	.0002	.0002	.0002	.0002	.0002	.0002	.0001	.0001
1	.0025	.0023	.0021	.0019	.0017	.0016	.0014	.0013	.0012	.0011
2	.0100	.0092	.0086	.0079	.0074	.0068	.0063	.0058	.0054	.0050
3	.0269	.0252	.0237	.0222	.0208	.0195	.0183	.0171	.0160	.0150
4	.0544	.0517	.0491	.0466	.0443	.0420	.0398	.0377	.0357	.0337
5	.0882	.0849	.0816	.0784	.0752	.0722	.0692	.0663	.0635	.0607
6	.1191	.1160	.1128	.1097	.1066	.1034	.1003	.0972	.0941	.0911
7	.1378	.1358	.1338	.1317	.1294	.1271	.1247	.1222	.1197	.1171
8	.1395	.1392	.1388	.1382	.1375	.1366	.1356	.1344	.1332	.1318
9	.1256	.1269	.1280	.1290	.1299	.1306	.1311	.1315	.1317	.1318
10	.1017	.1040	.1063	.1084	.1104	.1123	.1140	.1157	.1172	.1186
11	.0749	.0776	.0802	.0828	.0853	.0878	.0902	.0925	.0948	.0970
12	.0505	.0530	.0555	.0579	.0604	.0629	.0654	.0679	.0703	.0728
13	.0315	.0334	.0354	.0374	.0395	.0416	.0438	.0459	.0481	.0504
14	.0182	.0196	.0210	.0225	.0240	.0256	.0272	.0289	.0306	.0324
15	.0098	.0107	.0116	.0126	.0136	.0147	.0158	.0169	.0182	.0194
16	.0050	.0055	.0060	.0066	.0072	.0079	.0086	.0093	.0101	.0109
17	.0024	.0026	.0029	.0033	.0036	.0040	.0044	.0048	.0053	.0058
18	.0011	.0012	.0014	.0015	.0017	.0019	.0021	.0024	.0026	.0029
19	.0005	.0005	.0006	.0007	.0008	.0009	.0010	.0011	.0012	.0014
20	.0002	.0002	.0002	.0003	.0003	.0004	.0004	.0005	.0005	.0006
21	.0001	.0001	.0001	.0001	.0001	.0002	.0002	.0002	.0002	.0003
22	.0000	.0000	.0000	.0000	.0001	.0001	.0001	.0001	.0001	.0001

					λ					
x	9.1	9.2	9.3	9.4	9.5	9.6	9.7	9.8	9.9	10
0	.0001	.0001	.0001	.0001	.0001	.0001	.0001	.0001	.0001	.0000
1	.0010	.0009	.0009	.0008	.0007	.0007	.0006	.0005	.0005	.0005
2	.0046	.0043	.0040	.0037	.0034	.0031	.0029	.0027	.0025	.0023
3	.0140	.0131	.0123	.0115	.0107	.0100	.0093	.0087	.0081	.0076
4	.0319	.0302	.0285	.0269	.0254	.0240	.0226	.0213	.0201	.0189
5	.0581	.0555	.0530	.0506	.0483	.0460	.0439	.0418	.0398	.0378
6	.0881	.0851	.0822	.0793	.0764	.0736	.0709	.0682	.0656	.0631
7	.1145	.1118	.1091	.1064	.1037	.1010	.0982	.0955	.0928	.0901
8	.1302	.1286	.1269	.1251	.1232	.1212	.1191	.1170	.1148	.1126
9	.1317	.1315	.1311	.1306	.1300	.1293	.1284	.1274	.1263	.1251
10	.1198	.1210	.1219	.1228	.1235	.1241	.1245	.1249	.1250	.1251
11	.0991	.1012	.1031	.1049	.1067	.1083	.1098	.1112	.1125	.1137
12	.0752	.0776	.0799	.0822	.0844	.0866	.0888	.0908	.0928	.0948
13	.0526	.0549	.0572	.0594	.0617	.0640	.0662	.0685	.0707	.0729
14	.0342	.0361	.0380	.0399	.0419	.0439	.0459	.0479	.0500	.0521
15	.0208	.0221	.0235	.0250	.0265	.0281	.0297	.0313	.0330	.0347
16	.0118	.0127	.0137	.0147	.0157	.0168	.0180	.0192	.0204	.0217
17	.0063	.0069	.0075	.0081	.0088	.0095	.0103	.0111	.0119	.0128
18	.0032	.0035	.0039	.0042	.0046	.0051	.0055	.0060	.0065	.0071
19	.0015	.0017	.0019	.0021	.0023	.0026	.0028	.0031	.0034	.0037

					λ					
x	9.1	9.2	9.3	9.4	9.5	9.6	9.7	9.8	9.9	10
20	.0007	.0008	.0009	.0010	.0011	.0012	.0014	.0015	.0017	.0019
21	.0003	.0003	.0004	0004	.0005	.0006	.0006	.0007	.0008	.0009
22	.0001	.0001	.0002	.0002	.0002	.0002	.0003	.0003	.0004	.0004
23	.0000	.0001	.0001	.0001	.0001	.0001	.0001	.0001	.0002	.0002
24	.0000	.0000	.0000	.0000	.0000	.0000	.0000	.0001	.0001	.0001

					λ					
x	11	12	13	14	15	16	17	18	19	20
0	.0000	.0000	.0000	.0000	.0000	.0000	.0000	.0000	.0000	.0000
1	.0002	.0001	.0000	.0000	.0000	.0000	.0000	.0000	.0000	.0000
2	.0010	.0004	.0002	.0001	.0000	.0000	.0000	.0000	.0000	.0000
3	.0037	.0018	.0008	.0004	.0002	.0001	.0000	.0000	.0000	.0000
4	.0102	.0053	.0027	.0013	.0006	.0003	.0001	.0001	.0000	.0000
5	.0224	.0127	.0070	.0037	.0019	.0010	.0005	.0002	.0001	.0001
6	.0411	.0255	.0152	.0087	.0048	.0026	.0014	.0007	.0004	.0002
7	.0646	.0437	.0281	.0174	.0104	.0060	.0034	.0018	.0010	.0005
8	.0888	.0655	.0457	.0304	.0194	.0120	.0072	.0042	.0024	.0013
9	.1085	.0874	.0661	.0473	.0324	.0213	.0135	.0083	.0050	.0029
10	.1194	.1048	.0859	.0663	.0486	.0341	.0230	.0150	.0095	.0058
11	.1194	.1144	.1015	.0844	.0663	.0496	.0355	.0245	.0164	.0106
12	.1094	.1144	.1099	.0984	.0829	.0661	.0504	.0368	.0259	.0176
13	.0926	.1056	.1099	.1060	.0956	.0814	.0658	.0509	.0378	.0271
14	.0728	.0905	.1021	.1060	.1024	.0930	.0800	.0655	.0514	.0387
15	.0534	.0724	.0885	.0989	.1024	.0992	.0906	.0786	.0650	.0516
16	.0367	.0543	.0719	.0866	.0960	.0992	.0963	.0884	.0772	.0646
17	.0237	.0383	.0550	.0713	.0847	.0934	.0963	.0936	.0863	.0760
18	.0145	.0256	.0397	.0554	.0706	.0830	.0909	.0936	.0911	.0844
19	.0084	.0161	.0272	.0409	.0557	.0699	.0814	.0887	.0911	.0888
20	.0046	.0097	.0177	.0286	.0418	.0559	.0692	.0798	.0866	.0888
21	.0024	.0055	.0109	.0191	.0299	.0426	.0560	.0684	.0783	.0846
22	.0012	.0030	.0065	.0121	.0204	.0310	.0433	.0560	.0676	.0769
23	.0006	.0016	.0037	.0074	.0133	.0216	.0320	.0438	.0559	.0669
24	.0003	.0008	.0020	.0043	.0083	.0144	.0226	.0328	.0442	.0557
25	.0001	.0004	.0010	.0024	.0050	.0092	.0154	.0237	.0336	.0446
26	.0000	.0002	.0005	.0013	.0029	.0057	.0101	.0164	.0246	.0343
27	.0000	.0001	.0002	.0007	.0016	.0034	.0063	.0109	.0173	.0254
28	.0000	.0000	.0001	.0003	.0009	.0019	.0038	.0070	.0117	.0181
29	.0000	.0000	.0001	.0002	.0004	.0011	.0023	.0044	.0077	.0125
30	.0000	.0000	.0000	.0001	.0002	.0006	.0013	.0026	.0049	.0083
31	.0000	.0000	.0000	.0000	.0001	.0003	.0007	.0015	.0030	.0054
32	.0000	.0000	.0000	.0000	.0001	.0001	.0004	.0009	.0018	.0034
33	.0000	.0000	.0000	.0000	.0000	.0001	.0002	.0005	.0010	.0020
34	.0000	.0000	.0000	.0000	.0000	.0000	.0001	.0002	.0006	.0012
35	.0000	.0000	.0000	.0000	.0000	.0000	.0000	.0001	.0003	.0007
36	.0000	.0000	.0000	.0000	.0000	.0000	.0000	.0001	.0002	.0004
37	.0000	.0000	.0000	.0000	.0000	.0000	.0000	.0000	.0001	.0002
38	.0000	.0000	.0000	.0000	.0000	.0000	.0000	.0000	.0000	.0001
39	.0000	.0000	.0000	.0000	.0000	.0000	.0000	.0000	.0000	.0001

Table 4

Cumulative Terms of the Poisson Distribution

This table contains the values of

$$\sum_{x=x'}^{\infty} \frac{e^{-\lambda}\lambda^x}{x!}$$

for specified values of x' and λ. The cumulative Poisson distribution and the cumulative chi-square (χ^2) distribution are related as follows:

$$\sum_{x=0}^{x'-1} \frac{e^{-\lambda}\lambda^x}{x!} = 1 - F(\chi^2)$$

$$= \frac{1}{2^{\frac{n}{2}}\Gamma\left(\frac{n}{2}\right)} \int_{\chi^2}^{\infty} x^{\frac{n}{2}-1} e^{-\frac{x}{2}}\, dx$$

where $\lambda = \frac{1}{2}\chi^2$ and $x' = \frac{1}{2}n$.

Source: William H. Beyer, ed. *Handbook of Tables for Probability and Statistics.* Cleveland: The Chemical Rubber Company, 1966. Reprinted by permission of the publisher.

					λ					
x'	0.1	0.2	0.3	0.4	0.5	0.6	0.7	0.8	0.9	1.0
0	1.0000	1.0000	1.0000	1.0000	1.0000	1.0000	1.0000	1.0000	1.0000	1.0000
1	.0952	.1813	.2592	.3297	.3935	.4512	.5034	.5507	.5934	.6321
2	.0047	.0175	.0369	.0616	.0902	.1219	.1558	.1912	.2275	.2642
3	.0002	.0011	.0036	.0079	.0144	.0231	.0341	.0474	.0629	.0803
4	.0000	.0001	.0003	.0008	.0018	.0034	.0058	.0091	.0135	.0190
5	.0000	.0000	.0000	.0001	.0002	.0004	.0008	.0014	.0023	.0037
6	.0000	.0000	.0000	.0000	.0000	.0000	.0001	.0002	.0003	.0006
7	.0000	.0000	.0000	.0000	.0000	.0000	.0000	.0000	.0000	.0001

					λ					
x'	1.1	1.2	1.3	1.4	1.5	1.6	1.7	1.8	1.9	2.0
0	1.0000	1.0000	1.0000	1.0000	1.0000	1.0000	1.0000	1.0000	1.0000	1.0000
1	.6671	.6988	.7275	.7534	.7769	.7981	.8173	.8347	.8504	.8647
2	.3010	.3374	.3732	.4082	.4422	.4751	.5068	.5372	.5663	.5940
3	.0996	.1205	.1429	.1665	.1912	.2166	.2428	.2694	.2963	.3233
4	.0257	.0338	.0431	.0537	.0656	.0788	.0932	.1087	.1253	.1429
5	.0054	.0077	.0107	.0143	.0186	.0237	.0296	.0364	.0441	.0527
6	.0010	.0015	.0022	.0032	.0045	.0060	.0080	.0104	.0132	.0166
7	.0001	.0003	.0004	.0006	.0009	.0013	.0019	.0026	.0034	.0045
8	.0000	.0000	.0001	.0001	.0002	.0003	.0004	.0006	.0008	.0011
9	.0000	.0000	.0000	.0000	.0000	.0000	.0001	.0001	.0002	.0002

					λ					
x'	2.1	2.2	2.3	2.4	2.5	2.6	2.7	2.8	2.9	3.0
0	1.0000	1.0000	1.0000	1.0000	1.0000	1.0000	1.0000	1.0000	1.0000	1.0000
1	.8775	.8892	.8997	.9093	.9179	.9257	.9328	.9392	.9450	.9502
2	.6204	.6454	.6691	.6916	.7127	.7326	.7513	.7689	.7854	.8009
3	.3504	.3773	.4040	.4303	.4562	.4816	.5064	.5305	.5540	.5768
4	.1614	.1806	.2007	.2213	.2424	.2640	.2859	.3081	.3304	.3528
5	.0621	.0725	.0838	.0959	.1088	.1226	.1371	.1523	.1682	.1847
6	.0204	.0249	.0300	.0357	.0420	.0490	.0567	.0651	.0742	.0839
7	.0059	.0075	.0094	.0116	.0142	.0172	.0206	.0244	.0287	.0335
8	.0015	.0020	.0026	.0033	.0042	.0053	.0066	.0081	.0099	.0119
9	.0003	.0005	.0006	.0009	.0011	.0015	.0019	.0024	.0031	.0038
10	.0001	.0001	.0001	.0002	.0003	.0004	.0005	.0007	.0009	.0011
11	.0000	.0000	.0000	.0000	.0001	.0001	.0001	.0002	.0002	.0003
12	.0000	.0000	.0000	.0000	.0000	.0000	.0000	.0000	.0001	.0001

					λ					
x'	3.1	3.2	3.3	3.4	3.5	3.6	3.7	3.8	3.9	4.0
0	1.0000	1.0000	1.0000	1.0000	1.0000	1.0000	1.0000	1.0000	1.0000	1.0000
1	.9550	.9592	.9631	.9666	.9698	.9727	.9753	.9776	.9798	.9817
2	.8153	.8288	.8414	.8532	.8641	.8743	.8838	.8926	.9008	.9084
3	.5988	.6201	.6406	.6603	.6792	.6973	.7146	.7311	.7469	.7619
4	.3752	.3975	.4197	.4416	.4634	.4848	.5058	.5265	.5468	.5665

x'	3.1	3.2	3.3	3.4	λ 3.5	3.6	3.7	3.8	3.9	4.0
5	.2018	.2194	.2374	.2558	.2746	.2936	.3128	.3322	.3516	.3712
6	.0943	.1054	.1171	.1295	.1424	.1559	.1699	.1844	.1994	.2149
7	.0388	.0446	.0510	.0579	.0653	.0733	.0818	.0909	.1005	.1107
8	.0142	.0168	.0198	.0231	.0267	.0308	.0352	.0401	.0454	.0511
9	.0047	.0057	.0069	.0083	.0099	.0117	.0137	.0160	.0185	.0214
10	.0014	.0018	.0022	.0027	.0033	.0040	.0048	.0058	.0069	.0081
11	.0004	.0005	.0006	.0008	.0010	.0013	.0016	.0019	.0023	.0028
12	.0001	.0001	.0002	.0002	.0003	.0004	.0005	.0006	.0007	.0009
13	.0000	.0000	.0000	.0001	.0001	.0001	.0001	.0002	.0002	.0003
14	.0000	.0000	.0000	.0000	.0000	.0000	.0000	.0000	.0001	.0001

x'	4.1	4.2	4.3	4.4	λ 4.5	4.6	4.7	4.8	4.9	5.0
0	1.0000	1.0000	1.0000	1.0000	1.0000	1.0000	1.0000	1.0000	1.0000	1.0000
1	.9834	.9850	.9864	.9877	.9889	.9899	.9909	.9918	.9926	.9933
2	.9155	.9220	.9281	.9337	.9389	.9437	.9482	.9523	.9561	.9596
3	.7762	.7898	.8026	.8149	.8264	.8374	.8477	.8575	.8667	.8753
4	.5858	.6046	.6228	.6406	.6577	.6743	.6903	.7058	.7207	.7350
5	.3907	.4102	.4296	.4488	.4679	.4868	.5054	.5237	.5418	.5595
6	.2307	.2469	.2633	.2801	.2971	.3142	.3316	.3490	.3665	.3840
7	.1214	.1325	.1442	.1564	.1689	.1820	.1954	.2092	.2233	.2378
8	.0573	.0639	.0710	.0786	.0866	.0951	.1040	.1133	.1231	.1334
9	.0245	.0279	.0317	.0358	.0403	.0451	.0503	.0558	.0618	.0681
10	.0095	.0111	.0129	.0149	.0171	.0195	.0222	.0251	.0283	.0318
11	.0034	.0041	.0048	.0057	.0067	.0078	.0090	.0104	.0120	.0137
12	.0011	.0014	.0017	.0020	.0024	.0029	.0034	.0040	.0047	.0055
13	.0003	.0004	.0005	.0007	.0008	.0010	.0012	.0014	.0017	.0020
14	.0001	.0001	.0002	.0002	.0003	.0003	.0004	.0005	.0006	.0007
15	.0000	.0000	.0000	.0001	.0001	.0001	.0001	.0001	.0002	.0002
16	.0000	.0000	.0000	.0000	.0000	.0000	.0000	.0000	.0001	.0001

x'	5.1	5.2	5.3	5.4	λ 5.5	5.6	5.7	5.8	5.9	6.0
0	1.0000	1.0000	1.0000	1.0000	1.0000	1.0000	1.0000	1.0000	1.0000	1.0000
1	.9939	.9945	.9950	.9955	.9959	.9963	.9967	.9970	.9973	.9975
2	.9628	.9658	.9686	.9711	.9734	.9756	.9776	.9794	.9811	.9826
3	.8835	.8912	.8984	.9052	.9116	.9176	.9232	.9285	.9334	.9380
4	.7487	.7619	.7746	.7867	.7983	.8094	.8200	.8300	.8396	.8488
5	.5769	.5939	.6105	.6267	.6425	.6579	.6728	.6873	.7013	.7149
6	.4016	.4191	.4365	.4539	.4711	.4881	.5050	.5217	.5381	.5543
7	.2526	.2676	.2829	.2983	.3140	.3297	.3456	.3616	.3776	.3937
8	.1440	.1551	.1665	.1783	.1905	.2030	.2159	.2290	.2424	.2560
9	.0748	.0819	.0894	.0974	.1056	.1143	.1234	.1328	.1426	.1528

					λ					
x	5.1	5.2	5.3	5.4	5.5	5.6	5.7	5.8	5.9	6.0
10	.0356	.0397	.0441	.0488	.0538	.0591	.0648	.0708	.0772	.0839
11	.0156	.0177	.0200	.0225	.0253	.0282	.0314	.0349	.0386	.0426
12	.0063	.0073	.0084	.0096	.0110	.0125	.0141	.0160	.0179	.0201
13	.0024	.0028	.0033	.0038	.0045	.0051	.0059	.0068	.0078	.0088
14	.0008	.0010	.0012	.0014	.0017	.0020	.0023	.0027	.0031	.0036
15	.0003	.0003	.0004	.0005	.0006	.0007	.0009	.0010	.0012	.0014
16	.0001	.0001	.0001	.0002	.0002	.0002	.0003	.0004	.0004	.0005
17	.0000	.0000	.0000	.0001	.0001	.0001	.0001	.0001	.0001	.0002
18	.0000	.0000	.0000	.0000	.0000	.0000	.0000	.0000	.0000	.0001

					λ					
x'	6.1	6.2	6.3	6.4	6.5	6.6	6.7	6.8	6.9	7.0
0	1.0000	1.0000	1.0000	1.0000	1.0000	1.0000	1.0000	1.0000	1.0000	1.0000
1	.9978	.9980	.9982	.9983	.9985	.9986	.9988	.9989	.9990	.9991
2	.9841	.9854	.9866	.9877	.9887	.9897	.9905	.9913	.9920	.9927
3	.9423	.9464	.9502	.9537	.9570	.9600	.9629	.9656	.9680	.9704
4	.8575	.8658	.8736	.8811	.8882	.8948	.9012	.9072	.9129	.9182
5	.7281	.7408	.7531	.7649	.7763	.7873	.7978	.8080	.8177	.8270
6	.5702	.5859	.6012	.6163	.6310	.6453	.6594	.6730	.6863	.6993
7	.4098	.4258	.4418	.4577	.4735	.4892	.5047	.5201	.5353	.5503
8	.2699	.2840	.2983	.3127	.3272	.3419	.3567	.3715	.3864	.4013
9	.1633	.1741	.1852	.1967	.2084	.2204	.2327	.2452	.2580	.2709
10	.0910	.0984	.1061	.1142	.1226	.1314	.1404	.1498	.1505	.1695
11	.0469	.0514	.0563	.0614	.0668	.0726	.0786	.0849	.0916	.0985
12	.0224	.0250	.0277	.0307	.0339	.0373	.0409	.0448	.0490	.0534
13	.0100	.0113	.0127	.0143	.0160	.0179	.0199	.0221	.0245	.0270
14	.0042	.0048	.0055	.0063	.0071	.0080	.0091	.0102	.0115	.0128
15	.0016	.0019	.0022	.0026	.0030	.0034	.0039	.0044	.0050	.0057
16	.0006	.0007	.0008	.0010	.0012	.0014	.0016	.0018	.0021	.0024
17	.0002	.0003	.0003	.0004	.0004	.0005	.0006	.0007	.0008	.0010
18	.0001	.0001	.0001	.0001	.0002	.0002	.0002	.0003	.0003	.0004
19	.0000	.0000	.0000	.0000	.0001	.0001	.0001	.0001	.0001	.0001

					λ					
x'	7.1	7.2	7.3	7.4	7.5	7.6	7.7	7.8	7.9	8.0
0	1.0000	1.0000	1.0000	1.0000	1.0000	1.0000	1.0000	1.0000	1.0000	1.0000
1	.9992	.9993	.9993	.9994	.9994	.9995	.9995	.9996	.9996	.9997
2	.9933	.9939	.9944	.9949	.9953	.9957	.9961	.9964	.9967	.9970
3	.9725	.9745	.9764	.0781	.9797	.9812	.9826	.9839	.9851	.9862
4	.9233	.9281	.9326	.9368	.9409	.9446	.9482	.9515	.9547	.9576
5	.8359	.8445	.8527	.8605	.8679	.8751	.8819	.8883	.8945	.9004
6	.7119	.7241	.7360	.7474	.7586	.7693	.7797	.7897	.7994	.8088
7	.5651	.5796	.5940	.6080	.6218	.6354	.6486	.6616	.6743	.6866
8	.4162	.4311	.4459	.4607	.4754	.4900	.5044	.5188	.5330	.5470
9	.2840	.2973	.3108	.3243	.3380	.3518	.3657	.3796	.3935	.4075
10	.1798	.1904	.2012	.2123	.2236	.2351	.2469	.2589	.2710	.2834
11	.1058	.1133	.1212	.1293	.1378	.1465	.1555	.1648	.1743	.1841
12	.0580	.0629	.0681	.0735	.0792	.0852	.0915	.0980	.1048	.1119
13	.0297	.0327	.0358	.0391	.0427	.0464	.0504	.0546	.0591	.0638
14	.0143	.0159	.0176	.0195	.0216	.0238	.0261	.0286	.0313	.0342

λ

x'	7.1	7.2	7.3	7.4	7.5	7.6	7.7	7.8	7.9	8.0
15	.0065	.0073	.0082	.0092	.0103	.0114	.0127	.0141	.0156	.0173
16	.0028	.0031	.0036	.0041	.0046	.0052	.0059	.0066	.0074	.0082
17	.0011	.0013	.0015	.0017	.0020	.0022	.0026	.0029	.0033	.0037
18	.0004	.0005	.0006	.0007	.0008	.0009	.0011	.0012	.0014	.0016
19	.0002	.0002	.0002	.0003	.0003	.0004	.0004	.0005	.0006	.0006
20	.0001	.0001	.0001	.0001	.0001	.0001	.0002	.0002	.0002	.0003
21	.0000	.0000	.0000	.0000	.0000	.0000	.0001	.0001	.0001	.0001

λ

x'	8.1	8.2	8.3	8.4	8.5	8.6	8.7	8.8	8.9	9.0
0	1.0000	1.0000	1.0000	1.0000	1.0000	-1.0000	1.0000	1.0000	1.0000	1.0000
1	.9997	.9997	.9998	.9998	.9998	.9998	.9998	.9998	.9999	.9999
2	.9972	.9975	.9977	.9979	.9981	.9982	.9984	.9985	.9987	.9988
3	.9873	.9882	.9891	.9900	.9907	.9914	.9921	.9927	.9932	.9938
4	.9604	.9630	.9654	.9677	.9699	.9719	.9738	.9756	.9772	.9788
5	.9060	.9113	.9163	.9211	.9256	.9299	.9340	.9379	.9416	.9450
6	.8178	.8264	.8347	.8427	.8504	.8578	.8648	.8716	.8781	.8843
7	.6987	.7104	.7219	.7330	.7438	.7543	.7645	.7744	.7840	.7932
8	.5609	.5746	.5881	.6013	.6144	.6272	.6398	.6522	.6643	.6761
9	.4214	.4353	.4493	.4631	.4769	.4906	.5042	.5177	.5311	.5443
10	.2959	.3085	.3212	.3341	.3470	.3600	.3731	.3863	.3994	.4126
11	.1942	.2045	.2150	.2257	.2366	.2478	.2591	.2706	.2822	.2940
12	.1193	.1269	.1348	.1429	.1513	.1600	.1689	.1780	.1874	.1970
13	.0687	.0739	.0793	.0850	.0909	.0971	.1035	.1102	.1171	.1242
14	.0372	.0405	.0439	.0476	.0514	.0555	.0597	.0642	.0689	.0739
15	.0190	.0209	.0229	.0251	.0274	.0299	.0325	.0353	.0383	.0415
16	.0092	.0102	.0113	.0125	.0138	.0152	.0168	.0184	.0202	.0220
17	.0042	.0047	.0053	.0059	.0066	.0074	.0082	.0091	.0101	.0111
18	.0018	.0021	.0023	.0027	.0030	.0034	.0038	.0043	.0048	.0053
19	.0008 •	.0009	.0010	.0011	.0013	.0015	.0017	.0019	.0022	.0024
20	.0003	.0003	.0004	.0005	.0005	.0006	.0007	.0008	.0009	.0011
21	.0001	.0001	.0002	.0002	.0002	.0002	.0003	.0003	.0004	.0004
22	.0000	.0000	.0001	.0001	.0001	.0001	.0001	.0001	.0002	.0002
23	.0000	.0000	.0000	.0000	.0000	.0000	0000	.0000	.0001	.0001

λ

x'	9.1	9.2	9.3	9.4	9.5	9.6	9.7	9.8	9.9	10
0	1.0000	1.0000	1.0000	1.0000	1.0000	1.0000	1.0000	1.0000	1.0000	1.0000
1	.9999	.9999	.9999	.9999	.9999	.9999	.9999	.9999	1.0000	1.0000
2	.9989	.9990	.9991	.9991	.9992	.9993	.9993	.9994	.9995	.9995
3	.9942	.9947	.9951	.9955	.9958	.9962	.9965	.9967	.9970	.9972
4	.9802	.9816	.9828	.9840	.9851	.9862	.9871	.9880	.9889	.9897
5	.9483	.9514	.9544	.9571	.9597	.9622	.9645	.9667	.9688	.9707
6	.8902	.8959	.9014	.9065	.9115	.9162	.9207	.9250	.9290	.9329
7	.8022	.8108	.8192	.8273	.8351	.8426	.8498	.8567	.8634	.8699
8	.6877	.6990	.7101	.7208	.7313	.7416	.7515	.7612	.7706	.7798
9	.5574	.5704	.5832	.5958	.6082	.6204	.6324	.6442	.6558	.6672

					λ					
x′	9.1	9.2	9.3	9.4	9.5	9.6	9.7	9.8	9.9	10
10	.4258	.4389	.4521	.4651	.4782	.4911	.5040	.5168	.5295	.5421
11	.3059	.3180	.3301	.3424	.3547	.3671	.3795	.3920	.4045	.4170
12	.2068	.2168	.2270	.2374	.2480	.2588	.2697	.2807	.2919	.3032
13	.1316	.1393	.1471	.1552	.1636	.1721	.1809	.1899	.1991	.2084
14	.0790	.0844	.0900	.0958	.1019	.1081	.1147	.1214	.1284	.1355
15	.0448	.0483	.0520	.0559	.0600	.0643	.0688	.0735	.0784	.0835
16	.0240	.0262	.0285	.0309	.0335	.0362	.0391	.0421	.0454	.0487
17	.0122	.0135	.0148	.0162	.0177	.0194	.0211	.0230	.0249	.0270
18	.0059	.0066	.0073	.0081	.0089	.0098	.0108	.0119	.0130	.0143
19	.0027	.0031	.0034	.0038	.0043	.0048	.0053	.0059	.0065	.0072
20	.0012	.0014	.0015	.0017	.0020	.0022	.0025	.0028	.0031	.0035
21	.0005	.0006	.0007	.0008	.0009	.0010	.0011	.0013	.0014	.0016
22	.0002	.0002	.0003	.0003	.0004	.0004	.0005	.0005	.0006	.0007
23	.0001	.0001	.0001	.0001	.0001	.0002	.0002	.0002	.0003	.0003
24	.0000	.0000	.0000	.0000	.0001	.0001	.0001	.0001	.0001	.0001

					λ					
x′	11	12	13	14	15	16	17	18	19	20
0	1.0000	1.0000	1.0000	1.0000	1.0000	1.0000	1.0000	1.0000	1.0000	1.0000
1	1.0000	1.0000	1.0000	1.0000	1.0000	1.0000	1.0000	1.0000	1.0000	1.0000
2	.9998	.9999	1.0000	1.0000	1.0000	1.0000	1.0000	1.0000	1.0000	1.0000
3	.9988	.9995	.9998	.9999	1.0000	1.0000	1.0000	1.0000	1.0000	1.0000
4	.9951	.9977	.9990	.9995	.9998	.9999	1.0000	1.0000	1.0000	1.0000
5	.9849	.9924	.9963	.9982	.9991	.9996	.9998	.9999	1.0000	1.0000
6	.9625	.9797	.9893	.9945	.9972	.9986	.9993	.9997	.9998	.9999
7	.9214	.9542	.9741	.9858	.9924	.9960	.9979	.9990	.9995	.9997
8	.8568	.9105	.9460	.9684	.9820	.9900	.9946	.9971	.9985	.9992
9	.7680	.8450	.9002	.9379	.9626	.9780	.9874	.9929	.9961	.9979
10	.6595	.7576	.8342	.8906	.9301	.9567	.9739	.9846	.9911	.9950
11	.5401	.6528	.7483	.8243	.8815	.9226	.9509	.9696	.9817	.9892
12	.4207	.5384	.6468	.7400	.8152	.8730	.9153	.9451	.9653	.9786
13	.3113	.4240	.5369	.6415	.7324	.8069	.8650	.9083	.9394	.9610
14	.2187	.3185	.4270	.5356	.6368	.7255	.7991	.8574	.9016	.9339
15	.1460	.2280	.3249	.4296	.5343	.6325	.7192	.7919	.8503	.8951
16	.0926	.1556	.2364	.3306	.4319	.5333	.6285	.7133	.7852	.8435
17	.0559	.1013	.1645	.2441	.3359	.4340	.5323	.6250	.7080	.7789
18	.0322	.0630	.1095	.1728	.2511	.3407	.4360	.5314	.6216	.7030
19	.0177	.0374	.0698	.1174	.1805	.2577	.3450	.4378	.5305	.6186
20	.0093	.0213	.0427	.0765	.1248	.1878	.2637	.3491	.4394	.5297
21	.0047	.0116	.0250	.0479	.0830	.1318	.1945	.2693	.3528	.4409
22	.0023	.0061	.0141	.0288	.0531	.0892	.1385	.2009	.2745	.3563
23	.0010	.0030	.0076	.0167	.0327	.0582	.0953	.1449	.2069	.2794
24	.0005	.0015	.0040	.0093	.0195	.0367	.0633	.1011	.1510	.2125
25	.0002	.0007	.0020	.0050	.0112	.0223	.0406	.0683	.1067	.1568
26	.0001	.0003	.0010	.0026	.0062	.0131	.0252	.0446	.0731	.1122
27	.0000	.0001	.0005	.0013	.0033	.0075	.0152	.0282	.0486	.0779
28	.0000	.0001	.0002	.0006	.0017	.0041	.0088	.0173	.0313	.0525
29	.0000	.0000	.0001	.0003	.0009	.0022	.0050	.0103	.0195	.0343

x'	11	12	13	14	15	16	17	18	19	20
30	.0000	.0000	.0000	.0001	.0004	.0011	.0027	.0059	.0118	.0218
31	.0000	.0000	.0000	.0001	.0002	.0006	.0014	.0033	.0070	.0135
32	.0000	.0000	.0000	.0000	.0001	.0003	.0007	.0018	.0040	.0081
33	.0000	.0000	.0000	.0000	.0000	.0001	.0004	.0010	.0022	.0047
34	.0000	.0000	.0000	.0000	.0000	.0001	.0002	.0005	.0012	.0027
35	.0000	.0000	.0000	.0000	.0000	.0000	.0001	.0002	.0006	.0015
36	.0000	.0000	.0000	.0000	.0000	.0000	.0000	.0001	.0003	.0008
37	.0000	.0000	.0000	.0000	.0000	.0000	.0000	.0001	.0002	.0004
38	.0000	.0000	.0000	.0000	.0000	.0000	.0000	.0000	.0001	.0002
39	.0000	.0000	.0000	.0000	.0000	.0000	.0000	.0000	.0000	.0001
40	.0000	.0000	.0000	.0000	.0000	.0000	.0000	.0000	.0000	.0001

λ

Table 5

Hypergeometric Distribution

The hypergeometric probability function is given by

$$f(x;N,n,k) = \frac{\binom{k}{x}\binom{N-k}{n-x}}{\binom{N}{n}} = \frac{\dfrac{k!}{x!(k-x)!}\dfrac{(N-k)!}{(n-x)!(N-k-n+x)!}}{\dfrac{N!}{n!(N-n)!}}$$

$$= \frac{k!n!}{x!(k-x)!(n-x)!}\frac{(N-k)!(N-n)!}{N!(N-k-n+x)!} \; ,$$

where N = number of items in a finite population consisting of A successes and B failures
  $(A + B = N)$
  n = number of items drawn in sample without replacement, from the N items
  k = number of failures in finite population = B
  x = number of failures in sample .
  $f(x;N,n,k)$ gives the probability of exactly x failures and $n - x$ successes in the sample of n items.

$$F(x;N,n,k) = \sum_{r=0}^{x} \frac{\binom{k}{r}\binom{N-k}{n-r}}{\binom{N}{n}} \; .$$

$F(x;N,n,k)$ gives the probability of x or fewer failures in the sample of n items.

Source: Gerald J. Lieberman and Donald B. Owen. *Tables of the Hypergeometric Probability Distribution.* Stanford, Calif.: Stanford University Press, 1961. Reprinted by permission of the publishers.

$$f(x;N,n,k) = \frac{\binom{k}{x}\binom{N-k}{n-x}}{\binom{N}{n}}, \qquad F(x;N,n,k) = \sum_{r=0}^{x} \frac{\binom{k}{r}\binom{N-k}{n-r}}{\binom{N}{n}}$$

N	n	k	x	F(x)	f(x)	N	n	k	x	F(x)	f(x)
2	1	1	0	0.500000	0.500000	6	2	2	2	1.000000	0.066667
2	1	1	1	1.000000	0.500000	6	3	1	0	0.500000	0.500000
3	1	1	0	0.666667	0.666667	6	3	1	1	1.000000	0.500000
3	1	1	1	1.000000	0.333333	6	3	2	0	0.200000	0.200000
3	2	1	0	0.333333	0.333333	6	3	2	1	0.800000	0.600000
3	2	1	1	1.000000	0.666667	6	3	2	2	1.000000	0.200000
3	2	2	1	0.666667	0.666667	6	3	3	0	0.050000	0.050000
3	2	2	2	1.000000	0.333333	6	3	3	1	0.500000	0.450000
4	1	1	0	0.750000	0.750000	6	3	3	2	0.950000	0.450000
4	1	1	1	1.000000	0.250000	6	3	3	3	1.000000	0.050000
4	2	1	0	0.500000	0.500000	6	4	1	0	0.333333	0.333333
4	2	1	1	1.000000	0.500000	6	4	1	1	1.000000	0.666667
4	2	2	0	0.166667	0.166667	6	4	2	0	0.066667	0.066667
4	2	2	1	0.833333	0.666667	6	4	2	1	0.600000	0.533333
4	2	2	2	1.000000	0.166667	6	4	2	2	1.000000	0.400000
4	3	1	0	0.250000	0.250000	6	4	3	1	0.200000	0.200000
4	3	1	1	1.000000	0.750000	6	4	3	2	0.800000	0.600000
4	3	2	1	0.500000	0.500000	6	4	3	3	1.000000	0.200000
4	3	2	2	1.000000	0.500000	6	4	4	2	0.400000	0.400000
4	3	3	2	0.750000	0.750000	6	4	4	3	0.933333	0.533333
4	3	3	3	1.000000	0.250000	6	4	4	4	1.000000	0.066667
5	1	1	0	0.800000	0.800000	6	5	1	0	0.166667	0.166667
5	1	1	1	1.000000	0.200000	6	5	1	1	1.000000	0.833333
5	2	1	0	0.600000	0.600000	6	5	2	1	0.333333	0.333333
5	2	1	1	1.000000	0.400000	6	5	2	2	1.000000	0.666667
5	2	2	0	0.300000	0.300000	6	5	3	2	0.500000	0.500000
5	2	2	1	0.900000	0.600000	6	5	3	3	1.000000	0.500000
5	2	2	2	1.000000	0.100000	6	5	4	3	0.666667	0.666667
5	3	1	0	0.400000	0.400000	6	5	4	4	1.000000	0.333333
5	3	1	1	1.000000	0.600000	6	5	5	4	0.833333	0.833333
5	3	2	0	0.100000	0.100000	6	5	5	5	1.000000	0.166667
5	3	2	1	0.700000	0.600000	7	1	1	0	0.857143	0.857143
5	3	2	2	1.000000	0.300000	7	1	1	1	1.000000	0.142857
5	3	3	1	0.300000	0.300000	7	2	1	0	0.714286	0.714286
5	3	3	2	0.900000	0.600000	7	2	1	1	1.000000	0.285714
5	3	3	3	1.000000	0.100000	7	2	2	0	0.476190	0.476190
5	4	1	0	0.200000	0.200000	7	2	2	1	0.952381	0.476190
5	4	1	1	1.000000	0.800000	7	2	2	2	1.000000	0.047619
5	4	2	1	0.400000	0.400000	7	3	1	0	0.571429	0.571429
5	4	2	2	0.000000	0.600000	7	3	1	1	1.000000	0.428571
5	4	3	2	0.600000	0.600000	7	3	2	0	0.285714	0.285714
5	4	3	3	1.000000	0.400000	7	3	2	1	0.857143	0.571429
5	4	4	3	0.800000	0.800000	7	3	2	2	1.000000	0.142857
5	4	4	4	1.000000	0.200000	7	3	3	0	0.114286	0.114286
6	1	1	0	0.833333	0.833333	7	3	3	1	0.628571	0.514286
6	1	1	1	1.000000	0.166667	7	3	3	2	0.971428	0.342857
6	2	1	0	0.666667	0.666667	7	3	3	3	1.000000	0.028571
6	2	1	1	1.000000	0.333333	7	4	1	0	0.428571	0.428571
6	2	2	0	0.400000	0.400000	7	4	1	1	1.000000	0.571429
6	2	2	1	0.933333	0.533333	7	4	2	0	0.142857	0.142857

N	n	k	x	F(x)	f(x)	N	n	k	x	F(x)	f(x)
7	4	2	1	0.714286	0.571429	8	3	3	2	0.982143	0.267857
7	4	2	2	1.000000	0.285714	8	3	3	3	1.000000	0.017857
7	4	3	0	0.028571	0.028571	8	4	1	0	0.500000	0.500000
7	4	3	1	0.371429	0.342857	8	4	1	1	1.000000	0.500000
7	4	3	2	0.885714	0.514286	8	4	2	0	0.214286	0.214286
7	4	3	3	1.000000	0.114286	8	4	2	1.	0.785714	0.571429
7	4	4	1	0.114286	0.114286	8	4	2	2	1.000000	0.214286
7	4	4	2	0.628571	0.514286	8	4	3	0	0.071429	0.071429
7	4	4	3	0.971428	0.342857	8	4	3	1	0.500000	0.428571
7	4	4	4	1.000000	0.028571	8	4	3	2	0.928571	0.428571
7	5	1	0	0.285714	0.285714	8	4	3	3	1.000000	0.071429
7	5	1	1	1.000000	0.714286	8	4	4	0	0.014286	0.014286
7	5	2	0	0.047619	0.047619	8	4	4	1	0.242857	0.228571
7	5	2	1	0.523809	0.476190	8	4	4	2	0.757143	0.514286
7	5	2	2	1.000000	0.476190	8	4	4	3	0.985714	0.228571
7	5	3	1	0.142857	0.142857	8	4	4	4	1.000000	0.014286
7	5	3	2	0.714286	0.571429	8	5	1	0	0.375000	0.375000
7	5	3	3	1.000000	0.285714	8	5	1	1	1.000000	0.625000
7	5	4	2	0.285714	0.285714	8	5	2	0	0.107143	0.107143
7	5	4	3	0.857143	0.571429	8	5	2	1	0.642857	0.535714
7	5	4	4	1.000000	0.142857	8	5	2	2	1.000000	0.357143
7	5	5	3	0.476190	0.476190	8	5	3	0	0.017857	0.017857
7	5	5	4	0.952381	0.476190	8	5	3	1	0.285714	0.267857
7	5	5	5	1.000000	0.047619	8	5	3	2	0.821429	0.535714
7	6	1	0	0.142857	0.142857	8	5	3	3	1.000000	0.178571
7	6	1	1	1.000000	0.857143	8	5	4	1	0.071429	0.071429
7	6	2	1	0.285714	0.285714	8	5	4	2	0.500000	0.428571
7	6	2	2	1.000000	0.714286	8	5	4	3	0.928571	0.428571
7	6	3	2	0.428571	0.428571	8	5	4	4	1.000000	0.071429
7	6	3	3	1.000000	0.571429	8	5	5	2	0.178571	0.178571
7	6	4	3	0.571429	0.571429	8	5	5	3	0.714286	0.535714
7	6	4	4	1.000000	0.428571	8	5	5	4	0.982143	0.267857
7	6	5	4	0.714286	0.714286	8	5	5	5	1.000000	0.017857
7	6	5	5	1.000000	0.285714	8	6	1	0	0.250000	0.250000
7	6	6	5	0.857143	0.857143	8	6	1	1	1.000000	0.750000
7	6	6	6	1.000000	0.142857	8	6	2	0	0.035714	0.035714
8	1	1	0	0.875000	0.875000	8	6	2	1	0.464286	0.428571
8	1	1	1	1.000000	0.125000	8	6	2	2	1.000000	0.535714
8	2	1	0	0.750000	0.750000	8	6	3	1	0.107143	0.107143
8	2	1	1	1.000000	0.250000	8	6	3	2	0.642857	0.535714
8	2	2	0	0.535714	0.535714	8	6	3	3	1.000000	0.357143
8	2	2	1	0.964286	0.428571	8	6	4	2	0.214286	0.214286
8	2	2	2	1.000000	0.035714	8	6	4	3	0.785714	0.571429
8	3	1	0	0.625000	0.625000	8	6	4	4	1.000000	0.214286
8	3	1	1	1.000000	0.375000	8	6	5	3	0.357143	0.357143
8	3	2	0	0.357143	0.357143	8	6	5	4	0.892857	0.535714
8	3	2	1	0.892857	0.535714	8	6	5	5	1.000000	0.107143
8	3	2	2	1.000000	0.107143	8	6	6	4	0.535714	0.535714
8	3	3	0	0.178571	0.178571	8	6	6	5	0.964286	0.428571
8	3	3	1	0.714286	0.535714	8	6	6	6	1.000000	0.035714

N	n	k	x	F(x)	f(x)	N	n	k	x	F(x)	f(x)
8	7	1	0	0.125000	0.125000	9	5	3	1	0.404762	0.357143
8	7	1	1	1.000000	0.875000	9	5	3	2	0.880952	0.476190
8	7	2	1	0.250000	0.250000	9	5	3	3	1.000000	0.119048
8	7	2	2	1.000000	0.750000	9	5	4	0	0.007936	0.007936
8	7	3	2	0.375000	0.375000	9	5	4	1	0.166667	0.158730
8	7	3	3	1.000000	0.625000	9	5	4	2	0.642857	0.476190
8	7	4	3	0.500000	0.500000	9	5	4	3	0.960317	0.317460
8	7	4	4	1.000000	0.500000	9	5	4	4	1.000000	0.039683
8	7	5	4	0.625000	0.625000	9	5	5	1	0.039683	0.039683
8	7	5	5	1.000000	0.375000	9	5	5	2	0.357143	0.317460
8	7	6	5	0.750000	0.750000	9	5	5	3	0.833333	0.476190
8	7	6	6	1.000000	0.250000	9	5	5	4	0.992063	0.158730
8	7	7	6	0.875000	0.875000	9	5	5	5	1.000000	0.007936
8	7	7	7	1.000000	0.125000	9	6	1	0	0.333333	0.333333
9	1	1	0	0.888889	0.888889	9	6	1	1	1.000000	0.666667
9	1	1	1	1.000000	0.111111	9	6	2	0	0.083333	0.083333
9	2	1	0	0.777778	0.777778	9	6	2	1	0.583333	0.500000
9	2	1	1	1.000000	0.222222	9	6	2	2	1.000000	0.416667
9	2	2	0	0.583333	0.583333	9	6	3	0	0.011905	0.011905
9	2	2	1	0.972222	0.388889	9	6	3	1	0.226190	0.214286
9	2	2	2	1.000000	0.027778	9	6	3	2	0.761905	0.535714
9	3	1	0	0.666667	0.666667	9	6	3•	3	1.000000	0.238095
9	3	1	1	1.000000	0.333333	9	6	4	1	0.047619	0.047619
9	3	2	0	0.416667	0.416667	9	6	4	2	0.404762	0.357143
9	3	2	1	0.916667	0.500000	9	6	4	3	0.880952	0.476190
9	3	2	2	1.000000	0.083333	9	6	4	4	1.000000	0.119048
9	3	3	0	0.238095	0.238095	9	6	5	2	0.119048	0.119048
9	3	3	1	0.773809	0.535714	9	6	5	3	0.595238	0.476190
9	3	3	2	0.988095	0.214286	9	6	5	4	0.952381	0.357143
9	3	3	3	1.000000	0.011905	9	6	5	5	1.000000	0.047619
9	4	1	0	0.555556	0.555556	9	6	6	3	0.238095	0.238095
9	4	1	1	1.000000	0.444444	9	6	6	4	0.773809	0.535714
9	4	2	0	0.277778	0.277778	9	6	6	5	0.988095	0.214286
9	4	2	1	0.833333	0.555556	9	6	6	6	1.000000	0.011905
9	4	2	2	1.000000	0.166667	9	7	1	0	0.222222	0.222222
9	4	3	0	0.119048	0.119048	9	7	1	1	1.000000	0.777778
9	4	3	1	0.595238	0.476190	9	7	2	0	0.027778	0.027778
9	4	3	2	0.952381	0.357143	9	7	2	1	0.416667	0.388889
9	4	3	3	1.000000	0.047619	9	7	2	2	1.000000	0.583333
9	4	4	0	0.039683	0.039683	9	7	3	1	0.083333	0.083333
9	4	4	1	0.357143	0.317460	9	7	3	2	0.583333	0.500000
9	4	4	2	0.833333	0.476190	9	7	3	3	1.000000	0.416667
9	4	4	3	0.992063	0.158730	9	7	4	2	0.166667	0.166667
9	4	4	4	1.000000	0.007936	9	7	4	3	0.722222	0.555556
9	5	1	0	0.444444	0.444444	9	7	4	4	1.000000	0.277778
9	5	1	1	1.000000	0.555556	9	7	5	3	0.277778	0.277778
9	5	2	0	0.166667	0.166667	9	7	5	4	0.833333	0.555556
9	5	2	1	0.722222	0.555556	9	7	5	5	1.000000	0.166667
9	5	2	2	1.000000	0.277778	9	7	6	4	0.416667	0.416667
9	5	3	0	0.047619	0.047619	9	7	6	5	0.916667	0.500000

N	n	k	x	F(x)	f(x)	N	n	k	x	F(x)	f(x)
9	7	6	6	1.000000	0.083333	10	5	1	0	0.500000	0.500000
9	7	7	5	0.583333	0.583333	10	5	1	1	1.000000	0.500000
9	7	7	6	0.972222	0.388889	10	5	2	0	0.222222	0.222222
9	7	7	7	1.000000	0.027778	10	5	2	1	0.777778	0.555556
9	8	1	0	0.111111	0.111111	10	5	2	2	1.000000	0.222222
9	8	1	1	1.000000	0.888889	10	5	3	0	0.083333	0.083333
9	8	2	1	0.222222	0.222222	10	5	3	1	0.500000	0.416667
9	8	2	2	1.000000	0.777778	10	5	3	2	0.916667	0.416667
9	8	3	2	0.333333	0.333333	10	5	3	3	1.000000	0.083333
9	8	3	3	1.000000	0.666667	10	5	4	0	0.023810	0.023810
9	8	4	3	0.444444	0.444444	10	5	4	1	0.261905	0.238095
9	8	4	4	1.000000	0.555556	10	5	4	2	0.738095	0.476190
9	8	5	4	0.555556	0.555556	10	5	4	3	0.976190	0.238095
9	8	5	5	1.000000	0.444444	10	5	4	4	1.000000	0.023810
9	8	6	5	0.666667	0.666667	10	5	5	0	0.003968	0.003968
9	8	6	6	1.000000	0.333333	10	5	5	1	0.103175	0.099206
9	8	7	6	0.777778	0.777778	10	5	5	2	0.500000	0.396825
9	8	7	7	1.000000	0.222222	10	5	5	3	0.896825	0.396825
9	8	8	7	0.888889	0.888889	10	5	5	4	0.996032	0.099206
9	8	8	8	1.000000	0.111111	10	5	5	5	1.000000	0.003968
10	1	1	0	0.900000	0.900000	10	6	1	0	0.400000	0.400000
10	1	1	1	1.000000	0.100000	10	6	1	1	1.000000	0.600000
10	2	1	0	0.800000	0.800000	10	6	2	0	0.133333	0.133333
10	2	1	1	1.000000	0.200000	10	6	2	1	0.666667	0.533333
10	2	2	0	0.622222	0.622222	10	6	2	2	1.000000	0.333333
10	2	2	1	0.977778	0.355556	10	6	3	0	0.033333	0.033333
10	2	2	2	1.000000	0.022222	10	6	3	1	0.333333	0.300000
10	3	1	0	0.700000	0.700000	10	6	3	2	0.833333	0.500000
10	3	1	1	1.000000	0.300000	10	6	3	3	1.000000	0.166667
10	3	2	0	0.466667	0.466667	10	6	4	0	0.004762	0.004762
10	3	2	1	0.933333	0.466667	10	6	4	1	0.119048	0.114286
10	3	2	2	1.000000	0.066667	10	6	4	2	0.547619	0.428571
10	3	3	0	0.291667	0.291667	10	6	4	3	0.928571	0.380952
10	3	3	1	0.816667	0.525000	10	6	4	4	1.000000	0.071429
10	3	3	2	0.991667	0.175000	10	6	5	1	0.023810	0.023810
10	3	3	3	1.000000	0.008333	10	6	5	2	0.261905	0.238095
10	4	1	0	0.600000	0.600000	10	6	5	3	0.738095	0.476190
10	4	1	1	1.000000	0.400000	10	6	5	4	0.976190	0.238095
10	4	2	0	0.333333	0.333333	10	6	5	5	1.000000	0.023810
10	4	2	1	0.866667	0.533333	10	6	6	2	0.071429	0.071429
10	4	2	2	1.000000	0.133333	10	6	6	3	0.452381	0.380952
10	4	3	0	0.166667	0.166667	10	6	6	4	0.880952	0.428571
10	4	3	1	0.666667	0.500000	10	6	6	5	0.995238	0.114286
10	4	3	2	0.966667	0.300000	10	6	6	6	1.000000	0.004762
10	4	3	3	1.000000	0.033333	10	7	1	0	0.300000	0.300000
10	4	4	0	0.071429	0.071429	10	7	1	1	1.000000	0.700000
10	4	4	1	0.452381	0.380952	10	7	2	0	0.066667	0.066667
10	4	4	2	0.880952	0.428571	10	7	2	1	0.533333	0.466667
10	4	4	3	0.995238	0.114286	10	7	2	2	1.000000	0.466667
10	4	4	4	1.000000	0.004762	10	7	3	0	0.008333	0.008333

Table 6

Negative Binomial Distribution

The negative binomial probability function is given by

$$f(x;r,\theta) = \binom{x + r - 1}{r - 1} \theta^r (1 - \theta)^x, \qquad x = 0, 1, 2, \ldots ;$$

where θ is the probability of success and $1 - \theta$ the probability of failure of a given event. $f(x)$ is the probability that exactly $x + r$ trials will be required to produce r successes. The cumulative distribution is given by

$$F(x;r,\theta) = \sum_{x'=0}^{x} \binom{x' + r - 1}{r - 1} \theta^r (1 - \theta)^{x'} .$$

The cumulative negative binomial distribution is related to the cumulative binomial distribution as follows:

$$\sum_{x'=0}^{x} \binom{x' + r - 1}{r - 1} \theta^r (1 - \theta)^{x'} = \sum_{x'=r}^{x+r} \binom{x + r}{x'} \theta^{x'} (1 - \theta)^{x+r-x'} .$$

NEGATIVE BINOMIAL PROBABILITY AND DISTRIBUTION FUNCTIONS

$$f(x;r,\theta) = \binom{x + r - 1}{r - 1} \theta^r (1 - \theta)^x, \qquad F(x;r,\theta) = \sum_{x'=0}^{x} \binom{x' + r - 1}{r - 1} \theta^r (1 - \theta)^{x'}$$

$\theta = 0.900, r = 1$			$\theta = 0.900, r = 4$		
$x + r$	$f(x)$	$F(x)$	$x + r$	$f(x)$	$F(x)$
1	0.90000	0.9000	4	0.65610	0.6561
2	0.09000	0.9900	5	0.26244	0.9185
			6	0.06561	0.9841
			7	0.01312	0.9973

$\theta = 0.900, r = 2$			$\theta = 0.900, r = 5$		
$x + r$	$f(x)$	$F(x)$	$x + r$	$f(x)$	$F(x)$
2	0.81000	0.8100	5	0.59049	0.5905
3	0.16200	0.9720	6	0.29524	0.8857
4	0.02430	0.9963	7	0.08857	0.9743
			8	0.02067	0.9950

$\theta = 0.900, r = 3$			$\theta = 0.900, r = 6$		
$x + r$	$f(x)$	$F(x)$	$x + r$	$f(x)$	$F(x)$
3	0.72900	0.7290	6	0.53144	0.5314
4	0.21870	0.9477	7	0.31886	0.8503
5	0.04374	0.9914	8	0.11160	0.9619
			9	0.02976	0.9917

Source: William H. Beyer, ed. *Handbook of Tables for Probability and Statistics.* Cleveland: The Chemical Rubber Company, 1966. Reprinted by permission of the publishers.

Table 7

Exponential Functions

Values of e^x, log e^x and e^{-x} where e is the base of the natural system of logarithms 2.71828 . . . and x has values from 0 to 10. Facilitating the solution of exponential equations, these tables also serve as a table of natural or Naperian antilogarithms. For instance, if the logarithm or exponent $x = 3.26$, the corresponding number or value of e^x is 26.050. Its reciprocal e^{-x} is .038388.

Source: William H. Beyer, ed. *Handbook of Tables for Probability and Statistics.* Cleveland: The Chemical Rubber Company, 1966. Published by permission of the publishers.

x	e^x	$Log_{10}\left(e^x\right)$	e^{-x}	x	e^x	$Log_{10}\left(e^x\right)$	e^{-x}
0.00	1.0000	0.00000	1.000000	**0.50**	1.6487	0.21715	0.606531
0.01	1.0101	.00434	0.990050	0.51	1.6653	.22149	.600496
0.02	1.0202	.00869	.980199	0.52	1.6820	.22583	.594521
0.03	1.0305	.01303	.970446	0.53	1.6989	.23018	.588605
0.04	1.0408	.01737	.960789	0.54	1.7160	.23452	.582748
0.05	1.0513	0.02171	0.951229	**0.55**	1.7333	0.23886	0.576950
0.06	1.0618	.02606	.941765	0.56	1.7507	.24320	.571209
0.07	1.0725	.03040	.932394	0.57	1.7683	.24755	.565525
0.08	1.0833	.03474	.923116	0.58	1.7860	.25189	.559898
0.09	1.0942	.03909	.913931	0.59	1.8040	.25623	.554327
0.10	1.1052	0.04343	0.904837	**0.60**	1.8221	0.26058	0.548812
0.11	1.1163	.04777	.895834	0.61	1.8404	.26492	.543351
0.12	1.1275	.05212	.886920	0.62	1.8589	.26926	.537944
0.13	1.1388	.05646	.878095	0.63	1.8776	.27361	.532592
0.14	1.1503	.06080	.869358	0.64	1.8965	.27795	.527292
0.15	1.1618	0.06514	0.860708	**0.65**	1.9155	0.28229	0.522046
0.16	1.1735	.06949	.852144	0.66	1.9348	.28663	.516851
0.17	1.1853	.07383	.843665	0.67	1.9542	.29098	.511709
0.18	1.1972	.07817	.835270	0.68	1.9739	.29532	.506617
0.19	1.2092	.08252	.826959	0.69	1.9937	.29966	.501576
0.20	1.2214	0.08686	0.818731	**0.70**	2.0138	0.30401	0.496585
0.21	1.2337	.09120	.810584	0.71	2.0340	.30835	.491644
0.22	1.2461	.09554	.802519	0.72	2.0544	.31269	.486752
0.23	1.2586	.09989	.794534	0.73	2.0751	.31703	.481909
0.24	1.2712	.10423	.786628	0.74	2.0959	.32138	.477114
0.25	1.2840	0.10857	0.778801	**0.75**	2.1170	0.32572	0.472367
0.26	1.2969	.11292	.771052	0.76	2.1383	.33006	.467666
0.27	1.3100	.11726	.763379	0.77	2.1598	.33441	.463013
0.28	1.3231	.12160	.755784	0.78	2.1815	.33875	.458406
0.29	1.3364	.12595	.748264	0.79	2.2034	.34309	.453845
0.30	1.3499	0.13029	0.740818	**0.80**	2.2255	0.34744	0.449329
0.31	1.3634	.13463	.733447	0.81	2.2479	.35178	.444858
0.32	1.3771	.13897	.726149	0.82	2.2705	.35612	.440432
0.33	1.3910	.14332	.718924	0.83	2.2933	.36046	.436049
0.34	1.4049	.14766	.711770	0.84	2.3164	.36481	.431711
0.35	1.4191	0.15200	0.704688	**0.85**	2.3396	0.36915	0.427415
0.36	1.4333	.15635	.697676	0.86	2.3632	.37349	.423162
0.37	1.4477	.16069	.690734	0.87	2.3869	.37784	.418952
0.38	1.4623	.16503	.683861	0.88	2.4109	.38218	.414783
0.39	1.4770	.16937	.677057	0.89	2.4351	.38652	.410656
0.40	1.4918	0.17372	0.670320	**0.90**	2.4596	0.39087	0.406570
0.41	1.5068	.17806	.663650	0.91	2.4843	.39521	.402524
0.42	1.5220	.18240	.657047	0.92	2.5093	.39955	.398519
0.43	1.5373	.18675	.650509	0.93	2.5345	.40389	.394554
0.44	1.5527	.19109	.644036	0.94	2.5600	.40824	.390628
0.45	1.5683	0.19543	0.637628	**0.95**	2.5857	0.41258	0.386741
0.46	1.5841	.19978	.631284	0.96	2.6117	.41692	.382893
0.47	1.6000	.20412	.625002	0.97	2.6379	.42127	.379083
0.48	1.6161	.20846	.618783	0.98	2.6645	.42561	.375311
0.49	1.6323	.21280	.612626	0.99	2.6912	.42995	.371577
0.50	1.6487	0.21715	0.606531	**1.00**	2.7183	0.43429	0.367879

x	e^x	$Log_{10}\left(e^x\right)$	e^{-x}	x	e^x	$Log_{10}\left(e^x\right)$	e^{-x}
1.00	2.7183	0.43429	0.367879	**1.50**	4.4817	0.65144	0.223130
1.01	2.7456	.43864	.364219	1.51	4.5267	.65578	.220910
1.02	2.7732	.44298	.360595	1.52	4.5722	.66013	.218712
1.03	2.8011	.44732	.357007	1.53	4.6182	.66447	.216536
1.04	2.8292	.45167	.353455	1.54	4.6646	.66881	.214381
1.05	2.8577	0.45601	0.349938	**1.55**	4.7115	0.67316	0.212248
1.06	2.8864	.46035	.346456	1.56	4.7588	.67750	.210136
1.07	2.9154	.46470	.343009	1.57	4.8066	.68184	.208045
1.08	2.9447	.46904	.339596	1.58	4.8550	.68619	.205975
1.09	2.9743	.47338	.336216	1.59	4.9037	.69053	.203926
1.10	3.0042	0.47772	0.332871	**1.60**	4.9530	0.69487	0.201897
1.11	3.0344	.48207	.329559	1.61	5.0028	.69921	.199888
1.12	3.0649	.48641	.326280	1.62	5.0531	.70356	.197899
1.13	3.0957	.49075	.323033	1.63	5.1039	.70790	.195930
1.14	3.1268	.49510	.319819	1.64	5.1552	.71224	.193980
1.15	3.1582	0.49944	0.316637	**1.65**	5.2070	0.71659	0.192050
1.16	3.1899	.50378	.313486	1.66	5.2593	.72093	.190139
1.17	3.2220	.50812	.310367	1.67	5.3122	.72527	.188247
1.18	3.2544	.51247	.307279	1.68	5.3656	.72961	.186374
1.19	3.2871	.51681	.304221	1.69	5.4195	.73396	.184520
1.20	3.3201	0.52115	0.301194	**1.70**	5.4739	0.73830	0.182684
1.21	3.3535	.52550	.298197	1.71	5.5290	.74264	.180866
1.22	3.3872	.52984	.295230	1.72	5.5845	.74699	.179066
1.23	3.4212	.53418	.292293	1.73	5.6407	.75133	.177284
1.24	3.4556	.53853	.289384	1 74	5.6973	75567	175520
1.25	3.4903	0.54287	0.286505	**1.75**	5.7546	0.76002	0.173774
1.26	3.5254	.54721	.283654	1.76	5.8124	.76436	.172045
1.27	3.5609	.55155	.280832	1.77	5.8709	.76870	170333
1.28	3.5966	.55590	.278037	1.78	5.9299	.77304	168638
1.29	3.6328	.56024	.275271	1.79	5.9895	.77739	.166960
1.30	3.6693	0.56458	0.272532	**1.80**	6.0496	0.78173	0.165299
1.31	3.7062	.56893	.269820	1.81	6.1104	.78607	.163654
1.32	3.7434	.57327	.267135	1.82	6.1719	.79042	.162026
1.33	3.7810	.57761	.264477	1.83	6.2339	.79476	.160414
1.34	3.8190	.58195	.261846	1.84	6.2965	79910	.158817
1.35	3.8574	0.58630	0.259240	**1.85**	6.3598	0.80344	0.157237
1.36	3.8962	.59064	.256661	1.86	6.4237	.80779	.155673
1.37	3.9354	.59498	.254107	1.87	6.4883	.81213	.154124
1.38	3.9749	.59933	.251579	1.88	6.5535	.81647	.152590
1.39	4.0149	.60367	.249075	1.89	6.6194	.82082	.151072
1.40	4.0552	0.60801	0.246597	**1.90**	6.6859	0.82516	0.149569
1.41	4.0960	.61236	.244143	1.91	6.7531	.82950	.148080
1.42	4.1371	.61670	.241714	1.92	6.8210	.83385	.146607
1.43	4.1787	.62104	.239309	1.93	6.8895	.83819	.145148
1.44	4.2207	.62538	.236928	1.94	6.9588	.84253	.143704
1.45	4.2631	0.62973	0.234570	**1.95**	7.0287	0.84687	0.142274
1.46	4.3060	.63407	.232236	1.96	7.0993	.85122	.140858
1.47	4.3492	.63841	.229925	1.97	7.1707	.85556	.139457
1.48	4.3929	.64276	.227638	1.98	7.2427	.85990	.138069
1.49	4.4371	.64710	.225373	1.99	7.3155	.86425	.136695
1.50	4.4817	0.65144	0.223130	**2.00**	7.3891	0.86859	0.135335

x	e^x	$\text{Log}_{10}\left(e^x\right)$	e^{-x}	x	e^x	$\text{Log}_{10}\left(e^x\right)$	e^{-x}
2.00	7.3891	0.86859	0.135335	**2.50**	12.182	1.08574	0.082085
2.01	7.4633	.87293	.133989	2.51	12.305	1.09008	.081268
2.02	7.5383	.87727	.132655	2.52	12.429	1.09442	.080460
2.03	7.6141	.88162	.131336	2.53	12.554	1.09877	.079659
2.04	7.6906	.88596	.130029	2.54	12.680	1.10311	.078866
2.05	7.7679	0.89030	0.128735	**2.55**	12.807	1.10745	0.078082
2.06	7.8460	.89465	.127454	2.56	12.936	1.11179	.077305
2.07	7.9248	.89899	.126186	2.57	13.066	1.11614	.076536
2.08	8.0045	.90333	.124930	2.58	13.197	1.12048	.075774
2.09	8.0849	.90768	.123687	2.59	13.330	1.12482	.075020
2.10	8.1662	0.91202	0.122456	**2.60**	13.464	1.12917	0.074274
2.11	8.2482	.91636	.121238	2.61	13.599	1.13351	.073535
2.12	8.3311	.92070	.120032	2.62	13.736	1.13785	.072803
2.13	8.4149	.92505	.118837	2.63	13.874	1.14219	.072078
2.14	8.4994	.92939	.117655	2.64	14.013	1.14654	.071361
2.15	8.5849	0.93373	0.116484	**2.65**	14.154	1.15088	0.070651
2.16	8.6711	.93808	.115325	2.66	14.296	1.15522	.069948
2.17	8.7583	.94242	.114178	2.67	14.440	1.15957	.069252
2.18	8.8463	.94676	.113042	2.68	14.585	1.16391	.068563
2.19	8.9352	.95110	.111917	2.69	14.732	1.16825	.067881
2.20	9.0250	0.95545	0.110803	**2.70**	14.880	1.17260	0.067206
2.21	9.1157	.95979	.109701	2.71	15.029	1.17694	.066537
2.22	9.2073	.96413	.108609	2.72	15.180	1.18128	.065875
2.23	9.2999	.96848	.107528	2.73	15.333	1.18562	.065219
2.24	9.3933	.97282	.106459	2.74	15.487	1.18997	.064570
2.25	9.4877	0.97716	0.105399	**2.75**	15.643	1.19431	0.063928
2.26	9.5831	.98151	.104350	2.76	15.800	1.19865	.063292
2.27	9.6794	.98585	.103312	2.77	15.959	1.20300	.062662
2.28	9.7767	.99019	.102284	2.78	16.119	1.20734	.062039
2.29	9.8749	.99453	.101266	2.79	16.281	1.21168	.061421
2.30	9.9742	0.99888	0.100259	**2.80**	16.445	1.21602	0.060810
2.31	10.074	1.00322	.099261	2.81	16.610	1.22037	.060205
2.32	10.176	1.00756	.098274	2.82	16.777	1.22471	.059606
2.33	10.278	1.01191	.097296	2.83	16.945	1.22905	.059013
2.34	10.381	1.01625	.096328	2.84	17.116	1.23340	.058426
2.35	10.486	1.02059	0.095369	**2.85**	17.288	1.23774	0.057844
2.36	10.591	1.02493	.094420	2.86	17.462	1.24208	.057269
2.37	10.697	1.02928	.093481	2.87	17.637	1.24643	.056699
2.38	10.805	1.03362	.092551	2.88	17.814	1.25077	.056135
2.39	10.913	1.03796	.091630	2.89	17.993	1.25511	.055576
2.40	11.023	1.04231	0.090718	**2.90**	18.174	1.25945	0.055023
2.41	11.134	1.04665	.089815	2.91	18.357	1.26380	.054476
2.42	11.246	1.05099	.088922	2.92	18.541	1.26814	.053934
2.43	11.359	1.05534	.088037	2.93	18.728	1.27248	.053397
2.44	11.473	1.05968	.087161	2.94	18.916	1.27683	.052866
2.45	11.588	1.06402	0.086294	**2.95**	19.106	1.28117	0.052340
2.46	11.705	1.06836	.085435	2.96	19.298	1.28551	.051819
2.47	11.822	1.07271	.084585	2.97	19.492	1.28985	.051303
2.48	11.941	1.07705	.083743	2.98	19.688	1.29420	.050793
2.49	12.061	1.08139	.082910	2.99	19.886	1.29854	.050287
2.50	12.182	1.08574	0.082085	**3.00**	20.086	1.30288	0.049787

x	e^x	$\text{Log}_{10}\left(e^x\right)$	e^{-x}	x	e^x	$\text{Log}_{10}\left(e^x\right)$	e^{-x}
3.00	20.086	1.30288	0.049787	**3.50**	33.115	1.52003	0.030197
3.01	20.287	1.30723	.049292	3.51	33.448	1.52437	.029897
3.02	20.491	1.31157	.048801	3.52	33.784	1.52872	.029599
3.03	20.697	1.31591	.048316	3.53	34.124	1.53306	.029305
3.04	20.905	1.32026	.047835	3.54	34.467	1.53740	.029013
3.05	21.115	1.32460	0.047359	**3.55**	34.813	1.54175	0.028725
3.06	21.328	1.32894	.046888	3.56	35.163	1.54609	.028439
3.07	21.542	1.33328	.046421	3.57	35.517	1.55043	.028156
3.08	21.758	1.33763	.045959	3.58	35.874	1.55477	.027876
3.09	21.977	1.34197	.045502	3.59	36.234	1.55912	.027598
3.10	22.198	1.34631	0.045049	**3.60**	36.598	1.56346	0.027324
3.11	22.421	1.35066	.044601	3.61	36.966	1.56780	.027052
3.12	22.646	1.35500	.044157	3.62	37.338	1.57215	.026783
3.13	22.874	1.35934	.043718	3.63	37.713	1.57649	.026516
3.14	23.104	1.36368	.043283	3.64	38.092	1.58083	.026252
3.15	23.336	1.36803	0.042852	**3.65**	38.475	1.58517	0.025991
3.16	23.571	1.37237	.042426	3.66	38.861	1.58952	.025733
3.17	23.807	1.37671	.042004	3.67	39.252	1.59386	.025476
3.18	24.047	1.38106	.041586	3.68	39.646	1.59820	.025223
3.19	24.288	1.38540	.041172	3.69	40.045	1.60255	.024972
3.20	24.533	1.38974	0.040762	**3.70**	40.447	1.60689	0.024724
3.21	24.779	1.39409	.040357	3.71	40.854	1.61123	.024478
3.22	25.028	1.39843	.039955	3.72	41.264	1.61558	.024234
3.23	25.280	1.40277	.039557	3.73	41.679	1.61992	.023993
3.24	25.534	1.40711	.039164	3.74	42.098	1.62426	.023754
3.25	25.790	1.41146	0.038774	**3.75**	42.521	1.62860	0.023518
3.26	26.050	1.41580	.038388	3.76	42.948	1.63295	.023284
3.27	26.311	1.42014	.038006	3.77	43.380	1.63729	.023052
3.28	26.576	1.42449	.037628	3.78	43.816	1.64163	.022823
3.29	26.843	1.42883	.037254	3.79	44.256	1.64598	.022596
3.30	27.113	1.43317	0.036883	**3.80**	44.701	1.65032	0.022371
3.31	27.385	1.43751	.036516	3.81	45.150	1.65466	.022148
3.32	27.660	1.44186	.036153	3.82	45.604	1.65900	.021928
3.33	27.938	1.44620	.035793	3.83	46.063	1.66335	.021710
3.34	28.219	1.45054	.035437	3.84	46.525	1.66769	.021494
3.35	28.503	1.45489	0.035084	**3.85**	46.993	1.67203	0.021280
3.36	28.789	1.45923	.034735	3.86	47.465	1.67638	.021068
3.37	29.079	1.46357	.034390	3.87	47.942	1.68072	.020858
3.38	29.371	1.46792	.034047	3.88	48.424	1.68506	.020651
3.39	29.666	1.47226	.033709	3.89	48.911	1.68941	.020445
3.40	29.964	1.47660	0.033373	**3.90**	49.402	1.69375	0.020242
3.41	30.265	1.48094	.033041	3.91	49.899	1.69809	.020041
3.42	30.569	1.48529	.032712	3.92	50.400	1.70243	.019841
3.43	30.877	1.48963	.032387	3.93	50.907	1.70678	.019644
3.44	31.187	1.49397	.032065	3.94	51.419	1.71112	.019448
3.45	31.500	1.49832	0.031746	**3.95**	51.935	1.71546	0.019255
3.46	31.817	1.50266	.031430	3.96	52.457	1.71981	.019063
3.47	32.137	1.50700	.031117	3.97	52.985	1.72415	.018873
3.48	32.460	1.51134	.030807	3.98	53.517	1.72849	.018686
3.49	32.786	1.51569	.030501	3.99	54.055	1.73283	.018500
3.50	33.115	1.52003	0.030197	**4.00**	54.598	1.73718	0.018316

x	e^x	$\text{Log}_{10}\left(e^x\right)$	e^{-x}	x	e^x	$\text{Log}_{10}\left(e^x\right)$	e^{-x}
4.00	54.598	1.73718	0.018316	**4.50**	90.017	1.95433	0.011109
4.01	55.147	1.74152	.018133	4.51	90.922	1.95867	.010998
4.02	55.701	1.74586	.017953	4.52	91.836	1.96301	.010889
4.03	56.261	1.75021	.017774	4.53	92.759	1.96735	.010781
4.04	56.826	1.75455	.017597	4.54	93.691	1.97170	.010673
4.05	57.397	1.75889	0.017422	**4.55**	94.632	1.97604	0.010567
4.06	57.974	1.76324	.017249	4.56	95.583	1.98038	.010462
4.07	58.557	1.76758	.017077	4.57	96.544	1.98473	.010358
4.08	59.145	1.77192	.016907	4.58	97.514	1.98907	.010255
4.09	59.740	1.77626	.016739	4.59	98.494	1.99341	.010153
4.10	60.340	1.78061	0.016573	**4.60**	99.484	1.99775	0.010052
4.11	60.947	1.78495	.016408	4.61	100.48	2.00210	.009952
4.12	61.559	1.78929	.016245	4.62	101.49	2.00644	.009853
4.13	62.178	1.79364	.016083	4.63	102.51	2.01078	.009755
4.14	62.803	1.79798	.015923	4.64	103.54	2.01513	.009658
4.15	63.434	1.80232	0.015764	**4.65**	104.58	2.01947	0.009562
4.16	64.072	1.80667	.015608	4.66	105.64	2.02381	.009466
4.17	64.715	1.81101	.015452	4.67	106.70	2.02816	.009372
4.18	65.366	1.81535	.015299	4.68	107.77	2.03250	.009279
4.19	66.023	1.81969	.015146	4.69	108.85	2.03684	.009187
4.20	66.686	1.82404	0.014996	**4.70**	109.95	2.04118	0.009095
4.21	67.357	1.82838	.014846	4.71	111.05	2.04553	.009005
4.22	68.033	1.83272	.014699	4.72	112.17	2.04987	.008915
4.23	68.717	1.83707	.014552	4.73	113.30	2.05421	.008826
4.24	69.408	1.84141	.014408	4.74	114.43	2.05856	.008739
4.25	70.105	1.84575	0.014264	**4.75**	115.58	2.06290	0.008652
4.26	70.810	1.85009	.014122	4.76	116.75	2.06724	.008566
4.27	71.522	1.85444	.013982	4.77	117.92	2.07158	.008480
4.28	72.240	1.85878	.013843	4.78	119.10	2.07593	.008396
4.29	72.966	1.86312	.013705	4.79	120.30	2.08027	.008312
4.30	73.700	1.86747	0.013569	**4.80**	121.51	2.08461	0.008230
4.31	74.440	1.87181	.013434	4.81	122.73	2.08896	.008148
4.32	75.189	1.87615	.013300	4.82	123.97	2.09330	.008067
4.33	75.944	1.88050	.013168	4.83	125.21	2.09764	.007987
4.34	76.708	1.88484	.013037	4.84	126.47	2.10199	.007907
4.35	77.478	1.88918	0.012907	**4.85**	127.74	2.10633	0.007828
4.36	78.257	1.89352	.012778	4.86	129.02	2.11067	.007750
4.37	79.044	1.89787	.012651	4.87	130.32	2.11501	.007673
4.38	79.838	1.90221	.012525	4.88	131.63	2.11936	.007597
4.39	80.640	1.90655	.012401	4.89	132.95	2.12370	.007521
4.40	81.451	1.91090	0.012277	**4.90**	134.29	2.12804	0.007447
4.41	82.269	1.91524	.012155	4.91	135.64	2.13239	.007372
4.42	83.096	1.91958	.012034	4.92	137.00	2.13673	.007299
4.43	83.931	1.92392	.011914	4.93	138.38	2.14107	.007227
4.44	84.775	1.92827	.011796	4.94	139.77	2.14541	.007155
4.45	85.627	1.93261	0.011679	**4.95**	141.17	2.14976	0.007083
4.46	86.488	1.93695	.011562	4.96	142.59	2.15410	.007013
4.47	87.357	1.94130	.011447	4.97	144.03	2.15844	.006943
4.48	88.235	1.94564	.011333	4.98	145.47	2.16279	.006874
4.49	89.121	1.94998	.011221	4.99	146.94	2.16713	.006806
4.50	90.017	1.95433	0.011109	**5.00**	148.41	2.17147	0.006738

x	e^x	$\text{Log}_{10}\left(e^x\right)$	e^{-x}	x	e^x	$\text{Log}_{10}\left(e^x\right)$	e^{-x}
5.00	148.41	2.17147	0.006738	**5.50**	244.69	2.38862	0.0040868
5.01	149.90	2.17582	.006671	5.55	257.24	2.41033	.0038875
5.02	151.41	2.18016	.006605	5.60	270.43	2.43205	.0036979
5.03	152.93	2.18450	.006539	5.65	284.29	2.45376	.0035175
5.04	154.47	2.18884	.006474	5.70	298.87	2.47548	.0033460
5.05	156.02	2.19319	0.006409	**5.75**	314.19	2.49719	0.0031828
5.06	157.59	2.19753	.006346	5.80	330.30	2.51891	.0030276
5.07	159.17	2.20187	.006282	5.85	347.23	2.54062	.0028799
5.08	160.77	2.20622	.006220	5.90	365.04	2.56234	.0027394
5.09	162.39	2.21056	.006158	5.95	383.75	2.58405	.0026058
5.10	164.02	2.21490	0.006097	**6.00**	403.43	2.60577	0.0024788
5.11	165.67	2.21924	.006036	6.05	424.11	2.62748	.0023579
5.12	167.34	2.22359	.005976	6.10	445.86	2.64920	.0022429
5.13	169.02	2.22793	.005917	6.15	468.72	2.67091	.0021335
5.14	170.72	2.23227	.005858	6.20	492.75	2.69263	.0020294
5.15	172.43	2.23662	0.005799	**6.25**	518.01	2.71434	0.0019305
5.16	174.16	2.24096	.005742	6.30	544.57	2.73606	.0018363
5.17	175.91	2.24530	.005685	6.35	572.49	2.75777	.0017467
5.18	177.68	2.24965	.005628	6.40	601.85	2.77948	.0016616
5.19	179.47	2.25399	.005572	6.45	632.70	2.80120	.0015805
5.20	181.27	2.25833	0.005517	**6.50**	665.14	2.82291	0.0015034
5.21	183.09	2.26267	.005462	6.55	699.24	2.84463	.0014301
5.22	184.93	2.26702	.005407	6.60	735.10	2.86634	.0013604
5.23	186.79	2.27136	.005354	6.65	772.78	2.88806	.0012940
5.24	188.67	2.27570	.005300	6.70	812.41	2.90977	.0012309
5.25	190.57	2.28005	0.005248	**6.75**	854.06	2.93149	0.0011709
5.26	192.48	2.28439	.005195	6.80	897.85	2.95320	.0011138
5.27	194.42	2.28873	.005144	6.85	943.88	2.97492	.0010595
5.28	196.37	2.29307	.005092	6.90	992.27	2.99663	.0010078
5.29	198.34	2.29742	.005042	6.95	1043.1	3.01835	.0009586
5.30	200.34	2.30176	0.004992	**7.00**	1096.6	3.04006	0.0009119
5.31	202.35	2.30610	.004942	7.05	1152.9	3.06178	.0008674
5.32	204.38	2.31045	.004893	7.10	1212.0	3.08349	.0008251
5.33	206.44	2.31479	.004844	7.15	1274.1	3.10521	.0007849
5.34	208.51	2.31913	.004796	7.20	1339.4	3.12692	.0007466
5.35	210.61	2.32348	0.004748	**7.25**	1408.1	3.14863	0.0007102
5.36	212.72	2.32782	.004701	7.30	1480.3	3.17035	.0006755
5.37	214.86	2.33216	.004654	7.35	1556.2	3.19206	.0006426
5.38	217.02	2.33650	.004608	7.40	1636.0	3.21378	.0006113
5.39	219.20	2.34085	.004562	7.45	1719.9	3.23549	.0005814
5.40	221.41	2.34519	0.004517	**7.50**	1808.0	3.25721	0.0005531
5.41	223.63	2.34953	.004472	7.55	1900.7	3.27892	.0005261
5.42	225.88	2.35388	.004427	7.60	1998.2	3.30064	.0005005
5.43	228.15	2.35822	.004383	7.65	2100.6	3.32235	.0004760
5.44	230.44	2.36256	.004339	7.70	2208.3	3.34407	.0004528
5.45	232.76	2.36690	0.004296	**7.75**	2321.6	3.36578	0.0004307
5.46	235.10	2.37125	.004254	7.80	2440.6	3.38750	.0004097
5.47	237.46	2.37559	.004211	7.85	2565.7	3.40921	.0003898
5.48	239.85	2.37993	.004169	7.90	2697.3	3.43093	.0003707
5.49	242.26	2.38428	.004128	7.95	2835.6	3.45264	.0003527
5.50	244.69	2.38862	0.004087	**8.00**	2981.0	3.47436	0.0003355

x	e^x	$\text{Log}_{10}\left(e^x\right)$	e^{-x}	x	e^x	$\text{Log}_{10}\left(e^x\right)$	e^{-x}
8.00	2981.0	3.47436	0.0003355	**9.00**	8103.1	3.90865	0.0001234
8.05	3133.8	3.49607	.0003191	9.05	8518.5	3.93037	.0001174
8.10	3294.5	3.51779	.0003035	9.10	8955.3	3.95208	.0001117
8.15	3463.4	3.53950	.0002887	9.15	9414.4	3.97379	.0001062
8.20	3641.0	3.56121	.0002747	9.20	9897.1	3.99551	.0001010
8.25	3827.6	3.58293	0.0002613	**9.25**	10405	4.01722	0.0000961
8.30	4023.9	3.60464	.0002485	9.30	10938	4.03894	.0000914
8.35	4230.2	3.62636	.0002364	9.35	11499	4.06065	.0000870
8.40	4447.1	3.64807	.0002249	9.40	12088	4.08237	.0000827
8.45	4675.1	3.66979	.0002139	9.45	12708	4.10408	.0000787
8.50	4914.8	3.69150	0.0002035	**9.50**	13360	4.12580	0.0000749
8.55	5166.8	3.71322	.0001935	9.55	14045	4.14751	.0000712
8.60	5431.7	3.73493	.0001841	9.60	14765	4.16923	.0000677
8.65	5710.1	3.75665	.0001751	9.65	15522	4.19094	.0000644
8.70	6002.9	3.77836	.0001666	9.70	16318	4.21266	.0000613
8.75	6310.7	3.80008	0.0001585	**9.75**	17154	4.23437	0.0000583
8.80	6634.2	3.82179	.0001507	9.80	18034	4.25609	.0000555
8.85	6974.4	3.84351	.0001434	9.85	18958	4.27780	.0000527
8.90	7332.0	3.86522	.0001364	9.90	19930	4.29952	.0000502
8.95	7707.9	3.88694	.0001297	9.95	20952	4.32123	0.0000477
9.00	8103.1	3.90865	0.0001234	10.00	22026	4.34294	0.0000454

Table 8

Normal Distribution

This table gives values of:

a) $f(x)$ = the probability density of a standardized random variable

$$= \frac{1}{\sqrt{2\pi}} e^{-\frac{1}{2}x^2}$$

For negative values of x, one uses the fact that $f(-x) = f(x)$.

b) $F(x)$ = the cumulative distribution function of a standardized normal random variable

$$= \int_{-\infty}^{x} \frac{1}{\sqrt{2\pi}} e^{-\frac{1}{2}t^2} dt$$

For negative values of x, one uses the relationship $F(-x) = 1 - F(x)$. Values of x corresponding to a few special values of $F(x)$ are given in a separate table following the main table.

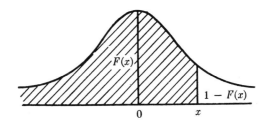

c) $f'(x)$ = the first derivative of $f(x)$ with respect to x

$$= -\frac{x}{\sqrt{2\pi}} e^{-\frac{1}{2}x^2} = -xf(x)$$

d) $f''(x)$ = the second derivative of $f(x)$ with respect to x

$$= \frac{(x^2 - 1)}{\sqrt{2\pi}} e^{-\frac{1}{2}x^2} = (x^2 - 1)f(x)$$

e) $f'''(x)$ = the third derivative of $f(x)$ with respect to x

$$= \frac{3x - x^3}{\sqrt{2\pi}} e^{-\frac{1}{2}x^2} = (3x - x^3)f(x)$$

f) $f^{iv}(x)$ = the fourth derivative of $f(x)$ with respect to x

$$= \frac{x^4 - 6x^2 + 3}{\sqrt{2\pi}} e^{-\frac{1}{2}x^2} = (x^4 - 6x^2 + 3)f(x)$$

Source: William H. Beyer, ed. *Handbook of Tables for Probability and Statistics.* Cleveland: The Chemical Rubber Company, 1966. Reprinted by permission of the publishers.

It should be noted that other probability integrals can be evaluated by the use of these tables. For example,

$$\int_0^x f(t)dt = \tfrac{1}{2} \, \mathrm{erf}\left(\frac{x}{\sqrt{2}}\right),$$

where $\mathrm{erf}\left(\dfrac{x}{\sqrt{2}}\right)$ represents the error function associated with the normal curve.

To evaluate erf (2.3) one proceeds as follows: Since $\dfrac{x}{\sqrt{2}} = 2.3$, one finds $x = (2.3)(\sqrt{2}) = 3.25$. In the entry opposite $x = 3.25$, the value 0.9994 is given. Subtracting 0.5000 from the tabular value, one finds the value 0.4994. Thus erf (2.3) = 2(0.4994) = 0.9988.

x	$F(x)$	$1 - F(x)$	$f(x)$	$f'(x)$	$f''(x)$	$f'''(x)$	$f^{\mathrm{iv}}(x)$
.00	.5000	.5000	.3989	− .0000	− .3989	.0000	1.1968
.01	.5040	.4960	.3989	− .0040	− .3989	.0120	1.1965
.02	.5080	.4920	.3989	− .0080	− .3987	.0239	1.1956
.03	.5120	.4880	.3988	− .0120	− .3984	.0359	1.1941
.04	.5160	.4840	.3986	− .0159	− .3980	.0478	1.1920
.05	.5199	.4801	.3984	− .0199	− .3975	.0597	1.1894
.06	.5239	.4761	.3982	− .0239	− .3968	.0716	1.1861
.07	.5279	.4721	.3980	− .0279	− .3960	.0834	1.1822
.08	.5319	.4681	.3977	− .0318	− .3951	.0952	1.1778
.09	.5359	.4641	.3973	− .0358	− .3941	.1070	1.1727
.10	.5398	.4602	.3970	− .0397	− .3930	.1187	1.1671
.11	.5438	.4562	.3965	− .0436	− .3917	.1303	1.1609
.12	.5478	.4522	.3961	− .0475	− .3904	.1419	1.1541
.13	.5517	.4483	.3956	− .0514	− .3889	.1534	1.1468
.14	.5557	.4443	.3951	− .0553	− .3873	.1648	1.1389
.15	.5596	.4404	.3945	− .0592	− .3856	.1762	1.1304
.16	.5636	.4364	.3939	− .0630	− .3838	.1874	1.1214
.17	.5675	.4325	.3932	−.0668	− .3819	.1986	1.1118
.18	.5714	.4286	.3925	− .0707	− .3798	.2097	1.1017
.19	.5753	.4247	.3918	− .0744	− .3777	.2206	1.0911
.20	.5793	.4207	.3910	− .0782	− .3754	.2315	1.0799
.21	.5832	.4168	.3902	− .0820	− .3730	.2422	1.0682
.22	.5871	.4129	.3894	− .0857	− .3706	.2529	1.0560
.23	.5910	.4090	.3885	− .0894	− .3680	.2634	1.0434
.24	.5948	.4052	.3876	− .0930	− .3653	.2737	1.0302
.25	.5987	.4013	.3867	− .0967	− .3625	.2840	1.0165
.26	.6026	.3974	.3857	− .1003	− .3596	.2941	1.0024
.27	.6064	.3936	.3847	− .1039	− .3566	.3040	0.9878
.28	.6103	.3897	.3836	− .1074	− .3535	.3138	0.9727
.29	.6141	.3859	.3825	−.1109	− .3504	.3235	0.9572
.30	.6179	.3821	.3814	− .1144	− .3471	.3330	0.9413
.31	.6217	.3783	.3802	− .1179	− .3437	.3423	0.9250
.32	.6255	.3745	.3790	− .1213	− .3402	.3515	0.9082
.33	.6293	.3707	.3778	− .1247	− .3367	.3605	0.8910
.34	.6331	.3669	.3765	− .1280	− .3330	.3693	0.8735
.35	.6368	.3632	.3752	− .1313	− .3293	.3779	0.8556
.36	.6406	.3594	.3739	− .1346	− .3255	.3864	0.8373
.37	.6443	.3557	.3725	− .1378	− .3216	.3947	0.8186
.38	.6480	.3520	.3712	− .1410	− .3176	.4028	0.7996
.39	.6517	.3483	.3697	− .1442	− .3135	.4107	0.7803
.40	.6554	.3446	.3683	− .1473	− .3094	.4184	0.7607
.41	.6591	.3409	.3668	− .1504	− .3051	.4259	0.7408
.42	.6628	.3372	.3653	− .1534	− .3008	.4332	0.7206
.43	.6664	.3336	.3637	− .1564	− .2965	.4403	0.7001
.44	.6700	.3300	.3621	− .1593	− .2920	.4472	0.6793
.45	.6736	.3264	.3605	− .1622	− .2875	.4539	0.6583
.46	.6772	.3228	.3589	− .1651	− .2830	.4603	0.6371
.47	.6808	.3192	.3572	− .1679	− .2783	.4666	0.6156
.48	.6844	.3156	.3555	− .1707	− .2736	.4727	0.5940
.49	.6879	.3121	.3538	− .1734	− .2689	.4785	0.5721
.50	.6915	.3085	.3521	− .1760	− .2641	.4841	0.5501

x	$F(x)$	$1 - F(x)$	$f(x)$	$f'(x)$	$f''(x)$	$f'''(x)$	$f^{\mathrm{iv}}(x)$
.50	.6915	.3085	.3521	− .1760	− .2641	.4841	.5501
.51	.6950	.3050	.3503	− .1787	− .2592	.4895	.5279
.52	.6985	.3015	.3485	− .1812	− .2543	.4947	.5056
.53	.7019	.2981	.3467	− .1837	− .2493	.4996	.4831
.54	.7054	.2946	.3448	− .1862	− .2443	.5043	.4605
.55	.7088	.2912	.3429	− .1886	− .2392	.5088	.4378
.56	.7123	.2877	.3410	− .1920	− .2341	.5131	.4150
.57	.7157	.2843	.3391	− .1933	− .2289	.5171	.3921
.58	.7190	.2810	.3372	− .1956	− .2238	.5209	.3691
.59	.7224	.2776	.3352	− .1978	− .2185	.5245	.3461
.60	.7257	.2743	.3332	− .1999	− .2133	.5278	.3231
.61	.7291	.2709	.3312	− .2020	− .2080	.5309	.3000
.62	.7324	.2676	.3292	− .2041	− .2027	.5338	.2770
.63	.7357	.2643	.3271	− .2061	− .1973	.5365	.2539
.64	.7389	.2611	.3251	− .2080	− .1919	.5389	.2309
.65	.7422	.2578	.3230	− .2099	− .1865	.5411	.2078
.66	.7454	.2546	.3209	− .2118	− .1811	.5431	.1849
.67	.7486	.2514	.3187	− .2136	− .1757	.5448	.1620
.68	.7517	.2483	.3166	− .2153	− .1702	.5463	.1391
.69	.7549	.2451	.3144	− .2170	− .1647	.5476	.1164
.70	.7580	.2420	.3123	− .2186	− .1593	.5486	.0937
.71	.7611	.2389	.3101	− .2201	− .1538	.5495	.0712
.72	.7642	.2358	.3079	− .2217	− .1483	.5501	.0487
.73	.7673	.2327	.3056	− .2231	− .1428	.5504	.0265
.74	.7704	.2296	.3034	− .2245	− .1373	.5506	.0043
.75	.7734	.2266	.3011	− .2259	− .1318	.5505	− .0176
.76	.7764	.2236	.2989	− .2271	− .1262	.5502	− .0394
.77	.7794	.2206	.2966	− .2284	− .1207	.5497	− .0611
.78	.7823	.2177	.2943	− .2296	− .1153	.5490	− .0825
.79	.7852	.2148	.2920	− .2307	− .1098	.5481	− .1037
.80	.7881	.2119	.2897	− .2318	− .1043	.5469	− .1247
.81	.7910	.2090	.2874	− .2328	− .0988	.5456	− .1455
.82	.7939	.2061	.2850	− .2337	− .0934	.5440	− .1660
.83	.7967	.2033	.2827	− .2346	− .0880	.5423	− .1862
.84	.7995	.2005	.2803	− .2355	− .0825	.5403	− .2063
.85	.8023	.1977	.2780	− .2363	− .0771	.5381	− .2260
.86	.8051	.1949	.2756	− .2370	− .0718	.5358	− .2455
.87	.8078	.1922	.2732	− .2377	− .0664	.5332	− .2646
.88	.8106	.1894	.2709	− .2384	− .0611	.5305	− .2835
.89	.8133	.1867	.2685	− .2389	− .0558	.5276	− .3021
.90	.8159	.1841	.2661	− .2395	− .0506	.5245	− .3203
.91	.8186	.1814	.2637	− .2400	− .0453	.5212	− .3383
.92	.8212	.1788	.2613	− .2404	− .0401	.5177	− .3559
.93	.8238	.1762	.2589	− .2408	− .0350	.5140	− .3731
.94	.8264	.1736	.2565	− .2411	− .0299	.5102	− .3901
.95	.8289	.1711	.2541	− .2414	− .0248	.5062	− .4066
.96	.8315	.1685	.2516	− .2416	− .0197	.5021	− .4228
.97	.8340	.1660	.2492	− .2417	− .0147	.4978	− .4387
.98	.8365	.1635	.2468	− .2419	− .0098	.4933	− .4541
.99	.8389	.1611	.2444	− .2420	− .0049	.4887	− .4692
1.00	.8413	.1587	.2420	− .2420	.0000	.4839	− .4839

x	$F(x)$	$1 - F(x)$	$f(x)$	$f'(x)$	$f''(x)$	$f'''(x)$	$f^{\mathrm{iv}}(x)$
1.00	.8413	.1587	.2420	− .2420	.0000	.4839	− .4839
1.01	.8438	.1562	.2396	− .2420	.0048	.4790	− .4983
1.02	.8461	.1539	.2371	− .2419	.0096	.4740	− .5122
1.03	.8485	.1515	.2347	− .2418	.0143	.4688	− .5257
1.04	.8508	.1492	.2323	− .2416	.0190	.4635	− .5389
1.05	.8531	.1469	.2299	− .2414	.0236	.4580	− .5516
1.06	.8554	.1446	.2275	− .2411	.0281	.4524	− .5639
1.07	.8577	.1423	.2251	− .2408	.0326	.4467	− .5758
1.08	.8599	.1401	.2227	− .2405	.0371	.4409	− .5873
1.09	.8621	.1379	.2203	− .2401	.0414	.4350	− .5984
1.10	.8643	.1357	.2179	− .2396	.0458	.4290	− .6091
1.11	.8665	.1335	.2155	− .2392	.0500	.4228	− .6193
1.12	.8686	.1314	.2131	− .2386	.0542	.4166	− .6292
1.13	.8708	.1292	.2107	− .2381	.0583	.4102	− .6386
1.14	.8729	.1271	.2083	− .2375	.0624	.4038	− .6476
1.15	.8749	.1251	.2059	− .2368	.0664	.3973	− .6561
1.16	.8770	.1230	.2036	− .2361	.0704	.3907	− .6643
1.17	.8790	.1210	.2012	− .2354	.0742	.3840	− .6720
1.18	.8810	.1190	.1989	− .2347	.0780	.3772	− .6792
1.19	.8830	.1170	.1965	− .2339	.0818	.3704	− .6861
1.20	.8849	.1151	.1942	− .2330	.0854	.3635	− .6926
1.21	.8869	.1131	.1919	− .2322	.0890	.3566	− .6986
1.22	.8888	.1112	.1895	− .2312	.0926	.3496	− .7042
1.23	.8907	.1093	.1872	− .2303	.0960	.3425	− .7094
1.24	.8925	.1075	.1849	− .2293	.0994	.3354	− .7141
1.25	.8944	.1056	.1826	− .2283	.1027	.3282	− .7185
1.26	.8962	.1038	.1804	− .2273	.1060	.3210	− .7224
1.27	.8980	.1020	.1781	− .2262	.1092	.3138	− .7259
1.28	.8997	.1003	.1758	− .2251	.1123	.3065	− .7291
1.29	.9015	.0985	.1736	− .2240	.1153	.2992	− .7318
1.30	.9032	.0968	.1714	− .2228	.1182	.2918	− .7341
1.31	.9049	.0951	.1691	− .2216	.1211	.2845	− .7361
1.32	.9066	.0934	.1669	− .2204	.1239	.2771	− .7376
1.33	.9082	.0918	.1647	− .2191	.1267	.2697	− .7388
1.34	.9099	.0901	.1626	− .2178	.1293	.2624	− .7395
1.35	.9115	.0885	.1604	− .2165	.1319	.2550	− .7399
1.36	.9131	.0869	.1582	− .2152	.1344	.2476	− .7400
1.37	.9147	.0853	.1561	− .2138	.1369	.2402	− .7396
1.38	.9162	.0838	.1539	− .2125	.1392	.2328	− .7389
1.39	.9177	.0823	.1518	− .2110	.1415	.2254	− .7378
1.40	.9192	.0808	.1497	− .2096	.1437	.2180	− .7364
1.41	.9207	.0793	.1476	− .2082	.1459	.2107	− .7347
1.42	.9222	.0778	.1456	− .2067	.1480	.2033	− .7326
1.43	.9236	.0764	.1435	− .2052	.1500	.1960	− .7301
1.44	.9251	.0749	.1415	− .2037	.1519	.1887	− .7274
1.45	.9265	.0735	.1394	− .2022	.1537	.1815	− .7243
1.46	.9279	.0721	.1374	− .2006	.1555	.1742	− .7209
1.47	.9292	.0708	.1354	− .1991	.1572	.1670	− .7172
1.48	.9306	.0694	.1334	− .1975	.1588	.1599	− .7132
1.49	.9319	.0681	.1315	− .1959	.1604	.1528	− .7089
1.50	.9332	.0668	.1295	− .1943	.1619	.1457	− .7043

x	$F(x)$	$1 - F(x)$	$f(x)$	$f'(x)$	$f''(x)$	$f'''(x)$	$f^{\text{iv}}(x)$
1.50	.9332	.0668	.1295	−.1943	.1619	.1457	−.7043
1.51	.9345	.0655	.1276	−.1927	.1633	.1387	−.6994
1.52	.9357	.0643	.1257	−.1910	.1647	.1317	−.6942
1.53	.9370	.0630	.1238	−.1894	.1660	.1248	−.6888
1.54	.9382	.0618	.1219	−.1877	.1672	.1180	−.6831
1.55	.9394	.0606	.1200	−.1860	.1683	.1111	−.6772
1.56	.9406	.0594	.1182	−.1843	.1694	.1044	−.6710
1.57	.9418	.0582	.1163	−.1826	.1704	.0977	−.6646
1.58	.9429	.0571	.1145	−.1809	.1714	.0911	−.6580
1.59	.9441	.0559	.1127	−.1792	.1722	.0846	−.6511
1.60	.9452	.0548	.1109	−.1775	.1730	.0781	−.6441
1.61	.9463	.0537	.1092	−.1757	.1738	.0717	−.6368
1.62	.9474	.0526	.1074	−.1740	.1745	.0654	−.6293
1.63	.9484	.0516	.1057	−.1723	.1751	.0591	−.6216
1.64	.9495	.0505	.1040	−.1705	.1757	.0529	−.6138
1.65	.9505	.0495	.1023	−.1687	.1762	.0468	−.6057
1.66	.9515	.0485	.1006	−.1670	.1766	.0408	−.5975
1.67	.9525	.0475	.0989	−.1652	.1770	.0349	−.5891
1.68	.9535	.0465	.0973	−.1634	.1773	.0290	−.5806
1.69	.9545	.0455	.0957	−.1617	.1776	.0233	−.5720
1.70	.9554	.0446	.0940	−.1599	.1778	.0176	−.5632
1.71	.9564	.0436	.0925	−.1581	.1779	.0120	−.5542
1.72	.9573	.0427	.0909	−.1563	.1780	.0065	−.5452
1.73	.9582	.0418	.0893	−.1546	.1780	.0011	−.5360
1.74	.9591	.0409	.0878	−.1528	.1780	−.0042	−.5267
1.75	.9599	.0401	.0863	−.1510	.1780	−.0094	−.5173
1.76	.9608	.0392	.0848	−.1492	.1778	−.0146	−.5079
1.77	.9616	.0384	.0833	−.1474	.1777	−.0196	−.4983
1.78	.9625	.0375	.0818	−.1457	.1774	−.0245	−.4887
1.79	.9633	.0367	.0804	−.1439	.1772	−.0294	−.4789
1.80	.9641	.0359	.0790	−.1421	.1769	−.0341	−.4692
1.81	.9649	.0351	.0775	−.1403	.1765	−.0388	−.4593
1.82	.9656	.0344	.0761	−.1386	.1761	−.0433	−.4494
1.83	.9664	.0336	.0748	−.1368	.1756	−.0477	−.4395
1.84	.9671	.0329	.0734	−.1351	.1751	−.0521	−.4295
1.85	.9678	.0322	.0721	−.1333	.1746	−.0563	−.4195
1.86	.9686	.0314	.0707	−.1316	.1740	−.0605	−.4095
1.87	.9693	.0307	.0694	−.1298	.1734	−.0645	−.3995
1.88	.9699	.0301	.0681	−.1281	.1727	−.0685	−.3894
1.89	.9706	.0294	.0669	−.1264	.1720	−.0723	−.3793
1.90	.9713	.0287	.0656	−.1247	.1713	−.0761	−.3693
1.91	.9719	.0281	.0344	−.1230	.1705	−.0797	−.3592
1.92	.9726	.0274	.0632	−.1213	.1697	−.0832	−.3492
1.93	.9732	.0268	.0620	−.1196	.1688	−.0867	−.3392
1.94	.9738	.0262	.0608	−.1179	.1679	−.0900	−.3292
1.95	.9744	.0256	.0596	−.1162	.1670	−.0933	−.3192
1.96	.9750	.0250	.0584	−.1145	.1661	−.0964	−.3093
1.97	.9756	.0244	.0573	−.1129	.1651	−.0994	−.2994
1.98	.9761	.0239	.0562	−.1112	.1641	−.1024	−.2895
1.99	.9767	.0233	.0551	−.1096	.1630	−.1052	−.2797
2.00	.9772	.0228	.0540	−.1080	.1620	−.1080	−.2700

x	$F(x)$	$1 - F(x)$	$f(x)$	$f'(x)$	$f''(x)$	$f'''(x)$	$f^{\mathrm{iv}}(x)$
2.00	.9773	.0227	.0540	− .1080	.1620	− .1080	− .2700
2.01	.9778	.0222	.0529	− .1064	.1609	− .1106	− .2603
2.02	.9783	.0217	.0519	− .1048	.1598	− .1132	− .2506
2.03	.9788	.0212	.0508	− .1032	.1586	− .1157	− .2411
2.04	.9793	.0207	.0498	− .1016	.1575	− .1180	− .2316
2.05	.9798	.0202	.0488	− .1000	.1563	− .1203	− .2222
2.06	.9803	.0197	.0478	− .0985	.1550	− .1225	− .2129
2.07	.9808	.0192	.0468	− .0969	.1538	− .1245	− .2036
2.08	.9812	.0188	.0459	− .0954	.1526	− .1265	− .1945
2.09	.9817	.0183	.0449	− .0939	.1513	− .1284	− .1854
2.10	.9821	.0179	.0440	− .0924	.1500	− .1302	− .1765
2.11	.9826	.0174	.0431	− .0909	.1487	− .1320	− .1676
2.12	.9830	.0170	.0422	− .0894	.1474	− .1336	− .1588
2.13	.9834	.0166	.0413	− .0879	.1460	− .1351	− .1502
2.14	.9838	.0162	.0404	− .0865	.1446	− .1366	− .1416
2.15	.9842	.0158	.0396	− .0850	.1433	− .1380	− .1332
2.16	.9846	.0154	.0387	− .0836	.1419	− .1393	− .1249
2.17	.9850	.0150	.0379	− .0822	.1405	− .1405	− .1167
2.18	.9854	.0146	.0371	− .0808	.1391	− .1416	− .1086
2.19	.9857	.0143	.0363	− .0794	.1377	− .1426	− .1006
2.20	.9861	.0139	.0355	− .0780	.1362	− .1436	− .0927
2.21	.9864	.0136	.0347	− .0767	.1348	− .1445	− .0850
2.22	.9868	.0132	.0339	− .0754	.1333	− .1453	− .0774
2.23	.9871	.0129	.0332	− .0740	.1319	− .1460	− .0700
2.24	.9875	.0125	.0325	− .0727	.1304	− .1467	− .0626
2.25	.9878	.0122	.0317	− .0714	.1289	− .1473	− .0554
2.26	.9881	.0119	.0310	− .0701	.1275	− .1478	− .0484
2.27	.9884	.0116	.0303	− .0689	.1260	− .1483	− .0414
2.28	.9887	.0113	.0297	− .0676	.1245	− .1486	− .0346
2.29	.9890	.0110	.0290	− .0664	.1230	− .1490	− .0279
2.30	.9893	.0107	.0283	− .0652	.1215	− .1492	− .0214
2.31	.9896	.0104	.0277	− .0639	.1200	− .1494	− .0150
2.32	.9898	.0102	.0270	− .0628	.1185	− .1495	− .0088
2.33	.9901	.0099	.0264	− .0616	.1170	− .1496	− .0027
2.34	.9904	.0096	.0258	− .0604	.1155	− .1496	.0033
2.35	.9906	.0094	.0252	− .0593	.1141	− .1495	.0092
2.36	.9909	.0091	.0246	− .0581	.1126	− .1494	.0149
2.37	.9911	.0089	.0241	− .0570	.1111	− .1492	.0204
2.38	.9913	.0087	.0235	− .0559	.1096	− .1490	.0258
2.39	.9916	.0084	.0229	− .0548	.1081	− .1487	.0311
2.40	.9918	.0082	.0224	− .0538	.1066	− .1483	.0362
2.41	.9920	.0080	.0219	− .0527	.1051	− .1480	.0412
2.42	.9922	.0078	.0213	− .0516	.1036	− .1475	.0461
2.43	.9925	.0075	.0208	− .0506	.1022	− .1470	.0508
2.44	.9927	.0073	.0203	− .0496	.1007	− .1465	.0554
2.45	.9929	.0071	.0198	− .0486	.0992	− .1459	.0598
2.46	.9931	.0069	.0194	− .0476	.0978	− .1453	.0641
2.47	.9932	.0068	.0189	− .0467	.0963	− .1446	.0683
2.48	.9934	.0066	.0184	− .0457	.0949	− .1439	.0723
2.49	.9936	.0064	.0180	− .0448	.0935	− .1432	.0762
2.50	.9938	.0062	.0175	− .0438	.0920	− .1424	.0800

x	$F(x)$	$1 - F(x)$	$f(x)$	$f'(x)$	$f''(x)$	$f'''(x)$	$f^{iv}(x)$
2.50	.9938	.0062	.0175	$-.0438$	.0920	$-.1424$	.0800
2.51	.9940	.0060	.0171	$-.0429$	.0906	$-.1416$	.0836
2.52	.9941	.0059	.0167	$-.0420$	.0892	$-.1408$	.0871
2.53	.9943	.0057	.0163	$-.0411$	.0878	$-.1399$	.0905
2.54	.9945	.0055	.0158	$-.0403$	.0864	$-.1389$	.0937
2.55	.9946	.0054	.0155	$-.0394$	.0850	$-.1380$	.0968
2.56	.9948	.0052	.0151	$-.0386$	.0836	$-.1370$	.0998
2.57	.9949	.0051	.0147	$-.0377$	.0823	$-.1360$	.1027
2.58	.9951	.0049	.0143	$-.0369$	.0809	$-.1350$	.1054
2.59	.9952	.0048	.0139	$-.0361$	.0796	$-.1339$	.1080
2.60	.9953	.0047	.0136	$-.0353$	.0782	$-.1328$	.1105
2.61	.9955	.0045	.0132	$-.0345$	.0769	$-.1317$	.1129
2.62	.9956	.0044	.0129	$-.0338$	.0756	$-.1305$	.1152
2.63	.9957	.0043	.0126	$-.0330$	.0743	$-.1294$	.1173
2.64	.9959	.0041	.0122	$-.0323$	.0730	$-.1282$	.1194
2.65	.9960	.0040	.0119	$-.0316$	.0717	$-.1270$	.1213
2.66	.9961	.0039	.0116	$-.0309$	.0705	$-.1258$	.1231
2.67	.9962	.0038	.0113	$-.0302$	.0692	$-.1245$	.1248
2.68	.9963	.0037	.0110	$-.0295$	.0680	$-.1233$	.1264
2.69	.9964	.0036	.0107	$-.0288$	.0668	$-.1220$	.1279
2.70	.9965	.0035	.0104	$-.0281$	.0656	$-.1207$	.1293
2.71	.9966	.0034	.0101	$-.0275$	.0644	$-.1194$	.1306
2.72	.9967	.0033	.0099	$-.0269$	.0632	$-.1181$	.1317
2.73	.9968	.0032	.0096	$-.0262$	.0620	$-.1168$	.1328
2.74	.9969	.0031	.0093	$-.0256$	.0608	$-.1154$	.1338
2.75	.9970	.0030	.0091	$-.0250$	.0597	$-.1141$	.1347
2.76	.9971	.0029	.0088	$-.0244$	.0585	$-.1127$	.1356
2.77	.9972	.0028	.0086	$-.0238$	.0574	$-.1114$	.1363
2.78	.9973	.0027	.0084	$-.0233$	.0563	$-.1100$	.1369
2.79	.9974	.0026	.0081	$-.0227$	.0552	$-.1087$	.1375
2.80	.9974	.0026	.0079	$-.0222$	.0541	$-.1073$	.1379
2.81	.9975	.0025	.0077	$-.0216$	.0531	$-.1059$	.1383
2.82	.9976	.0024	.0075	$-.0211$	.0520	$-.1045$	.1386
2.83	.9977	.0023	.0073	$-.0206$	.0510	$-.1031$	.1389
2.84	.9977	.0023	.0071	$-.0201$	.0500	$-.1017$	.1390
2.85	.9978	.0022	.0069	$-.0196$	.0490	$-.1003$	.1391
2.86	.9979	.0021	.0067	$-.0191$	.0480	$-.0990$	.1391
2.87	.9979	.0021	.0065	$-.0186$	.0470	$-.0976$	.1391
2.88	.9980	.0020	.0063	$-.0182$	.0460	$-.0962$	.1389
2.89	.9981	.0019	.0061	$-.0177$	.0451	$-.0948$	.1388
2.90	.9981	.0019	.0060	$-.0173$	.0441	$-.0934$	.1385
2.91	.9982	.0018	.0058	$-.0168$	.0432	$-.0920$	.1382
2.92	.9982	.0018	.0056	$-.0164$	.0423	$-.0906$	.1378
2.93	.9983	.0017	.0055	$-.0160$	.0414	$-.0893$	.1374
2.94	.9984	.0016	.0053	$-.0156$	.0405	$-.0879$	.1369
2.95	.9984	.0016	.0051	$-.0152$	.0396	$-.0865$	.1364
2.96	.9985	.0015	.0050	$-.0148$	.0388	$-.0852$	.1358
2.97	.9985	.0015	.0048	$-.0144$	.0379	$-.0838$	.1352
2.98	.9986	.0014	.0047	$-.0140$	.0371	$-.0825$	.1345
2.99	.9986	.0014	.0046	$-.0137$	.0363	$-.0811$	.1337
3.00	.9987	.0013	.0044	$-.0133$	.0355	$-.0798$	.1330

x	$F(x)$	$1 - F(x)$	$f(x)$	$f'(x)$	$f''(x)$	$f'''(x)$	$f^{iv}(x)$
3.00	.9987	.0013	.0044	− .0133	.0355	− .0798	.1330
3.01	.9987	.0013	.0043	− .0130	.0347	− .0785	.1321
3.02	.9987	.0013	.0042	− .0126	.0339	− .0771	.1313
3.03	.9988	.0012	.0040	− .0123	.0331	− .0758	.1304
3.04	.9988	.0012	.0039	− .0119	.0324	− .0745	.1294
3.05	.9989	.0011	.0038	− .0116	.0316	− .0732	.1285
3.06	.9989	.0011	.0037	− .0113	.0309	− .0720	.1275
3.07	.9989	.0011	.0036	− .0110	.0302	− .0707	.1264
3.08	.9990	.0010	.0035	− .0107	.0295	− .0694	.1254
3.09	.9990	.0010	.0034	− .0104	.0288	− .0682	.1243
3.10	.9990	.0010	.0033	− .0101	.0281	− .0669	.1231
3.11	.9991	.0009	.0032	− .0099	.0275	− .0657	.1220
3.12	.9991	.0009	.0031	− .0096	.0268	− .0645	.1208
3.13	.9991	.0009	.0030	− .0093	.0262	− .0633	.1196
3.14	.9992	.0008	.0029	− .0091	.0256	− .0621	.1184
3.15	.9992	.0008	.0028	− .0088	.0249	− .0609	.1171
3.16	.9992	.0008	.0027	− .0086	.0243	− .0598	.1159
3.17	.9992	.0008	.0026	− .0083	.0237	− .0586	.1146
3.18	.9993	.0007	.0025	− .0081	.0232	− .0575	.1133
3.19	.9993	.0007	.0025	− .0079	.0226	− .0564	.1120
3.20	.9993	.0007	.0024	− .0076	.0220	− .0552	.1107
3.21	.9993	.0007	.0023	− .0074	.0215	− .0541	.1093
3.22	.9994	.0006	.0022	− .0072	.0210	− .0531	.1080
3.23	.9994	.0006	.0022	− .0070	.0204	− .0520	.1066
3.24	.9994	.0006	.0021	− .0068	.0199	− .0509	.1053
3.25	.9994	.0006	.0020	− .0066	.0194	− .0499	.1039
3.26	.9994	.0006	.0020	− .0064	.0189	− .0488	.1025
3.27	.9995	.0005	.0019	− .0062	.0184	− .0478	.1011
3.28	.9995	.0005	.0018	− .0060	.0180	− .0468	.0997
3.29	.9995	.0005	.0018	− .0059	.0175	− .0458	.0983
3.30	.9995	.0005	.0017	− .0057	.0170	− .0449	.0969
3.31	.9995	.0005	.0017	− .0055	.0166	− .0439	.0955
3.32	.9995	.0005	.0016	− .0054	.0162	− .0429	.0941
3.33	.9996	.0004	.0016	− .0052	.0157	− .0420	.0927
3.34	.9996	.0004	.0015	− .0050	.0153	− .0411	.0913
3.35	.9996	.0004	.0015	− .0049	.0149	− .0402	.0899
3.36	.9996	.0004	.0014	− .0047	.0145	− .0393	.0885
3.37	.9996	.0004	.0014	− .0046	.0141	− .0384	.0871
3.38	.9996	.0004	.0013	− .0045	.0138	− .0376	.0857
3.39	.9997	.0003	.0013	− .0043	.0134	− .0367	.0843
3.40	.9997	.0003	.0012	− .0042	.0130	− .0359	.0829
3.41	.9997	.0003	.0012	− .0041	.0127	− .0350	.0815
3.42	.9997	.0003	.0012	− .0039	.0123	− .0342	.0801
3.43	.9997	.0003	.0011	− .0038	.0120	− .0334	.0788
3.44	.9997	.0003	.0011	− .0037	.0116	− .0327	.0774
3.45	.9997	.0003	.0010	− .0036	.0113	− .0319	.0761
3.46	.9997	.0003	.0010	− .0035	.0110	− .0311	.0747
3.47	.9997	.0003	.0010	− .0034	.0107	− .0304	.0734
3.48	.9997	.0003	.0009	− .0033	.0104	− .0297	.0721
3.49	.9998	.0002	.0009	− .0032	.0101	− .0290	.0707
3.50	.9998	.0002	.0009	− .0031	.0098	− .0283	.0694

x	$F(x)$	$1 - F(x)$	$f(x)$	$f'(x)$	$f''(x)$	$f'''(x)$	$f^{\mathrm{iv}}(x)$
3.50	.9998	.0002	.0009	− .0031	.0098	− .0283	.0694
3.51	.9998	.0002	.0008	− .0030	.0095	− .0276	.0681
3.52	.9998	.0002	.0008	− .0029	.0093	− .0269	.0669
3.53	.9998	.0002	.0008	− .0028	.0090	− .0262	.0656
3.54	.9998	.0002	.0008	− .0027	.0087	− .0256	.0643
3.55	.9998	.0002	.0007	− .0026	.0085	− .0249	.0631
3.56	.9998	.0002	.0007	− .0025	.0082	− .0243	.0618
3.57	.9998	.0002	.0007	− .0024	.0080	− .0237	.0606
3.58	.9998	.0002	.0007	− .0024	.0078	− .0231	.0594
3.59	.9998	.0002	.0006	− .0023	.0075	− .0225	.0582
3.60	.9998	.0002	.0006	− .0022	.0073	− .0219	.0570
3.61	.9998	.0002	.0006	− .0021	.0071	− .0214	.0559
3.62	.9999	.0001	.0006	− .0021	.0069	− .0208	.0547
3.63	.9999	.0001	.0005	− .0020	.0067	− .0203	.0536
3.64	.9999	.0001	.0005	− .0019	.0065	− .0198	.0524
3.65	.9999	.0001	.0005	− .0019	.0063	− .0192	.0513
3.66	.9999	.0001	.0005	− .0018	.0061	− .0187	.0502
3.67	.9999	.0001	.0005	− .0017	.0059	− .0182	.0492
3.68	.9999	.0001	.0005	− .0017	.0057	− .0177	.0481
3.69	.9999	.0001	.0004	− .0016	.0056	− .0173	.0470
3.70	.9999	.0001	.0004	− .0016	.0054	− .0168	.0460
3.71	.9999	.0001	.0004	− .0015	.0052	− .0164	.0450
3.72	.9999	.0001	.0004	− .0015	.0051	− .0159	.0440
3.73	.9999	.0001	.0004	− .0014	.0049	− .0155	.0430
3.74	.9999	.0001	.0004	− .0014	.0048	− .0150	.0420
3.75	.9999	.0001	.0004	− .0013	.0046	− .0146	.0410
3.76	.9999	.0001	.0003	− .0013	.0045	− .0142	.0401
3.77	.9999	.0001	.0003	− .0012	.0043	− .0138	.0392
3.78	.9999	.0001	.0003	− .0012	.0042	− .0134	.0382
3.79	.9999	.0001	.0003	− .0012	.0041	− .0131	.0373
3.80	.9999	.0001	.0003	− .0011	.0039	− .0127	.0365
3.81	.9999	.0001	.0003	− .0011	.0038	− .0123	.0356
3.82	.9999	.0001	.0003	− .0010	.0037	− .0120	.0347
3.83	.9999	.0001	.0003	− .0010	.0036	− .0116	.0339
3.84	.9999	.0001	.0003	− .0010	.0034	− .0113	.0331
3.85	.9999	.0001	.0002	− .0009	.0033	− .0110	.0323
3.86	.9999	.0001	.0002	− .0009	.0032	− .0107	.0315
3.87	.9999	.0001	.0002	− .0009	.0031	− .0104	.0307
3.88	.9999	.0001	.0002	− .0008	.0030	− .0100	.0299
3.89	1.0000	.0000	.0002	− .0008	.0029	− .0098	.0292
3.90	1.0000	.0000	.0002	− .0008	.0028	− .0095	.0284
3.91	1.0000	.0000	.0002	− .0008	.0027	− .0092	.0277
3.92	1.0000	.0000	.0002	− .0007	.0026	− .0089	.0270
3.93	1.0000	.0000	.0002	− .0007	.0026	− .0086	.0263
3.94	1.0000	.0000	.0002	− .0007	.0025	− .0084	.0256
3.95	1.0000	.0000	.0002	− .0006	.0024	− .0081	.0250
3.96	1.0000	.0000	.0002	− .0006	.0023	− .0079	.0243
3.97	1.0000	.0000	.0002	− .0006	.0022	− .0076	.0237
3.98	1.0000	.0000	.0001	− .0006	.0022	− .0074	.0230
3.99	1.0000	.0000	.0001	− .0006	.0021	− .0072	.0224
4.00	1.0000	.0000	.0001	− .0005	.0020	− .0070	.0218

x	1.282	1.645	1.960	2.326	2.576	3.090
$F(x)$	.90	.95	.975	.99	.995	.999
$2[1 - F(x)]$	.20	.10	.05	.02	.01	.002

Answers to Selected Odd-Numbered Exercises and Problems

Chapter 0

0.1 (a) $x_0 x_1 x_2 x_3 x_4$, (b) $\prod_{i=1}^{r} x_i \Big/ \prod_{i=1}^{r} y_{i-1}$, (c) $-\dfrac{x_1}{2} + \dfrac{x_2}{3} - \dfrac{x_3}{4} + \dfrac{x_4}{5} - \dfrac{x_5}{6}$.

0.3 (a) $A_3 = \{x: 11 \leq x < 66\}$,   (b) $A_1 = \{x: 16 < x \leq 41\}$,
   (c) $A_1 = \{x: 16 < x \leq 41\}$,   (d) $A_1 \cap \bar{A}_2 = \{x: 16 < x < 29\}$,
   (e) $A_3 \cap A_2 = \{x: 29 \leq x \leq 56\}$,
   (f) $A_2 \cup \bar{A}_3 = \{x: x < 11 \text{ or } 29 \leq x \leq 56 \text{ or } x \geq 66\}$,
   (g) $A_1 \cap A_2 = \{x: 16 \leq x \leq 56\}$,   (h) $A_1 \cup A_2 = \{x: 16 < x \leq 56\}$,
   (i) $\bar{A}_3 = \{x: x < 11 \text{ or } x \geq 66\}$,   (j) A_3.

0.5 ϕ $\{1, 2\}$ $\{1, 2, 3\}$
    $\{1\}$ $\{1, 3\}$ $\{1, 2, 4\}$
    $\{2\}$ $\{1, 4\}$ $\{1, 3, 4\}$
    $\{3\}$ $\{2, 3\}$ $\{2, 3, 4\}$
    $\{4\}$ $\{2, 4\}$ $\{1, 2, 3, 4\}$.
       $\{3, 4\}$

0.11 $P_5^{17} = 742{,}560$, $P_0^5 = 1$, $P_{r+1}^n = n(n-1)\cdots(n-r)$,
    $P_{r-1}^{n-1} = (n-1)(n-2)\cdots(n-r+1)$.

0.13 (a) 180,   (b) 100.   **0.15** (a) $n = 20$,   (b) $k = 4$.

0.17 495.   **0.21** 2,598,960.   **0.23** $2^{16} - \binom{16}{0} = 2^{16} - 1$.

0.25 (a) $x^{5/2} + 10x^2 y + 40x^{3/2} y^2 + 80xy^3 + 80x^{1/2} y^4 + 32y^5$,

   (b) $64x^6 - 96x^5 y^2 + 60x^4 y^4 - 20x^3 y^6 + \dfrac{15}{4} x^2 y^8 - \dfrac{3}{8} y^{10} + \dfrac{1}{64} y^{12}$.

0.27 $\binom{10}{3-j}$ for $j \geq -3$.   **0.29** (a) 25,200,   (b) -560.

0.31 11,732,745,024,   **0.33** $J = \dfrac{2}{23}$.   **0.35** (a) $\left(\dfrac{1}{t}\right)^{t+1} \Gamma(t+1)$,   (b) $\Gamma(5)$,

   (c) $\dfrac{1}{2^7} \Gamma(7)$,   (d) $\dfrac{1}{3} \Gamma\left(\dfrac{1}{2}\right)$,   (e) $\dfrac{1}{6\sqrt{\ln 4}} \Gamma\left(\dfrac{1}{2}\right)$.

0.37 (a) $\begin{bmatrix} 9 & 2 & 7 \\ 4 & 1 & -1 \\ 3 & -1 & 4 \end{bmatrix}$,   (b) $\begin{bmatrix} 5 & -3 & 0 \\ -3 & 1 & -5 \\ 0 & 1 & -2 \end{bmatrix}$,   (c) $\begin{bmatrix} -12 & -3 & -13 \\ -5 & 4 & -4 \\ -5 & -2 & -6 \end{bmatrix}$,

(d) $AB = \begin{bmatrix} 24 & 10 & 31 \\ 4 & 0 & 0 \\ 3 & 3 & 6 \end{bmatrix}$, $BA = \begin{bmatrix} 27 & -1 & 7 \\ 16 & -4 & 11 \\ 13 & -3 & 7 \end{bmatrix}$, (e) $\begin{bmatrix} 9 & -1 & 5 \\ 0 & 0 & -3 \\ 2 & 1 & 1 \end{bmatrix}$,

(f) $\begin{bmatrix} 14 & -1 & 12 \\ 6 & 9 & 16 \\ -5 & -5 & 7 \end{bmatrix}$.   **0.39** (a) -8,   (b) 0,

(c) $c_{11}c_{22}c_{33} - c_{11}c_{23}c_{32} - c_{21}c_{12}c_{33} + c_{21}c_{32}c_{13} + c_{31}c_{12}c_{23} - c_{31}c_{22}c_{13}$.

0.41 $A^T = \begin{bmatrix} 5 & 1 & 1 \\ 0 & 2 & -1 \\ 2 & -3 & 1 \end{bmatrix}$, $B^T = \begin{bmatrix} 4 & 3 & 2 \\ 2 & -1 & 0 \\ 5 & 2 & 3 \end{bmatrix}$, $C^T = \begin{bmatrix} 0 & 4 & 1 \\ 3 & 1 & -2 \\ 2 & 2 & 3 \end{bmatrix}$.

0.45 $\begin{vmatrix} 1 & -3 & 1 \\ 2 & 1 & 2 \\ 1 & 5 & 3 \end{vmatrix} = 14$, nonsingular.

Chapter 1

Exercises:

1.11 When the probability of either or both of the events equals zero.
1.21 0.5.   **1.23** 0.25.

Problems:

1.1 (a) $k = 2 : \dfrac{1}{36}$, $k = 8 : \dfrac{5}{36}$,   (b) $k = 2 : \dfrac{1}{36}$, $k = 8 : \dfrac{26}{36}$,

$k = 3 : \dfrac{2}{36}$, $k = 9 : \dfrac{4}{36}$, $k = 3 : \dfrac{3}{36}$, $k = 9 : \dfrac{30}{36}$,

$k = 4 : \dfrac{3}{36}$, $k = 10 : \dfrac{3}{36}$, $k = 4 : \dfrac{6}{36}$, $k = 10 : \dfrac{33}{36}$,

$k = 5 : \dfrac{4}{36}$, $k = 11 : \dfrac{2}{36}$, $k = 5 : \dfrac{10}{36}$, $k = 11 : \dfrac{35}{36}$,

$k = 6 : \dfrac{5}{36}$, $k = 12 : \dfrac{1}{36}$. $k = 6 : \dfrac{15}{36}$, $k = 12 : \dfrac{36}{36}$.

$k = 7 : \dfrac{6}{36}$, $k = 7 : \dfrac{21}{36}$,

(c) $k = 2 : \dfrac{36}{36}$, $k = 5 : \dfrac{30}{36}$, $k = 8 : \dfrac{15}{36}$, $k = 11 : \dfrac{3}{36}$,

$k = 3 : \dfrac{35}{36}$, $k = 6 : \dfrac{36}{36}$, $k = 9 : \dfrac{10}{36}$, $k = 12 : \dfrac{1}{36}$.

$k = 4 : \dfrac{33}{36}$, $k = 7 : \dfrac{21}{36}$, $k = 10 : \dfrac{6}{36}$,

1.3 (a) $k = 0 : \dfrac{12}{40}$,　(b) $k = 0 : 1$,　(c) $k = 0 : \dfrac{12}{40}$,

$\qquad k = 1 : \dfrac{18}{40}$,　$\qquad k = 1 : \dfrac{28}{40}$,　$\qquad k = 1 : \dfrac{30}{40}$,

$\qquad k = 2 : \dfrac{9}{40}$,　$\qquad k = 2 : \dfrac{10}{40}$,　$\qquad k = 2 : \dfrac{39}{40}$,

$\qquad k = 3 : \dfrac{1}{40}$.　$\qquad k = 3 : \dfrac{1}{40}$.　$\qquad k = 3 : 1$.

1.5 (a) $\dfrac{25}{108}$,　(b) $\dfrac{25}{81}$,　(c) 0,　(d) $\dfrac{25}{189}$,　(e) $\dfrac{7}{108}$,　(f) $\dfrac{1}{27}$,

$\qquad$ (g) $\dfrac{3}{20}$,　(h) $\dfrac{7}{90}$,　(i) $\dfrac{1}{6}$.

1.7 (a) $\dfrac{2}{5}$,　(b) $\dfrac{2}{5}$,　(c) $\dfrac{1}{5}$.

1.9 $k = 1 : 0$,　$k = 5 : \dfrac{10}{126}$,　$k = 9 : \dfrac{8}{126}$,

$\qquad k = 2 : \dfrac{1}{126}$,　$k = 6 : \dfrac{15}{126}$,　$k = 10 : \dfrac{15}{126}$,

$\qquad k = 3 : \dfrac{3}{126}$,　$k = 7 : \dfrac{21}{126}$,　$k = 11 : \dfrac{11}{126}$,

$\qquad k = 4 : \dfrac{6}{126}$,　$k = 8 : \dfrac{20}{126}$,　$k = 12 : \dfrac{6}{126}$.

1.11 3.　**1.13** (a) 0.0154,　(b) 0.2315,　(c) 0.1543.

1.15 $\dfrac{244}{495}$.　**3.17** the former.　**1.19** (a) $\dfrac{1}{2^{n-1}}$,　(b) $\dfrac{31}{32}$,　(c) $\dfrac{2}{3}$.

1.21 $\dfrac{w_2(w_1 + b_1) + w_1}{(w_1 + b_1)(w_2 + b_2 + 1)}$.　**1.23** $n2^{1-n}$.

Chapter 2

Exercises:

2.1 (a) $f(x) = \begin{cases} \dfrac{\binom{13}{x}\binom{39}{7-x}}{\binom{52}{7}}, & x = 0, 1, 2, 3, 4, 5, 6, 7, \\ 0, & \text{elsewhere.} \end{cases}$

$\qquad$ (b) $F(x) = \begin{cases} 1, & x > 7, \\ \displaystyle\sum_{k=0}^{[x]} \dfrac{\binom{13}{k}\binom{39}{7-k}}{\binom{52}{7}}, & 0 \le x \le 7, \\ 0, & x < 0. \end{cases}$

2.3 (a) $f(x) = \begin{cases} \dfrac{1}{2^x}, & x = 1, 2, 3, \ldots, \\ 0, & \text{elsewhere.} \end{cases}$

(b) $F(x) = \begin{cases} \sum\limits_{k=1}^{[x]} \dfrac{1}{2^k}, & x \geq 1, \\ 0, & x < 1. \end{cases}$

2.5

$f(x) = \begin{cases} \dfrac{1}{6}\left(\dfrac{5}{6}\right)^{x-1}, & x = 1, 2, 3, \ldots, \\ 0, & \text{elsewhere.} \end{cases}$

$F(x) = \begin{cases} \sum\limits_{k=1}^{[x]} \dfrac{1}{6}\left(\dfrac{5}{6}\right)^{k-1}, & x \geq 1, \\ 0, & x < 1. \end{cases}$

2.7 $k = \dfrac{60}{77}$.   **2.9** (a) $k = \dfrac{3}{\pi^2}$,   (b) $F(x) = \begin{cases} \dfrac{6}{\pi^2}\sum\limits_{i=1}^{[x]} \dfrac{1}{i^2}, & x \geq 1, \\ 0, & x < 1. \end{cases}$

Problems:

2.1 (a) $\dfrac{\binom{13}{5}\binom{39}{2}}{\binom{52}{7}}$,   (b) $\dfrac{\binom{13}{5}\binom{39}{2}}{\binom{52}{7}} - \dfrac{\binom{13}{2}\binom{39}{5}}{\binom{52}{7}}$.

2.3 (a) $\dfrac{1}{16}$,   (b) $\dfrac{7}{8}$.

2.5 (a) $\dfrac{27}{77}$,   (b) $\dfrac{27}{77}$.

2.7 0.5008.   **2.9** (a) binomial: $\binom{7}{4}\left(\dfrac{1}{6}\right)^4\left(\dfrac{5}{6}\right)^3$,   (b) geometric: $\dfrac{1}{6}\left(\dfrac{5}{6}\right)^6$,

(c) negative binomial: $\binom{6}{3}\left(\dfrac{1}{6}\right)^4\left(\dfrac{5}{6}\right)^3$.   **2.11** (a) $\sum\limits_{k=13}^{16}\binom{20}{k}\left(\dfrac{1}{5}\right)^k\left(\dfrac{4}{5}\right)^{20-k}$,

(b) $\binom{20}{17}(0.2)^{17}(0.8)^3 - \binom{20}{12}(0.2)^{12}(0.8)^8$.

2.13 (a) $\dfrac{\binom{4}{2}\binom{48}{5}}{\binom{52}{7}}$,   (b) $1 - \sum\limits_{x=0}^{2}\dfrac{\binom{4}{4}\binom{48}{7-x}}{\binom{52}{7}}$,   (c) $\sum\limits_{x=0}^{1}\dfrac{\binom{4}{x}\binom{48}{7-x}}{\binom{52}{7}}$.

2.15 5.   **2.17** (a) 0.375,   (b) 0.8050.

2.19 (a) 0.125,   (b) 0.1301,   (c) 0.00005.

2.21 (a) binomial: 0.455, Poisson: 0.451;
       (b) binomial: 0.9994, Poisson: 0.9999.

2.23 Probability he breaks the record: 0.459 (binomial),
                                            0.4512 (Poisson).

2.25 (a) $\dfrac{\binom{4}{0}\binom{48}{5}}{\binom{52}{5}}$,   (b) $1 - \sum\limits_{x=0}^{1} \dfrac{\binom{4}{x}\binom{48}{5-x}}{\binom{52}{5}}$,   (c) $\sum\limits_{x=0}^{1} \dfrac{\binom{4}{x}\binom{48}{5-x}}{\binom{52}{5}}$.

2.27 $\dfrac{11}{42}$.   **2.29** 0.0648.   **2.31** 0.109.

2.33 Probability of qualifying: 0.3482, winning: 0.5;
         Probability of qualifying: 0.8, winning: 0.9.

2.35 0.00099.

2.37 (a) 0.0904,   (b) 0.0054.

Chapter 3

Exercises:

3.1 (a) $k = \dfrac{1}{2}$,   (b) $F(x) = \begin{cases} 1, & x \geq \pi, \\ \dfrac{1}{2}(1 - \cos x), & 0 < x < \pi, \\ 0, & x \leq 0. \end{cases}$

3.3 (a) $F(x) = \begin{cases} 1, & x > 1, \\ \dfrac{x^3}{2} + \dfrac{1}{2}, & -1 \leq x \leq 1, \\ 0, & x < -1. \end{cases}$

3.5 (a) $f(x) = \begin{cases} 1, & 0 < x \leq \dfrac{1}{2}, \\ 2, & \dfrac{3}{4} < x \leq 1, \\ 0, & \text{elsewhere.} \end{cases}$

3.9 (a) $c = 3$,   (b) $c = 1$,   (c) $c = 3$,   (d) $c = \dfrac{1}{2}$,   (e) $c = \dfrac{1}{\theta}$,

   (f) $c = \dfrac{1}{\pi}$,   (g) $c = \dfrac{6}{5}$,   (h) $c = \dfrac{1}{2}$,   (i) $c = 1$,   (k) $c = 4$,

   (l) $c = \dfrac{1}{6}$,   (m) $c = \dfrac{21}{440}$,   (n) $c = \dfrac{1 - e^{-1}}{1 - e}$,   (o) $c = \dfrac{1}{\sqrt{2\pi}}$,

   (p) $c = 2$,   (q) $c = 1$,   (r) $c = 1$,   (s) $c = \dfrac{1}{6}$.

Problems:

3.1 (a) $\frac{1}{2}$,   (b) 0,   (c) $\frac{7}{8}$,   (d) 0,   (e) $\frac{7}{8}$,   (f) $\frac{1}{8}$,   (g) $\frac{3}{8}$,

(h) $\frac{3}{8}$,   (i) 1,   (j) $\frac{1}{8}$.

3.3 $\left(\frac{20}{27}\right)^2$.   **3.5** (a) $\frac{7}{8}$,   (b) $\frac{7}{8}$,   (c) $\frac{3}{4}$.

3.7 (a) $\frac{2}{59}$,   (b) $\frac{41}{118}$.   **3.9** (b) $\dfrac{\pi^2 + 6(3 - \sqrt{3})\pi - 18}{18(\pi - 2)}$,

$\dfrac{-\sqrt{3}\,\pi^2 + 12\pi - 72(2 - \sqrt{3})}{72(\pi - 2)}$.   **3.11** $\frac{3}{2}\,e^{-1/2} - 117e^{-10}, \frac{17}{e^{16}}$.   **3.13** 0.40.

3.15 \$250,000.   **3.17** 655.   **3.19** 87.8.   **3.21** (a) 0.64,   (b) 0.471196.
3.23 0.595.   **3.25** 0.45.   **3.27** 0.274.   **3.29** 0.0276.   **3.31** 0.03213.
3.33 0.554, 1, 1.80.   **3.35** 0.067.   **3.37** 0.77.

Chapter 4

Exercises:

4.1 (a) $f(y) = \begin{cases} \frac{1}{12}, & y = -1, \frac{1}{2}, \\ \frac{1}{6}, & y = -\frac{3}{2}, -\frac{1}{2}, \\ \frac{1}{4}, & y = 0, 1, \\ 0, & \text{elsewhere.} \end{cases}$ (b) $f(z) = \begin{cases} \frac{1}{12}, & z = 1, 10, \\ \frac{1}{4}, & z = 5, 17, \\ \frac{1}{3}, & z = 2, \\ 0, & \text{elsewhere.} \end{cases}$

4.3 (a) $f(g) = \begin{cases} \dfrac{e^{-\lambda}\lambda^{-y}}{(-y)!}, & y = 0, -1, -2, \ldots, \\ 0, & \text{elsewhere.} \end{cases}$

(b) $f(z) = \begin{cases} \dfrac{e^{-\lambda}\lambda^{z^2}}{(z^2)!}, & z = 0, 1, \sqrt{2}, \sqrt{3}, \ldots, \\ 0, & \text{elsewhere.} \end{cases}$

(c) $f(w) = \begin{cases} \dfrac{e^{-\lambda}\lambda^{(w+1)/2}}{\left(\dfrac{w+1}{2}\right)!}, & w = -1, 1, 3, 5, 7, \ldots, \\ 0, & \text{elsewhere.} \end{cases}$

(d) $h(y) = \begin{cases} \dfrac{e^{-\lambda}\lambda^{y^{1/\alpha}}}{(y^{1/\alpha})!}, & \begin{aligned} & y^{1/\alpha} = 0, 1, 2, 3, \ldots, \\ & \text{or } y = 0, 1, 2\alpha, 3\alpha, \ldots, \end{aligned} \\ 0, & \text{elsewhere.} \end{cases}$

4.5 (a) $f(y) = \begin{cases} \binom{n}{\sqrt{y/a}} p^{\sqrt{y/a}}(1-p)^{n-\sqrt{y/a}}, & \sqrt{\dfrac{y}{a}} = 0, 1, 2, 3, \ldots, n, \\ & \text{or } y = 0, a, 4a, \ldots n^2 a, \\ 0, & \text{elsewhere.} \end{cases}$

(b) $f(z) = \begin{cases} \binom{n}{\ln y} p^{\ln y}(1-p)^{n-\ln y}, & \ln y = 0, 1, 2, \ldots, n, \\ & \text{or } y = 1, e^1, e^2, \ldots, e^n, \\ 0, & \text{elsewhere.} \end{cases}$

4.7 $F(y) = \begin{cases} 1 - e^{-(\sqrt{y}-6)}, & y \geq 36, \\ 0, & y < 36. \end{cases}$ $F(x) = \begin{cases} 1 - e^{-(x-6)}, & x \geq 6, \\ 0, & x < 6. \end{cases}$

4.9 (a) $f(y) = \begin{cases} \dfrac{y-\beta}{4\alpha^2} e^{-(y-\beta)/2\alpha}, & y > \beta, \\ 0, & \text{elsewhere.} \end{cases}$

(b) $f(z) = \begin{cases} \dfrac{1}{4} z^{-1}\ln z e^{-(\ln z)/2}, & z > 1, \\ 0, & \text{elsewhere.} \end{cases}$

(c) $f(y) = \begin{cases} \dfrac{1}{4} y^{-3}e^{-1/2y}, & y > 0, \\ 0, & \text{elsewhere.} \end{cases}$

(d) $h(z) = \begin{cases} \dfrac{1}{2} z^3 e^{-z^2/2}, & z > 0, \\ 0, & \text{elsewhere.} \end{cases}$

4.11 $f(x) = \dfrac{1}{\pi} \dfrac{\alpha}{\alpha^2 + (x-\mu)^2}, \quad -\infty < x < \infty.$

4.13 (a) $f(y) = \dfrac{1}{2\sqrt{2\pi}} \exp\left[-\dfrac{1}{2}\left(\dfrac{y-1}{2}\right)^2\right], \quad -\infty < y < \infty.$

(b) $f(z) = \begin{cases} \dfrac{1}{2\sqrt{2\pi}} \left(\dfrac{z+1}{2}\right)^{-1/2} \exp\left[-\dfrac{1}{2}\left(\dfrac{z+1}{2}\right)^2\right], & z > -1, \\ 0, & \text{elsewhere.} \end{cases}$

(c) $f(y) = \begin{cases} \dfrac{2\sqrt{2}}{\sqrt{\pi}} ye^{-y^4/2}, & y > 0, \\ 0, & \text{elsewhere.} \end{cases}$

4.15 $F(y) = \begin{cases} 1, & y \geq 2, \\ 1 - e^{-3/2}, & -2 \leq y < 2, \\ 0, & y < -2. \end{cases}$

4.17 $g(y) = \begin{cases} 1, & 0 \leq y \leq 1, \\ 0, & \text{elsewhere.} \end{cases}$

4.19 $g(y) = \begin{cases} \left[2\Gamma\left(\dfrac{n+1}{2}\right)\left(1+\dfrac{y}{n}\right)^{-(n+1)/2}, & y \geq 0, \\ 0, & \text{elsewhere.} \end{cases}$

Problems:

4.1 (a) 0,
   (b) if $4 < \alpha a + b$, $Pr(y < 4) = 0$,

   if $\alpha a + b \leq 4 \leq \beta a + b$, $Pr(y < 4) = \dfrac{4 - \alpha a - b}{a(\beta - \alpha)}$,

   if $4 > \beta a + b$, $Pr(y < 4) = 1$,
   (c) 0,
   (d) x must be such that $0 < x < \pi$,

   $$g(t) = \begin{cases} \dfrac{1}{\pi} \dfrac{1}{\sqrt{1 - t^2}}, & -1 < t < 1 \\ 0, & \text{elsewhere.} \end{cases}$$

   Then $Pr\left(0 < T < \dfrac{\pi}{2}\right) = \dfrac{1}{2}$.

4.3 (a) $1 - 3e^{-2}$, (b) $7e^{-6} - 9e^{-8}$, (c) $13e^{-12}$.

4.5 $h(c) = \dfrac{1}{\sqrt{2\pi \frac{5}{9}\sigma}} \exp\left\{ -\dfrac{1}{2}\left[\dfrac{c - \frac{5}{9}(\mu - 32)}{\frac{5}{9}\sigma} \right]^2 \right\}$, $-\infty < c < \infty$.

4.7 $f(p) = \begin{cases} \dfrac{1}{20}\sqrt{\dfrac{r}{p}}, & \dfrac{100}{r} \leq p \leq \dfrac{400}{r}, \\ 0, & \text{elsewhere.} \end{cases}$

Chapter 5

Exercises

5.1 $\dfrac{k}{p}$. **5.3** (a) $\dfrac{33}{64}$, (b) $\dfrac{1723}{20{,}480}$. **5.5** $c = 2$, $E(X) = 1$, $\text{Var}(X) = \dfrac{1}{6}$.

5.9 $c = \dfrac{1}{2}$, $E(X) = 0$, $\text{Var}(X) = 2$. **5.11** (a) $c = \dfrac{1}{95}$, (b) $\dfrac{79}{19}$,

(c) $\dfrac{1733}{95}$, (d) $\dfrac{1163}{190}$, (e) $\dfrac{1722}{1805}$.

5.13 (a) $c = \dfrac{3}{\pi^2}$, (b) $E(|X|) = \infty$. **5.15** (a) $\phi_X(t) = \dfrac{1}{3}(1 + 2e^{2it})$, (b) $\mu = \dfrac{4}{3}$,

(c) $\eta_2 = \dfrac{8}{9}$, (d) $\gamma = \dfrac{-\sqrt{2}}{2}$, (e) $V = \dfrac{\sqrt{2}}{2}$, (f) $\xi = -\dfrac{3}{2}$.

5.17 (a) $\phi_X(t) = \dfrac{e^{it\beta} - e^{it\alpha}}{it(\beta - \alpha)}$, (b) $\mu = \dfrac{\beta + \alpha}{2}$, (c) $\eta_2 = \dfrac{(\beta - \alpha)^2}{12}$,

(d) $\sigma^2 = \dfrac{(\beta - \alpha)^2}{12}$, (e) $\gamma = 0$, (f) $\xi = -\dfrac{6}{5}$.

5.21 $\mu_k = \begin{cases} 0 & \text{for } k \text{ odd,} \\ \dfrac{1}{k+1} & \text{for } k \text{ even.} \end{cases}$

Problems:

5.1 $k=1$: $\quad E(X) = 3.5, \quad k=2$: $\quad E(X) = 7, \quad k=3$: $\quad E(X) = 10.5.$

5.3 (a) $\dfrac{35}{12}$, (b) $\dfrac{35}{3}$, (c) $\dfrac{35}{12}$, (d) 0. **5.5** $\dfrac{13144}{9075}$. **5.7** (a) σ^2,

(b) $\alpha\sigma^2 + \beta$, (c) $\alpha^2\sigma^2$. **5.9** (a) $E(X) = \dfrac{1}{p}$, $\quad \text{Var}(X) = \dfrac{1-p}{p^2}$;

(b) $E(X) = \dfrac{k(1-p)}{p}$, $\quad \text{Var}(X) = \dfrac{k(1-p)}{p^2}$. **5.11** (a) 28, (b) $\dfrac{38}{75}$.

5.13 (a) $E[g(X)] = \beta^k \dfrac{(\alpha+k-1)!}{(\alpha-1)!}$ if α is an integer, $\beta^k(\alpha+k-1)(\alpha+k-2)\ldots\alpha$, otherwise.

Chapter 6

Exercises:

6.3 $c = \dfrac{1}{4}$. **6.5** $f(x, y)$ is a probability density function.

6.9 $F(x, y) = \begin{cases} 1, & x > 1 \text{ and } y > 1, \\ y(2x - y), & 0 \le y \le x \le 1, \\ x^2, & 0 \le x \le 1, y > x, \\ y(2 - y), & x > 1, 0 \le y \le 1, \\ 0, & x < 0 \text{ or } y < 0. \end{cases}$ **6.11** $f(x, y) = \begin{cases} 2, & 1 < x < y < 2, \\ 0, & \text{elsewhere.} \end{cases}$

6.13 $f_1(x) = \begin{cases} \dfrac{1}{3}, & x = 1, \\ \dfrac{1}{6}, & x = 2, 3, 4, 5, \\ 0, & \text{elsewhere.} \end{cases}$ $\quad f_2(y) = \begin{cases} \dfrac{1}{5}, & y = 1, 2, 3, 4, 5, \\ 0, & \text{elsewhere.} \end{cases}$

6.15 (a) $f_1(x) = \begin{cases} \dfrac{(\lambda p)^x e^{-\lambda p}}{x!}, & x = 0, 1, 2, \ldots \\ 0, & \text{elsewhere.} \end{cases}$ (b) $f_2(y) = \begin{cases} \dfrac{\lambda^y e^{-\lambda}}{y!}, & y = 0, 1, 2, \ldots, \\ 0, & \text{elsewhere.} \end{cases}$

(c) $Pr(x \le r) = e^{-\lambda p} \displaystyle\sum_{x=0}^{r} \dfrac{(\lambda p)^x}{x!}$, (d) $Pr(y \ge k) = 1 - e^{-\lambda} \displaystyle\sum_{y=0}^{k-1} \dfrac{\lambda^r}{r!}$.

6.17 (a) $F(x, y) = \begin{cases} (1 - e^{-x})(1 - e^{-y}), & x, y > 0, \\ 1 - e^{-x}, & x > y, y = \infty, \\ 1 - e^{-y}, & y > 0, x = \infty, \\ 0, & x \le 0 \text{ or } y \le 0. \end{cases}$ (b) $f_1(x) = \begin{cases} e^{-x}, & x > 0, \\ 0, & \text{elsewhere.} \end{cases}$

(c) $f_2(y) = \begin{cases} e^{-y}, & y > 0, \\ 0, & \text{elsewhere.} \end{cases}$ (d) $F_1(x) = \begin{cases} 1 - e^{-x}, & x > 0, \\ 0, & x \le 0. \end{cases}$

(e) $F_2(y) = \begin{cases} 1 - e^{-y}, & y > 0, \\ 0, & y \le 0. \end{cases}$ (f) $h_1(x \mid y) = f_1(x)$, (g) $h_2(y \mid x) = f_2(y)$,

(h) $F_X(x \mid y) = F_1(x)$, (i) $F_Y(y \mid x) = F_2(y)$, (j) yes, they are independent.

6.21 (a) $h_1(x \mid y) = \begin{cases} \binom{y}{x} p^x (1-p)^{y-x}, & x = 0, 1, 2, \ldots, y, \\ 0, & \text{elsewhere.} \end{cases}$

(b) $h_2(y \mid x) = \begin{cases} \dfrac{e^{-\lambda(1-p)}[\lambda(1-p)]^{y-x}}{(y-x)!}, & y = x, x+1, \ldots, \\ 0, & \text{elsewhere.} \end{cases}$

(c) X and Y are not independent.

6.23 $f_2(y) = \begin{cases} \left(\dfrac{1}{2}\right)^{y+1}, & y \geq 0, \\ 0, & \text{elsewhere.} \end{cases}$

6.25 (a) $h_1(x \mid y) = \begin{cases} \dfrac{6x^2}{n(n+1)(2n+1)}, & x = 1, 2, \ldots, n, \\ 0, & \text{elsewhere.} \end{cases}$

(b) $h_2(y \mid x) = \begin{cases} \dfrac{6y^2}{n(n+1)(2n+1)}, & y = 1, 2, \ldots, n, \\ 0, & \text{elsewhere.} \end{cases}$

6.27 (a) $f_2(z_1, z_2) = \begin{cases} \dfrac{1}{\Gamma(\alpha)\Gamma(\beta)} z_1^{\alpha-1}(1-z_1)^{\beta-1} z_2^{\alpha+\beta-1} e^{-z_2}, & 0 \leq z_1 \leq 1, z_2 \geq 0, \\ 0, & \text{elsewhere.} \end{cases}$

(b) $g_1(z_1) = \begin{cases} \dfrac{\Gamma(\alpha+\beta)}{\Gamma(\alpha)\Gamma(\beta)} z_1^{\alpha-1}(1-z_1)^{\beta-1}, & 0 \leq z_1 \leq 1, \\ 0, & \text{elsewhere.} \end{cases}$

$g_2(z_2) = \begin{cases} \dfrac{1}{\Gamma(\alpha+\beta)} z_2^{\alpha+\beta-1} e^{-z_2}, & z_2 \geq 0, \\ 0, & \text{elsewhere.} \end{cases}$

(c) Z_1 and Z_2 are independent,   (d) $Pr(Z_2 < Z_1) = 3e^{-1} - 1$.

6.29 (a) $f(z) = \begin{cases} z(z - 1 - \ln z), & 1 \leq z < 2, \\ 2\left[\dfrac{1}{z-1} - \ln\left(\dfrac{z}{z-1}\right)\right], & z \geq 2, \\ 0, & \text{elsewhere.} \end{cases}$

(b) $f(z) = \begin{cases} 2\left[\ln\left(\dfrac{1-z}{-z}\right) - \dfrac{1}{1-z}\right], & z < -1, \\ z\left[\ln(1-z) - \dfrac{z^2}{1-z}\right], & z \geq -1, \\ 0, & \text{elsewhere.} \end{cases}$

(c) $f(z) = \begin{cases} 2(1-z), & 0 \le z < 1, \\ 0, & \text{elsewhere.} \end{cases}$ (d) $f(z) = \begin{cases} \dfrac{2}{3}z, & 0 \le z < 1, \\ \dfrac{2}{3}z^2, & z \ge 1, \\ 0, & \text{elsewhere.} \end{cases}$

6.33 (a) yes, X and Y are independent,   (b) yes, X and Y are identically distributed,
(c) $Pr(X^2 + Y^2 \le 4) = 1 - e^{-8}$,

(d) $f(z) = \begin{cases} \dfrac{1}{2^{1/2}\Gamma(\frac{1}{2})}z^{1/2-1}e^{-3/2}, & z \ge 0, \\ 0, & \text{elsewhere.} \end{cases}$ $Z = X^2$ has a gamma distribution with $\alpha = \dfrac{1}{2}$, $\beta = 2$.

Problems:

6.1 (a) $f(x,y) = \begin{cases} \dfrac{\binom{9}{x}\binom{8}{y}\binom{3}{6-x-y}}{\binom{20}{6}}, & x, y = 0, 1, 2, 3, 4, 5, 6 \\ & \text{such that } 3 \le x+y \le 6, \\ 0, & \text{elsewhere.} \end{cases}$

(b) $\dfrac{\binom{9}{3}\binom{8}{3}\binom{3}{0}}{\binom{20}{6}}$,   (c) $\dfrac{\binom{9}{1}}{\binom{20}{6}}\left[\binom{11}{5} - \binom{8}{5}\right].$

6.3 (a) $f(x,y) = \begin{cases} \binom{20}{x, y, 20-x-y}\left(\dfrac{1}{3}\right)^x\left(\dfrac{1}{2}\right)^y\left(\dfrac{11}{26}\right)^{20-x-y}, & x, y = 0, 1, \dots, 20, \\ 0, & \text{elsewhere.} \end{cases}$

(b) $f(x,y) = \begin{cases} \dfrac{\binom{13}{x}\binom{26}{y}\binom{44}{20-x-y}}{\binom{52}{20}}, & \begin{aligned} & x = 0, 1, 2, \dots, 13, \\ & y = 0, 1, 2, \dots, 20, \\ & \text{such that } 7 \le x+y \le 20, \end{aligned} \\ 0, & \text{elsewhere.} \end{cases}$

6.5 (a) 0.1,   (b) .2124,   (c) 0.
6.7 (a) $e^{-5/4}$,   (b) $e^{-3}(1 - e^{-9})$,   (c) $1 - e^{-1/4}$.

6.9 (a) $f(x) = \begin{cases} \dfrac{\binom{4}{x}\binom{10}{6-x}}{\binom{14}{6}}, & x = 0, 1, 2, 3, 4, \\ 0, & \text{elsewhere.} \end{cases}$ $f(y) = \begin{cases} \dfrac{\binom{5}{y}\binom{9}{6-y}}{\binom{14}{6}}, & \begin{aligned} & y = 0, 1, 2, 3, \\ & 4, 5, \end{aligned} \\ 0, & \text{elsewhere.} \end{cases}$

(b) $1 - \dfrac{\binom{10}{2}}{\binom{14}{6}}$,   (c) $\dfrac{1}{\binom{14}{6}}\sum_{y=2}^{4}\binom{5}{y}\binom{9}{6-y}.$

6.11 (a) $h_1(x \mid y_0) = \begin{cases} \dfrac{\dbinom{9}{x}\dbinom{11}{15-x-y_0}}{\dbinom{20}{15-y_0}}, & \begin{array}{l} x \text{ and } y_0 \text{ integers such that} \\ 0 \le x \le 9, \\ 4 - y_0 \le x \le 15 - y_0, \\ 0 \le y_0 \le 10, \end{array} \\ 0, \quad \text{elsewhere.} \end{cases}$

(b) $h_2(y \mid x_0) = \begin{cases} \dfrac{\dbinom{10}{y}\dbinom{11}{15-x_0-y}}{\dbinom{21}{15-x_0}}, & \begin{array}{l} y \text{ and } x_0 \text{ integers such that} \\ 0 \le y \le 10, \\ 4 - x_0 \le y \le 15 - x_0, \\ 0 \le x_0 \le 9, \end{array} \\ 0, \quad \text{elsewhere.} \end{cases}$

(c) $h_1(x \mid 5) = \begin{cases} \dfrac{\dbinom{9}{x}\dbinom{11}{10-x}}{\dbinom{20}{10}}, & \begin{array}{l} x \text{ an integer such that} \\ 0 \le x \le 9, \end{array} \\ 0, \quad \text{elsewhere.} \end{cases}$

(d) $h_2(y \mid 5) = \begin{cases} \dfrac{\dbinom{10}{y}\dbinom{11}{10-y}}{\dbinom{21}{10}}, & \begin{array}{l} y \text{ an integer such that} \\ 0 \le y \le 10, \end{array} \\ 0, \quad \text{elsewhere.} \end{cases}$

(e) X and Y are not independent.

6.13 (a) $\dfrac{1}{8}$, **(b)** $\dfrac{1}{8}$, **(c)** $\dfrac{3}{4}$, **(d)** $f(x) = \begin{cases} x, & 0 \le x < 1, \\ 2 - x, & 1 \le x < 2, \\ 0, & \text{elsewhere.} \end{cases}$

6.15 (a) $\dfrac{9}{5}$, **(b)** $\dfrac{47}{10}$, **(c)** $\dfrac{84}{10}$.

6.17 (Exercise 6.9) **(a)** $E(X) = \dfrac{2}{3}$, **(b)** $E(Y) = \dfrac{1}{3}$.

6.19 (a) Exercise 6.2 $E(X) = \dfrac{2n+1}{3}$, $E(X^2) = \dfrac{n(n+1)}{n}$, $\mathrm{Var}(X) = \dfrac{(n+2)(n-1)}{18}$;

(Exercise 6.6) $E(X) = \Gamma\!\left(\dfrac{3}{2}\right)$, $E(X^2) = \Gamma(2)$, $\mathrm{Var}(X) = 1 - \dfrac{\pi}{4}$;

(b) (Exercise 6.2) $E(Y) = \mathrm{Var}(X) = \dfrac{(n+2)(n-1)}{18}$;

(Exercise 6.6) $E(Y) = 1$, $E(Y^2) = 2$, $\mathrm{Var}(Y) = 1$;
(c) (Exercises 6.2 and 6.6) $\mathrm{Cov}(X, Y) = 0$.

6.23 (a) $E(Z_1) = \dfrac{\alpha}{\alpha + \beta}$, **(b)** $E(Z_2) = \alpha + \beta$, **(d)** $\mathrm{Cov}(Z_1, Z_2) = 0$.

6.25 $E(Z) = -\dfrac{95}{3}$, $\mathrm{Var}(Z) = \dfrac{241607}{360}$.

6.27 $E(X^k Y^m) = \dfrac{1}{4}\left\{\dfrac{(2k+3)(-1)^{k+2}-1}{(k+1)(k+2)}\right\}\left\{\dfrac{(2m+3)(-1)^{m+2}-1}{(m+1)(m+2)}\right\}.$

6.29 $\mu_{10} = \dfrac{9}{5},\qquad \mu_{01} = \dfrac{47}{10},\qquad \mu_{11} = \dfrac{84}{10},\qquad \mu_{20} = \dfrac{112}{25},\qquad \mu_{02} = \dfrac{301}{50}.$

6.31 (a) $E(X\,|3) = \dfrac{11}{24},$ (b) $E(X\,|5) = \dfrac{7}{12},$ (c) $E(Y\,|3) = \dfrac{7}{12},$ (d) $E(Y\,|5) = \dfrac{1}{2}.$

Chapter 7

7.1 $f(x,y,z) = \begin{cases} \left(\dfrac{10}{x,\,y,\,z,\,(10-x-y-z)}\right)\left(\dfrac{1}{6}\right)^{x+y+z}\left(\dfrac{1}{2}\right)^{10-x-y-z}, & \begin{array}{l}0\le x+y+z\le 10,\\ x,y,z \text{ integers,}\end{array} \\ 0, & \text{elsewhere.}\end{cases}$

7.3 $f(w,x,y,z) = \begin{cases} \left(\dfrac{n}{w,\,x,\,y,\,z,\,(n-w-y-x-z)}\right)\left(\dfrac{1}{32}\right)^{w}\left(\dfrac{5}{32}\right)^{x}\left(\dfrac{10}{32}\right)^{y}\left(\dfrac{10}{32}\right)^{z} \\ \qquad\qquad\left(\dfrac{6}{32}\right)^{n-w-x-y-z}, \qquad 0\le w+x+y+z\le n, \\ 0, \quad\text{elsewhere.}\end{cases}$

7.5 $f(x,y,z) = \begin{cases} 1, & 3\le x\le 4,\ \ 2\le y\le 3,\ \ \ 0\le z\le 1, \\ 0, & \text{elsewhere.}\end{cases}$

7.7 $k = \dfrac{32\sqrt{2}}{15}.$ **7.9** $f(w,x,y,z) = \begin{cases} 4, & 0\le w\le 1,\ 1\le x\le \frac{3}{2},\ 1\le y\le 2,\ 2\le z\le \frac{5}{2}, \\ 0, & \text{elsewhere.}\end{cases}$

7.11 (7.5) $F(x,y,z) = \begin{cases} 1, & x\ge 4,\ \ y\ge 3,\ \ z\ge 1, \\ xyz - 3yz - 2xy + 6y, & 3\le x < 4,\ \ 2\le y < 3,\ \ 0\le z < 1, \\ 0, & x < 3,\ \ y < 2,\ \ z < 0.\end{cases}$

  (7.6) $F(x,y,z) = \begin{cases} 1, & x,y,z > 1, \\ 6xyz, & 0\le x\le y\le z\le 1, \\ 0, & x < 0.\end{cases}$

7.13 (7.1) (a) $f_1(x) = \begin{cases} \dbinom{10}{x}\left(\dfrac{1}{6}\right)^{x}\left(\dfrac{5}{6}\right)^{10-x}, & 0\le x\le 10,\ x \text{ an integer}, \\ 0, & \text{elsewhere.}\end{cases}$

  (b) $f_2(y) = \begin{cases} \dbinom{10}{y}\left(\dfrac{1}{6}\right)^{y}\left(\dfrac{5}{6}\right)^{10-y}, & 0\le y\le 10,\ y \text{ an integer}, \\ 0, & \text{elsewhere.}\end{cases}$

  (c) $f_{13}(x,z) = \begin{cases} \left(\dfrac{10}{x,\,z,\,(10-x-z)}\right)\left(\dfrac{1}{6}\right)^{x+z}\left(\dfrac{2}{3}\right)^{10-x-z}, & \begin{array}{l}0\le x+z\le 10\\ x \text{ and } z \text{ integers},\end{array} \\ 0, & \text{elsewhere.}\end{cases}$

  (d) $f_{23}(y,z) = \begin{cases} \left(\dfrac{10}{y,\,z,\,(10-y-z)}\right)\left(\dfrac{1}{6}\right)^{y+3}\left(\dfrac{2}{3}\right)^{10-y-z}, & \begin{array}{l}0\le y+z\le 10,\\ y \text{ and } z \text{ integers},\end{array} \\ 0, & \text{elsewhere.}\end{cases}$

(7.5) (a) $f_1(x) = \begin{cases} 1, & 3 \le x \le 4, \\ 0, & \text{elsewhere.} \end{cases}$ (b) $f_2(y) = \begin{cases} 1, & 2 \le y \le 3, \\ 0, & \text{elsewhere.} \end{cases}$

(c) $f_{13}(x, z) = \begin{cases} 1, & 3 \le x \le 4, \quad 0 \le z \le 1 \\ 0, & \text{elsewhere.} \end{cases}$

(d) $f_{23} = \begin{cases} 1, & 2 \le y \le 5, \ 0 \le z \le 1, \\ 0, & \text{elsewhere.} \end{cases}$

(7.7) (a) $f_1(x) = \begin{cases} \dfrac{32\sqrt{2}}{15}\left(2 - 2x^2 + \dfrac{1}{2}x^4\right), & -\sqrt{2} \le x \le \sqrt{2}, \\ 0, & \text{elsewhere.} \end{cases}$

(b) $f_2(y) = \begin{cases} \dfrac{64\sqrt{2}}{15}\sqrt{y}(2 - y), & 0 \le y \le 2, \\ 0, & \text{elsewhere.} \end{cases}$

(c) $f_{13}(x, z) = \begin{cases} \dfrac{32\sqrt{2}}{15}(z - x^2), & 0 \le x^2 \le z \le 2, \\ 0, & \text{elsewhere.} \end{cases}$

(d) $f_{23}(y, z) = \begin{cases} \dfrac{64\sqrt{2}}{15}\sqrt{y}, & 0 \le y \le z \le 2, \\ 0, & \text{elsewhere.} \end{cases}$

7.15 (7.1) (a) $f(x \mid y) = \begin{cases} \dbinom{10-y}{x}\left(\dfrac{1}{5}\right)^x\left(\dfrac{4}{5}\right)^{10-y}, & \begin{array}{l} x = 0, 1, 2, \ldots, (10 - y), \\ \text{where } y = 0, 1, \ldots, 10 \end{array} \\ 0, & \text{elsewhere.} \end{cases}$

(b) $g(y \mid z) = \begin{cases} \dbinom{10-z}{y}\left(\dfrac{1}{5}\right)^y\left(\dfrac{4}{5}\right)^{10-z}, & \begin{array}{l} y = 0, 1, 2, \ldots, (10 - z), \\ \text{where } z = 0, 1, \ldots, 10 \end{array} \\ 0, & \text{elsewhere.} \end{cases}$

(7.5) (a) $f(x \mid y) = \begin{cases} 1, & 3 \le x \le 4, \\ 0, & \text{elsewhere.} \end{cases}$ (b) $g(y \mid z) = \begin{cases} 1, & 2 \le y \le 3, \\ 0, & \text{elsewhere.} \end{cases}$

(7.7) (a) $f(x \mid y) = \begin{cases} \dfrac{1}{2\sqrt{y}}, & -\sqrt{y} \le x \le \sqrt{y}, \ 0 < y \le 2 \\ 0, & \text{elsewhere.} \end{cases}$

(b) $f(y \mid z) = \begin{cases} \dfrac{3\sqrt{y}}{2z\sqrt{z}}, & 0 \le y \le z \le 2, \\ 0, & \text{elsewhere.} \end{cases}$

7.17 (7.3) (a) $h(w \mid x) = \begin{cases} \dbinom{n-x}{n}\left(\dfrac{1}{27}\right)^w\left(\dfrac{26}{27}\right)^{n-x-w}, & \begin{array}{l} w = 0, 1, 2, \ldots, (n - x), \\ \text{where } x = 0, 1, \ldots, n \end{array} \\ 0, & \text{elsewhere.} \end{cases}$

(b) $f(x \mid w, y) = \begin{cases} \dbinom{n-w-y}{x}\left(\dfrac{5}{21}\right)^x\left(\dfrac{16}{21}\right)^{n-w-y-x}, & \begin{array}{l} x = 0, 1, 2, \ldots, (n - w - y), \\ \text{where } w, y = 0, 1, \ldots, n \\ \text{such that } w + y = 0, 1, \ldots, n \end{array} \\ 0, & \text{elsewhere.} \end{cases}$

(c) $g(y \mid w, x, z) = \begin{cases} \dbinom{n-x-z}{y}\left(\dfrac{5}{8}\right)^y\left(\dfrac{3}{8}\right)^{n-w-x-z-y}, & \begin{array}{l} y = 0, 1, \ldots, \\ \quad (n - w - x - z), \\ \text{where } w, x, z = 0, 1, \ldots, n \\ \text{such that} \\ w + x + z = 0, 1, \ldots, n \end{array} \\ 0, & \text{elsewhere.} \end{cases}$

(d) $\quad l(w, z \mid y) = \begin{cases} \left(\left(w, z, (n - w - y - z) \atop n - y \right) \right) \left(\frac{1}{22} \right)^w \left(\frac{10}{22} \right)^z \left(\frac{1}{2} \right)^{n-w-y-z}, & w + z = 0, 1, \\ & \dots, n - y \\ & \text{where } y = 0, \\ 0, \quad \text{elsewhere.} & 1, \dots, n, \end{cases}$

(e) $\quad m(w, x, y \mid z) = \begin{cases} \left(\left(w, x, y, (n - w - x - y - z) \atop n - z \right) \right) \left(\frac{1}{22} \right)^w \left(\frac{5}{22} \right)^x \left(\frac{10}{22} \right)^y \\ \qquad \times \left(\frac{6}{22} \right)^{n-w-x-y-z}, \quad w + x + y = \\ \qquad\qquad\qquad\qquad\qquad\qquad 0, 1, \dots, n - z \\ \qquad\qquad\qquad\qquad\qquad\qquad \text{where } z = 0, 1, \dots, n, \\ 0, \quad \text{elsewhere.} \end{cases}$

(7.9) (a) $\quad h(w \mid x) = \begin{cases} 1, & 0 \le w \le 1, \\ 0, & \text{elsewhere.} \end{cases}$ (b) $\quad f(x \mid w, y) = \begin{cases} 2, & 1 \le x \le \frac{3}{2}, \\ 0, & \text{elsewhere.} \end{cases}$

(c) $\quad g(y \mid w, x, z) = \begin{cases} 1, & 1 \le y \le 2, \\ 0, & \text{elsewhere.} \end{cases}$

(d) $\quad l(w, z \mid y) = \begin{cases} 2, & 0 \le w \le 1, \quad 2 \le z \le \frac{5}{2}, \\ 0, & \text{elsewhere.} \end{cases}$

(e) $\quad m(w, x, y \mid z) = \begin{cases} 2, & 0 \le w \le 1, \quad 1 \le x \le \frac{3}{2}, \quad 1 \le y \le 2, \\ 0, & \text{elsewhere.} \end{cases}$

7.19 (7.1) no; (7.2) (a) with replacement—no, (b) without replacement—no; (7.3) no; (7.4) no; (7.5) yes.

7.23 (a) $\quad g(y_1, y_2, \dots, y_n) = \dfrac{1}{(2\pi)^{n/2} \sigma^n} \exp \left\{ - \dfrac{1}{2\sigma^2} \left(2 \sum_{i=1}^{n} y_i^2 - 2 \sum_{i=2}^{n} y_i y_{i-1} - y_n^2 - n\mu^2 \right) \right\}$

$$0 < y_1 \le y_2 \le \dots \le y_n < \infty.$$

(b) $\quad g(y_1, y_2, \dots, y_n) = \dfrac{1}{\beta^{n\alpha}[\Gamma(\alpha)]^n} \, y_1 \prod_{j=2}^{n} (y_j - y_{j-1}) e^{-1/\beta y_n},$

$$0 < y_1 \le y_2 \le \dots \le y_n < \infty.$$

(c) $\quad g(y_1, y_2, \dots, y_n) = \dfrac{\lambda^{y_n} e^{-\lambda}}{y_1! \prod_{i=2}^{n} (y_i - y_{i-1})!}, \quad 0 \le y_1 \le y_2 \le \dots \le y_n < \infty.$

7.27 (a) $\quad m_Y(t) = \exp(2t + 18t^2),$ (b) $\quad Pr(Y > 8) = .1587.$

7.29 (7.5) (a) $\quad \eta_{1, 2, 3} = 0,$ (b) $\quad \eta_{3, 3, 3} = 0.$

7.37 (a) $\quad g(\bar{x}) = \begin{cases} \dbinom{nm}{n\bar{x}} p^{n\bar{x}} (1 - p)^{n(m - \bar{x})}, & \bar{x} = 0, \dfrac{1}{n}, \dfrac{2}{n}, \dots, m, \\ 0, & \text{elsewhere.} \end{cases}$

(b) $\quad g(\bar{x}) = \begin{cases} \dfrac{e^{-n\lambda}(n\lambda)^{n\bar{x}}}{(n\bar{x})!}, & \bar{x} = 0, \dfrac{1}{n}, \dfrac{2}{n}, \dots, \\ 0, & \text{elsewhere.} \end{cases}$

(c) $\quad g(\bar{x}) = \begin{cases} \dbinom{n\bar{x} - 1}{n - 1} p^n (1 - p)^{n(x-1)}, & \bar{x} = 1, 1 + \dfrac{1}{n}, 1 + \dfrac{2}{n}, \dots, \\ 0, & \text{elsewhere.} \end{cases}$

(d) $g(\bar{x}) = \begin{cases} \binom{n\bar{x}-1}{nk-1} p^{nk}(1-p)^{n(\bar{x}-k)}, & \bar{x} = k, k+\dfrac{1}{n}, k+\dfrac{2}{n}, \ldots, \\ 0, & \text{elsewhere.} \end{cases}$

(e) $g(\bar{x}) = \begin{cases} \dfrac{1}{\left(\dfrac{\beta}{n}\right)^{n\alpha} \Gamma(n\alpha)} \bar{x}^{n\alpha-1} e^{-\bar{x}/(\beta/n)}, & \bar{x} > 0, \\ 0, & \text{elsewhere.} \end{cases}$

7.39 (7.3) (d) $\dfrac{5(n-y)(n-y-1)}{484}$,   (e) $\dfrac{5(n-y-3)(n-y-3-1)}{144}$,

(f) $\dfrac{50(n-z)(n-z-1)(n-z-2)}{10{,}648}$.

(7.9) (a) $\dfrac{1}{2}$,   (b) $\dfrac{1}{2}$,   (c) $\dfrac{1}{2}$,   (d) $\dfrac{5}{8}$,   (e) $\dfrac{5}{8}$,   (d) $\dfrac{15}{16}$.

Chapter 8

8.1 $1 - \dfrac{1}{k^2} = \dfrac{7}{10}$.   **8.3** $n \geq 250$.   **8.7** $n \geq 23$.

8.9 $n \geq 228$.   **8.13** yes, by Theorem 9.3.2.   **8.15** $\dfrac{S_n}{n} \to 0$ as $n \to \infty$ for $c > 1$.

8.17 $n = 25$: .00002, $n = 64$: $\Phi \approx 0$.

8.19 .00007.   **8.21** (a) .9979,   (b) .00004,   (c) .1549.   **8.25** $n \geq 90$, $n > 109$.   **8.27** 0.9213.

Chapter 9

9.1 (a)

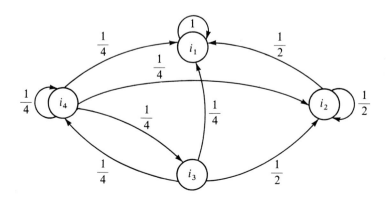

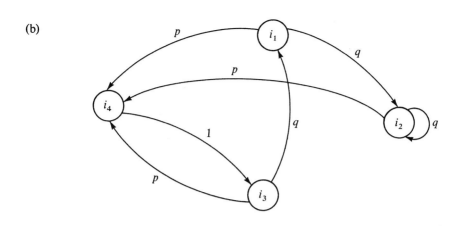

(b)

$$
\mathbf{9.3 \ (b)} \quad \begin{array}{c} \\ c \\ t \\ b \end{array}
\begin{array}{c} c \quad t \quad b \end{array}
\begin{bmatrix} 0 & \dfrac{1}{2} & \dfrac{1}{2} \\[2mm] \dfrac{1}{2} & 0 & \dfrac{1}{2} \\[2mm] \dfrac{1}{4} & \dfrac{3}{4} & 0 \end{bmatrix}
\qquad \text{(c)}
$$

$$
\mathbf{9.5} \quad
\begin{array}{c}
i_1 \\ i_2 \\ i_3 \\ i_4 \\ i_5 \\ i_6 \\ i_7
\end{array}
\begin{array}{c} i_1 \quad i_2 \quad i_3 \quad i_4 \quad i_5 \quad i_6 \quad i_7 \end{array}
\begin{bmatrix}
0 & \dfrac{1}{6} & \dfrac{1}{6} & \dfrac{1}{6} & \dfrac{1}{6} & \dfrac{1}{6} & \dfrac{1}{6} \\[2mm]
\dfrac{1}{3} & 0 & \dfrac{1}{3} & \dfrac{1}{3} & 0 & 0 & 0 \\[2mm]
\dfrac{1}{3} & \dfrac{1}{3} & 0 & 0 & \dfrac{1}{3} & 0 & 0 \\[2mm]
\dfrac{1}{3} & \dfrac{1}{3} & 0 & 0 & 0 & \dfrac{1}{3} & 0 \\[2mm]
\dfrac{1}{3} & 0 & \dfrac{1}{3} & 0 & 0 & 0 & \dfrac{1}{3} \\[2mm]
\dfrac{1}{3} & 0 & 0 & \dfrac{1}{3} & 0 & 0 & \dfrac{1}{3} \\[2mm]
\dfrac{1}{3} & 0 & 0 & 0 & \dfrac{1}{3} & \dfrac{1}{3} & 0
\end{bmatrix}
$$

$$
\mathbf{9.7} \quad
\begin{array}{c}
i_1 \\ i_2 \\ i_3 \\ i_4 \\ i_5 \\ i_6
\end{array}
\begin{array}{c} i_1 \quad i_2 \quad i_3 \quad i_4 \quad i_5 \quad i_6 \end{array}
\begin{bmatrix}
0 & 1 & 0 & 0 & 0 & 0 \\
q & 0 & p & 0 & 0 & 0 \\
0 & q & 0 & p & 0 & 0 \\
0 & 0 & q & 0 & p & 0 \\
0 & 0 & 0 & q & 0 & p \\
0 & 0 & 0 & 0 & 1 & 0
\end{bmatrix}
$$

9.7 (b)

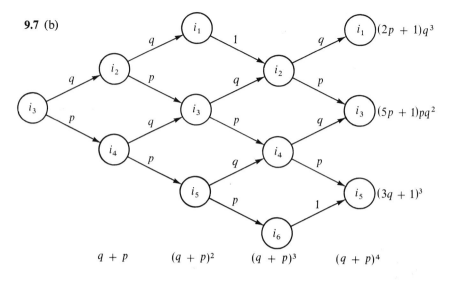

$q + p$ $(q + p)^2$ $(q + p)^3$ $(q + p)^4$

9.9 (a) $(.6)^3$,   **(b)** $9(.6)^4(.4)^2$.

9.13 (b) $i_1 : \dfrac{7}{27}$, $i_3 : \dfrac{2}{27}$, $i_5 : \dfrac{5}{27}$, $i_7 : \dfrac{2}{27}$.

$i_2 : \dfrac{5}{27}$, $i_4 : \dfrac{2}{27}$, $i_6 : \dfrac{4}{27}$,

9.15 $\dfrac{1}{4}$, $\dfrac{3}{4}$, 1.

9.17 $J^k = (\Lambda + M)^k =
\begin{bmatrix}
1 & 0 & 0 & 0 \\
0 & \frac{2}{3} & 0 & 0 \\
0 & 0 & \frac{1}{3} & 1 \\
0 & 0 & 0 & \frac{1}{3}
\end{bmatrix}^k
=
\begin{bmatrix}
1 & 0 & 0 & 0 \\
0 & \left(\frac{2}{3}\right)^k & 0 & 0 \\
0 & 0 & \left(\frac{1}{3}\right)^k & k\left(\frac{1}{3}\right)^k \\
0 & 0 & 0 & \left(\frac{1}{3}\right)^k
\end{bmatrix}$;

Eigenvector for $\lambda_1 = 1 : x_1 = \begin{bmatrix} 1 \\ 1 \\ 1 \\ 1 \end{bmatrix}$,

Eigenvector for $\lambda_2 = \dfrac{2}{3} : x_2 = \begin{bmatrix} 0 \\ 2 \\ 2 \\ 3 \end{bmatrix}$,

Eigenvector for $\lambda_3 = \dfrac{1}{3} : x_3 = \begin{bmatrix} 0 \\ 0 \\ 0 \\ 1 \end{bmatrix}$,

Eigenvector for $\lambda_4 = \frac{1}{3}$: $x_4 = \begin{bmatrix} 0 \\ 0 \\ 4 \\ 1 \end{bmatrix}$;

$$C = \begin{bmatrix} 1 & 0 & 0 & 0 \\ 1 & 2 & 0 & 0 \\ 1 & 2 & 0 & 4 \\ 1 & 3 & 1 & 1 \end{bmatrix} \quad \text{and} \quad C^{-1} = \frac{1}{4}\begin{bmatrix} 4 & 0 & 0 & 0 \\ -2 & 2 & 0 & 0 \\ 2 & -5 & -1 & 4 \\ 0 & -1 & 1 & 0 \end{bmatrix};$$

$P^k = CJ^kC^{-1} = C(\Lambda + M)^kC^{-1} =$

$$\begin{bmatrix} 1 & 0 & 0 & 0 \\ 1-\left(\frac{2}{3}\right)^k & \left(\frac{2}{3}\right)^k & 0 & 0 \\ 1-\left(\frac{2}{3}\right)^k & (2^k-1)\left(\frac{1}{3}\right)^k & \left(\frac{1}{3}\right)^k & 0 \\ 1-\frac{1}{2}(3\cdot 2^k-1)\left(\frac{1}{3}\right)^k & \frac{3}{4}(2^{k+1}-2-k)\left(\frac{1}{3}\right)^k & \frac{3}{4}k\left(\frac{1}{3}\right)^k & \left(\frac{1}{3}\right)^k \end{bmatrix}.$$

9.19 $\lambda_1 = 1, \quad \lambda_2 = \lambda_3 = \frac{1}{2}; \quad J^k = (\Lambda + M)^k = \begin{bmatrix} 1 & 0 & 0 \\ 0 & \left(\frac{1}{2}\right)^k & n\left(\frac{1}{2}\right)^{k-1} \\ 0 & 0 & \left(\frac{1}{2}\right)^k \end{bmatrix};$

$$x_1 = \begin{bmatrix} 1 \\ 1 \\ 1 \end{bmatrix}, \quad x_2 = \begin{bmatrix} 0 \\ 1 \\ 0 \end{bmatrix}, \quad x_3 = \begin{bmatrix} 2 \\ 1 \\ 0 \end{bmatrix};$$

$$C = \begin{bmatrix} 1 & 0 & 2 \\ 1 & 1 & 1 \\ 1 & 0 & 0 \end{bmatrix}; \quad C^{-1} = \frac{1}{2}\begin{bmatrix} 0 & 0 & 2 \\ -1 & 2 & -1 \\ 1 & 0 & -1 \end{bmatrix};$$

$$P^k = CJ^kC^{-1} = C(\Lambda + M)^kC^{-1} = \begin{bmatrix} \left(\frac{1}{2}\right)^k & 0 & 1-\left(\frac{1}{2}\right)^k \\ n\left(\frac{1}{2}\right)^k & \left(\frac{1}{2}\right)^k & 1-(n+1)\left(\frac{1}{2}\right)^k \\ 0 & 0 & 1 \end{bmatrix};$$

$$P^{20} = \begin{bmatrix} \left(\frac{1}{2}\right)^{20} & 0 & 1-\left(\frac{1}{2}\right)^{20} \\ 20\left(\frac{1}{2}\right)^{20} & \left(\frac{1}{2}\right)^{20} & 1-21\left(\frac{1}{2}\right)^{20} \\ 0 & 0 & 1 \end{bmatrix}.$$

Index

655